Economic Analysis
and
Industrial Management

PRENTICE-HALL INTERNATIONAL SERIES IN MANAGEMENT

Baumol	*Economic Theory and Operations Analysis*
Brown	*Smoothing, Forecasting and Prediction of Discrete Time Series*
Churchman	*Prediction and Optimal Decision: Philosophical Issues of a Science of Values*
Clarkson	*The Theory of Consumer Demand: A Critical Appraisal*
Cyert and March	*A Behavioral Theory of the Firm*
Greenlaw, Herron, and Rawdon	*Business Simulation in Industrial and University Education*
Hadley and Whiten	*Analysis of Inventory Systems*
Holt, Modigliani, Muth, and Simon	*Planning, Production, Inventories, and Work Force*
Kaufmann	*Methods and Models of Operations Research*
Lesourne	*Economic Analysis and Industrial Management*
Miller and Starr	*Executive Decisions and Operations Research*
Muth and Thompson	*Industrial Scheduling*
Pfiffner and Sherwood	*Administrative Organization*

PRENTICE-HALL QUANTITATIVE METHODS SERIES
Dr. W. Allen Spivey, Editor

Brown	*Smoothing, Forecasting and Prediction of Discrete Time Series*
Cyert and Davidson	*Statistical Sampling for Accounting Information*
Hadley and Whiten	*Analysis of Inventory Systems*
Kemeny, Schleifer, Snell, and Thompson	*Finite Mathematics with Business Applications*
Lesourne	*Economic Analysis and Industrial Management*
Massé	*Optimal Investment Decisions: Rules for Action and Criteria for Choice*
Stern	*Mathematics for Management*

Economic Analysis
and
Industrial Management

Jacques Lesourne

Ancien Elève de l'Ecole Polytechnique
Directeur Général de la
Société d'Economie et de Mathématique Appliquées

Translated by *Scripta Technica, Inc.*

Prentice-Hall Inc.
Englewood Cliffs, N. J.

PRENTICE-HALL, INC.
PRENTICE-HALL INTERNATIONAL, INC., UNITED-KINGDOM AND EIRE
PRENTICE-HALL OF CANADA, LTD., CANADA
J. H. DE BUSSY, LTD., HOLLAND AND FLEMISH-SPEAKING BELGIUM
DUNOD PRESS, FRANCE
MARUZEN COMPANY, LTD., FAR EAST
C. BERTELSMANN VERLAG, WEST GERMANY AND AUSTRIA
HERRERO HERMANOS, SUCS., SPAIN AND LATIN AMERICA

Originally published as *Technique Economique et Gestion Industrielle, 2eme edition.* ©—1960 by Dunod, Paris.

HB
71
L 523

Library of Congress Catalog Card Number 63-18815

Printed in the United States of America—C

Acknowledgments

I wish to express my deep gratitde to the Rockefeller Foundation which, by granting me a year's fellowship to pursue studies in the United States, made it possible for me to prepare this text.

Thanks to that fellowship, I was able to obtain time for the thought that such a work entails and to perform the necessary bibliographic research in the splendid libraries of American universities.

In addition, I extend my thanks to all persons whose names are given below, who kindly examined this book before its publication and who offered comments and suggestions. These observations were very valuable to me and my only regret is that I have been unable, because of the time element, to take them into account as much as I would have wished.

M. ALLAIS—Professor of Political Economy at the Ecole Nationale Supérieure des Mines de Paris.

M. BOITEUX—Associate Director of Electricité de France.

M. DESROUSSEAUX—General Director of the Services Economiques des Charbonnages de France.

M. GARDENT—Director of the Service des Etudes générales et du Marché commun de Charbonnages de France.

M. GRUSON—Chief of the Service des Etudes économiques au Ministère des Finances.

M. MAINGUY—Chief of Service à Gaz de France.

M. MASSE—Associate General Director of Electricité de France.

M. VENTURA—Director of the Bureau de Documentation minière.

May M. ALGAN, Chief of the Département de Recherche opérationnelle de la Société de Mathématiques appliquées, also find here a special expression of my gratitude for his assistance in putting the finishing touches to the text of this book by suggesting the elimination of certain unnecessary passages and permitting me to clarify a great number of obscure points.

J. LESOURNE

Contents

Part II

Cost Structure

Part III

Problems of Synthesis

Conclusion

Introduction

In attaining a certain maturity a science creates new methods and analyses. In addition to the core inherited from the general principles of science, a new methodology borrows elements from many other sciences and supplements them with its own observed facts and empirical rules. Because it is directed toward action, methodology cannot lag but must develop a synthesis, however temporary and imperfect, which will permit decision-making.

At present, this phenomenon is taking place in the science of economics. Although as yet tentative, the synthesis is beginning to present facts in a sufficiently organized and comprehensive manner to permit the creation of analytical techniques. These techniques are closely related and appear to be developing around two poles of interest: namely, the direction and control of the national economy and that of business management. The techniques of analysis and decision-making in the business sector constitute the subject of this book. Here we are concerned with decisions by a micro-economic unit as represented by the firm. Economic analysis, relative to business management, emerges as an area of contact between the science of economics and many other disciplines. For this reason, as can be demonstrated by a review of the history of the subject, economic analysis incorporates elements far more varied than the majority of other analytical techniques. To purely economic considerations are added elements derived from statistics, psychology, sociology, market analysis, and, finally, from industrial engineering and related activities. It remains closely linked to operations research without completely merging with the latter. Furthermore, its efficacy rests upon a correct use of the applied techniques of the physical sciences.

Before any other task can be undertaken, a definition of economic analysis is in order. The examination which will lead to it should then permit a presentation of the organizational setup of this book and its objectives.*

---

*We shall consider as economic analysis only those portions of economics which relate to business management.

I

THE SEARCH FOR A DEFINITION OF ECONOMIC
ANALYSIS

During a firm's lifetime it is largely concerned with making and acting on correct decisions. Its prosperity depends on these activities. Relationships between the various levels in the company are so organized that necessary information is collected and distributed to the proper recipients; that the decisions which are made conform to the policy and aims of the firm; and that the decisions are carried out under proper controls. Because of its central role, an analysis of the decision concept must necessarily be the starting point of any management study, regardless of the aspects forming the subject of the study.

Considered in the abstract, a decision is a choice between a set of possible actions. This decision is considered correct if, having been made in accordance with a certain criterion of value which permits classification of the consequences of such actions, it selects the action most likely to bear consequences of the highest value. Such a definition may appear to be glib; we all know from experience how little is generally known concerning an area of possibilities, how very difficult it is to accurately evaluate the consequences of our actions, and how very rarely we can explicitly formulate our criteria of value.

Nevertheless, by isolating the elements which constitute a decision, namely, the range of alternative actions, their consequences, and the maximization of a criterion of value, the foregoing definition forms the basis of certain very profitable economic analyses. It will be useful to pinpoint our area of study. It will be observed that we have avoided characterizing a correct decision as the selection of the best means of attaining a given objective. Indeed, what is an end result within a certain framework can well be merely a means when viewed in a broader perspective. Thus, the maximization of production, which may be the final objective from the shop foreman's point of view, is, in the eyes of management, merely one of several means of eventually arriving at a maximization of profit. In other words, there exists a hierarchy of value criteria; and according to the type of decisions contemplated, it will be necessary to consider criteria that are generally highly located in the hierarchy.

The implicit criterion of value used in an enterprise requires the consideration of many factors, i.e., technical, economic, sociological, psychological, cultural, and at times even moral factors. The business executives seek a certain combination of profit, technical perfection, economic or political power. They are not disinterested in the general welfare, the wellbeing of their employees or their sociological impact on society. Because of the complexity of this criterion of value, important decisions must of necessity be made by the head of the firm. Analyses cannot be substituted for decision; they merely help top management to find its way among numerous problems.

Despite the complexity of the bulk of a firm's criteria, it is often possible to be content with simpler criteria. This occurs notably in two cases which we shall now discuss in order to arrive at a definition of economic analysis.

1. In the case of certain decisions, the consequences of alternative actions differ only in a limited number of viewpoints. The following example will provide a clarification of this point.

The sales volume of a given firm increases regularly. An extensive survey indicates that, to meet the demand, it will be necessary either to increase the number of employees in the sales department, or to change the present organizational setup. It is obvious that the differences between these two possibilities in the sociological, cultural, etc. . . . planes will probably be minor in relation to the economic advantage to be gained by using available employees to the best advantage. Here, therefore, we are faced with the kind of choice in which the criterion to be used is fairly simple. It reduces to minimization or maximization of a given quantity (in this case, the maximization of the number of orders which can be filled by a given number of employees). We can call this type of choice a technical choice. It consists in maximizing output for given production factors or minimizing the number of production factors used for a given output.

Such problems usually relate to the area of industrial engineering as conceived in France. Technical choices which do not affect prices are among the simplest to conceive in the business life of a firm. As such, they are encountered at the lowest levels of the organization. They condition the efficiency of the firm and form the basis of an appropriate system of decisions. However, a constant danger to which management sometimes succumbs is that of treating as technical choices decisions which involve more complex criteria.

Returning to the example of the sales department, if mechanization is contemplated in some of the operations which can reduce manpower, a more subtle criterion must be used, i.e., one which will take into account two types of expenditure, namely, the cost of manpower and the purchase price of the machines. This example leads us, therefore, to a second class of simple choices which we designate as economic choices whose only important differences can be expressed by solely considering the values, i.e., expressions which involve not merely quantities, but also prices.

On the basis of the foregoing example, the danger of failing to distinguish between technical alternatives and economic alternatives appears very minor. The actual operation of firms, however, teaches us that this is not so. The history of the French coal industry during the first few years following nationalization provides an excellent illustration of this fact. In this industry, where manpower costs are primary, representing approximately 60% of total costs, the procedure has been adopted of using as a criterion the maximization of man-station yield, i.e., the number of tons of coal extracted at each miner station. Clearly, this criterion coincides with minimization of salary costs. Now, pressing for mechanization means that, all other things being equal, men are replaced by machines. Mechanization cannot, however, be judged without studying its repercussions on the value of the coal extracted, on the cost of manpower replacement, and on the cost of the machines introduced. Taking into account solely the yield, a decision of an economic nature is obviously treated as a technical choice [2].*

There are many other types of simple choices. The selection of personnel where, for instance, temperament is an important criterion, can be characterized as a psychological alternative. But such an analysis would divert us from our subject.

2. Some decisions can be made on the basis of simple criteria while others require complex criteria which take into account very disparate elements. Among these, the economic element of profit** will frequently be the most important measure of decision effectiveness.

Decisions by business executives can therefore be facilitated when they know the manner in which the various alternatives are classified in relation to the single economic criterion of profit maximization. They will then be in a better position to compare the economic disadvantages (or advantages) presented by an alternative related to the relevant social, psychological, political, etc., advantages (or disadvantages). Because the former are often measurable and the others are not, this method permits an evaluation of the accepted price to be charged, as it were, to benefit from the psychological, social, or political advantages of an operation. For example, it should be possible to eliminate all automobile accidents by prohibiting speeds in excess of 30 km. an hour, and by having a sufficiently large police force to enforce traffic rules. But society, which deplores the loss of lives resulting from accidents, is unwilling to pay the price to preserve these lives.

The decisions which a business executive is called upon to make between measurable and nonmeasurable elements rarely offer

---

*This criterion of yield nevertheless retains its full value in the coal-mining industry when it is used in the numerous technical choices which are required to be made at short notice.

**Profit may take on a different form in the case of a private or a public enterprise.

such extreme alternatives. But they are greatly facilitated by purely economic study.

Assume that a firm decides to close an unprofitable plant in area A and to construct another plant for which an economic study has determined an optimum location B. The same study makes it possible to calculate the loss which would result from constructing the new plant in area A. It is incumbent upon the head of the firm to balance this loss against the social aspects of the operation (i.e., the extent to which the employees at Plant A are unemployed or are forced to move and work at Plant B).

Therefore, even in the case of complex decisions, simple criteria, and more particularly economic criteria, can provide invaluable assistance to the executive staff of a firm in arriving at decisions.

The foregoing discussion now makes it possible to define economic analysis while avoiding the misunderstandings which usually accompany such definitions: Economic analysis is a scientific method aimed at providing the executive staff of an enterprise with elements which can serve as a basis for their decisions. These elements, measured whenever possible, are derived from a comparison of the various alternative solutions in the light of economic criteria, that is to say, of criteria introducing the price factor.

The scope of economic analysis is restricted on two levels: on one hand, its role is not to effect a comparison of various solutions whose classification is independent of price (technical, psychological choices, etc.); on the other hand, its utility ceases when it begins to compare economic with extraeconomic elements.

To accomplish its task, economic analysis must develop (at least in part) empirically: past information is derived from the statistics of the economy as a whole, from the internal statistics of the firm, and from data established by the accounting department; it is up to management to analyse these data, to make projections regarding their future development, and to make the modifications required for comparison.

The different parts of the foregoing definition are each important:

(a) The use of the word "analysis" emphasized the close relationship which exists between economics and methodology. In fact, by applying certain concepts of economics to actual cases, the methods evolved have tended to enrich economic theory and to open new avenues for pure research.

(b) The reference to a "scientific method" is not merely lip service to present trends. It means that in dealing with problems economic analysis follows well-defined stages determined by scientific philosophy.

(c) The reference to "executive staff" is to emphasize two fundamental and complementary aspects of economic analysis:

1. The problems dealt with are primarily problems of synthesis,

such as confront the responsible staff of the firm at the policy level.

2. It can therefore be effective only if the economists who put it into effect are assigned to the executive echelons. If the conclusions derived through the studies are not promptly communicated to the staff empowered to make decisions, the use of economic analysis merely becomes an exercise where imagination and the ingenuity of analysts are exploited fruitlessly. We touch here upon a delicate subject: the implementation of economic analysis poses, within the firm, certain problems of organization which should not be underestimated.

The economic elements that are basic to decision-making cover only some of the factors to be taken into consideration in a final decision. We wish to stress the basic differences between the roles of the executive and of the economic analyst. The role of the latter is to analyze, conclude, and recommend; the role of the former is to make decisions. This distinction has such important psychological consequences that it would be difficult for the same individual to be simultaneously an excellent executive and a professional economist. The economist must be a free man who, in the quiet of his office, spends his time analyzing, discussing, criticizing, and reflecting. He observes the precautions of scientific method and presents results of limited value which have matured gradually. The executive, on the other hand, is much too absorbed in reaching decisions to find time to devote to this painstaking task. He has to make decisions and any decision must necessarily assume an arbitrary character in which the intuition and personality of the executive play an important role. The executive is not interested in the subtleties of economic methods; he needs to know merely what he can expect from the economists. Should the economists and the executives not be aware of these psychological differences and should they not realize the necessity for them, they will run headlong into serious difficulties: the economists become irritated upon observing executives sometimes making decisions contrary to their conclusions, and the executives become sceptical and discontented with the spirit of criticism and caution demonstrated by the economists. In a well-organized enterprise the functions of these individuals remain distinct, but there is no restriction on the flow of information between top management and the economists. The head of the economics department must not be isolated from action and must be intimately acquainted with the policy of the firm in order to provide correct orientation to the studies of his associates. Inasmuch as the concluding chapter will be devoted in its entirety to these problems, it is unnecessary to dwell on them further at this time.

The concept of measurement is also vital and its implications cannot be taken for granted. The economics department seeks to measure the phenomena under study and this is not the easiest part of its task. One would be seriously mistaken, for example, in believing that the information supplied by the accounting department can be used in the form in which it is provided. Experience has indicated that when an economic study is undertaken, few of the necessary elements are ever available in measurable form. These must be developed on the basis of ad hoc operational concepts and it is the quality of these measurable elements which conditions the entire study. The economist must therefore never lose sight of the reliability of the data available to him and he must avoid presenting results based on erroneous data. Generally, the application of scientific method helps minimize error.

According to the English economist Lionel Robbins, "The science of economics is that science which makes a study of production and of the widespread use of unconventional means on an alternating or reciprocal basis."

This appears to be an obscure definition since an uninformed reader cannot, at first, see its connection with the science of economics. A moment's thought, however, reveals that it does, in fact, include the study of the distribution of income between savings and consumption, of land areas among various crops, of manpower among various areas of activity, etc. Economic analysis may then be characterized as an analysis devoted to a study of the manner in which the firm can apply "unconventional means on an alternating basis" from the country as a whole. As shown very clearly by the duality theorem in mathematical programs (Chapter 13), there is a very strong link between the notion of price, on one hand, and scarcity and the possibility of reciprocal uses on the other, and it is found that through this powerful link the second notion becomes related to the first. It may not be amiss to observe the place occupied by economic analysis in relation to two related disciplines also concerned with business management, namely operations research and industrial engineering.

Operations research was developed in Great Britain and in the United States for the study of military problems during World War II and has since been applied to the solution of industrial and governmental problems. Many definitions thereof have been suggested. For example, according to Morse and Kimball [11], "Operations research is a scientific method whose object is to provide executive personnel with quantitative elements which can serve as a basis for decisions concerning operations which they control." The similarity of the two definitions gives particular import to the complexity of the relationships between operations research and economic analysis. Historically, this phenomenon may be described as follows: scientific knowledge develops on the levels of both pure science and analysis, each analysis having some relationship with one or more disciplines of pure science. Around 1940 there existed a vast no man's land which corresponded to the field of applied science, e.g., economics, administration, political science, military science, etc. This no man's land has been invaded by armies of various persuasions: the operations research army, consisting mainly of mathematicians, physicists, and chemists camping throughout the field, whereas the economic analysis army was content to remain within the area closely related to economic science. It is still too early to determine the redistribution of areas among the various armies. The operations research army may perhaps merge with the others or may camp within the restricted area of the actual application of certain mathematical structures [8].

Industrial engineering needs less comment for, while its area of application overlaps in practice that of economic analysis, it still remains quite distinct in theory and relevance. In seeking the best technical procedure for the fulfillment of a given operation, in order to permit maximization of production for given manpower and equipment, industrial engineering remains entirely within the area of analytical choice. It conditions the efficiency of the economics department without encroaching thereon. However, industrial engineering is also traditionally concerned with the remuneration of personnel, which always presents an economic aspect. And experience has demonstrated that within small and average size firms which cannot afford an economics department and which from time to time call upon outside consultants, economic aspects of wage and related problems are sometimes unavoidable.

Since we now have a definition of economic analysis, it will be possible to begin the second part of this introduction and to present the chapters that are to follow.

II

GENERAL PLAN ADOPTED FOR THIS BOOK

This book is in the nature of a textbook rather than a creative work. It systematically defines methods and problems of economic analysis as they appear at the present state of the art. We have attempted to present it in a form which, on the average, would be of the greatest utility for persons of varying backgrounds interested in rational business management; it is with this criterion in mind that we have sought to solve a few problems of presentation:

1. At the expense of conciseness of text, we have attempted to make this book a complete entity which, aside from a certain basic background in mathematics, would not require any particular training. We have sought to avoid, in particular, restricting its usefulness to economists, and so we have presented some elementary considerations of basic economic theories. Along the same line of reasoning, an important chapter is devoted to the statistical aspects o

econometrics, which, of course, are familiar to statisticians but may also be of interest to engineers and economists.

2. We found it particularly difficult to select the level of mathematical exposition. A complete and rigorous mathematical treatment of the problems considered would have made this book incomprehensible to many who might otherwise derive some use from it. Furthermore, it might have contributed to spreading the false impression that economic analysis is a branch of mathematics. Finally, it might have concealed the essential elements. The absence of any mathematical development, on the other hand, would have deprived the reader of the means of applying, in his field, certain methods of economic analysis. A middle-of-the-road approach had to be adopted which provided considerable latitude. We have generally made use of mathematics only as currently taught in engineering schools; where exceptions had to be made we have given definitions and complementary theorems either in the text or in a final appendix. Finally, we have systematically omitted demonstrations of theorems except when these were brief or contained particularly valuable information.

3. For each type of problem, abstract development is followed by a discussion of a few examples, enabling the reader to form an opinion as to possibilities of actual application. We have multiplied these examples to the utmost extent possible because it is through their richness and diversity that comprehension and conviction are truly born.

4. As a manual, this book does not aim to be more than an introduction. To facilitate access to original sources, a detailed bibliography is provided at the end of each chapter. An author index and subject index (indispensable in any text and all too often omitted from French publications) will be found at the back of this book.

5. Finally, we have refrained from considering subjects which were just barely within the range of application of economic analysis and which could not have been observed in true perspective. Therefore, company wage policy is not considered because this could be discussed adequately only by introducing concepts of time and motion analysis, psychology, and sociology (which extend considerably beyond the economic framework). For analogous reasons, the research techniques of marketing studies are merely touched upon, although the utilization of their results by economic analysis is discussed at some length.

Chapters 1 and 2 are devoted, respectively, to an analysis of the relationships existing between scientific method and economic analysis, and to problems in selecting economic criteria. Understanding the precepts and methods of scientific method is basic to understanding the presentation of the problems and methods of economic analysis in this book. As a matter of fact, the entire significance of this book might be lost or distorted were it not preceded by a brief review of scientific method.

The problem of economic criteria is basic. A mere reference to profit and loss is not sufficient. Economic criteria must be expressed in terms of economic life as well as uncertainty regarding the future. In practice, the results of a study, however excellently conducted, are no better than the least adequate criterion and an economist must endeavor to select these judiciously.

The substance of the three main parts of the book has been dictated by the various aspects of the activities of the firm itself:

1) It disposes of its production on a market within the framework of an economy;

2) It maintains a cost structure which fluctuates in a certain manner to meet production modifications;

3) Decisions concerning the firm's policy are made by combining information regarding these two areas.

In accordance with this plan, the first part (Chapters 3 to 7), entitled "Econometrics In The Service Of Business," is devoted to market and demand analysis. The second part (Chapters 8 to 10) is devoted, as indicated by its title, to "Cost Structure" and analyzes the development of the cost concept in both accounting and economics, as well as the characteristics of marginal costs. The third part (Chapters 11 to 14) deals with "Problems Of Synthesis": regulation of production, management of inventories, investment and price policies. This concludes the exposition of the program we have outlined for ourselves.

It becomes possible thereafter to discuss in Chapter 15, by way of conclusion, problems of organization and formation whose solution strongly affects the efficacy of economic analysis.

BIBLIOGRAPHY

1. CHURCHMAN, ACKOFF, AND ARNOFF:
   Introduction to Operations Research. Wiley, New York, 1957.

2. M. ALLAIS:
   La gestion des houilières nationaliséés et la théorie économique (The management of nationalized coal-mining operations, and economic theory). Imprimerie Nationale, 1953.

3. Lieutenant-Colonel CHANDESSAIS:
   La Recherche Opérationelle (Operations Research). Revue de Défense nationale, May 1955.

4. Ch. GOODEVE:
   Operations Research as a science. Journal of the Operations Research Society of America, 1953, I, 4.

5. G. Th. GUILBAUD:
   La Recherche Opérationnelle et ses applications (Operations Research and its applications). Revue de statistique appliquée, 1956, IV, No. 3.

6. G. Th. GUILBAUD:
   Pour une étude de la Recherche Opérationnelle (For a study on Operations Research). Revue de Recherche Opérationnelle, 1956, I, No. 1.

7. A. LEROY:
   La Recherche Opérationnelle (Operations Research). Revue de statistique appliquée, 1955, III, No. 2.

8. J. LESOURNE:
   La place de la recherche opérationnelle dans l'évolution sociale contemporaine (The role of operations research in contemporary social development).

9. J. F. McCLOSKEY and F. N. TREFETHEN:
   Operations Research for Management (I), Baltimore. The Johns Hopkins Press, 1954. French edition: Introduction à la Recherche opérationnelle, translated and adapted by M. VERHULST and J. LAVAULT.

10. J. F. McCLOSKEY and J. M. COPPINGER:
    Operations Research for Management (II): The Johns Hopkins Press, 1956.

11. P. M. MORSE AND G. E. KIMBALL:
    Methods of Operations Research (5th edition 1954): U.S.A.: The Technology Press of Massachusetts Institute of Technology and John Wiley and Sons, Inc., New York. Great Britain: Chapman and Hall, Ltd., London.

12. R. F. RINEHART:
    Threats to the growth of Operations Research in business and industry. Journal of the Operations Research Society of America, 1954, II, No. 3.

13. C. SALZMANN:
    La Recherche Opérationnelle (Introduction a son application industrielle). [Operations Research (Introduction to its

industrial application).] Revue de statistique appliquée.
1954, II, No. 1.

14. H. A. SIMON:
    Administrative behavior. The MacMillan Company, New
    York, 1948.

15. Society for the Advancement of Management: Proceedings of
    the Conference on Operations Research. New York, 1954.

16. E. VENTURA:
    La Recherche Opérationnelle. [Operations Research.] Revue
    de statistique appliquée. 1956, IV, No. 1.

Economic Analysis
and
Industrial Management

Chapter 1

The scientific method

and economic analysis

The tremendous advances in science—particularly in the physical sciences—during the past hundred and fifty years have given luster to the word "science"; so all disciplines now seek the seal of "scientific" even when it is only a matter of doctrines or scholarship. Many of our contemporaries believe that to deserve this designation one merely needs to undertake objective or systematic studies. The scientific method must be based on intellectual honesty and good faith. However, daily experience reaffirms the meagerness of such an opinion. Scientific method is a severe taskmaster requiring of the researcher something more than an absence of prejudice. It prescribes stages which are admirably described by J. Ullmo in his book, "Modern Scientific Thought" [15], and which are essentially uniform for diverse scientific disciplines.

At the other extreme there is the opinion that scientific method is primarily a mental outlook. Persons trained and working in the "hard" sciences assert that true scientific discipline exists only in the physical and biological fields. In referring to scientific method they allude constantly to the theoretical physics of the 19th century, interpreting its intellectual ramifications very inaccurately. Due to the very narrow margin separating the experimental from the theoretically anticipated results in this field, they assign to the latter a significance which is rejected by prevailing modern scientific thought.

In this book the methodological debate is of primary importance because, if economic analysis is to be equated with scientific method, it becomes necessary to ascertain what is meant by this term. This is not mere intellectual curiosity, but stems from a desire to become familiar with a procedure which can prescribe those tools of economic analysis that are most likely to lead to successful results.

Briefly, the scientific method consists of inferring from known facts a number of hypotheses which are then verified through observation. This, in brief, is the environment within which the techniques of economic analysis are considered in this chapter under the following four phases: analysis of facts, construction of models, verification of hypotheses, and review and presentation of conclusions.

I

ANALYSIS OF FACTS

An economic study starts with recognition by the economic analyst or management that a "problem" exists. Once the problem is identified, it must then be defined with respect to its scope, context, and meaning. The analyst must develop precise definitions of the concepts he will deal with to avoid error and inconsistency.

For example, the term "client" appears to be simple and susceptible to little variation in meaning. But measurement of the economic impact of a client will vary significantly depending on the specific aspect of the term used by the analyst. The client may be regarded as a purchaser, as a consumer, as a user of credit, or from the standpoint of the way in which he spreads his purchases over time or among different suppliers, or using any of a large number of different considerations.

The notion of "cost" also contains a number of possible meanings. "Cost" can be average, marginal, short-term or long-term, fixed or variable, etc. If the type of cost is not specifically defined, it becomes impossible to judge what is involved.

What is significant here is that different facts and considerations are necessary to develop a problem, depending on the meaning and the context of the terms involved.*

Following completion of this initial stage of analysis (where the need for rigor and the exigencies of scientific method have already manifested themselves) the analyst is ready to consider his first major decision: should a study of the problem be undertaken? Such a decision must be made in accordance with the objectives of management. Economic analysis, per se, is of little importance to management. The analyst who serves management should restrict his research to problems that hold promise of return. Time and pertinence are important criteria. There are examples of over-zealous researchers who devote a lifetime carefully studying the details of problems which offer little hope of success. Most of them fail. The fact that some succeed tends to obscure the essential wastefulness of a procedure that ignores the tests of timeliness and pertinence.

---

*[3] page 5.

The economist serving management, unlike the analyst working in pure research, cannot afford to consider problems other than those of interest to management. An economic study is an investment which must yield return. It is of little importance that it is very difficult to predict the possible results of a study at the outset. Repeated evaluations, though lacking in precision, make it possible to avoid the more serious errors. Timeliness is an important factor because executives are often called upon to make a decision within a given period of time; a brief study, however imperfect, prepared in time to meet a deadline is more valuable than a voluminous and complete document presented six months too late.

The next step, after the problem has passed its first tests, consists of assembling the various sources of information pertinent to the study. The initial search is in-house and can take several forms: discussions with the staff, gathering internal statistics, and study and review of work already performed within the organization on a similar or related subject. The analyst next turns to outside sources of information. He reviews the available literature and examines the various abstracts and bibliographies to ascertain whether similar or related research has been done. Such research can provide — especially in the case of market research — quantitative data and can indicate possible methods to be used or avoided. Leads from bibliographies should be followed up, keeping in mind that the search is not only for data but for hypotheses and, sometimes, a rationale.

At this stage, as well as in all the early stages, the following question must be answered repeatedly: should the study be pursued further? This preliminary survey may reveal that previous attempts failed because of insurmountable difficulties which were not immediately apparent. This knowledge may provide the basis for a decision as to the feasibility of the current study.

This first phase in the application of scientific method to economic research can be easily developed and satisfactorily completed because of its systematic character. The next phase, unfortunately, requires a little more sophistication in approach and in methodology.

II

CONSTRUCTION OF MODELS

The analysis of facts and the review of available literature may suggest a certain number of concepts which we will attempt to tie together in order to obtain the elements of a theory, or, in more modern parlance, a model. It would be a serious mistake to suppose that the concepts utilized are preexistent in nature and merely need to be unearthed. As a matter of fact, they are constructed, and the use of a precise vocabulary is one aspect of such development. J. Ullmo, for instance, has demonstrated the extent to which discussions which took place during the last few years regarding national income highlighted this point [14]. It is therefore necessary for the analyst to develop his concepts in such a manner that they will be operational (that is, capable of providing a basis for measurement). The expansion of studies on marginal costs during recent years is a brilliant confirmation of this latter point. Long ago, the science of economics had introduced a general notion of marginal cost in its explanatory diagrams, though it did not attempt to use the concept in quantitative analysis. However, the development of the economic theory of the firm led to an interest in the operational aspects of marginal costs which required the introduction of quantification and measurement.

A scientific theory in the form of a model is a construct of interrelated concepts. The following analogy will perhaps demonstrate how concepts can be related and tested. A child observes a crane unloading a ship in a harbor, and then plans to build a model crane. What may appear to him to be essential, and what he will attempt to reproduce, are the crane's movements. The crane can move a load vertically as well as horizontally in an area circumscribed by the length of the boom and in such directions as are permitted by the ability of the cable control to articulate from the mast. The miniature crane will possess these characteristics. It will be a model of the actual crane, but this model may not be equipped with the same system of electrical control nor will it have a lubricating system. The cable will be represented by a string. Nevertheless, if the ratios between the main dimensions are maintained, the child can predict with this miniature crane the ranges within which the crane will be able to lift or deposit a load. Should the miniature crane fail, the child will decide that there must be an important difference between his toy and the machine he observed in the harbor. This realization may lead him to observe more closely certain aspects which he had at first overlooked. Any scientific theory can be considered to be analogous to the crane erected by the child. As in the case of the toy, it retains only a few essential parameters and some necessary relationships. Naturally, an analyst can add parameters and relationships, just as the child can install a control system on his crane that duplicates the larger one on the real crane. Each complication, however, makes it more difficult to handle the model and causes greater and greater cost in constructing the theory in exchange for refinements of less and less utility.

Model construction is a very common technique employed in science and technology. For instance, in order to determine the best method of straightening the course of a river, a scale model is constructed reproducing the shape of its banks and the configurations affecting the speed of the water. A study is then undertaken to test the effect of various engineering devices on the flow of the water. This reduced model is none other than a theory of the river.

The theory incorporates a great number of important variables. Some of these variables are introduced explicitly by the constructor — the configuration of the banks and the speed of the water, for example. Others are introduced implicitly and result from the fact that water, sand, and soil are used, to conform with reality. It can then be assumed that the essential variables have been taken into consideration.

There remains, however, a major difference between the model and the actual river: namely, size. However, the ingenuity of the analyst has been devoted to developing a model that contains what he considers to be the essential characteristics with respect to function and is, through testing, susceptible to verification. He believes that if certain consequences of his model are verified by tests the likelihood of other confirmations will be enhanced.

It must be emphasized that the analyst does not construct his model haphazardly; he adheres strictly to the necessity for similitude and determines the relations existing in reality between forces, speeds, lengths, etc., for duplication in the scale model.

The Monte Carlo method, introduced in studies in operations research, bears an astonishing resemblance, at least with regard to its simulation aspect,* to the construction of scale models. It can be used in studies relating to the behavior of a system containing random variables when the traditional methods, based on the calculus of probability, become too complicated and difficult. It consists of repeating a great number of simulated experiments based on numerical data drawn at random.

For instance, in the relatively simple example of a survey on the time-use element of a telephone line, the length of call periods and conversation duration can be gathered at random and a diagram of line use can be established for a given period on the basis of initially specified conditions. The frequency distribution of the system can thus be ascertained experimentally by frequent repetition of the same operation.**

This method has been used to determine the optimum firing patterns for a combat vessel based on simulated attacks realized under all possible conditions of offense and defense.

---

*The Monte Carlo method can also be compared to classical methods of calculation by approximation for the determination of definite quantities. It is merely necessary to define these quantities as functions of random variables.

**In cases of this particular type it is frequently of value to conduct only one experiment, but over a very long hypothetical period.

Let us now set aside "material representation"* (i.e., specific quantitative models) and consider only mathematical formulations about relationships between various magnitudes. This is commonly called a scientific theory. Actually, there is no essential difference between a mathematical formulation and a model construct.

Here again, the analyst has selected the essential variables and has assumed functional relations between them. He has a priori confidence in the validity of this theory to the extent that some of the consequences are verified by experience, and to the extent that his theory is consistent with more general theories.

The models of economic analysis extend over a very wide range, from single relationship models with few variables to more extensive models that bring together several hundred variables with many relationships. Various examples of the foregoing will be encountered later, but a few are given here by way of illustration.

Électricité de France, in order to forecast consumption of electricity, assumed that annual consumption of electrical energy was linked, on the one hand, to industrial production and that it increased, on the other, at a constant rate independently of any growth in production. This autonomous expansion was assumed to be due to a steady substitution of electric power for other sources of energy, and to the fact that, given fixed income, the public consumes more and more electricity by modifying the distribution of its income. It is therefore possible to assume mathematically that r, the rate of growth in electrical consumption, per year t is as follows:

$$r_t = u + av_t ,$$

u representing the rate of autonomous growth and v_t the rate of increase of industrial production in the year t. The verification of the model through experience consists in finding the best estimators of the parameters u and a, and testing whether the difference between the calculated r_t and the true r_t is significant. As a matter of fact, the study demonstrated that the model is valid for u = 5% and a = 0.4%.

We shall borrow the second example from Whitman [16]. He examined the problem of the demand for steel, and used the following variables: Y — index of steel sales (by volume), p — the price of steel, $\frac{dp}{dt}$ — the fluctuation rate in the price of steel, I — index of industrial production, and time t. He then constructed a model in the form of the following differential equation:

---

*"Material representation" can be mentioned in the case of the Monte Carlo method, since the model is provided with a "history." For instance, one can refer to the plane which was first to hit a target.

$$Y = Y_0 - ap + b\frac{dp}{dt} + cI + dt \quad a, b, c, \text{ positive.}$$

The characteristics inherent in the development of theories are again encountered in connection with this model. Whitman selected the variables which seemed important to him, being aided in that selection by general economic analysis on the influence of prices, speculative trends, etc. He investigated validity of the model over a long period in the past, and was then able to estimate its value as a forecasting tool.

A study by Henderson [8] on the production and distribution of coal in the United States can serve to illustrate a general type of model to which an entire chapter will be devoted later.

The territory of the United States can be divided into m regions of coal consumption, the annual requirement of region j, expressed in calories, being D_j. With regard to production, it can be considered to be obtained from n homogeneous groups of mines, all mines in a group being substantially within the same geographical location and having the same cost structure. The annual productive capacity of group i is P_i calories and the cost of production of one calorie is c_i,* t_{ij} representing the transportation cost of one calorie from the producing group i to region j. Production and distribution curves remain to be developed which, when account is taken of demand and capacity, minimize the total cost of coal delivered. Let us now introduce x_{ij}, the number transported from group i to region j. The problem can now be expressed mathematically as follows:

The following is to be minimized: $\sum_{ij} (c_i + t_{ij})\, x_{ij}$,

taking into consideration constants: $\sum_i x_{ij} \geq D_j$

$$\sum x_{ij} \leq P_i,$$

x_{ij} being positive or zero.

The number of variables in the model is mn and the number of relation links m + n.

The selection of the degree of complexity of the model requires considerable skill, and care must be exercised that all of the principles of scientific method (especially the testing of theory) are followed.

III

TESTING OF HYPOTHESES

Testing is unquestionably the most neglected link in the application of scientific method in economic analysis. This weakness can

---

*We shall find subsequently that the cost to be taken into account in this case is the marginal cost at short term.

threaten the entire structure. Between the establishment of hypotheses and their testing, an attempt is usually made to deduce mathematically the consequences of the inferences derived from the model; the difficulty of such an operation is variable. At times, as in the foregoing example on the consumption of electricity, the model is tested directly. Frequently, however, it is difficult to subject the model in a decisive manner to the test of facts. The checking is therefore limited to testing specific values of the parameters. In the case of models which represent the structure of demand and the costs of a firm, and which express profit with respect to variables of decision (such as production, prices, etc.), a rule of optimum decision is arrived at mathematically. The test consists of a hypothetical application of the rule to past periods or, experimentally, to the present. Evidently, the tremendous interest in the mathematical formulation of models lies in the fact that this is the only technique that lends itself conveniently to determination of consequences.

Measured information can represent either complete information derived from systematic statistics or incomplete information derived either through sampling or from experiments.

When several methods of approach are possible, it is usually advisable to begin with the least costly. Although these provide less information, they permit a more rational utilization of other procedures. Thus, a discussion of existing statistics can facilitate a pilot survey which can itself increase efficiency in conducting the main survey.

The research decision must take into account the cost of each procedure. Generally, the cost of constructing a model is inversely related to the likelihood of arriving at an incorrect decision from its use.

The economist must analyze his data in order to ascertain whether or not they are compatible with his primary hypotheses. Statistical techniques are frequently employed, but care must be taken to avoid the potentially fatal use of pseudostatistical methods or sophisticated methods which may not have been completely mastered.

Assuming that the analysis has survived to this point, several possibilities must now be considered.

The model may not be verified by experience. This is of the greatest concern, because it establishes either that the hypotheses are not consistent with the facts or that management did not understand the problem. The analyst should generally be more sceptical of his own rationale than of the intuitive judgment of management. Lorie [10] cites the following case.

A few years ago, the director of a large American aircraft company initiated an investigation to determine why people are reluctant to travel by air. His suspicion that fear of accidents was significantly involved became the hypothesis to be tested. The investigation rejected this hypothesis. The reasons given were the cost of air travel, difficulty in reaching the airport, and fears expressed by their families. The director was not convinced by the results of this investigation. He determined to question people about the motives of their friends and relatives rather than their own, surmising correctly that ego would dictate a biased response where the admission of fear was involved. This time, the survey placed fear as the most frequently indicated cause, and the company invested in a publicity campaign to stress the safety of air travel. The first investigation had made use of a faulty method in order to test the hypothesis.

If a countertest is not indicated, suspicion is warranted that the model is not realistic. The process must then be repeated and a new model must be established whose construct utilizes the negative results of the first study.

There are models whose verification is acceptable but whose implementation appears impracticable. For example, if testing the decision derived from the solution of the mathematical formulation requires a specific expense that is not acceptable to management, the expenditure itself should be made part of an amended model. The new solution would be useful in convincing either the analyst or management that his original opinion was not justified.

If the facts and the model are in substantial agreement implementation of the results of the survey can be considered, but this still requires some precautions.

IV

REVIEW AND PRESENTATION OF CONCLUSIONS

Before presenting his conclusions and recommendations to management, the analyst must reconsider the problem in its entirety. The techniques of analysis, model formation, simulation, and formulation reduce a problem to its essential components. Reviewing the results in the context of the original, complete problem is an important verification of their validity and pertinence.

The survey is then presented to management. This requires successful practice of the art of communication. The economic analyst, unlike the researcher in pure science, must communicate at all levels if the firm as a whole is to prosper. The art of communication requires two qualities that are not normally pertinent to the practice of the scientific method: diplomacy and simplicity.

The economic staff, on the strength of a relatively short-run study, must sometimes advise men with many years of experience that their procedures or products can be improved. These men will alternate between defending themselves and attacking the study. Both positions must be taken seriously. First of all, the cooperation of these people is essential to the successful implementation of the results of the study. And, second, they may be right. In any event, a tactful presentation enlisting the advice and aid of these men will go far toward allaying their scepticism and fear. Furthermore, their point of view should be given as much attention by management as the results of the study to insure that the final decision will stem from a consideration of all pertinent facts and opinions. In the end, the firm may be able to arrive at a correct decision because of a diplomatic presentation of the study as well as from the persuasive content of the study's results.

The results of economic analysis must be expressed in understandable form to other members of the firm. Excessive use of technical language will serve only to obscure the issues to the discredit of the economics staff, and will tend to increase the scepticism of the other departments. Detoeuf stated that when a consulting engineer presented his results by employing an esoteric vocabulary and was incapable of summarizing in ordinary language, he had to be driven into a corner; behind the pedantic front, one found "a small, trembling, naked man. . ." [4]. Charts can clarify the text and emphasize the main issues, and if a few technical words must be introduced, it is an easy matter to provide definitions of these in footnotes.

Thus, with the formulated model, the cycle of the scientific method is completed. The various precautions taken along the way will insure consistency in the structure and will make it possible to consider new questions which relate to the main problem. The scientific method will have constantly channeled the analyst's efforts and will have enabled him to travel a straight and rigorous road between his introduction to the problem and his presentation of the solution.

BIBLIOGRAPHY

1. M. ALLAIS:
   L'emploi de mathématiques en economique (The use of mathematics in economics). Metroeconomica, October 1949.

2. M. ALLAIS:
   Puissance et danger de l'utilisation de l'outil mathématique en economique (Power and danger of the use of the mathematical tool in economics). Nouvelle Revue de l'Economie Contemporaine, January 1955.

3. BLANKERTZ, FERBER, WALES:
   Cases and problems in marketing research. The Ronald Press Company, New York, 1954.

4. A. DETOEUF:
Les propos d'Oscar Barenton, Confiseur, ancien élève de l'Ecole Polytechnique (Observations by Oscar Barenton, Confectioner, former student at Polytechnique).

5. J. DUMONTIER:
Le concept opérationnel dans l'economie (The operational concept in the economy). Econometrica, Vol. 17, supplément, July 1949.

6. I. FISHER:
Mathematical methods in the social sciences. Econometrica, July 1941.

7. Sir Ronald FISHER:
Statistical methods and scientific induction. Journal of the Royal Statistical Society, Series B, Vol. 17, No. 1, 1955.

8. HENDERSON:
Efficiency and pricing in the coal industry. Review of economics and statistics, January 1956.

9. J. LESOURNE:
Quelques réflexions sur la science économique (A few remarkd on economics). Les cahiers économiques, April 1956.

10. LORIE and ROBERTS:
Basic methods of marketing research. McGraw Hill, New York, 1951.

11. A. MARCHAL:
De la theorie a la prevision par la méthode de modèles (From theory to prediction by the method of models). Rev. Econ. Pol., 1948, 58, 481-512.

12. R. P. RICH:
Simulation as an aid in model building. Journal of the Operations Research Society of America, Vol. III, No. 1, February 1955.

13. P. THIONET:
Décisions a propos de sondages (Decisions relating to soundings). Revue de statistique appliquee, 1955, Vol. III, No. 4.

14. J. ULLMO:
Le revenu national (The national revenue). Lecture delivered at the Institut de Science Economique Appliquée, Paris.

15. J. ULLMO:
La pensee scientifique moderne (Modern scientific thinking).

16. WHITMAN:
The statistical law of demand for a producer's good, as
illustrated by the demand for steel. Econometrica, Vol. 4,
1936.

Chapter 2

The selection
of economic criteria

It is widely recognized that the nature of the criteria selected affects the outcome of economic studies. The criteria used must reflect the objectives; mathematical techniques, no matter how precise or sophisticated, cannot resolve the difficulty caused by using criteria that are inconsistent with them. Studies are frequently seen in which the authors have adopted criteria which, under analysis, are found to be inconsistent with management policy. The economic analyst must select his criteria with care so that his analysis will reflect the needs of management.

In this chapter we shall concentrate on the criterion of profit maximization and its importance as a forecasting tool. Before examining the meaning and economic implications of profit, however, it might be useful to examine the following considerations:

1. The influence of extraeconomic factors in economic studies.
2. The significance of profit.
3. The hierarchy of criteria.

I

PRELIMINARY CONSIDERATIONS

1. Extraeconomic factors.

Early in the Introduction, in attempting to determine the usefulness of economic criteria, it was demonstrated that, for management, certain decisions are purely economic. Many decisions involving extraeconomic factors are facilitated if, initially, one treats them as though they were economic factors. In such case, however, the conclusions must later be examined in the light of management's overall criteria.

Economic analysis could be facilitated if the extraeconomic factors were to be considered apart from, as well as part of, the general economic context and in such a manner as to permit the decision-maker to interpret their net effect. This can be done in three ways.

a) When the number of choices is small, it is frequently possible to compare the cost of a purely economic solution with the cost of a solution that has been optimized with respect to economic and non-economic considerations. This was observed briefly in the Introduction in the example dealing with the location of plants.

b) Noneconomic considerations are, at times, absolute "restraints" in the sense that their influence on the decision-maker is not diminished by the economic factors.

Thus, in a study on the optimization of coal production and distribution, minimal values are set for production in each mine since lower production might result in unemployment of socially undesirable magnitude.

Another type of restraint (an advantageous one) for a firm seeking to avoid layoffs is the lower limit that can be attributed to employment reduction from one year to another because of natural attrition of manpower.

Frequently, uncertainty about the future brings about new restraints. For example, Électricité de France can produce electricity through both steam generating stations and hydroelectric plants. But the volume of production at hydroelectric plants is not completely predictable because of rainfall variations. Therefore, for given equipment, there is a probability p that the production of hydroelectric plants would be so low that E.D.F. would not be able to supply normal demand. Should this eventuality arise, power cuts would become necessary and E.D.F. would default on its responsibilities. This would not only lose money for the company, but would tend to diminish public confidence. In addition, this could create an unfavorable wave of opinion toward nationalized enterprises, and possibly provoke political reprecussions. It is therefore important to minimize the likelihood of failure. A simple though not perfect method of accomplishing this consists in investing in a plant mix whose value of p is less than or equal to any pre-assigned value p_0.

Failure can also result from the uncertainty of demand. For instance, because of irregularity in hydroelectric production, E.D.F. varies the output of its steam generating stations. The variation in its coal consumption poses a problem for the French coal industry, which is also seeking to minimize cost. The fluctuating demand for coal has an effect on mining workload which tends to create inefficiencies in the utilization of labor and capital at the expense of profits and employment. In order to minimize fluctuations in production, the mines will stock a certain tonnage of coal at each pithead. However, stockpiling is costly. The problem which faces coal mine operators can be formulated as the determination of optimum combinations of stockpiling and changing output. This can be done by taking into account the probability of a given failure p_0 in demand for coal by E.D.F.

It is important to note that the specific effects of restraints are not readily apparent. However, they are parametric and can be tested. Thus, in the case of E.D.F., instead of an a priori selection of p_0, a study should be undertaken to determine the nature of cost variations with respect to the probability of failure; the resulting distribution would be helpful in selecting the p_0 value.

c) Extraeconomic factors can, at times, be costed so that they can be validly integrated with the economic factors in a cost minimization model. For instance, the discharge of an employee can be costed by adding to his severance pay — a direct charge — the additional costs attributable to loss in output, decreased average efficiency of plant personnel, and cost of later recruitment and training.

There is considerable overlapping between the methods outlined above. For example, each value of attributed costs mentioned in the third method corresponds to a parameter value of the restraints described in the second method. The cost of failure, for instance, can be determined by studying the variations of profit with respect to the probability of failure. The first method is the simplest, but its use is limited. The third method is of greater mathematical convenience than the second, for it introduces no asymmetry whatever to the problem, but it is usually very difficult to assign costs to extraeconomic factors. The second method, therefore, seems to be the most satisfactory, especially when the restraints are parametric. The use of these various methods does not exhaust the problem of extraeconomic considerations. Such methods merely facilitate the utilization of conclusions inferred from economic studies.

2. Significance of profit.

From a purely economic point of view, the most pervasive objective for management — and, therefore, the major consideration in selecting the criteria for economic analysis — is maximization of profit. On the microeconomic, short-run level, this is a valid objective. However, from a macroeconomic point of view, a current profit advantage for an individual firm might not be consistent with the long-term interests of the overall economy.

It would be premature, at this point, to give full consideration to problems of optimization with respect to the national economy. However, at the risk of oversimplification, a few observations might be helpful at this point.

In considering the disposition of national resources, we can generalize that the allocation of the factors of production is not optimal if a modification thereto can effect an increase in overall production. Conversely, conditions can be said to be economically optimized when it is impossible to increase total output by varying the allocation of the factors of production.

Economists have long sought to determine the conditions necessary for reaching a state of optimum production. In their analysis, they frequently consider the problem in the light of perfect competition and monopoly. Firms operating in perfect competition establish and implement internal policy independent of the market price for their products. Their profits are maximized by controlling costs and varying production. Under conditions of imperfect competition, market price is influenced by production policy; the monopolist seeks to maximize his profit by varying his output to the point where his marginal cost is equal to a price that can attract an equivalent demand.

It should not be inferred from the foregoing that free competition is the only system which approaches perfect competition. The idea that one can approach this ideal through planning is not precluded. It does demonstrate, however, that if free competition constitutes a valid approximation (if not the best) of perfect competition, then the thesis of maximization of profit by private enterprises, provided they do not constitute a monopoly, can be defended, even from the point of view of general interests. Monopolies (and nationalized industries which are frequently monopolistic in character) must also seek to maximize their profit, but without utilizing the relationship existing between their selling price and the volume of their output if their activities are to be consistent with the public interest.

Under these conditions, when the price system is optimal each firm contributes to the general welfare by maximizing its profit. As a matter of fact, this problem has many ramifications and we can observe the effects of an individual firm's policies in areas other than the pricing system. The development of a theory of general interest which takes into consideration all possible interactions still remains to be accomplished. However, even if the scope and methods of econometrics were to be vastly enlarged, we would continue to use concepts analogous to profit.

It is therefore reasonable to continue to use the criterion of maximization of profit regardless of whether the context is a business viewpoint or a more general interest.

3. The hierarchy of criteria.

The criterion of maximizing the profit of the firm suffers frequently from the defect of being too broad. In the case of large firms, it leads to a systematic introduction of very many variables. Under such conditions, subordinate criteria are introduced and maximum conditions are sought with respect to each new criterion. Following are two illustrative examples.

A group of operations analysts in the United States studying the Battle of the Atlantic in 1943. Naturally, the objective which corresponds to a maximization of returns in industry is to win the war. Theoretically, one should therefore consider the effect of decisions concerning the Battle of the Atlantic on the battles in Africa and in Russia and on the war in the Pacific. However, within limits, a single objective can be considered: namely, to win the Battle of the Atlantic. This is a subordinate criterion which may not be consistent with objectives in other theatres or with the overall objective of winning the war.

Let us now consider the problems of a large French mining firm, Les Charbonnages de France. This company manages nine coalfields. Let us suppose that an economic study is being made in one coalfield. Which criterion should be adopted? In the interest of the company, it should be the criterion of maximization of profit for the company as a whole. But such a criterion may be unwieldy. It would certainly be simpler to use the criterion of maximizing the return of the individual field.

Subordinate criteria are necessary because, once established, they are useful guides for eliminating a great number of secondary variables. This makes it possible to concentrate on the main aspects of a problem and on the task of rational simplification that is undertaken at the time of model construction.

Care must be exercised in the selection of subordinate criteria before undertaking the study, to insure that they are consistent with the general criterion of maximization of profit.

It is difficult to establish rules governing the selection of subordinate criteria. The choice depends upon the particular problem under study. A few generalizations, however, can be set forth.

1. Every effort should be made to use simple criteria.

2. Relationships expressed as ratios can be misleading. A ratio is a quotient of two numbers in which changes in value may have a variety of interpretations, depending on whether the source of the change is in the numerator or in the denominator.

3. The major criterion of maximization of profit for the firm as a whole may be approximated by considering the subordinate problems of maximizing profits in each component of the firm, provided the values of the inputs and outputs for each component can be determined. Furthermore, if gross income is known, and prices and output are stable, the problem of maximizing profit may be analyzed from the viewpoint of minimization of expenditures. Minimization of expenditures is equivalent to a minimization of the average cost or to a maximization of the difference between sale price and average cost.

4. Criteria that are subordinate to the objective of profit maximization can, almost always, be expressed in value terms, i.e., the product of a unit price and a quantity.

II

CALCULATION OF PROFIT

Profit is the difference between a firm's gross income and expenses of all types. But such a definition, as simple as it appears, must be closely scrutinized because much depends upon what is incorporated in the costs.

For instance, should the salaries paid to top management staff be included? Some economists insist that top management's salaries are essentially different from other salaries. Management is paid to coordinate the diverse activities of a firm and to define its policy. Management is responsible for the introduction of innovations and shoulders the blame for failure. Wages paid to labor are fixed by convention, law, and, quite frequently, by union contract. Top management's salary is more directly related to profits. However, this is a distinction with little practical difference. A statistical investigation undertaken in the United States demonstrated that the salaries of executives did not follow the variations of profits, but remained substantially stable.* It therefore appears reasonable to consider them as costs.

Should hypothetical interest on the firm's capital be incorporated in the definition of costs? From E. L. Grant's point of view, "Where ownership funds are available without borrowing, it is not necessary to pay out interest to any creditor. Nevertheless, interest is a cost just as much as if it had to be paid out. There is always the alternative of lending money at interest (or perhaps paying off a debt on which interest is being paid) or somehow investing funds productively so as to yield a return. If this opportunity does not exist for the private corporation or government body, it does exist for the stockholder or the citizen who pays the taxes. Thus, in this situation, interest is a cost in the sense of an opportunity foregone, an economic sacrifice of a possible income that might have been obtained by investment elsewhere."** As a matter of fact, interest is a price similar to others associated with the exchange of sums available now against sums to become available in the future.

Economic studies should account for interest on corporate capital just as though it were borrowed capital. The determination of the

_____

*[29] page 5.
**[16] page 71.

rate of interest to be retained constitutes another problem which will be examined later.

Profit and its calculation are affected by the fact that receipts and expenditures are not static with respect to time.

Let us consider an enterprise established during the year 0. Let us designate the consecutive years by $0, 1, 2, \ldots, p, \ldots$; R_p then represents the receipts of the enterprise during the year p, and D_p the expenditures. The profits for the year p are, therefore, $R_p - D_p$.

If all annual profits are equal, there is no difficulty in selecting the best solution. But if this is not the case, it is useful to consider annual variations in terms of borrowed funds.

If all one-year loans made in the economy are at the same interest rate i (a reasonable hypothesis because the problems of risk are excluded here), and if this interest rate is constant over time, having 1 franc this year or the certainty of having (1 + i) francs next year amounts to the same thing for anyone. For if he has the certainty of having (1 + i) francs next year, but desires to have 1 franc now, he can borrow the franc and the sum he will receive in a year will permit him to repay his loan upon payment of interest. If, on the other hand, he currently has 1 franc but wishes to have (1 + i) next year, he can lend the franc and he will receive exactly (1 + i) in a year. In other words, to possess 1 franc within a year is equal to possessing

$$v = \frac{1}{1 + i} \text{ francs}$$

now, v representing the present value of 1 franc within a year. If we now consider 1 franc payable in two years, and if the rate of interest on loans remains i, this sum is equal to 1/1 + i francs payable in one year's time or to $1/(1 + i)^2$ francs payable now. The present worth of a franc payable in p years is $1/(1 + i)^p$.

The concept of present value is one of the most convenient tools in economic analysis [3] [6]. Through the use of this concept, the sequence of a firm's future profits can be represented in terms of its present worth (calculated from the year 0):

$$V = R_0 - D_0 + \frac{R_1 - D_1}{(1 + i)} + \cdots + \frac{R_p - D_p}{(1 + i)^p} + \cdots = \sum_{p=0} \frac{R_p - D_p}{(1 + i)^p}.$$

It can be demonstrated that V is equal to the present value of the future profits of an enterprise in the accounting sense of the term. In order to do this, let E_p be the value of the company's net assets at the end of the year p (value of the equipment, stocks, available funds, etc.).

The company's net assets during the year p vary from E_p to $(1 + i) E_{p-1}$. If assets E_{p-1} existing at the end of the year p - 1 were loaned during the year p, the company would collect at the end of year p interest in an amount equal to iE_{p-1}.

The profit for the year p is therefore:

$$R_p - D_p + E_p - (1 + i) E_{p-1}.$$

The present value of future profits is (for the years p - 1 and p):

$$\cdots + \frac{R_{p-1} - D_{p-1} + E_{p-1} - (1 + i) E_{p-2}}{(1 + i)^{p-1}} +$$

$$+ \frac{R_p - D_p + E_p - (1 + i) E_{p-1}}{(1 + i)^p}$$

which indicates that E_{p-1} and all similar terms disappear.

Thus, the present value of a company's profits is equal to the present value of the difference between future receipts and expenditures. It should be noted that the latter, which do not include interest, are calculated at the time payment is actually made. Instead of the term "present value of profit," the expression "effective income" is also commonly used.

At one time, the concept of present values was not utilized; efforts were made to solve problems created by the inequality of yearly profits by calculating yearly profit averages. Thus, let us consider the case of a company in which annual receipts and expenditures remain constant over the years and are equal to R and D, respectively. In the year o, some initial expenditures D_0 become necessary. Without the counterpart of equivalent receipts, the income is:

$$- D_0 + \sum_{p=1} \frac{R - D}{(1 + i)^p}$$

However, there exists a yearly sum d such that $D_0 = \sum_{p=1} \frac{d}{(1 + i)^p}$.

It can therefore be considered that the company has an annual (constant) profit equal to R - D - d.

Although, when correctly used, this second method is equivalent to the use of present values, its utilization requires more extensive calculation when the flow of receipts or of expenditures is not constant.

Because of the importance of effective income, we list its main properties below.

1. The calculation of effective income assumes that it will be computed on the basis of compound interest. This results directly from the equivalence between 1 franc during a particular year and $(1 + i)^p$ francs during the year p. Any method used by the company which does not make use of compound interest is therefore at variance with calculations based upon the present value. This applies especially to methods of calculating simple interest,

amortization, and financing costs. Moreover, by erecting a definitive and unjustified screen between capital and interest, simple interest calculations do not make sense from an economic viewpoint.

2. According to its own definition, effective income takes into account interests which are associated with the different sums R_p, D_p, etc. There is no point, therefore, in introducing them elsewhere. If this were properly attempted, they would be self-canceling. If this reasoning were incorrect, interest would be counted twice.

3. By bringing total yearly expenditures and receipts into the picture, the calculation of effective income does not require any arbitrary apportionment of expenditures among the various units produced. This advantage is a considerable one.

4. The R_p and D_p quantities represent the actual receipts and expenditures of the company during the year in which they are incurred. Thus, investment expenditures are credited in the year during which the contractor who performed the work was paid rather than during successive amortization periods. For this reason, the calculation of effective income is relatively direct: it is merely necessary to record the expenditures and the receipts at the precise moment payments are effected.

5. Effective income does not depend upon the sequence of values of the company's net assets at the end of each year. This sequence of values is simply used as a basis for developing a series of annual profits. Through loans, the company can always convert its profits into any succession of incomes which is equivalent in actual value.

6. The calculation of effective income presumes an estimate of future expenditures and receipts. The past is not pertinent, since past expenditures and receipts can no longer be affected by our decisions. This is perfectly logical. The fact that one has expended billions in the construction of a plant does not necessarily imply that it should not be abandoned if, for example, its continued utilization were to be more costly than its replacement.

Once the method of calculating the actual value of profit for a series of future, well-defined situations in the company is known, all that remains is to apply this knowledge in the selection of one of alternative decisions. This will depend on the manner in which we may be able to link our present decision with future situations of the company.

III

PREDICTABILITY OF THE FUTURE AND FORMULATION OF SELECTED CRITERIA

It is helpful to distinguish four types of knowledge concerning the future, each of which leads to problems of making entirely different decisions.

1. The future is treated as though it were perfectly known.

Each decision is associated with a well-defined sequence of future situations in the company, principally a sequence of annual expenditures and receipts. It is then possible to characterize each decision by the effective income which it provides, and to select the one for which the effective income represents a maximum. It will be noted that, if the information is complete, this decision is also one which maximizes the company's market value (i.e., the sum of its debt and the value of its shares, the latter representing the present value of future profits of the company). Because the future cannot be predicted with certainty, an attempt is made to estimate the effect of errors in prediction on effective income.

Particular attention should be given to the period over which effective income is calculated. For example, there are alternative choices available to a firm in considering economic retention policies for its capital equipment which can have varying effects on calculations of long-term effective income. Let us consider two large coalfields of varying age, both currently producing the same effective income. However, by taking into account almost any alternative course of future action with respect to retention and replacement of the fields, estimates of future income can no longer be based on assumptions of equivalence.

If all units of equipment have the same life expectancy, say n years, all that remains, in order to make a decision, is to ascertain what is likely to occur in each eventuality during these n years, unless the choice which favors one solution over another could be followed by important consequences after discarding this equipment.

If all units of equipment do not have the same life expectancy, and if it is believed that it will be necessary to replace them with substantially identical equipment, one should consider as a retention period the smallest common multiple of the life expectancies of such units of equipment.

In all other instances, it would be theoretically necessary to predict the future ad infinitum. This is actually what the Électricité de France has been doing in its studies. This method is practical and less speculative than would appear on the surface, since computations of future income for extremely remote periods for which very little information is available are given a very low value.

When a decision can be characterized by the choice of a certain number of parameters which include all values of a given interval (for example, daily production, average volume of stocks, sale price, etc.), and when the effective income is a continuous function of such parameters, then the analytical conditions required for the determination of a maximum will be introduced. For example, if x and y are the parameters of decision and are linked by the relationship $r(x, y) = 0$, then the problem is to maximize the effective income R (x, y), taking into account the preceding restraint. If x and y take on increments, then dx, dy,

$$R'_x\,dx + R'_y\,dy \leqslant 0$$

with $\qquad\qquad r'_x\,dx + r'_y\,dy = 0$

which, if the presence of maxima at the end points is excluded, leads to the condition

$$\frac{R'_x}{r'_x} = \frac{R'_y}{r'_y}.$$

This condition demonstrates that for variations in x and y the marginal variation of income due to x, $R'_x dx$ is equal to the marginal variation of income due to y, $R'_y dy$. In other words, in a maximum situation, there is equilibrium of marginal effects of the various factors. A translation into economic terms of this property of the maximum frequently permits a clearer meaning to be given to the results of the mathematical study.

2. Each current decision is associated with future random situations.

The word random is used in the mathematical probability sense. More precisely, the present value of future profits engendered by a decision is a random variable with a known probability distribution. This is no longer a case of choosing between various decisions each leading to different effective incomes; the choice is now between various decisions each leading to different probability distributions of effective income.

For example a newsdealer knows that he has a certain number of regular customers each day, plus a certain number of nonregular customers. If one assumes that the unsold copies are not returnable, how many newspapers should he buy each day? Should he purchase a small quantity, he would rarely have any unsold copies, but he would also frequently miss sales. If, on the other hand, he purchases a large number of newspapers, he will always satisfy his customers, but he will often be left with unsold copies. The optimum number will maximize the difference between his gross receipts and his losses.

What method should be used by an insurance company to determine its premium charges? The effective yield is not given for each premium value, but it is a random variable which depends upon the number of insurees and the frequency of accidents resulting in paid claims.

Another example is the irregularity in hydroelectric production and its repercussions on the consumption of coal. Électricité de France's annual expenditures constitute a random variable which depends upon the degree of rainfall during the year.

In the same manner, an oil company's receipts based on the sale of fuel oil depend upon the random variable represented by temperature.

Further consideration of the complexities of alternative choices can be facilitated by dividing the possibilities into two major categories.

The first presupposes that the firm belongs to a single individual, and that he has no intention of selling his business. In other words, it is the case of the newsdealer who does not anticipate changing his trade.

The second covers the case of a company which is owned by a large number of stockholders.

It may seem that the second hypothesis is the only realistic one, and that, consequently, it is unnecessary to consider the first one. As a matter of fact, the criteria which emanate from the first hypothesis are practical ones, and, in general, even for firms established as limited liability companies. Whereas those which evolve from the second hypothesis, though theoretically much more satisfactory, are more difficult to apply.

When a firm is owned by a single individual, the choice depends upon the individual's preferences. An attempt must therefore be made to represent the individual's total preferences. We start by presupposing that the individual is rational, i.e., we assume that his field of preferences follows certain axioms in which the symbol x indicates a random income with a given probability distribution and (X) represents all possible x's. (In order to facilitate this reasoning, these random incomes can be likened to hypothetical lottery tickets.)

In order to carry the analysis further, it is necessary, at this time, to state five axioms.

Axiom I. For any x_1 and x_2 in (X), the individual is able to determine whether he prefers x_1 to x_2, x_2 to x_1, or if he considers x_1 and x_2 as equivalent. This axiom is merely the statement that the individual has certain preferences.

Axiom II. If x_1 is preferred to x_2, and x_2 is preferred or equal to x_3, x_1 is preferred to x_3. If x_1 is preferred or equal to x_2, and x_2 is preferred to x_3, x_1 is preferred to x_3. Finally, if x_1 and x_2, on one hand, and x_2 and x_3 on the other hand, are equivalent, x_1 and x_3 are also equal. This axiom, which states that preferences are transitive, simply means that if we prefer an apple to a pear, and an orange to an apple, we prefer the orange to the pear.

If these two axioms are accepted, it can then be demonstrated that it is possible to associate with any x a number U (x), which is the utility function of x, for the individual under consideration.

If x_1 and x_2 are equal, then U (x_1) = U (x_2). If x_1 is preferred to x_2 U (x_1) > U (x_2).

Axiom III. If x_1 is preferred or equal to x_2, and x_2 is preferred or equal to x_3, there exists a lottery ticket with prizes: x_1 with the probability p and x_3 with a probability $(1 - p)$ which is equivalent to x_2.*

This axiom expresses the continuity of preferences.

Thus, with x_1 = certainty of winning 500,000 francs,

x_2 = one chance out of two of winning 400,000 and one chance out of two of not winning anything,

x_3 = certainty of winning 100,000 francs,

one can assume that for any individual who prefers x_1 to x_2 and x_2 to x_3, there will be a ticket equivalent to x_2 which provides p chances of winning 500,000 francs, and $1 - p$ chances of winning 100,000 francs. For example, p can be equal to 1/4 for an individual who considers only the mathematical expectation.

Axiom IV. This axiom, evolved by P. Massé and Morlat, is extremely important and great care must be taken to have it verified in practice. Its equivalent in terms of an exact prediction would be: "We prefer two francs to one franc." In order to state this axiom, reference will once more be made to the example of the news-dealer. Assume n to be the number of newspapers purchased one morning. To each n value corresponds a certain probability distribution of the dealer's returns for the day. Thus, $P_n (r)$ would be the probability that these returns would be less than or equal to r if n newspapers are purchased. The inverse function $R_n (P)$ gives the income r with the probability P of not being exceeded. As P increases, so does r and for certainty $(P = 1)$, r is equal to the maximum possible income.

For two numbers n_1 and n_2, two cases are possible depending upon whether the curves $r_{n1} (P)$ and $r_{n2} (P)$ intersect or not.

1. If these curves do not intersect, for example

$$r_{n_1} (P) < r_{n_2} (P) \text{ (Figure 1)}.$$

then the above inequality is equivalent to:

$$P_{n_1} (r) > P_{n_2} (r) \text{ or: } 1 - P_{n_1} (r) < 1 - P_{n_2} (r)$$

and the latter inequality indicates that the probability of an income equal to or greater than r is greater with n_2 than with n_1, whatever r may be.

Under these circumstances, it would not be reasonable to prefer n_1 to n_2. Axiom IV may then be stated as follows:

"When one is called upon to choose between two random distributions of incomes 1 and 2, and when the probability of having an income equal to or greater than a value r is greater** with 2 than with 1, whatever r may be, distribution 2 is preferable to distribution 1."

---

*The illustrated process is a "balancing" of probability.

**Or equal for all r values except one.

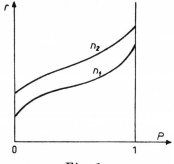

Fig. 1.

2. Let us now suppose that the two curves intersect (Fig. 2). For a weak r ($r < r_0$), the chances of securing gains greater than r are greater with n_1. For a large r ($r < r_0$) they are greater with n_2. In other words, lesser gains are rare with n_1, but large gains also are rare. With n_2 the possibility of larger gains is great, but there is also a risk of much lesser gains. In statistical language, the standard deviation of the distribution of income n_1 is smaller than the standard deviation of the distribution of income n_2.

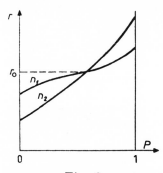

Fig. 2.

One needs to have tried his hunch but once with the French National Lottery to realize what this means. When one purchases 2,000 francs worth of National Lottery tickets, one may obtain either a single ticket, or one-tenth of each of ten tickets. In the first instance, one's chances are greater of winning large amounts, but the chances are quite strong that one will lose the entire stake. In the second case, one will probably not lose everything, for one or more of the tenths will be reimbursed, but if one of the numbers comes up with a sizable prize, only one-tenth will be won.

It should be realized, therefore, that, in the case of Fig. 2, there is no reason for choosing, a priori, either the n_1 or the n_2 distribution. Axiom IV cannot settle this issue.

To the four preceding axioms, American economists traditionally add a fifth known as the axiom of independence, the validity of which has been questioned by P. Massé and M. Allais.

Axiom V. If x_1 and x_2 are randomly distributed variates of equivalent incomes, then the joint distribution of x_1 and x_3 is equivalent to the joint distribution of x_2 and x_3.

As it stands, this axiom appears to be extremely reasonable. However, there are some disturbing consequences which lead certain economists to reject it. Mr. Allais' argument in this connection is essentially as follows [7]:

1. The axiom of independence leads to a rejection of criteria as nonrational which otherwise appear entirely satisfactory.

2. "It is an easy matter to construct numerous examples where persons considered perfectly rational will respond to the axiom in a contrary manner without any hesitation" [7].

In order to demonstrate the above, we shall reconstruct an example supplied by M. Allais.

It can be deduced from axiom V and the preceding axioms that, if the lottery ticket offering:

x_1 with the probability p
x_2 with the probability 1 - p

is preferred to a lottery ticket

x_2 with the probability p
x_3 with the probability 1 - p

this situation remains constant if a new x_4 distribution is substituted in the two x_3 tickets (x_1 and x_2 are no longer here equivalent distributions).

Let us select for x_1, x_2, x_3 the following distributions:

x_1: certainty of winning 100 million
x_2: 10 chances in 11 of winning 500 million
    1 chance in 11 of not winning anything
x_3: certainty of winning 100 million.

If we combine x_1 and x_3 on one hand, x_2 and x_3 on the other with $p = \dfrac{11}{100}$, we are then obliged to compare the following situations:

A   certainty of receiving 100 million

B $\begin{cases} \text{10 chances in 100 of winning 500 million} \\ \text{1 chance in 100 of not winning anything} \\ \text{89 chances in 100 of winning 100 million.} \end{cases}$

Let us select for x_4 the following distribution:

x_4: certainty of not winning anything

and substitute x_4 for x_3 in the A and B situations. We are led to compare the following situations:

$$
C \left\{ \begin{array}{l} \text{11 chances in 100 of winning 100 million} \\ \text{89 chances in 100 of not winning anything} \end{array} \right.
$$

$$
D \left\{ \begin{array}{l} \text{10 chances in 100 of winning 500 million} \\ \text{90 chances in 100 of not winning anything.} \end{array} \right.
$$

Axiom V implies that, if situation A is preferred to situation B, situation C is preferred to situation D. However, we find that many persons who are considered to be rational, while they prefer A to B, nevertheless prefer D to C.

3. The reasoning basic to axiom V is not satisfactory. It goes somewhat as follows: If the event occurs with probability (1 - p), one finally finds oneself in the same situation. If the probability of the event occurring is p, the first ticket gives x_1 and the second x_2, which are considered equal. The two tickets must therefore be equivalent. But this reasoning becomes "ex post" once the first drawing characterized by the probability p has been held, and eliminates the essential element which involves the simultaneous drawing of prospects x_1 and x_3, on one hand, and x_2 and x_3 on the other. As a matter of fact, if one assumes an "ex ante" position, as one must, it becomes difficult to justify axiom V.

A. If one accepts axioms I, II, III, IV, and V, the utility functions U (x)* possess properties which simplify their use considerably:

a) If x_3 is the lottery ticket with x_1 prizes, with probability p and x_2 with probability (1 - p) then

$$U (x_3) = pU (x_1) + (1 - p) U (x_2).$$

This relationship demonstrates that one will seek to maximize the mathematical expectation of the utility function U (x).

b) All possible utility functions may be derived by a linear transformation:

$$U' (x) = aU (x) + b \qquad a \text{ being positive.}$$

B. If axiom V is rejected, retaining axioms I, II, III, and IV, the utility functions lack the foregoing properties: if U (x) is a utility

---

*Properly, these functions do not then represent utility, but are selection indicators.

function, any transformation f (U), where f (U) is an increasing function of U, defines a new utility function.

Inasmuch as the utility function represents the preference field of an individual, a decision must be made which will maximize this function. However, economic studies cannot begin with complicated U (x) functions. They must be limited to a small number of functions leading to relatively simple criteria. The foregoing theoretical discussion will demonstrate the logic of these criteria:

1. The maximization of mathematical expectation.

For instance, in the case of a random distribution of x, p(x, r)dr is the probability of having an income between r and r + dr. This first criterion considers the utility of x to be its mathematical expectation:

$$U(x) = \int_{-\infty}^{+\infty} rp(x, r)\, dr.$$

The criterion, which maximizes the average gain from an operation if the operation is repeated many times, can be criticized for the following reasons:

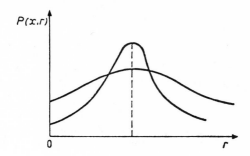

Fig. 3.

It assigns the same value to the two distributions of Fig. 3 which have the same mean but which have different variances. Now, as shown by the example of the purchase of Loterie Nationale tickets, the variance is one of the parameters to be taken into consideration when an operation is not repeated many times [7].

If the operation is repeated a great number of times — such as in the case of the newsdealer who buys his newspapers each morning — the effective average of daily gains will eventually approach its mathematical expectation, provided one has not become bankrupt in the meantime.

There is therefore, a tendency to substitute for the criterion of the mean, criteria which also depend upon the variance, or upon the probability of ruin.

2. Criteria which are conditioned by the mean and variance.

Let us assume R to be the mathematical expectation of income, and S the standard deviation. The problem is to maximize a utility function of the form U (R, S). It is possible to demonstrate, if only normal distributions are considered, that, for a function U (R, S) to satisfy the first 4 axioms, it is necessary and sufficient that the partial derivative of U with respect to S be positive. The curves of uniform utility in plane R, S are represented in Figs. 4 and 5. In Fig. 4, the partial derivative of U with respect to S is positive, which indicates a preference for security.

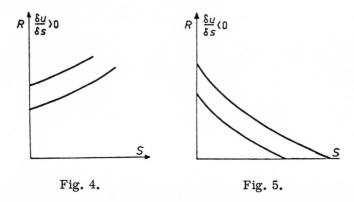

Fig. 4.   Fig. 5.

In order that the function U (R, S) should satisfy axiom V, rigorous conditions must be met. Among functions of this type compatible with axiom V, are found such functions as

$$U (R, S) = R + a S^2 \quad \text{(a positive or negative)}$$

because when random variables are independent, the means and the variances are respectively additive, and that consequently:

$$U (R, S) = p U (R_1, S_1) + (1 - p) U (R_2, S_2) \quad \text{(cf. Section A above).}$$

When income is not normally distributed, but is any random variable (particularly one from an asymmetrical distribution), the above criteria may not be in accord with axiom IV. One solution consists of substituting the probability of ruin for the standard deviation.

3. Criteria which are conditioned by the mean and probability of ruin [7].

Let the mean be represented by R and the probability of ruin by q which is defined as the probability that the present value of income is less than a certain R value, which is dependent upon the firm. The term "ruin" is not restricted here to its most drastic meaning. It is used to designate any state judged undesirable by management.

The utility function U (R, q) confirms the first four axioms under the following necessary and sufficient conditions:*

$$\frac{\partial U}{\partial R} > 0 \quad \frac{\partial U}{\partial q} \leqslant 0.$$

These conditions are much more restrictive than those imposed on function U in the preceding paragraph. The lines of utility in the R, q plane can assume the shape of Figs. 6, 7 and 8. In Fig. 7, management is determined not to go beyond a certain probability of ruin. In Fig. 8, he maximizes his mathematical expectation, but is determined not to go beyond a certain probability of ruin.

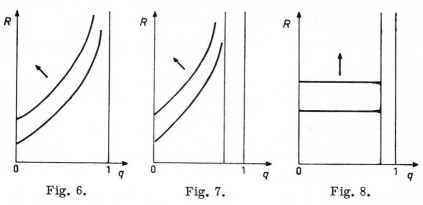

Fig. 6.   Fig. 7.   Fig. 8.

---

*We will demonstrate only that the $\frac{\partial U}{\partial q} \leq 0$ condition is necessary.

It is necessary only to observe that it is always possible to find two random distributions which will fulfill the following requirements:

The values of R and q are determined in advance.

q - dq is the probability of ruin, and R + dR is the mean where dR = edq, e being smaller than any preassigned number.

The latter requirement is preferred by virtue of axiom IV.

In going from the first to the second distribution dU must be positive.

$$dU = U'_R + dR + U'_q (- dq) = (eU'_R - U'_q) dq$$

U'_r being positive, U'_q must be negative or zero.

It is possible to demonstrate that the U (R, q) function is consistent with axiom V except that it takes the form U (R,q) = R - aq in which a is a positive constant. This formulation is not satisfactory unless it excludes the value q = 1, because it is apparent that when q approaches 1, R must approach a given value of U at infinity (Fig. 6) [7].

The criterion of maximization of mathematical expectation of income is extremely useful, provided the probability of ruin is less than a given value.

The utility of this criterion can, however, be improved by assigning a probability of ruin for each period, which imposes a restraint on the current income in each period as well as on the present value of future returns. The criterion can be made more meaningful by defining the probability of ruin as a probability that the cash in hand at the end of a period will be less than a given value, rather than the probability that the income during one period will be less than a given value. Management is as much interested in promoting a profitable and expanding enterprise as it is in avoiding bankruptcy. The conversion of fixed assets to cash might satisfy an immediate need but might also be counter to long-term interests.

In all cases, the responsibility rests with the "executives" of the firm to select the probabilities of ruin, and the parameters which appear in utility functions. Though this may appear to be a simple matter when the managers own the enterprise, it is another matter entirely for management to determine policy when it merely manages the firm on behalf of stockholders.

The following illustrations with respect to the problem of risk and its effects on a joint stock company are useful as a means of considering some of the factors and relationships that must be considered when selecting economic criteria for analysis of the market.

1. It may be assumed that investment plans are known on the money market. In addition — and this limits the flexibility of the model — all fluctuations of income engendered by existing or new investments are presumed to present identical risks. The property of risk consists of a series of available returns during successive years, with a given probability distribution each year, and each investment is characterized by the number of ΔP units of risk it procures.

2. Management, acting in the best interests of the owners of the company, must seek to maximize the market value of all shares existing at the time of the decision. Such behavior is entirely compatible with the criterion of profit maximization when the future is definitely known.

3. As a consequence of competition, the price for risk existing in the economy is established. The inverse of this price r, is the number of units of risk that one can buy for one franc.

Consequently, if V is the market value of the firm, A the value of its capital shares, D the amount of its indebtedness (or amount of its liabilities) and P the number of units of risk attendant upon its future profits, the market will tend to bring about the equality

$$V = A + D = \frac{P}{r}.$$

4. The future profits P* of the company are divided among the shares and the debentures. The following can then be established

$$P^* = rV = tD + jA$$

where t designates the fixed income guaranteed for each debenture and j the risk income associated with each share. Subject to a suitable selection of units, r, t, and j can be considered as the market interest rates for the firm's future profits from both the debentures and the shares.

5. An investment of an amount I will be desirable if the market value of the quantity of risk ΔP which it will purchase is higher than the amounts invested, that is, if

$$\frac{\Delta P}{r} \geqslant I$$

or, by $\frac{\Delta P}{I} = r'$, $r' \geq r$. r' can be considered as the rate of profit of the investment.

Such an investment will increase the market value of the total number of shares outstanding at the time of the decision, regardless of whether the investment is financed out of company surplus or from the sale of bonds or shares.

Where it is self-financed, an investment I provides the shareholders with future returns $r'I$. If the sum I were to be distributed among the shareholders instead, they could invest it on the market at the rate r in exchange for a quantity rI of risk. The investment is favorable to the shareholders if $r' \geq r$.

Before the investment is made, the market value of the company is $E = P/r$ and the value of the capital shares is E - D. If the enterprise borrows funds by selling bonds to make an investment I, its market value becomes

$$E' = \frac{P + r'I}{r} = E + \frac{r'I}{r}$$

and the value of the shares becomes

$$A' = E' - D - I = A + I\frac{r' - r}{r}$$

which demonstrates that the value of the shares increases if r' is greater than r.

If the quantities of r and r' were known at the time of making each decision, the above method would provide a criterion ($r' > r$) which would have the advantage of considering the risk preferences of the members of the group. But information about the money market is far from adequate, and there are many kinds of risk. It is therefore difficult to determine whether F. Modigliani's analysis, with regard to the present problem, is of considerable interest in demonstrating the links which exist between the selection of economic criteria and the psychology of lenders on the money market. A sound knowledge of this market is helpful to the "executives" of large private companies who must be aware of the risks they can assume. Reference to the market can be of assistance in selecting the value of the parameters which obtain in the selected criteria discussed above.

3. The decisions of a firm affect the interplay of economic factors and the decisions of other firms.

The head of a company, in reaching a decision, must take into account any strategies of which his competitors are aware. This interplay has been likened to the strategies of a game. The theory of games is still largely concerned with static problems and for this reason has limited utility in considering the dynamics of actual economic situations. It is mentioned here, however, because its concepts constitute a useful framework for anyone wishing to consider the notion of rationality of choice.

Let us therefore take the example of two firms, A and B, which share a market. They are called upon every three months to reach a decision as to the use to be made of their advertising budgets. We will assume that advertising merely transfers profits from one firm to another, so that, regardless of the behavior of the firms, what is gained by one is lost by the other. Two strategies are available to each firm in the form of media in which to expend their budgets: newspapers and billboards. If each firm reaches its decision independent of the other, then four eventualities are

Table I

		B Firm	
		Newspapers I	Billboards II
A Firm	Newspapers 1	a	c
	Billboards 2	b	d

possible. Table I demonstrates the additional profit reaped by the first firm from advertising in these four situations (the additional profits of the second enterprise appear opposite).

The A firm will seek to adopt a strategy which will maximize its profit, while the B firm will attempt to minimize A's profit. Two cases can be distinguished first and foremost which, for the sake of simplicity, we will handle by the numerical examples shown in Table II.

Table II

		B Firm	
		Newspapers I	Billboards II
A Firm	Newspapers 1	4	0
	Billboards 2	5	- 1

1. Table II indicates A's profits. If A adopts the first strategy, B will adopt the second, thus not losing anything. Conversely, if B adopts the second strategy, A will turn to the first. It is not in A's interest to adopt the second strategy — it would lose 1, — nor B the first — it would lose 4. Therefore, an equilibrium establishes itself and A adopts the first strategy and B the second.

Let us designate as P (i, j) the profit realized by the first firm when it adopts the i strategy and its competitor the j strategy.

A seeks to maximize P (i, j) and, consequently, adopts a strategy which, regardless of what j may be, will lead to a maximum with respect to i of P (i, j), which we will note as

$$M(j) = \text{Max}_i \, P(i, j).$$

If A so acts, B will attempt to minimize A's profit, and, consequently, will chose a j value which will minimize M (j). Let V_B be defined as

$$V_B = \text{Min}_j \, \text{Max}_i \, P(i, j)$$

B is therefore assured of being able to limit A's profit to V_B.

Similar reasoning, starting from the B enterprise, would indicate likewise that A is at least assured of a V_A profit with

$$V_A = \text{Max}_i \, \text{Min}_j \, P(i, j).$$

There are instances where V_B and V_A are equal to a common value, i.e., where A is assured of a V profit, but where B is assured of being able to prevent A from making a greater profit.

In the latter case

$$V = P(\text{I}, \text{II}).$$

2. Table III indicates A's profits.

Table III

		B Firm	
		Newspapers I	Billboards II
A Firm	Newspapers 1	1	0
	Billboards 2	- 1	2

It can be observed that there is no such pair of strategies as (1, II) in the example above. If, for instance, A selects strategy 1, B will choose strategy II, which will lead A to adopt strategy 2; but then B will adopt strategy I, and A will return to strategy 1, and so on. There is, therefore, no balance if each firm makes use of a single strategy.

Nevertheless, since the choice repeats itself frequently — at the beginning of each quarter — each firm can alternate strategies at random instead of constantly using the same one. This is described as a mixed strategy.*

The decision of firm A to use strategy 1 is then completely determined by the probability p. Figure 9 indicates the mathematical expectation of p of firm A, as firm B makes use of either strategy I (right ab) or strategy II (right cd).

Since p_0 is the abscissa at intersection P of ab and cd, it is in the interest of firm A to "mix" strategies 1 and 2 with p_0 and $1 - p_0$ probabilities. A's profit which is a function of p, when firm B employs strategies I and II with probabilities q and $1 - q$, is represented by a straight line through P and goes from a to b, and from c to d.** In selecting the value q_0 of q which makes this straight line horizontal, firm B can prevent firm A from making a profit greater than indicated by the ordinate P.

---

*Within the structure of the theoretical model, there is no difference between using one strategy during each period while varying from period to period, or using a mix of strategies during each period.

**The profit in the case of a mixed strategy is the arithmetic average of profits of the extreme strategies calculated with "balancing" ratios q and $1 - q$.

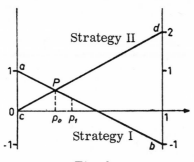

Fig. 9.

The ordinate P represents the maximum profit which can be made by firm A. By "playing" rationally, B can prevent A from making a greater profit. By mixing 1 and 2 with the probability p_0, firm A is assured of maximizing its profit. If it were to select a probability different from p_0 (p_1 for instance) firm B can, by constantly applying strategy I, reduce A's profits.

Figure 10 represents the equivalent of Fig. 9 from the standpoint of firm B. A's profit is shown by the ordinates, and the probability values q with which B "mixes" the opposing strategies are indicated by the abscissa. Point Q corresponds to point P and has the same ordinate.

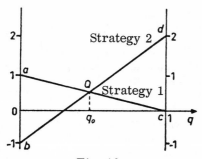

Fig. 10.

If the two firms play rationally, A is assured of eventually realizing the profit represented by the ordinates of points P and Q, but no more.

Consequently, if $P(p, q)$ indicates A's profit, while A and B mix their two strategies with probabilities p, $1 - p$; and q, $1 - q$, the probabilities p_0 and q_0 have the following property:

$$P(p_0, q_0) = \text{Max}_p \text{ Min}_q P(p, q) = \text{Min}_q \text{ Max}_p P(p, q).$$

The first example now appears as an individual case where p_0 and q_0 are both equal to 0 or 1 in the limit.

The above results remain valid regardless of the number of opposing strategies available to the two firms. In facing a rational adversary whose interests are directly opposed to your own, the appropriate criterion seems to be the maximization of the minimum profit (the minimum available under the conditions imposed by the entire series of the adversary's mixed strategies; and the maximum made available by use of the entire series of your own mixed strategies).

These conclusions are only of theoretical interest and are not likely to find many applications largely because these are strategies involved in a "two-person" game and also because the sum of the "profits" of both players has been held constant.

4. With each decision are associated several future events whose probabilities of occurrence are unknown.

Each of our decisions can be considered as a strategy, and the present value of profit to be derived therefrom relates to the future state of "nature" (which is unknown to us). Thus, nature can be considered as the second player, and its future states as its strategies. But which rule of decision should be adopted? An axiom similar to axiom IV restricts the area of possibilities, still allowing, however, a considerable margin of freedom. Each decision must be consistent with the state of nature. Unfortunately, there are numerous criteria that justify decisions regardless of the state of nature. The present trend among analysts is to construct criteria which make the fourth case compatible with either the second or third.

Joining the fourth case to the third amounts to considering nature as an adversary who will select the most unfavorable solution for you. A decision will therefore be selected which maximizes the minimum profit or — and this amounts to the same thing — minimizes the maximum loss. This is the minimax, at times referred to as the Wald criterion. It is a conservative approach about which there can be reasonable doubt for there is actually no reason to believe that nature "wishes us ill." Let us consider, for instance, the two tables below which furnish an indication, in two cases, of the profit to be derived from two possible strategies, 1 and 2, and the two conditions inherent in I and II.

	I	II
1	0	1
2	- 1	2

	I	II
1	0	1
2	- 1	10,000

In both cases, adoption of the Wald criterion has led to the adoption of strategy 1, whereas in the second case a gain of 10,000 could have been derived merely by risking - 1.

For this reason, Savage has suggested another criterion. He reasoned as follows: The fact that one state of nature prevails does not depend upon us. If one state occurs, the point solely to be considered is that of regret, i.e., the difference between the maximum profit which could have been derived from such state and the profit actually resulting from the decision chosen by us. In the case of the second table above, the table of regrets appears as follows:

	I	II
1	0	9999
2	1	0

Savage applies the minimax criterion to the second table and thus suggests that the second strategy be selected.

Joining the fourth case to the second amounts to an a priori assignment of probabilities to various states of nature to maximize the mathematical expectation. Certain writers have sought to determine the most reasonable a priori probabilities and have thus reached a criterion which had already been suggested by Lagrange. This criterion — when no previous element of information is available — assigns the same probability to all states of nature. The practical disadvantage of this criterion is that it is often difficult to enumerate the various states of nature. For example, we can divide, by means of a secondary symbol, state II into two sub-states II_a and II_b and set up the first of the following tables:

	I	II_a	II_b
1	0	1	1
2	- 1	2	2

Furthermore, certain preliminary elements of information are usually available which, subjectively, preclude the assignment of the same probability to all states of nature. The better method is to determine, a priori, any subjective probabilities which can be related to these various states. Values of such probabilities can be obtained by means of Wald, Savage, or Lagrange solutions.

In order to demonstrate more precisely the significance of the three (Wald, Savage, or Lagrange) solutions, let us attempt to determine to what extent they verify the three following axioms:

Axiom 1: A selected strategy must not be modified when a state of nature is subdivided into two sub-states leading to similar profits.

Axiom 2: A selected strategy must not be modified when a constant is added to all profits in one particular column.

Axiom 3: If, among the various strategies, a strategy is adjudged to be the most satisfactory, then such a strategy is considered better than any other one in the universe of all strategies.

In the following table, the axioms which are fulfilled by criteria are indicated by x, and those which are not are indicated by a dash.

Criterion	Wald	Savage	Lagrange
Axiom 1	x	x	-
2	-	x	x
3	x	-	x

Many problems are alleviated when, as a function of one's personality and available information, subjective probabilities are selected for the various states of nature. It is no longer necessary to assign to sub-states II_a and II_b, in their entirety, a probability greater than that assigned to state II. The criterion of maximization of mathematical expectation is then consistent with axioms I, II, III, [28].

All of the foregoing was intended to develop, among other things, the conviction that the selection of a proper criterion can assist in the statement of the problem and can be instrumental in pointing the analysis in the right direction. The following quotation is ample illustration [9].

"A group of operations research workers was, one day, presented with a problem concerned with the stockpiling of finished products. The factory's policy was to minimize the stock level within limits compatible with the need to guarantee deliveries. This intuitive criterion was therefore directed at minimizing stockpiling costs. In tackling this problem, the operations research group substituted for this criterion one of minimizing the plant's total expenditures. The selection of such a criterion led it, naturally, to an analysis of the repercussions of the stock level upon the expenditures of the plant's other departments. The group then discovered that in order to prevent a stock increase, certain production assembly lines were frequently halted and restarted. Such a policy was very costly. By the same token, the problem was properly posed. It merely became necessary to study the way stockpiling expenditures varied with the volume of stocks and the production costs relative to the number of units produced without halting the assembly line, and then to determine the policy which would provide a proper substitution rate between these two types of expenditures."

BIBLIOGRAPHY

1. M. ALLAIS:
   Traité d'Economie pure (Treatise on pure economics). Paris, Imprimerie Nationale, 1953. (A first edition of this publication appeared in 1943 under the title: A la recherche d'une discipline économique (In search of an economic discipline)).

2. M. ALLAIS:
   Economie pure et rendement social (Pure economics and corporate returns). Editions du Recueil Sirey, 1945, 72 pp.

3. M. ALLAIS:
   Economie et intérêt (Economics and interest). Paris, imprimerie Nationale, 1947, 2 volumes.

4. M. ALLAIS:
   Rendement social et productivité sociale (Corporate returns and corporate productivity). Econometrica, vol. XVII, Suppl., July, 1949.

5. M. ALLAIS:
   Quelques réflexions sur l'intérêt général et les intérêts particuliers (A few remarks on general and special interests). Nouvelle Revue de l'Economie Contemporaine, 1951.

6. M. ALLAIS:
   La gestion des Houillères nationalisées et la théorie économique (The management of nationalized coal fields and economic theory). Imprimerie Nationale, 1953.

7. M. ALLAIS:
   Le comportement de l'homme rationnel devant le risque: Critique des postulats et axiomes de l'école américaine (The behavior of rational man in the face of risk: Critique of the postulates and axioms of the American school). Econometrica XXI, October 1953.

8. M. ALLAIS:
   L'extension des théories de l'équilibre général et du rendement social au cas du risque (Extension to cases of risk of the theories of general equilibrium and corporate returns). Econometrica, April 1953.

9. R. L. ACKOFF:
   Production scheduling. Proceedings of the Conference on Operations Research. Society for the Advancement of Management. New York, Wiley, 1951.

10. K. J. ARROW:
Social choice and individual values. Cowles Commission Monograph, No. 12, New York, Wiley, 1951.

11. K. J. ARROW:
Le principe de rationalité dans les décisions collectives (The rationality principle in collective decisions). Economie appliquée, V, October-December 1952.

12. K. J. ARROW:
The role of securities in the optimal allocation of risk-bearing. Communication au Colloque International sur le Risque (Paper at the International Colloquium on Risk). Paris, May 1952.

13. D. BLACKWELL and M. A. GIRSCHIK:
Theory of games and statistical decisions. New York, Wiley, 1954.

14. DUBOURDIEU:
Théorie mathématique du risque dans les assurances de répartition (Mathematical theory of risk in distribution assurance). Gauthier-Villars, Paris.

15. M. FRIEDMANN and L. J. SAVAGE:
The utility analysis of choices involving risk. The Journal of Political Economy, April 1948.

16. E. L. GRANT:
Principles of engineering economy. The Ronald Press Company, New York [2nd edition, 1938; 3rd edition, 1950].

17. G. Th. GUILBAUD:
Les théories de l'intérêt général et le problème logique de l'agrégation (Theories on general interest and the logical problem of aggregation). Economie appliquée, 1952. October-December.

18. G. Th. GUILBAUD:
Leçons sur les élements principaux de la théorie mathématique des jeux (Lessons on the principal elements of the mathematical theory of games). Stratégies et décisions économiques. Editions of the CNRS, 1954.

19. J. R. HICKS:
Valeur et capital (Value and capital). French translation. Dunod, 1956.

20. J. R. HICKS:
    L'économie de bien-être et la théorie du surplus du con-
    sommateur (Welfare economics and the theory of con-
    sumer surplus). Economie appliquee, October-December
    1948.

21. Ch. HITCH:
    Sub-optimization in operations problems. Journal of the
    Operations Research Society of America, May 1, 1953.

22. G. E. KIMBALL:
    Decision theory. Proceedings of the conference on opera-
    tions research. Society for the Advancement of manage-
    ment. New York, January 1954.

23. O. LANGE:
    The practice of economic planning and the optimum allo-
    cation of resources. Econometrica, Vol. XVII, supplement,
    July 1949.

24. A. P. LERNER:
    Economics of control. Macmillan, 1944.

25. J. LESOURNE:
    Le comportement des entreprises et certains aspects de
    l'imprévisibilité (Business behavior and certain aspects
    of unpredictibility). Revue d'économie politique, January
    1954.

26. R. D. LUCE:
    Games and decisions. Wiley, 1957.

27. I. M. D. LITTLE:
    A critique of welfare economics. Clarendon Press, 1950.
    L'avantage collectif (Collective advantage). Economie
    appliquée, October-December 1952.

28. LUCE and RAIFFA:
    Games and decisions. Wiley, New York, 1958.

29. McKINSEY:
    Introduction to the theory of games. The Rand Corpora-
    tion, 1952.

30. L. McNAIR:
    Problems in business economics. McGraw Hill.

31. M. MARSCHAK:
    Rational behavior, uncertain prospects and measurable
    utility. Econometrica, April 1950.

32. M. MARSCHAK:
Why should statisticians and businessmen maximize moral expectation? Proceedings of the Second Berkeley Symposium on mathematical statistics and probability. Berkeley, University of California Press, 1951.

33. P. MASSE:
Les réserves et la régulation de l'avenir dans la vie économique (reserves and regulation of the future in economic life). Paris, Hermann, 1946.

34. P. MASSE:
Le taux d'intérêt et le risque (The interest rate and risk). Economie appliquée, 1951, No. 1.

35. P. MASSE:
Réflexions sur les comportements rationnels en économie aléatoire (Remarks on rational behavior in stochastic economics). Cahiers du séminaire d'économétrie, No. 2, 1953.

36. P. MASSE:
Le choix des investissements (The selection of investments). Dunod, Paris, 1959. Cf. Chapter V.

37. P. MASSE and G. MORLAT:
Sur le classement économique des perspectives aléatoires (Concerning economic classification of contingent expectations). Colloque International sur le risque (International Colloquium on Risk). Paris, May 1952.

38. Von NEUMANN AND O. MORGENSTERN:
Theory of games and economic behavior. Princeton University Press, 1944.

39. Göran NYBLEN:
Quelques réflexions sur le vieux problème de l'avantage collectif à la lumière des developpements récents (A few remarks on the old problem of collective welfare in the light of recent developments). Economie appliquée, October-December 1952.

40. G. ROTTIER:
Notes sur la maximation du profit (Notes on the maximization of profit). Economie appliquée, 1951, January-March.

41. P. A. SAMUELSON:
The foundations of economic analysis. Harvard University Press, 1948.

42. P. A. SAMUELSON:
Probability, utility, and the independence axiom. Econometrica, October 1952.

43. L. J. SAVAGE:
The theory of statistical decision. Journal of the American Statistical Association, March 1951.

44. L. J. SAVAGE:
An axiomatization of reasonable behavior in the face of uncertainty. Colloque international d'économétrie, May 1952.

45. L. J. SAVAGE:
The foundations of statistics. Wiley, 1954.

46. Tibor SCITOVSKY:
A note on profit maximization and its implications. Review of economic studies, 1943.

47. P. STREETEN:
La théorie moderne de l'économie de bien-être (The modern theory of welfare economics). Economie appliquée, October-December 1952.

48. R. M. THRALL, C. H. COOMBS, R. L. DAVIS:
Decision processes. Wiley, New York, 1954.

49. A. WALD:
Statistical decision functions. New York, Wiley; London, Chapman and Hall, 1950.

PART I

ECONOMETRICS IN THE SERVICE OF BUSINESS

Chapter 3

Marketing studies

A business, in order to survive in an intensely competitive environment, must constantly keep abreast of changing market requirements and must anticipate and evaluate the probable reactions that may follow each decision.

Within this general framework, one of the tasks of the economics research staff is to analyze the relationships between the firm and its market represented by its customers and suppliers.

In marketing studies, economic analysis must attempt to provide answers to two types of questions:

1. How will sales volume be affected by changing market conditions assuming an unchanging company policy, and on what basis can sales predictions be made?

2. What are likely to be the repercussions of company policy changes on the volume of its sales and what are the components of a policy structure that are amenable to such analysis?

Thus, for instance, when Electricité de France embarks on an investment program and seeks to ascertain what, in the absence of a modification of its rate policy, French demand for electricity would be during the next five years, the survey it would undertake would be characteristic of prediction analysis.

When the director of a group of chain stores would like to determine the potential increase in sales that would result from keeping the stores open one night a week, the survey he might require would depend upon analysis of structure.*

At the risk of oversimplification, the following generalizations will be made at this point. The first type of study relates to the establishment of budgets and the control of expenditures, to the regulation of production and the management of inventories, and to the development of investment programs. The second type of study is more closely linked to advertising, pricing policies, and sales practices.

---

* A short trial period would probably not provide a reliable basis for a decision.

The fact that these studies point toward a quantitative analysis of economic phenomena means that they probably can be classed as econometric studies. The word "econometrics" has had its supporters and its relentless adversaries in France during the last twenty years. Interest in the measurement of economic phenomena existed on both sides, but one side stressed its difficulties. The opposition associated econometrics with a "physical" concept of economics and proclaimed that problems of measurement were posed differently in the physical sciences. This debate is becoming obsolete because a better comprehension of scientific method, such as outlined in Chapter 1, insures a rational utilization of econometrics within the framework of a precise and carefully structured model.

We now turn our attention to examining various types of market studies by analyzing the factors influencing demand. Thereafter, we follow the stages of research from the establishment of hypotheses based on a rationale to the verification of the hypotheses through statistical analysis of empirical data. The closing paragraphs of this chapter are devoted to problems of data gathering, examination of existing statistics, and the completion of experiments.

I

FACTORS INFLUENCING DEMAND

In the field of economics, the term "demand" traditionally describes the quantity of a good that consumers would purchase within a given period and under given market conditions. The demand for certain goods by consumers is the sum of the demands for these goods upon all enterprises which produce them; and, the factors which govern total demand are not the same as those which determine the distribution of this demand among the various producers.

Goods may be demanded by final consumers or by intermediate consumers. For example, coal mines sell their coal for home use and also to Siderurgie, Electricite de France, and other industries. The intermediate consumers are also producers who use coal to manufacture their own products at a rate that is commensurate with the demand schedule for their output. For this reason, the variables which influence final demand and intermediate demand are not completely similar.

It is therefore possible to distinguish, from the standpoint of an industry, the variables in a final consumption market and the variables in an intermediate consumption market; and, from the standpoint of an enterprise, the factors of allocation of demand among the producers.

1. Variables in a final consumption market.

Many marketing studies have attempted to measure the impact on demand resulting from changes in one or more of the variables which affect final demand. Such a question can be answered only if the changing variables can be identified and the lag between the time of each change and the time of its actual impact can be measured.

Because of a tendency to overlook such limitations, the authors of some marketing studies are inclined to attribute to their conclusions a generality which is not warranted.

The following discussion of the principal variables can provide a basis for some protection against such oversights.

a) The sale price.

The influence of the sale price on the volume of demand is basic to economic theory. The curve which represents the variation of demand with respect to price can take on rather distinct aspects. In Fig. 1 demand decreases uniformly as price increases. In Fig. 2 the rate of change in demand with respect to price changes is not constant. The second illustration describes a common phenomenon which is usually linked to inelastic demand.

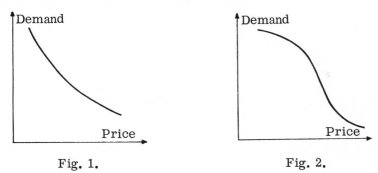

Fig. 1.   Fig. 2.

Certain commodities are substitutes for one another, such as butter and margarine, tea and coffee. Of course, there are taste preferences which affect the elasticity of response, as measured by demand, to price changes. But the tendency is there for consumers to switch brands or products as price changes make it worthwhile to make such substitutions. Coal and fuel oil are also substitutes but the demand for these items is quite inelastic. If a dwelling is equipped to heat with coal, for example, minor price changes would have small effect on total demand because demand for coal is more responsive to need (temperature) than to price. If, however, the price of fuel oil were to be lowered drastically, it would reach a point where the cost of changing the heating equipment (coupled with the added convenience of heating with oil) would appear worthwhile.

At this point, demand for oil would increase sharply. After that, it would again become relatively unresponsive to price changes.

Demand does not depend solely upon current prices. It can be strongly conditioned by anticipated prices, or by prices which existed in the past—especially if the latter have contributed to the development of an irreversible consumption habit or were translated into the purchase of permanent equipment.

b) The sale price of other products.

Demand is not only affected by varying prices and substitute commodities where the decreasing demand for an item whose cost is increasing is balanced by increasing demand for its substitute, but by complementary commodities as well. Complementary commodities are goods for which demand tends to vary in the same direction. For example, the price of and demand for automobiles certainly exercise a positive influence on the demand for gasoline, seatcovers, and accessories in general.

Nominally identical products whose only difference is that of quality may be either substitutes or complements. They are substitutes if consumers actually make the distinction, and complements if they do not.

c) Sales policy.

Sales policy and its practice can affect an individual firm with respect to its share of the market, and can also affect a total industry to the extent that total demand for the product (as distinct from the ''brand'') is affected. Quite frequently, marketing studies attempt to evaluate the efficiency of certain aspects of sales policy with respect to the influence of advertising, the presentation of the product, the organization of distribution, the sales methods of the sales force, and the various forms of price adjustments (discounts, rebates, premiums, and conditions of payment).

d) The income of consumers.

Income influences both the pattern and the level of demand. Consumer behavior is more responsive to (real) income than to most other economic or sociological factors. For the purpose of short run analysis of consumer patterns, the economic behavior of income groups can be used with confidence as a means of forecasting future patterns of similar income classes.

e) Stochastic variables.

The analysis of stochastic variables is basic to most studies of demand and consumer patterns. For example, the daily consumption

of gas, for heating purposes, is closely related to daily temperatures. The daily temperatures are stochastic variables whose
probability distributions can be studied. In determining their
influence upon demand, Gaz de France has been able to calculate the
maximum capacity it requires to meet peak demand. In addition, it
has successfully calculated the storage capacity requirement for
the Paris area.

f) Time factor.

Demand changes over time as a function of many variables. The
specific variables and their interrelationships with respect to
demand can be analyzed in terms of long-term modifications of consumption habits, short-run (e.g., seasonal, religious or political
holidays) fluctuations in demand patterns, and general economic
changes affecting income and price levels.

All of the foregoing applies to consumer demand. However, many
industries dispose of their products by selling to distributors. Under
these conditions, estimates of consumer demand are made by the
distributors who vary their inventory levels—sometimes abruptly—
in accordance with their anticipation of consumer demand patterns.

2. Variables in an intermediate consumption market.

Here, we need consider only those aspects which differ from the
preceding discussion of the final consumption market.

a) The production of consumer industries.

The intermediate consumption market is influenced strongly by
the production of consumer industries. Short-run variations in
demand relationships have little effect on prices and production
processes and influence only inventory levels and replenishment
policies. Long-term variations, however, ultimately result in re-
arrangement of the factors of production; adjustment of capacities,
manning, cost structure, and production techniques so as to retain
or advance profit ratios and shares of the market.

b) The sale price.

Prices to intermediate consumers have minor influence in the
short run. However, intermediate consumers are more sensitive to
price changes than are final consumers. The intermediate consumers have, individually, a greater stake in sophisticated response
by way of substitution, to price variations than the average household consumer and will react strongly, though rationally, to

long-term price trends. The notion of price equivalence becomes particularly useful in the study of easily substituted goods.

c) Reliability of supply.

Intermediate consumers are deeply concerned with the problem of reliability of sources of supply. Fixed overhead charges during relatively short periods of interrupted production can absorb profits earned during longer periods. The intermediate consumer will therefore show preference for local producers, domestic industries, strike-free plants, and firms in which they own an interest. The stability generally observed in relationships between intermediate consumers and their suppliers stems in part from this need for reliability of supply.

d) Company policy.

In order to be effective, a firm's policy must be expressed in terms of the actual advantages accruing to its customers. The variety of products offered, prompt execution of orders, advantageous conditions of payment, consistency of quality levels are some of the main aspects of successful policy.

e) Stochastic variables.

An example in Chapter 2 demonstrated the influence of hydro-electric plants on Electricité de France's demand for coal.

f) Time factor.

The influence of time assumes multiple aspects as in the case of final consumption goods. Technical progress effects changes in consumer habits. Demand is closely linked to economic fluctuations whose trends are not easily predictable.

The number of consumers in an intermediate market is much more limited than in a final market, and this can have appreciable effect on the methods used in marketing studies. A complete census, as opposed to a sample, might be feasible in a study of intermediate consumers.

3. Distribution of a market among producers.

The determination of an individual firm's share of the market depends not only on the quality of his product and related service, but on the structure of his competition: the number and quality of competing firms.

The structure of the producers' market is fundamental to many aspects of economic analysis. Accordingly, the various types of producers' markets will be reviewed briefly at this point.

a) Perfect competition is an ideal type of competition characterized by numerous sellers of identical products, each selling all he wishes at the going market price and whose sales tend neither to raise nor depress the market price.

Most industries are imperfectly competitive falling somewhere between perfect competition and the opposite extreme, monopoly.

b) Monopoly is characterized by a single-producer industry whose product is unique in that no other industry produces a satisfactory substitute. There are government regulated monopolies, like public utilities; competition in these industries would be extremely costly to both intermediate and final consumers. There are also de facto monopolies, i.e., firms which have succeeded in eliminating all competition. The de facto monopolist can increase his price somewhat with little danger to himself. Major price increases, however, can depress demand and encourage the reappearance of competition.

c) Duopoly and oligopoly describe industries where all supply of a specific product is provided either by two or a small number of firms. The important characteristic here is the identity of product and its quality sold by few producers. Accordingly, a minor change in pricing of one producer will rearrange consumer demand patterns affecting all producers. As a consequence, there is a greater tendency among oligopolists than among other types of competition to agree to eliminate price as a means of competing for markets. Each oligopolist, in order to maintain or increase his share of the market, will concentrate on product (and package) design, advertising, improved delivery and consumer credit.

Market analysis with respect to oligopolists or duopolists would evaluate all components of policies, except pricing, that might affect sales volume.

d) Monopolistic competition is a form of imperfect competition where the product of one monopolist (e.g., telegraph company) may be, at times, substituted for the product of another monopolist (e.g., telephone company). Price, here, is partially effective as a means of competing for demand.

In summation, the analysis of demand must be concentrated on the number of competitors and their relative shares of the market, the various aspects of sales policy, and the influence of prices.

Now that we have reviewed the factors which govern the distribution of demand, we are able to consider the common types of marketing studies.

II

VARIOUS TYPES OF MARKETING STUDIES

1. Predictions.

In general, firms attempt to develop both short-term and long-term predictions. Short-term predictions are made to cover periods from six to eighteen months, and are used for the establishment of annual budgets, for the regulation of production, and the management of inventories. Long-term predictions, on the other hand, look ahead five, ten, or twenty years, and serve as a basis for the establishment of internal investment policy (plant expansion, equipment replacement, personnel planning), and external investment policy (corporate expansion through purchase of controlling interest in diverse industries, suppliers, and competing firms).

Predictions are generally developed with respect to either the economy as a whole, an industry, or the individual firm. The point of some predictions derives from projections of the relationships between these three levels in the economic environment.

a) Short-term predictions.

An increasing number of firms attempt to analyze short-term business cycle projections and relate these trends to their own planning. The analysis of current trends of various economic indicators is sometimes helpful to the economist in developing forecasts of a firm's market opportunities. An understanding of the relationship between sales potential and such indicators as gross national product, disposable income, production indices of capital goods, consumer durables, commercial and residential construction, can be extremely helpful in predicting sales volume.

Various methods are available for developing sales predictions for a company or for an industry. One popular method on the industry level consists of requesting various firms to estimate their own sales trends. This method, though questionable on a long-term basis, can provide useful results on a short-term basis. It makes use of the experience and knowledge of those who are in close and constant contact with the market, and provides data which are easily allocated by product and geographical area. These advantages, however, are offset to an extent by certain disadvantages. Sellers run the risk of being too greatly influenced by the current psychological environment and are not sufficiently impressed with the actual (or projected) economic climate; for this reason, the quality of predictions is likely to deteriorate as the time-span covered by the study increases. If the number of consumers is not large—which occurs most frequently in the case of intermediate markets— the sellers can arrive at their predictions by direct inquiry of the buyers. On the average, much better predictions can be made with respect to intermediate consumption markets than for final consumption markets.

The validity of projected trends of sales is limited frequently by the lack of serious attention given the formulation of predictions by sellers who are naturally more concerned with current performance. Also, if their own predictions are going to be used as a basis for the establishment of sales quotas as a measure of their own performance they will tend to underestimate in order to more easily fulfill the goals.

Firms using this method of prediction should attempt to confirm the predicted values by developing estimates on totally different bases. To accomplish this, they can make use of basic statistical techniques including correlation and extrapolation.

Correlation analysis must first identify other measures of economic activity that might relate to sales volume. By correlating measures of past performance, we hope to discover high correlation coefficients in order to identify the factors that actually do relate to sales volume. Sometimes, two series of data will correlate significantly only if one is lagged in time with respect to the other. Such lags can be fortunate because such relationships lend themselves very directly to prediction. In other instances, high correlation coefficients permit the use of alternative projections as a means of arriving at or confirming sales predictions. In addition to general economic measures and market trends, sales volume can be correlated with consumption data, or volume of sales of substitute or complementary products.

For example, an American manufacturer of sanitary equipment observed for many years that the volume of his sales correlated closely with the number of permits issued for home building with an extremely useful time lag of three to four months.

Extrapolation consists of observing the pattern of sales over some past period and extending this pattern into some future period. In this connection, it is assumed that the volume of sales in the past can be represented, with respect to time, as the sum of a stochastic variable (i.e., the yearly seasonal component) and a "regular" function (i.e., the trend or tendency). Short-term predictions are obtained by extrapolating the general trends and correcting for seasonal variations. However, this method is risky and should not be used except for the purpose of estimating a monthly distribution of sales within a relatively short period. Long-term predictions are likely to be in error whenever the economy fluctuates between prosperity and depression. The most unpredictable aspects of business cycles are the location of the inflection points.

A few caveats are in order at this point with respect to the use of predictions derived from extrapolated data. First, the reliability of such predictions is least dubious for time periods when general economic analysis forecasts stability in the business cycle. Furthermore, use of this method should be restricted mainly to those products for which there is a relatively inelastic demand and whose sensitivity therefore to other economic fluctuations is minimal. Finally, this type of analysis is least helpful in intermediate consumer markets and for production of consumer durables which directly reflect cyclical trends.

As an example of this type of analysis, sales of light-weight fuel oils have been observed in France to be growing exponentially. By correcting this trend for seasonal variations and anticipated temperature levels, it is possible to predict the approximate volume of short-term sales.

b) Long-term predictions.

Long-term predictions of demand and sales possibilities are less dependent on the sales estimates of various sellers than are short-term analyses. Long term predictions might relate more directly to the firms' research and development programs, their plant expansion plans and equipment replacement policies, and their portfolio of external investments. Long-term predictions of the firm relate to projected developments in the economy as a whole.

The economist must study the probable progress of national income, its principal elements and related aspects since they all have direct bearing on the future of the individual firm. Basic to any consideration of national income are analyses of changes in total population, the size of the labor force, and measures of its productivity.

Demographic studies have made it possible to make accurate predictions of total population and, to some extent, its composition. Accordingly the size of the labor force can be predicted by analyzing the population and its stratification by age groups during predicted periods. Measures of productivity can be predicted by extrapolation of past and current rates as well as by analysis of current plans for modernization of plant and equipment.

Following an estimate of the total national income, an attempt should be made to obtain an approximation of the magnitudes of its major components:

a. In terms of expenditures: consumption, government investments and expenditures;

b. In terms of income: salaries, rent, interest, profit, taxes;

c. In terms of production: values added from various sectors (industry, agriculture, transportation, services).

For example, the Commissariat general au Plan (General Planning Commission) began its work on the third plan for modernization of equipment by studying the projected French economy for

1965. Its estimates are based on the total population (at that time approximately 45 million inhabitants), the civilian labor force (19.8 million), and on a distribution of this labor force between agriculture, industry, transportation, commerce, services and administration. The national income—the sum of the value added from the various sections—is estimated from the growth of each sector's productivity, defined as the value added per man-year, for a given period. The final step involves a study of the distribution of the national income, its probable utilization, and a verification as to whether it corresponds satisfactorily to the production hypotheses.

The long-term study of correlations between the sales volume and the various elements of national income poses problems that are similar to some raised by short-term predictions. However, it is frequently necessary to take account of supplemental variations (i.e., technical progress, changes in consumption habits, etc.) which, on a short-term basis, are treated as constants. For this reason, it is often necessary to use multiple regression models.

An American pharmaceutical company has observed over a long period of time that its sales volume varied by 5% for any 10% variation of available personal income, and that it grew, per unit of personal income, at a fixed rate due to the intrinsic expansion of consumption of pharmaceutical products.

When long-range forecasting relates to durable goods, the demand during the year t, d(t), can be analyzed as an expansion demand e(t) and a replacement demand r(t). An expansion in demand can be predicted on the basis of an analysis of its relationship with national income.

Insofar as replacement requirements are concerned, estimates are usually derived by analyzing the mortality experience of goods put into use in the past. Thus, during the year t, a fraction $u(t, \tau)$ of the goods first put into use during the year r comes to an end. Therefore:

$$d(t) = e(t) \times \sum_{\tau=0}^{t} d(\tau) \, u \, (t, \tau)$$

If t_0 represents the present moment, a knowledge of past sales and of the $u(t, \tau)$ function permits a calculation of $r(t_0 + 1)$. The $e(t_0 + 1)$ quantity having been predetermined, $d(t_0 + 1)$ can be calculated, and d(t) can then be derived.

Long-term analysis of economic trends is less hazardous than short-term analysis because the short-term predictions must take into account random fluctuations and inflections in the business cycle. Long-term predictions, on the other hand, can safely ignore periodic fluctuations and concentrate on the secular trends of general economic development.

Trend analysis has been particularly successful with new or redesigned products enjoying growth; these growth patterns are almost invariably exponential and predictions are generally well founded. The analysis of sales trends is less fruitful for products for which demand does not vary significantly over time, or whose variations are sometimes due to major crisis (e.g., the two world wars and the 1929 stock market break) whose impact is so large that the economic factors are totally obscured.

The demand structure is sometimes such that predicted trends can be cross-checked. For example, products frequently have multiple uses. Predictions of total demand can be extrapolated from past trends of total demand. Predictions of demand per specific use can be derived by relating its trend to a corollary trend; the aggregate of the individual trends can be compared with the extrapolation of total demand.

Sometimes, demand for a specific use or by a certain economic sector that cannot be estimated directly can be predicted as a residual. If the total demand can be estimated and if the other components of the total demand can be forecast, the residual demand can be identified. The demand for coal in the United States is a case in point. The demand for energy correlates strongly with national income and can therefore be forecast. The demand for fuel oil, natural gas, and hydroelectric power follow regular trends. The future demand for coal can be forecast as a residual.

Some predictions tend to underestimate the influence of a firm's policies on the volume of its future sales. In fact, what should be determined is not the level of demand but the demand function. For example, a monopolistic enterprise seeking to initiate an investment program should analyze the relationship between its price structure and the trend of its future demand schedule and determine simultaneously its investment policy and its price policy. Although the most practical predictions relate to the level of demand, interesting inferences with respect to the future can be drawn by supplementing demand analysis with studies of economic structure.

2. Structure analysis.

Of growing importance in studies involving the application of econometrics is the analysis of economic structure. This is a Pandora's box of multilevel complexity holding out both uncertainty and considerable hope. Although the concept of economic structure is not restricted to one pattern, a useful classification could include the influence of price and income, family budgets, the dynamics of markets, the firm's policy, sociological and ecological conditions of demand, and potential markets for new products.

a) The influence of price and income.

Since 1930, economists have undertaken numerous studies regarding the influence of price and income. The most remarkable work on the subject is that of Professor H. Schulz of the University of Chicago, as presented in 1938 in his book: Theory and Measurement of Demand.

These studies relate to total demand for one product or for a group of products produced by an industry. The data for most of these studies derive from general sources of published statistics rather than from special investigations. These studies appear in two forms: time series analysis and cross-section analysis.

The time series concept, covered at greater length in Chapter 6, is defined as a series of values measured during a succession of time intervals of identical lengths. For example, the annual consumption of sugar from 1920 to 1950 is compared with the average annual price of sugar, and the national income (both in constant monetary units) for the same years. By multiple correlation, we seek to establish the extent to which consumption is influenced by changes in real prices and in real income.

Cross-section analysis compares magnitudes between groups holding time constant. The technique here is to isolate the same variable in two samples by minimizing the influence of other variables. For example, to determine the influence of price on family gasoline consumption, a comparison is made between the consumption of regular customers and that of employee families of a gasoline company who are offered a discount. Providing that both samples are drawn from populations with similar social and economic backgrounds, differences in gasoline consumption can be attributed to price differences. Repeated tests with varying price discounts will not only verify the conclusion but will help establish the price function. Some cross-section analyses relate price differences to variations in geographic location. For example, demand for intermediate goods depends on the present location of plants; this, in turn, is linked to the geographical differentiation of prices in the past.

Independently of these methods which apply to total demand, a firm can explore the markets which become progressively open to it proportionate to the decrease in its prices.

For example, an industrialist studies possible foreign outlets for his products. His economic staff is able to approximate the following for each country: the price which prevails in each local market, and the quantities that can be sold at this price. For each foreign country, it is therefore possible to calculate an initial price which, taking into account transportation costs, can compete with the prices on the local market. A curve can then be drawn giving, for each initial price, the exportable quantity (equal to the sum of the outlets of countries where the delivery price is lower than the market price).

Another example is calculation of the increased receipts which will result from an increase in coal output of a given coal field. These increased receipts can be calculated by comparing the disposal structure before and after expansion. Before expansion, the field had a deficit of coal dust and a surplus in graded coal and found it necessary to pulverize some of its graded coal in order to feed its ovens. An increase in production makes it possible to both substitute coal dust for graded coal in the charging of its ovens, and to export a tonnage of graded coal more or less equal to the supplemental production. The price for the export tonnage is determined as in the previous example.

In these two examples, the enterprise utilized the geographical or economic differentiation of its markets to explore the structure of its demand. In assuming a constant total demand, it attempted to determine the conditions under which it could enter into some of its competitors' markets. This type of study is logically analogous to the computation of price equivalence between two products.

b) Household budgets.

Since Engel, the German economist, numerous studies have been undertaken to ascertain the manner in which families budgeted their income among various types of expenditures. Families have been requested to keep careful records of their purchases during one year. In order to analyze the influence of income, the same request was made of a great number of families drawn from populations that are homogeneous with respect to location and all social and economic factors except income. The data obtained permit a study of the correlation between the distribution of expenditures at various income levels.

c) Market dynamics.

The econometric models used in the above studies are often simple and reducible to a single equation. They are generally based on a static analysis of the mechanics of demand. Recently, more complex models have been developed which attempt to analyze the dynamic growth of markets, incorporating—in addition to prices and incomes—other characteristic variables of the problem. In such studies, there is no assumption that one year's demand is entirely dependent upon the values determined during that year from the other variables. The study on automobile demand presented in Chapter 7 illustrates the possibilities offered by this approach. The construction of these models calls for more imagination and care, but their utilization is likely to provide a great deal of information. They can remain valid over a much longer period of time than simple models which establish correlations between demand, price, and income.

d) The policy of the firm.

Here we have an area where problems are so varied in character that a systematic presentation of studies is hardly possible. But an outline of a few examples which will be discussed subsequently will provide a notion of the type of questions an economic analyst must attempt to answer.

A large department store has decided to remain open late one night a week. The management is anxious to know how this decision has affected profits. The increased cost of remaining open is well known, but an attempt must be made to determine the increase in sales. It is not feasible to use the volume of sales made during the additional hours because certain customers now await until the late night to make certain purchases which they might have made anyway. Nor can the total variation of monthly sales be used as a basis because the store's sales may have increased as a result of an improvement in the income of customers or due to other reasons not associated with the increased shopping time. Only a careful analysis can isolate the effect of the late shopping night on total sales [23].

A firm has been selling its products to a great number of retailers. Because the use of salesmen is expensive, their number is not sufficient to permit monthly visits to the customers. The firm decided, therefore, to have its salesmen pay monthly visits to the top 40% of its customers, i.e., those who purchased the largest dollar volume during the preceding month. This proposed policy should be compared with the alternative of a random selection of customers to be visited, or increasing the number of its salesmen. There are other alternatives that should be considered. The actual solution was based on a statistical analysis of the firm's data.

A chain of retail stores plans to open a new branch in an area where one of its stores is already established. In order to study the profit-making potential of this proposed investment, an estimate must be made of its probable effect on the receipts of the first store; the probable decrease in volume at the first store must be equated with the anticipated volume at the new store. Market analysts have traditionally considered this problem from the point of view of the population density in the area and its distribution with respect to both locations.

In order to adopt a reasonable advertising policy, a firm must constantly compare advertising costs to the advantages it derives therefrom; it must also attempt to expend its advertising budget as efficiently as possible. To attain such objectives, many analytical possibilities relating the firm to the market become imperative.

e) Sociological and ecological conditions of demand.

In our examples up to this point we have dealt with demand, its causes and consequences, solely from its economic implications. This is a potential defect because sociological and ecological aspects of demand are frequently significant and understanding them can contribute to developing a correct rationale and lead to a more perceptive analysis.

In the case of a final consumption market, the emphasis would be concerned with the consumer's knowledge, his intentions, and his behavior. It would be pertinent to almost any analysis of consumer demand to know how the consumers are stratified socially, economically, geographically, by age and by sex. It would also be important to obtain some idea of the qualities, both good and bad, that consumers attribute to a product as well as the reasons that impel them to purchase it or to look elsewhere. Answers, in the majority of cases, can best be obtained by means of survey.

In the case of an intermediate consumption market, the survey could be performed by an industry association, for example, in ecological terms. An attempt might be made to ascertain the number, size, and geographical location of the various firms in the industry. An analysis would then be made of the production and distribution techniques employed and the manner in which the product and competing products are utilized. A knowledge of the cost structure of the industry would make it possible to evaluate the significance of price with respect to purchaser behavior. It might be possible, as a follow-up to the foregoing, to deduce the etiology (other than cost) of price determination in terms of the psychological motivation of industrialists and their personal attitudes with respect to the importance of a product, as a means of evaluating apparent differences between cost and price. By further studying the industry's productive capacity, the structure of its outlets, long-term development prospects, sensitivity to the business cycles, and the volume of present investments, the analyst is then in possession of a sufficient number of factors to make an essential contribution to the determination of the firm's policy with regard to this industry.

f) Potential markets for new products.

Before undertaking the manufacture of a new product, a firm should consider its market potential. Either through examination of existing data or by means of a survey, the analyst must take into account the number of current competitors, the characteristics of their products, their means of distribution and their productive capacities; the price structure, its past development and future trends; the volume of production that the firm can hope to sell (account being taken of the reactions of existing competitors and the possible arrival of new competitors).

Although it is difficult to provide precise answers to these problems, approximations can frequently be of great value in enabling management to consider a problem rationally.

III

THE COMPILATION OF QUANTITATIVE DATA

The quantitative data that an economist uses are derived from research, from internal or external statistics, or from experiments. What follows is a brief and sketchy consideration of some of the problems involved in ascertaining the nature, validity and reliability of information derived from the various sources of quantitative data.

1. Research (Surveys, samples, and questionnaires).

Surveys and questionnaires generally entail canvassing a relatively small number of consumers constituting a sampling of opinion. Their use poses problems with respect to the wording of the questionnaires, the techniques for analyzing the responses, and means for ensuring the representativeness of the sample.

An analysis of the various types of questions which can be asked during the course of an inquiry has been made by Lorie. In our opinion, it is so very pertinent that it deserves to be considered a classic, and we shall derive inspiration from it, thus: [24]

Lorie distinguishes five types of research (these can be combined in actual practice):

a) behavior of consumers,
b) their intentions,
c) their attitudes,
d) their areas of knowledge and their thought processes,
e) their motives and their reasons for action.

a) Research on consumer behavior.

Understanding consumer behavior, in our opinion, constitutes an indispensable preliminary for any further inquiry. It helps clarify the nature of the market with respect to the consumers' living standards, social position, size of household, and other extra-economic influences. Without this sociological frame of reference, the analysis of attitudes, and opinions could lead to serious misunderstanding [18].

Research on consumer behavior can be carried on via observation of behavior, a questionnaire, or a report by the consumers themselves regarding their behavior during a given period.

Examples of observation are the inspection of a housewife's pantry, the silent survey of consumer behavior in a department store etc. The advantage of well conducted observation is that it registers facts and relates them to time. However, some pertinent information might not be available during this procedure. The fact of finding a package of cookies in the pantry does not tell the research worker whether it was a gift, a regular purchase or a chance purchase.

Observation, in the majority of cases, should therefore be combined with a questionnaire. In the case of behavior studies, persons approached are likely to understand the significance of the questions. However, they may not wish to answer correctly. In France, for example, a question relating to income is always unwelcome because of its personal nature and because the persons questioned fear tax repercussions. Likewise, answers are likely to be misleading when the persons questioned are not particularly proud of their behavior (Cf.: the example given concerning aerial transportation in Chapter 1). Finally, the memory of persons questioned should not be relied upon for extended periods; questions seeking precise answers should be limited to fairly recent time periods.

Daily reports by consumers concerning their own behavior obviate the need for long-lived memory. They also provide detailed information concerning the use of income. But considerable work is required on the part of the consumer, and certain consumers may refuse to cooperate. This reaction may be attributable to certain social characteristics which might also have considerable effect on the other aspects of behavior. The sampling of such responses runs the risk of not being representative.

The study of consumer behavior is certainly the surest form of inquiry, since it relates to facts that are generally easy to communicate.

b) Research on consumer intentions.

Understanding consumer intentions involves considerable complexity. The consumer, in exploring his own intentions, is less likely to predict his effective demand accurately than the trained analyst appraising consumer responses or patterns of past behavior.

In considering his intentions with respect to future purchases of, for example, major household appliances, the consumer frequently hedges his desire to acquire an item with questions about his future. He considers the possibility of not receiving a promised salary increase, or the chances of being transferred to another location, the likelihood of illness or accident in his family, or the prospect of not being able to find a suitably designed item at an acceptable price. Complete reliance on the consumers' expressed intentions could frequently be misleading. The analyst, on the other hand, is aware of the consumer's tendency to hedge.

Whereas the consumer assumes the most likely hypothesis for himself, the analyst is aware that the aggregate of most probable hypotheses for each individual is not the most probable hypothesis for all. There are among the people questioned some who will be hurt in automobile accidents, some whose children will be ill. In an overall statistical analysis, these probabilities are taken into consideration.

Many consumers questioned may experience difficulty in describing intentions. Sometimes the questions may be suggestive in that they invoke intentions that were not held before the questions were asked. We encounter similar problems in a study of attitudes.

c) Study of attitudes.

Consumer attitudes and opinions can give rise—still according to Lorie—to two types of investigations: thos which aim at classifying the various possibilities in the preference order of individuals, and those which aim at classifying the individuals according to their reaction when faced with only a single possibility. An example of the first type would be an inquiry relating to consideration of various types of packaging to determine the type preferred by consumers. An example of the second type of investigation would be the question: "What do you think of radio?"

Research on consumer opinions implicitly assumes a positive correlation between consumer opinions and consumer actions. But this correlation is frequently very weak, and, as a general rule, it is impossible to predict future sales solely on the basis of an investigation of consumer opinions.

Furthermore, such investigations are very narrowly based and often make use of concepts which are not operational. A discussion of both forms of investigation mentioned might help pinpoint these difficulties.

Let us suppose that we have three possible packagings: red, green, and white; designating these three possibilities as A, B, and C. The investigation will provide the order in which consumers have classified them. The results obtained are, for example, as follows (an ABC symbol would mean that A is preferred to B and C, and that B is preferred to C; the possibility that a consumer prefers A to B, B to C and C to A being excluded):

ABC	20%
ACB	10%
CAB	30%
CBA	—
BCA	30%
BAC	10%

A first examination indicates that A is cited first in 30% of the cases, B in 40%, and C in 30%. But it is impossible to conclude that consumers prefer B, because everything depends upon the opinion in relation to B of consumers who first indicated A or C. One is therefore led to prepare a table which will indicate the number of times one possibility is preferred to another: (a symbol such as AB means that A is preferred to B regardless of C's position):

AB	60%
BC	60%
CA	60%

A peculiarity in this table is immediately apparent. Although A is preferred to B, and B to C, C is preferred to A. This property has long been known under the name of the Condorcet effect [5][17]. Condorcet was initially interested in its appearance in successive votes at parliamentary assemblies.

This example demonstrates that, when consumers are asked their opinion as to certain possibilities, the inquiry should not be limited by requesting them to indicate what they prefer, since the table obtained would run the risk of being completely inaccurate.

In order to cause the "cyclic" effect of collective choices to disappear, one should be able to assign to each answer numbers measuring the degree of preference of each consumer for each possibility. By adding these numbers, the degree of preference of consumers for A, B, or C would be obtained. However, despite the efforts of economists, this question remains devoid of significance for the time being.

In an example of the second form of investigation, we find it very difficult to resolve the question as to whether Mr. X is more or less favorable to radio than Mr. Y? The usual survey poses a direct question and elicits a direct reply which, without understanding the background of the respondent, is usually meaningless. The following two answers, cited by Lorie, to the question, "Do you like radio?" — are not necessarily incompatible. "Listening to the radio is a bad habit for children." "Radio is excellent company when I am alone at night."

Furthermore, the consumer is frequently tempted to respond in a way that might not truly express his own preference. He might want to please the investigator or might simply be responsive to the framing of the question.

d) Study of consumer knowledge.

There is an implicit hypothesis that a relationship exists between the sales of a product and consumer knowledge. This hypothesis has a very limited area of application and it would seem advisable to resort to such studies only when other more direct methods are impossible.

On the other hand, implementation poses relatively few problems.

For example, a consumer can be requested to cite the various brand names he knows for a given product. Before selecting a name for a new product, it is similarly possible to offer a series of names to consumers and ascertain the names they remember best. In order to evaluate the effect of an advertising campaign, an attempt can be made at learning whether consumers remember the slogans that have been used. Another procedure that is used consists in exploring consumer idea associations by asking them to verbalize their reaction to each of a series of words or ideas.

e) Study of consumer motives.

Except for an asymmetrical and lagging time scale, consumer motives and consumer intentions are analytically similar. Research on consumer motivation assumes a continuity between some motives and ultimate action. The analysis of this function can help develop an understanding of the direction and potential scope of future markets. Such investigations can complement statistical analyses that do not themselves throw any light on causal relationships.

The individual questioned must understand the nature and objective of the inquiry. He must be able to express himself coherently. He must be able to distinguish between his basic motive and his immediate intention. For example, he may intend to replace his old automobile with a new one. His motive may be that he believes continued repair of the old automobile is uneconomical or he wants to improve the reliability of his transportation, or he wants to have as nice a car as neighbor Jones. For the analysis to be potentially fruitful, the respondent must understand his own motives, and must relate them completely and honestly. The analyst, on the other hand, must establish rapport with the respondent, enlist his cooperation and obtain full and frank responses.

Assuming that all of these difficulties have been resolved, it then becomes necessary for the analyst to classify the responses and collate them into homogeneous groupings whose significance can be interpreted.

Surveys pose problems not only of interrogation and interpretation but technical issues in connection with representative sampling as well. Theoretically, randomization derives the most accurate representation of a total population. However, a truly random selection might involve excessive costs to reach all types of people in many locations. Stratification, in terms of location and in accordance with population densities, permits sampling that can be both representative and relatively inexpensive. The accuracy of results can be considered as proportional to the square root of the number of persons questioned. Sample size will influence the probable error; the survey budget on one hand and the maximum acceptable error on the other will have a direct bearing on the number of respondents to be covered in the survey.

2. Statistics.

Much has been written about the significance of statistics. It is well-known that statistics and statistical correlations do not themselves imply causality. For instance, if a positive correlation is observed between sales and advertising expenditures, the explanation can be either that the advertising is effective and leads to an increase in the volume of sales, or that management has decided to spend a regular percentage of the volume of sales on advertising.

When statistics emanate from within the firm, problems of validity and reliability must be considered. Problems of communication and standardization of terms and techniques combine to render many collections of data suspect. Do they measure what is intended to be measured, and are the measurements reasonably accurate? In comparing a firm's internal statistics with other firms' or industry-wide aggregates, problems of validity and reliability become even more acute. Great care must be exercised in defining the terms and sources of statistical data and expert supervision is required at all levels of data gathering and collation.

Frequently, existing data do not provide a solution to a new problem and it appears to be necessary to obtain additional data. This is a serious problem of equating cost with benefit. Research staffs have a tendency to request ever increasing quantities of data. This sometimes contributes to the transformation of executives (whose work should be oriented toward concrete action) into bureaucrats. By reinforcing the administrative character of a firm's hierarchy, they increase the risk of ossification and put a brake on its dynamism. An economist must therefore accept the fact that he will only gather statistics that are indispensable to the solution of an important problem. Upon acceptance of his proposals by management, he must insure that the executives have the necessary means at their disposal to bring this new task to completion without excessive interference with their regular duties.

3. Experiments.

Experiments are another source for information pertinent to marketing research. This method differs from surveys in that studies are made of basic reactions of consumers in situations where certain variations are controlled. For example, a company wishes to launch a new product and hesitates between two brand names. It selects two distinct markets as close to each other in place and kind as possible, and introduces the product in both markets. Only the name differs from one market to the other. A study is thereafter made of consumer reactions on the two markets and the differences are attributed to the differences in the brand names. This example brings to light the advantages and disadvantages of experiments in marketing research:

1) A large advantage is in the fact that such an experiment is performed under conditions of an actual market. The consumer does not have to interpret his intentions, his motives, or his behavior. He is not even aware that he is participating in an experiment. There is, therefore, every reason to believe that he will behave as he would if the product were actually being marketed. The only difference between the experiment and actual practice lies in the quantity of the product placed on the market. In that there is a degree of extrapolation required.

2) Sometimes experiments tend to alter the conditions of a market or predispose it for future operations. For instance, an experimental price had better be based on real costs because sometimes a later marketing of a new product must hold to the earlier price. Because of such risks, an enterprise restricts itself, in general, to experiments of limited scope in order to avoid an irreversible action on the market structure.

3) Experiments require the expenditure of considerable amounts of money. They must be continued during a sufficiently long period of time to permit the markets to reach equilibrium, and that may necessitate the manufacture of two slightly different products during that period.

4) They take for granted the possibility of locating two markets sufficiently identical to warrant ascribing the differences observed to differences between the controlled variables. In economic life, where variables are numerous, this is a condition which is difficult to realize.

The collection of accurate and valid quantitative data does not lend itself to a display of brilliant intellectual virtuosity, but this small and often thankless task can condition an entire structure of planning and operation. This stage is a necessary prelude to the stages described in the following chapters.

BIBLIOGRAPHY

1. M. ADLER:
   A short course in market research. London, Fisher, 1952.

2. ALT and BRADFORD:
   Business economics. Principles and cases. Irwin, Homewood, Illinois, 1954.

3. O. ANGEHRN:
   Unternehmer und betriebliche Marktforschung Zurich St-Gall
   (Industrialists and operational market research, Zurich
   St-Gall). Polygr. Verlag A.G., 1954.

4. K. J. ARROW:
   Le principe de rationalité dans les décisions collectives (The
   principle of rationality in collective decisions). Economie
   appliquée V, October-December 1952.

5. K. J. ARROW:
   Social choice and individual values. Cowles Commision
   Monograph, No. 12, New York, Wiley, 1951.

6. Jane AUBERT-KRIER, J. BENOIT, R. B. THIBERT, C. CHAR-
   MONT, R. LABOURIER, J. POLY and P. LAUZEL:
   La prévision et le contrôle de la gestion (Predictions and
   managerial control). Journées d'études des 20-21.1.56
   Institut d'administration des entreprises de Rennes.

7. BLANKERTZ, FERLER, WALES:
   Cases and problems in marketing research. The Ronald
   Press Company, New York, 1954.

8. F. BOUQUEREL:
   L'étude des marchés au service de l'entreprise (Market
   research in the service of the firm), 2 vol. Presses
   Universitaires de France, 1953.

9. J. F. BOUQUEREL:
   Simples propos sur l'étude des marchés (Simple remarks
   concerning market research). Revue de statistique appliquée,
   1953, vol. 1, No. 1-2.

10. E. S. BRADFORD:
    Marketing research. How to analyze products, markets, and
    methods of distribution. McGraw-Hill, New York, 1951.

11. C.E.G.O.S.:
    L'étude du marché et ses applications pratiques (Marketing
    research and its practical applications). Exposé et enquête
    de la Commission "Commerce" C.E.G.O.S. oc. 15.

12. Committee on marketing research techniques. Design, size
    and validation of sample for market research. J. Marketing,
    1946, 10.

13. J. DEAN:
    Managerial economics. Prentice-Hall, New York, 1951.

14. A. H. R. DELENS:
    L'analisi del mercato (Market analysis). Edizioni Scientifiche Einaudi, Turin, 1954.

15. A. H. R. DELENS:
    Principles of market research. Ed. Crosby Lockwood. London, 1950. French edition: Les principes de l'étude des marchés. Dunod, 1955.

16. DUMAS:
    L'entreprise et la statistique (The enterprise and statistics). Paris, Dunod, 1959.

17. G. Th. GUILBAUD:
    Les théories de l'intérêt général et le problème logique de l'"agregation." (General interest theories and the logical problem of "aggregation.") Economie appliquée, IV, October-December 1952.

18. G. GURVITCH:
    La vocation actuelle de la sociologie (The present trend in sociology). Presses Universitaires de France, 1952.

19. Hrsg. von DONALD M. HOBART:
    Praxis der Markt forschung. Die deutsche Ausg. Besorgte Carl Hundhausen (Practices of market research. German edition prepared by Carl Hundhausen) Essen, Girardet, 1952.

20. H. S. HOUTHAKKER and S. J. PRAIS:
    Les variations de qualité dans les budget de famille (Quality variations in family budgets). Economie appliquée, V, 1952, No. 1.

21. A. G. IRVINE:
    Marketing research and management. London, Macdonald and Evans, 1954.

22. LEARNED:
    Problems in marketing. McGraw-Hill, New York.

23. H. C. LEVINSON:
    Experience in commercial operations research. Journal of the Operations Research Society of America, August 1953.

24. LORIE and ROBERTS:
    Basic methods of marketing research. McGraw-Hill, New York, 1951.

25. J. F. MAGEE:
The effect of promotional effort on sales. Journal of the
Operations Research Society of America, February 1953.

26. M. P. McNAIR and R. S. MERIAM:
Problems in business economics. McGraw-Hill, New York,
1941.

27. O.E.C.E.:
Les techniques de l'étude des marchés en Europe (Techniques
of European market research). Paris, 1956.

28. REDMAYNE, P. BREWIS, and H. WEEKS:
Market Research. London; Butterworth, 1951.

29. E. SCHAEFER:
Grundlagen der Markt forschung, Markt untersuchung und
Markt beobachtung (Fundamentals of market research, mar-
ket investigation, and market observation). Köln u. Opladen.
West deutscher Verlag, 1953.

30. E. SCHAEFER:
Betriebs wirtsschaftliche Markt forschung (Industrial economic market research). Essen, Girardet, 1955.

31. Ch. SCHERTENLEIB:
Traité théorique et pratique de l'étude du marché (Theoretical
and practical treatise on market research). Dunod, 1945.

32. H. SCHULZ:
The theory of measurement of demand. University Press,
Chicago, 1938.

33. SERVOISE:
L'étude scientifique des marchés (Scientific market research). Presses universitaires de France, 1954.

35. G. TINTNER:
Scope and methods of econometrics. Journal of the Statistical
Inquiry Society, Ireland, 1949, 21.

36. G. TINTNER:
La position de l'économétrie dans la hiérarchie des sciences
sociales (The position of econometrics in the hierarchy of
the social sciences). Revue d'Economie Politique, 1949, 59.

Chapter 4

The theoretical
analysis of demand

When an analyst undertakes to construct an economic model, he does so by attempting to synthesize the application of general theory with the specific variables of the problem.

A theoretical analysis of demand provides valuable assistance to the econometrician, but its effectiveness should not be over-estimated. The theory covers relatively few variables and it analyzes the behavior of both the consumer and the firm with considerable rigidity. The inadequate treatment of dynamic effects inhibits its usefulness as an analtyical tool.

The first three parts of this chapter are devoted to a consideration of consumer demand and the last part is devoted to a study of the middleman's demand. The first two parts analyze the static components of the consumer goods market, and the third part considers its dynamic elements. In developing a static analysis of consumer behavior, it is useful to postulate certain demand functions in order to define elasticities and to demonstrate a few relevant relationships which can lead, in turn, to some less obvious properties of demand functions. Finally, it will be recalled that, for a given product, there can be three different demand functions:

1. a single consumer or a single firm's demand for a given product or for a group of products;
2. the entire consumer demand, or the entire firm demand;
3. the consumer demand or the firm demand for the goods of a given firm.

The first two functions fall within the scope of this chapter. The third may have entirely different properties and may even be indefinable since it depends upon the state of competition existing between firms producing the same goods.

I

DEMAND FUNCTIONS

1. Single consumer demand functions.

Let us consider the case of an economy where goods or services 1, 2, ..., n are consumed. Within the static framework that we have postulated, the quantities requested by an individual during a given period, a year for example, will be functions of the different p_1, p_2, ..., p_n prices, of his income R and of the capital available to him at the beginning of the year in the shape of cash in hand or property owned. If, in order to simplify matters, we omit a clarification of variables which represent capital, one may consider that demand for an i product by an individual is a function of

$$q_i = q_i(p_1, ..., p_n, R) \tag{I.1}$$

In order to understand demand functions in the neighborhood of a given point, it is convenient to introduce the notion of elasticity. Given a function of (x, y, ...), its elasticity is defined with respect to the variable at a given point (x, y, ...) as

$$\frac{x}{f(x, y, .)} \frac{\partial f}{\partial x}(x, y, .)$$

preceded by the necessary sign to make it positive. This expression is none other than than the analytical form of the ratio

$$\frac{\Delta f}{f} \Big/ \frac{\Delta x}{x}$$

In applying this general definition according to customary usage, we designate for goods i:

a) Elasticity of demand with respect to income, by the expression

$$E_{iR} = \frac{R}{q_i} \frac{\partial q_i}{\partial R} \tag{I.2}$$

b) Elasticity of demand with respect to its price, by the expression

$$e_{ii} = -\frac{p_i}{q_i} \frac{\partial q_i}{\partial p_i} \tag{I.3}$$

c) Elasticity of demand with respect to other prices, or cross-elasticity, by the expression

$$e_{ij} = -\frac{p_j}{q_i} \frac{\partial q_i}{\partial p_j} \tag{I.4}$$

An understanding of elasticity is basic if one is to account for variations in the demand function when prices or income vary slightly. These variations may be characterized by magnitudes which are independent of the units of measurement, i.e., non-dimensional magnitudes which link the relative demand variation to the relative income or price variation. To state, for example, that the elasticity of demand with respect to income is 0.5, means that when income increases by 1%, the quantity demanded increases by 0.5%.

In addition to defining the elasticities of demand at a given point, average elasticities can be defined. Variables $p_1, \ldots, p_n$ (excluding p_i), as well as R having been specified, the average elasticity e_m of demand with respect to its price between price values p_i and p_i' is equal to the elasticity of the demand curve of constant elasticity passing through points (p_i, q_i) and (p_i', q_i'). It can be demonstrated that e_m is given by the expression

$$e_m = - \frac{\log q_i' - \log q_i}{\log p_i' - \log p_i} \tag{I.5}$$

A knowledge of elasticities of demand at a given point makes it possible to calculate, with respect to prices and income, how expenditures d for purchase of goods i by the consumer vary: $d_i = p_i \, q_i$,

a) Variation of expenditure with respect to income (price held constant):

$$\mathrm{d}d_i = p_i \, \mathrm{d}q_i = p_i \, q_i \, E_{iR} \frac{\mathrm{d}R}{R} = d_i \, E_{iR} \frac{\mathrm{d}R}{R} \tag{I.6}$$

This relationship indicates that elasticity of demand with respect to income could also be defined as elasticity of expenditure with respect to income.

b) Variation of expenditure with respect to price of goods purchased (income held constant):

$$\mathrm{d}d_i = p_i \, \mathrm{d}q_i + q_i \, \mathrm{d}p_i = d_i \, (1 - e_{ii}) \frac{\mathrm{d}p_i}{p_i} \tag{I.7}$$

Expenditure varies in the same direction as price if the elasticity with respect to prices is less than 1. It varies in the opposite direction if elasticity is greater than 1. When elasticity has a value of 1, the decrease in the quantity purchased when price increases compensates exactly for the increase in expenditure due to the price increases. In the case of a firm, it would be of interest to know whether the elasticity of demand for one of its products is less then, equal to, or greater than 1. If elasticity is less than 1, the demand is said to be inelastic. If it is greater than 1, the demand is said to be elastic.

c) Variation of expenditure with respect to the other prices (at constant income and prices — with the exception of one):

$$\mathrm{d}d_i = p_i \, \mathrm{d}q_i = - e_{ij} \, d_i \, \frac{\mathrm{d}p_j}{p_j} \qquad (\mathrm{I}.8)$$

This relation demonstrates that elasticity of demand with respect to the other prices could also be defined as expenditure elasticity with respect to the other prices.

Elasticity with respect to income is usually positive. There are, however, certain goods, regarded as inferior, for which this is not true. It could happen, for instance, that when an individual's income increases, he may wish to consume butter rather than margarine. In such a case, elasticity of demand for margarine with respect to income would be negative.

Elasticity of demand with respect to price is usually positive. Except in very rare cases (valuable stamps, paintings) demand decreases when the price increases.

Elasticity of demand with respect to the other prices can be positive or negative. In the case of butter and margarine, consumption of margarine may increase when the price of butter increases (negative elasticity). On the other hand, in the case of automobiles and gasoline, demand for gasoline increases when the price of automobiles decreases (positive elasticity).

Many econometric studies have attempted to demonstrate that demand functions in areas of large variation may often be represented by functions of constant elasticity. For instance, q_0 being a constant, demand for the product i (neglecting the symbol in order not to complicate the formula) will be

$$q = q_0 \, R^{E_R} \, p_1^{-e_1} \, p_2^{-e_2} \ldots\ldots\ldots p_n^{-e_n} \qquad (\mathrm{I}.9)$$

Such functions are represented in Figs. 1, 2, 3, and 4. In Figs. 1 and 2, the prices are presumed given, and the variables are income and demand in Fig. 1 and their logarithms in Fig. 2. In Figs. 3 and 4, income and prices of other goods are assumed given and the variables are demand and the price of the goods in Fig. 3 and their logarithms in Fig. 4.

On the logarithmic scale, the demand curves are straight lines, whose slopes represent elasticity with respect to income or inelasticity with respect to price.

For this reason preference is given, in statistical analyses, to correlating the logarithms of the variables rather than the variables themselves so as to utilize linear regression.

Constant elasticity functions can be utilized only in areas of limited variation. If we introduce the expenditure function, $d_i = p_i \, q_i$, it presents at least one minimum with respect to price (see Fig. 5).

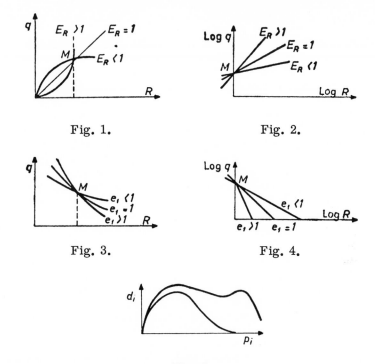

Fig. 1.

Fig. 2.

Fig. 3.

Fig. 4.

Fig. 5.

When the price is zero, the expenditure value is zero, and above a certain price, the demand approaches zero.

Intervals where expenditures increase with price increases correspond to inelastic demand; the intervals where expenditures decrease with price increases correspond to elastic demand.

Rather than adopt constant elasticity functions with respect to income, certain econometricians—Tornqvist, in particular—have suggested simple analytical functions, such as homographic functions.

2. Single consumer demand for a group of products.

At times, the composite demand for closely related products may be analytically more fruitful than the demand schedules for each of the individual products. For example, an analysis is made of the demand for fats and for heating fuels (coal and fuel oil). The composite demand can usually be measured in two different ways:

a) by using the total expenditure which, limiting oneself to goods 1 and 2, has the form: $d = d_1 + d_2 = p_1q_1 + p_2q_2$;

b) by using conversion coefficients. In the case of fuel oil and coal, for instance, the demand can be measured in terms of the caloric power of these two fuels. In such case, the total demand q is:

$$q = m_1 q_1 + m_2 q_2$$

where m_1 and m_2 indicate the conversion coefficients.

There are a few theorems which are at times useful in connection with total demand elasticities [36].

Elasticity of composite demand with respect to income is considered to be the average of the elasticities of the component goods with respect to income.

If the composite demand is measured by means of conversion coefficients, the weighting coefficients are the converted quantities of component goods.

If the composite demand is measured according to expenditure, the weighting coefficients are the expenditures corresponding to the component goods.

Therefore, in the case of two component goods,

$$E_q = \frac{m_1 q_1 E_1 + m_2 q_2 E_2}{m_1 q_1 + m_2 q_2} \quad (I.10) \qquad\qquad E_d = \frac{d_1 E_1 + d_2 E_2}{d_1 + d_2} \quad (I.11)$$

When composite demand is measured by means of conversion coefficients, its elasticity with respect to price is considered to be the average of the elasticities of the component goods, the weighted coefficients being the converted quantities. If we limit ourselves to the case of two goods, and if e_{qi}, e_{1i}, and e_{2i} represent, respectively, the elasticities of composite demand and of component demands with respect to p_i, we then have:

$$e_{qi} = \frac{m_1 q_1 e_{1i} + m_2 q_2 e_{2i}}{m_1 q_1 + m_2 q_2}. \quad (I.12)$$

Assuming now that all prices of component goods vary, let us designate p as a price index in such a way that the price of each component good is proportional to such index. The elasticity of total demand with respect to p is equal to the sum of the elasticities of that demand with respect to the prices of component goods.

Still limiting ourselves to two goods,

$$dq = \frac{\partial q}{\partial p_1} dp_1 + \frac{\partial q}{\partial p_2} dp_2.$$

But, by hypothesis,

$$\frac{dp_1}{p_1} = \frac{dp_2}{p_2} = \frac{dp}{p}.$$

Therefore

$$dq = -(e_{q1} + e_{q2}) \, q \, \frac{dp}{p}$$

3. Demand functions of consumer groups [36].

The total demand function for an i product by m consumers is, by definition, the sum of demands of individual consumers and, consequently, is mainly dependent upon prices $p_1, \ldots, p_n$ of the n goods and the m incomes $R_1, \ldots, R_m$ of consumers.

The definition of elasticity of total demand with respect to the various prices does not pose any problem. On the other hand, in order to define the elasticity of total demand with respect to total income $R = R_1 + \ldots + R_m$ of consumers, it is necessary to know how a surplus income dR is divided among the different consumers.

The relationships existing between total demand elasticities and the elasticities of component consumer demands are indicated by the following theorems:

1. Total demand elasticity with respect to price is the average of the elasticity of such demands weighted by component demands. Let q_i^j be the demand for a product i by the consumer j and let e_{ik}^j be the elasticity of this demand with respect to the price k. The elasticity e_{ik} of the total demand is then given by the formula:

$$e_{ik} = \frac{\sum\limits_{J=1}^{m} e_{ik}^j \, q_i^j}{\sum\limits_{J=1}^{M} q_i^j}. \tag{I.13}$$

2. The same relationship is valid in the case of elasticity with respect to income, when the incomes of consumers vary proportionately.

3. On the other hand, when the incomes of consumers do not vary proportionately, the computation of the elasticity of the total demand with respect to income requires the introduction of elasticity r_j of the income of the consumer j with respect to total income:

$$r_j = \frac{R}{R_j} \frac{dR_j}{dR}.$$

The elasticity of total demand with respect to consumer income is then provided by the formula:

$$E_i = \frac{\sum\limits_{J=1}^{m} E_i^j \, q_i^j \, r_j}{\sum\limits_{J=1}^{m} q_i^j} \tag{I.14}$$

where E_i^j indicates elasticity of consumer j's demand with respect to his income.

A fruitful method of representation in an analysis of total demand consists in assuming that, under given price conditions, all consumers with an R income have the same demand: q (R, p_1, ..., p_n). If f (R) dR represents the number of consumers with an income between R and R + dR, the total demand is then*

$$q = \int_0^\infty q\,(R, p_1, \cdots, p_n) f\,(R)\ dR$$

and the total income

$$r = \int_0^\infty R f\,(R)\ dR.$$

From a simple hypothesis relative to the q function (for instance, the hypothesis that q is a function of constant elasticity in R, p_1, ..., p_n) and a knowledge of the distribution of incomes, one can infer interesting information about the probable form of total demand. The statistical distribution functions of incomes are well known. They can be represented either by Gibrat's law, or Pareto's law, which are outlined as follows:

Gibrat's law: The logarithm of income is normally distributed (logarithmic-normal distribution).

Pareto's law: The frequency p (R) of an individual having an income between R and R + dR is, b being a positive constant:

$$p\,(R) = o \text{ for } R \leqslant b$$

$$p\,(R) = \frac{(a - 1)\,b^{a-1}}{R^a} \text{ for } R > b, \text{ a is a constant greater than 1.}$$

These are about the only theoretical elements concerning the functions of demand that can be developed without the assistance of a theory regarding consumer behavior. They reduce themselves to very ordinary properties because the more general the initial hypotheses, the more trite will be their consequences and the wider their application. The analyst always seeks an equilibrium between general hypotheses and the more specific hypotheses. The following section, concerned with the theory of consumer choice, is oriented toward hypotheses of a more specific nature whose applicability, therefore, though interesting, is fairly limited.

---

*Professor R. Roy is the author of this type of analysis.

II

THE THEORY OF CONSUMER CHOICE

1. The utility concept [1] [36].

The concept of utility, referred to in Chapter 2 in regard to choices involving risks, is presented here in regard to the consumption choices of an individual.

According to hypothesis, consumer behavior complies with the following axioms:

Axiom I. Taking into account two possible consumptions $(q_1, \ldots, q_n)$ and $(q_1', \ldots, q_n')$, the consumer is able to state whether they are equal in his scale of preference or if one is preferred to the other.

Axiom II. If a consumption $(q_i, \ldots, q_n)$ is preferred to consumption $(q_1^0, \ldots, q_n^0)$, any consumption preferred to $(q_1, \ldots, q_n)$ will be preferred to consumption $(q_i^0, \ldots, q_n^0)$.

Conversely, if a consumption $(q_1, \ldots, q_n)$ is such that consumption $(q_1^0, \ldots, q_n^0)$ is preferred instead, the latter will be preferred to any consumption to which $(q_1, \ldots, q_n)$ is preferred.

Axiom III. Any consumption $q_1, q_2, \ldots, q_n$, such as:
$q_1 \geq q_1^0, q_2 \geq q_2^0, \ldots\ldots\ldots\ldots q_n \geq q_n^0$ — the equal sign not being valid for all goods — is preferred by the consumer to consumption $(q_1^0, \ldots, q_n^0)$.

Conversely, any consumption $q_1, q_2, \ldots, q_n$, such as:
$q_1 \leq q_1^0, q_2 \leq q_0^2, \ldots\ldots\ldots\ldots q_n \leq q_n^0$ — the equal sign not being valid for all goods — is such that the consumer prefers consumption $(q_1^0, \ldots, q_n^0)$ to such a consumption.

Despite apparent similarities, there is a great difference between the axioms introduced in Chapter 2 and those above. The former established the conditions necessary for rational choice. Here, the axioms are utilized to describe the actual behavior of consumers which is understandably not always consistent with rational objectives of economic behavior.

With the help of the three preceding axioms, it can be demonstrated that total consumption equal to a given consumption $(q_1^0, \ldots, q_n^0)$ forms in an n dimensional space of n consumptions a surface known as an indifference surface.

Supposing for instance that n = 2. Let M_0 be the point $(q_1^0, q_2^0$. According to axiom III, any one Point M' of the shaded area in Fig. 6 is preferred to M_0. The straight line OM' contains, in the vicinity of the point of origin, points at which M_0 is preferred, and, in the vicinity of M', points preferred to M_0.

Any point M on OM' is such that points of segment MM' are preferable; however, it is preferred to points of segment OM. By

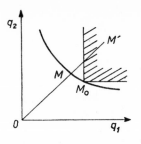

Fig. 6.

virtue of axiom II, there is, then, one M point, and one only point of OM' which would be equal to M_0'. When M' varies, M produces a curve passing through M_0 known as the curve of indifference.

In n dimensional space, indifference curves are replaced by a family of indifference surfaces. In order to define one such surface, it is merely necessary to know its point of intersection with a given straight line emanating from the point of origin. The indifference surfaces, therefore, depend on a parameter U and they can be represented by the equation

$$U = U(q_1, ..., q_n).$$

An index U must be chosen so that when one consumption is preferred to another, its U index will be greater. In this case one has, according to axiom III,

$$\frac{\partial U}{\partial q_i} > 0 \text{ for all } i.$$

Naturally, any function f (U), such as f' (U) > 0, can be substituted for a U function. Function U has been given the name of consumer utility.

The definition of utility having been taken into account, it is reasonable to stipulate as an axiom that the consumer will choose the maximum utility within the limits allowed by his budget. Subject to the hypothesis that a consumer's income is devoted entirely to the purchase of goods (1, 2, ..., n) (savings could be represented by the purchase of a durable product), the equilibrium of the consumer's budget can be translated by the relation

$$p_1 q_1 + p_2 q_2 + \cdots + p_n q_n = R. \tag{II.1}$$

Conditions required for a maximization of U $(q_1, ..., q_n)$ under the restraint (II.1) are given by the n - 1 equations:*

---

*At least, if one excludes the possibility of equilibrium limits because all consumptions must be positive or zero.

$$\frac{U'_{q_1}}{p_1} = \cdots = \frac{U'_{q_n}}{p_n}. \tag{II.2}$$

The n relations (II.1) and II.2) make it possible to calculate the n unknowns q_2, ..., q_n for given prices and income. They define a point of contact between an indifference surface and the plane of income defined by (II.1). This point of contact corresponds with a maximum utility if the indifference surface is entirely on the other side of the point of origin with respect to the tangent plane; in other words, if the indifference surface is convex at the point of contact. The significance of this property will be apparent in Fig. 7 in the case of n = 2.

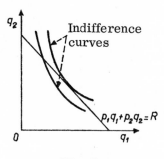

Fig. 7.

Subject to certain supplemental axioms it can be demonstrated that this condition of convexity is valid.

This, greatly condensed, is the theory of utility. A more detailed elaboration of this theory is not specifically useful to economic analysis.

2. Properties of consumer demand functions.

From the preceding theory three important theorems are deduced:

Theorem I: For given values of p_1, p_2, ..., p_n, R, the q_i demand has a well defined value. This theorem justifies, a posteriori, the analysis appearing in the first part of this chapter.

Theorem II: The demand functions are homogeneous and of zero degree. In other words, m being an arbitrary positive number,

$$q_i (mp_1, ..., mp_2, mR) = q_i (p_1, ..., p_n, R).$$

When all prices and income are multiplied by m, the systems (II.1 and II.2) remain unchanged. Its solutions, therefore, are the same demands. This theorem means, in effect, that consumers are not victims of a monetary illusion.

Corollary: By applying Euler's theorem to demand functions, the following relation is obtained:

$$R\frac{\partial q_i}{\partial R} + p_1\frac{\partial q_i}{\partial p_1} + \cdots + p_n\frac{\partial q_i}{\partial p_n} = 0. \qquad (II.3)$$

which means that elasticity with respect to income is equal to the sum of elasticities with respect to prices.

In reality, relation (II.1) is not quite valid because, for budgeted amounts, what one can spend depends upon the liquid capital initially available. Theorem II, therefore, is only approximately verified.

Theorem III: By using t as the common value of the ratios in relations (II.2), the system (II.1 and 2) becomes a system of $n + 1$ equations with $n + 1$ unknowns (t, $q_1, \ldots, q_n$). By differentiating the equations of the system (II.1 and 2) with respect to independent variables $p_1, \ldots, p_n$ R, one obtains $(n + 1)$ systems of $(n + 1)$ equations containing all the $(n + 1)^2$ unknown partial derivatives of (t, $q_1, \ldots, q_n$) with respect to the $n + 1$ variables $p_1, \ldots, p_n$, R.

The computation indicates that there exists between $\frac{\partial q_i}{\partial p_i}$ and $\frac{\partial q_i}{\partial R}$ the relation: $\frac{\partial q_i}{\partial p_j} = c_{ij} - q_j\frac{\partial q_i}{\partial R}$

where c_{ij} is a unique function of the partial derivatives of the first and second order of U ($q_1, \ldots, q_n$).

When the price of j goods varies by dp_j, all other prices and income being fixed, it is the same as though the consumer's income varied hypothetically by dR = q_j, dp_j.

Taking this dR value into consideration, the relation (II.4) can be written:

$$dq_i = c_{ij}\,dp_j + \frac{\partial q_i}{\partial R}\,dR. \qquad (II.5)$$

This interesting relation is known as Slutzky's equation. It indicates that, when a price varies, the variation in the demand is the sum of two effects:

a) An income effect $\frac{\partial q_i}{\partial R}$ dR which expresses the effect of the decrease in the actual income q_j dp_j, resulting from the increase in price, and which leads, all other things being equal, to a decrease in consumption when the price increases.

b) An effect of substitution, c_{ij} dp_j, which reflects the extent to which a consumer substitutes other goods for i goods when p_j varies, other prices and his real income being held constant. When i = j, it can be shown that c_{ii} is always negative. When i ≠ j, the relation defining c_{ij} is such that $c_{ij} = c_{ji}$.

The substitution effect is symmetrical. Consequently, two i and j goods bear the name of independent goods if $c_{ij} = 0$; substitute goods if $c_{ij} > 0$; complementary goods if $c_{ij} < 0$.

Now it is necessary to formulate the three theorems above to express total consumer demand.

3. Total consumer demand.

If q_i^k represents the demand for i goods by consumer k, the total demand is:

$$q_i = \sum_k q_i^k (p_1, \cdots, p_n, R_k).$$

Theorem I applies without difficulty. Since each q_i^k has a well defined value for given $p_1, \ldots, p_n, R_k$, the total demand has a well determined value for given prices and individual incomes.

Theorem II has the effect that when all prices and all incomes are multiplied by m, the demand functions remain unchanged. Consequently, the (II.3) relation becomes:

$$\sum_k R_k \frac{\partial q_i^k}{\partial R_k} + p_1 \frac{\partial q_i}{\partial p_1} + \cdots + p_n \frac{\partial q_i}{\partial p_n} = 0. \tag{II.6}$$

The summation of relations (II.4) for various consumers leads to the equivalent of theorem III:

$$\frac{\partial q_i}{\partial p_j} = \sum_k c_{ij}^k - \sum_k q_j^k \frac{\partial q_i^k}{\partial R_k} \tag{II.7}$$

i.e., by setting: $c_{ij} = \sum_k c_{ij}^k$:

$$dq_i = c_{ij}\, dp_j - \sum_k q_j^k \frac{\partial q_i^k}{\partial R_k}\, dp_j. \tag{II.8}$$

The second term represents the income effect for the total number of consumers. It is dependent upon the elasticity with respect to income for each consumer and the manner in which the decreases $q_j^k\, pd_j$ in real income are distributed.

The first term represents the substitution effect. The c_{ij} have the same properties as the c_{ij}^k.

The more interesting consequences of the theory of consumer's choice have been presented as concisely as possible. Although they may be difficult to verify empirically, they at least constitute a framework of practical reference for the analysis of specific cases.

III

THE DYNAMIC ASPECTS OF DEMAND
FOR CONSUMER GOODS

The theory outlined up to this point is essentially static. It presupposes that demand, during an entire period, is a function of prices and incomes during that period. This hypothesis has the disadvantage of neglecting a great number of routine phenomena of a dynamic character. A general dynamic theory of demand remains to be elaborated. Generally, the economic analyst retains only the essential variables; it is certainly less difficult for him to start from a static framework and to incorporate in his model one or two of the principal dynamic aspects of the market than it is to deduce his relationships from a completely dynamic theory. The following discussion will therefore be limited to an enumeration of certain dynamic aspects of demand without giving them a systematic form.

a) Demand functions can vary by reason of changes in consumer tastes. These changes can be seasonal or contingent upon the influence of external factors (as in the case of heating). They can be irreversible and long-term. R. Stone notes, for example [34], that in Great Britain, from 1920 to 1938, the demand for tobacco increased by about 3% per year (after eliminating the influence of incomes and prices). In such a case, the model assumes the form of:

$$q_{it} = q_{i_0} (p_{1t}, ..., p_{nt}, R_t) (1 + u)^t$$

where q_{i0} is a demand function of the year 0, q_{it} the demand function for the year t, $p_{1t}, ..., p_{nt}$ and R_t the prices and income of the year t, and u a rate of annual increase due to a transformation in consumer tastes.

Instead of assuming the shape of a uniform trend, these transformations sometimes occur rapidly under the influence of external causes, and assume the appearance of discontinuities in the observed correlations. The war of 1914-1918 is frequently associated with observations of this type.

b) A somewhat different phenomenon is the irreversibility of demand functions. If a consumer's income increases by dR, his demand will grow by dq. However, starting from this new situation, should his income return to its initial value, demand will decrease only by dq' quantity (which is less than dq). The consumer has become accustomed to higher consumption and, when his income decreases, he tends to diminish his savings rather than his consumption. The irreversibility of demand can also be observed when the variable is price instead of income. By using models which introduce two elasticities — an increase elasticity and a decrease elasticity — M. J. Farrel has demonstrated that he could explain, with the help of income and prices, a far greater percentage of the variation in consumption than with the classical models [12].

c) A certain period of time always elapses before consumer response to modification of a variable assumes its definitive value. If, in a city, streetcar fares are increased, the number of passengers will probably drop very sharply immediately following the increase. Many consumers may vow that at the increased price, they would use streetcars less often. Progressively, however, the consumers forget their "irrevocable" decisions and return to traveling by streetcar until a new equilibrium is reached. The number of passenger trips in relation to time assumes the shape of the curve in Fig. 8.

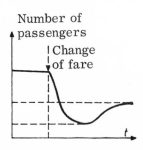

Fig. 8.

Conversely, demand can be maintained for a certain time above the level of equilibrium and then diminish progressively. Such is the case when one considers demand for electric power. It is only as changes progressively occur in their equipment that consumers substitute one source of energy for another.

d) Demand functions do not depend solely upon current income and prices. They are influenced by past income and prices as illustrated in the second example in paragraph (c). Finally, they are influenced by consumer predictions of the state of the economy. For example, if prices begin to mount, the consumer may fear a continual increase in prices and immediately increase his consumption. In other words, an increase in prices will have a static influence which will tend to diminish demand, and a dynamic influence which will tend to increase it. A knowledge of static elasticity alone is not sufficient to determine the direction of variations in demand.

These brief considerations of dynamic aspects of demand have been included to complement, only in a general way, the static theories.

IV

DEMAND FUNCTIONS OF FIRMS

Completely analogous to the analysis of consumer demand is the analysis of the demands made by business for the factors of production. However, the possibility of substitution between production factors are limited in the short run and the demand for factors is closely linked to the markets of the firm. Consequently, a theory of interindustry relations is frequently used in lieu of demand analysis; this neglects possibilities of substitution and emphasizes the interdependence of production of the various branches of industry.

1. The classical analysis.

Assume that an enterprise produces a product 0 using factors of production 1, 2, ..., n. If the enterprise is well managed technically, it will make use of a technique so that, for given quantities q_1, q_2, ..., q_n of factors of production, it will produce the maximum possible Q. Q depends naturally upon q_1, q_2, ..., q_n and this relation is known as a production function.*

$$Q = Q(q_1, q_2, ..., q_n) \qquad \text{(IV.1)}$$

The same quantity of Q can be produced with varying proportions of q_1, ..., q_n. For example, according to respective prices of energy and manpower, handling can or cannot be mechanized.

If the prices of the various goods are respectively P, p_1, ..., p_n, the profit of the enterprise for a given period is:

$$R = PQ - p_1 q_1 - ... - p_n q_n \qquad \text{(IV.2)}$$

Given prices, the enterprise seeks to determine the Q, q_1, ..., q_n quantities in order to maximize its profit R.

Taking into account the restraint (IV.1), this maximization is expressed by the n relations:**

$$\frac{Q'_{q1}}{p_1} = \frac{Q'_{q2}}{p_2} = \cdots\cdots\cdots = \frac{Q'_{q_n}}{p_n} = \frac{1}{P} \qquad \text{(IV.3)}$$

which, when considered with (IV.1), make it possible to calculate the $n + 1$ variables Q, q_1, ..., q_n.

---

*This problem is discussed in greater detail in Chapter 10.
**At least, if one excludes the possibility of a terminal-equilibrium resulting from the fact that all the variables entering into (IV.1) must be positive or zero.

The demand for the i factor of production then appears as a well determined function of the $n + 1$ prices P, p_1, ..., P_n.

Conditions (IV.3) indicate that these demand functions are homogeneous.

By differentiating relations (IV.1 and 3), it is possible, as in the case of the consumer, to calculate the derivatives $\frac{\partial q_i}{\partial p_j}$. It will then be observed that:

$$\frac{\partial q_i}{\partial p_j} = \frac{\partial q_j}{\partial p_i} \qquad \text{(IV.4)}$$

which can be written:

$$\frac{\partial q_i}{\partial p_j} = c_{ij} \text{ with } c_{ij} = c_{ji}. \qquad \text{(IV.5)}$$

Relation (IV.5) is completely analogous to relation (II.4) but, in the case of business, there will be only one effect of substitution.

The properties of demand functions for groups of firms can be very easily deduced from a summation of individual demand functions.

In an existing plant, it is generally impossible at short notice to vary, except within very narrow limits, the proportions of the different factors which contribute to production. Substitutions are scarcely possible except in the core of sub-groups of well determined factors, such as sources of energy.

Furthermore, this analysis has the disadvantage of not making evident the effect on the demand for the Q quantity produced. Models of interindustry relations which rigidly link demands for factors to production do not have this disadvantage.

2. Models of interindustry relations [18].

In these models, all of the enterprises of a country are grouped in n homogeneous areas, each producing only one type of good. For such production, each sector makes use of goods derived from other sectors and primary factors of production, such as, land, labor, and capital.

Assume x_j to be the annual production of area j. $(j = 1, 2, ..., n)$. It requires quantities x_{1j}, x_{2j}, ..., x_{nj} of goods produced by other areas. The x_{ij} and the x_j can be measured with the aid of physical units currently in effect, but it is more convenient to measure them in monetary values of constant francs. The difference between x_j and Σx_{ij} then represents that portion of the sales value which is set aside for the payment of taxes, for the remuneration of primary factors of production, and for profit. It is often referred to as value added V_j:

$$V_j = x_j - \sum_{i=1}^{n} x_{ij}. \qquad (IV.6)$$

Another relation is verified for each product. If, for the sake of simplification, one operates within the framework of a closed economy which neither imports nor exports, the production of each type of good x_i must be equal to the sum of the final demand (consumer demand, government demand, investments) Y_i and of the intermediate demand of the other sectors x_{ij}:

$$Y_i = x_i - \sum_{=1}^{n} x_{ij}. \qquad (IV.7)$$

The summation of relations (IV.6) with respect to j and of relations (IV.7) with respect to i creates a total value added V and the national income Y:

$$V = \sum_j V_j = \sum_j x_j - \sum_{ij} x_{ij} = \sum_i x_i - \sum_{ij} x_{ij} = \sum_i Y_i = Y. \qquad (IV.8)$$

The above relation demonstrates that these quantities are equal. The following table presents the various magnitudes which have now been introduced.

Until the present time, no hypothesis has been made concerning the production functions. The simplest hypothesis is to assume that, in a long interval, x_j and x_{ij} are proportional. In other words, when production is doubled, the quantities of the different factors consumed are also doubled.

Mathematically, this hypothesis is expressed by the relations:

$$x_{ij} = a_{ij} x_j \qquad (IV.9)$$

		Purchasing sectors			Final demand
		1	2	j	
Selling	1	x_{11}	$x_{12} \ldots \ldots$	$x_{1j} \ldots \ldots x_{1n}$	Y_1
	2	x_{21}	$x_{22} \ldots \ldots$	$x_{2j} \ldots \ldots x_{2n}$	Y_2
sectors	.	.	. $\ldots \ldots$	$\ldots \ldots$	.
	i	x_{i1}	$x_{i2} \ldots \ldots$	$x_{ij} \ldots \ldots x_{in}$	Y_i
	.	.	. $\ldots \ldots$	$\ldots \ldots$	.
	n	x_{n1}	$x_{n2} \ldots \ldots$	$x_{nj} \ldots \ldots x_{nn}$	Y_n
Value added		V_1	$V_2 \ldots \ldots$	$V_j \ldots \ldots V_n$	V = Y
Production		x_1	$x_2 \ldots \ldots$	$x_j \ldots \ldots x_n$	

where the a_{ij} are constant coefficients which form a square matrix with n lines and n columns. A supposition that coefficients a_{ij} are constant amounts to excluding two possibilities:

1. Substitutions between factors of production—at least between factors derived from different sectors. This is a reasonable exclusion in the short run if easily substituted goods can be grouped into the same sector of production, such as the different sources of energy.

2. Variation in the cost structure when the scale of production varies.

This is a well known phenomenon which can, moreover, manifest itself under two opposite forms. If it were desired to increase the production of coal in France by 25%, it would be necessary to draw upon less desirable coal fields where the extraction of a ton of coal would consume more factors of production. If, on the other hand, the outlets of our automobile industry could be considerably extended, it should be possible to reduce production costs very substantially. This modification of the cost structure, when the scale of production varies, is encountered mainly in sectors: where exhaustion of natural resources becomes apparent; and where the technically optimum size of the enterprise is very large with respect to the market.

Taking (IV.9) into account, relations (IV.7) can be written:

$$x_i = Y_i + \sum_j a_{ij} x_j \qquad (IV.10)$$

and now constitute, if one assumes the end-demand Y_i to be known, a system of equations in which the unknowns are the x_i productions of the various sectors. This famous analysis of interindustry relations is the work of the U. S. economist Leontief. Following his leadership, many studies were undertaken in the United States to determine the a_{ij} coefficients and to set up a table of interindustry relations. The same work has been undertaken in the Netherlands, Japan, Norway, the United Kingdom, and Italy. It is currently in progress in France.

A solution of system (IV.10) can be achieved directly by means of computations of determinants. x_i is obtained in the form of a linear combination of final demands for the various goods:

$$x_i = A_{i1} Y_1 + \dots + A_{ij} Y_j + \dots + A_{in} Y_n \qquad (IV.11)$$

$A_{ij} Y_j$ (i ≠ j) represents the intermediate demand for the product i resulting from the end-demand of product j and $(A_{ii} - 1) Y_i$, the intermediate demand of product i resulting from the final demand for this product. Rather than try to solve system (IV.10) directly, it is at times more practical to make use of a method of successive approximations. In a first stage, the final demand will induce on the part of the various productions: $x_i' = Y_i$. These productions will create intermediate demands $a_{ij} x_i'$ which will increase the total production to:

$$x_i'' = Y_i + \sum_j a_{ij} x_i'$$

thereupon creating a new expression of intermediate demand, and so on. The interest presented by such a method is that the production required of the various sectors is known at each stage. However, certain sectors may have a limited capacity of production. When the limit is reached, it will be necessary to resort to imports or to another method of production, i.e., to change the a_{ij}. The computation by successive approximations makes it possible to achieve this easily, and, consequently, to obtain freedom, in part, from the hypothesis of stability of the a_{ij} coefficients.

The number of sectors can vary from 20 to 200, but the magnitude of calculations increases as the square of n. For this reason, an effort is made at maintaining n within reasonable limits by regrouping various closely related activities into sectors. The available figures, furthermore, closely limit the possibilities in that connection. Firms that have similar structures are generally grouped within the same sector. These include vertically integrated firms, firms producing complementary goods, and, at times, firms producing substitute goods.

The interindustry models are extremely flexible. Imports and exports can be introduced as well as exchanges between different geographical areas of a country. Finally, assuming that the same product can be produced by several different sectors, linear programming models become feasible.* They can provide valuable information to industry in studies of intermediate demand, and through knowledge of relations between intermediate and final demand. One of their main disadvantages is that they link factor demand to product demand, thus neglecting the acceleration phenomenon (which will be discussed in Chapter 5). This can be remedied by assuming that each sector uses a special factor of production which is its "capacity" and which is initially available in given quantities. When a limit of capacity is reached for a sector, an increase in production necessitates an enlargement of capacity. This new activity is considered as an additional sector with its own a_{ij} coefficients. The pattern then distinguishes 2n sectors, the latter n corresponding to the creation of the capacities of production of the first n.

---

*See Chapter 12.

Note: The patterns of interindustry relations can even be used in connection with studies which include price factors, but the basic hypotheses then become more open to criticism. Assuming, for example, that one wishes to know the influence of indirect taxes upon the system, e.g., a tax on production, let T_j represent the official rate of indirect taxes on the sale of product j, and t_i the effective rate of taxes incorporated in the price of j, taking into account all of the repercussions. The percentage of taxes incorporated in the production cost of product j is $\sum_i a_{ij} t_i$. If the premise is accepted that the sale price closely follows the cost price, the percentage of taxes incorporated in the sale price is then:

$$t_j = T_j + \sum_i a_{ij} t_i.$$

The solution of this system of equations of n unknowns permits the calculation of the t_j's on the basis of a knowledge of the T_j's.

3. Certain dynamic aspects.

The first two types of analyses presented are static. In practice, it is advisable to perfect them by taking into account the main dynamic aspects:

a) The variables of static models can undergo seasonal variations, long run variations, or cyclical variations with respect to fluctuations of business cycle.

b) Aside from the general development of the economy, technical progress is one of the essential elements of long run transformations. It requires a complete revision of interindustry relations tables every ten years. Its development, at times, is sufficiently uniform to be predicted—as in the case of the consumption of calories per kw.-hr. of steam generating stations. When such is not the case, a knowledge of theoretical limits of consumption — if there are such —, a comparison of the most recent existing plants, and, finally, the state of progress of research undertaken make it possible to obtain some idea of the progress that may be anticipated in a given field.

c) In relation to the fluctuations of the business cycle, the inventory problem is often more significant than the demand for consumer goods. The demands of industry are made with respect to their predictions of future production, but this mechanical phenomenon is supplemented by a psychological reaction. When prices begin to rise, firms increase their demand not only because they anticipate greater production, but because they wish to antici-pate the increase and augment the volume of their inventories. This phenomenon, which was clearly observed in France during the few months which followed the beginning of the Korean war, was reversed when prices decreased. It will be studied in greater detail in the next chapter.

BIBLIOGRAPHY

1. M. ALLAIS:
   Traité d'économie pure (Treatise on pure economics). Imprimerie nationale, Paris, 1953.

2. R. L. BASMAN:
   "A theory of demand with consumer's preferences varia-ble." Econometrica, No. 1, January 1956.

3. B. CAMERON:
   "The production function in Leontief models." Review of economic studies, 1952-1953.

4. A. CHABERT:
   "Le système d'input-output de W. Leontief et l'analyse économique quantitative." (The W. Leontief input-output system and quantitative economic analysis). Economie appliquée, Vol. III, 1950, No. 1, January-March.

5. H. B. CHENERY, P. CLARK, and CAO PINNA:
   The structure and growth of the Italian economy. Rome, 1953.

6. H. B. CHENERY:
   "Development policy in underdeveloped countries. The role of industrialization in development programs." The American Economic Review, May 1955.

7. CORNFIELD, W. D. EVANS, and M. HOFFENBERG:
   "Full employment patterns, 1950." Monthly Labor Re-view, 1947.

8. F. DIVISIA:
   Cours d'Economie politique de l'Ecole Polytechnique (Course in political economy at the Ecole Polytechnique). 1949-1950.

9. R. DORFMAN:
   "The nature and significance of input-output." Review of economics and statistics. May 1954.

10. W. D. EVANS:
    "Marketing uses of input-output data." Journal of Mark-eting, July 1952.

11. W. D. EVANS and M. HOFFENBERG:
    "The interindustry relations study for 1947." The Review
    of economics and statistics, May 1952.

12. M. J. FARREL:
    "Irreversible demand functions." Econometrica, XX, 2,
    April 1952.

13. N. GEORGESCU-ROEGEN:
    "Leontief's system in the light of recent results." The
    Review of economics and statistics, August 1950.

14. R. GIBRAT:
    Les inégalitiés économiques (Economic inequalities). Li-
    brairies du Recueil Sirey, Paris, 1952.

15. J. R. HICKS:
    Value and Capital. Oxford, Clarendon Press, 1st edition,
    1939. Valeur et Capital. Dunod, Paris, 1956.

16. L. HURWICZ:
    "Input-output analysis and economic structure." Ameri-
    can Economic Review, September 1955.

17. Tj. KOOPMANS:
    Activity analysis of production and allocation. Wiley, 1951.

18. W. LEONTIEF:
    Structure of the American economy, 1919-1939. 2nd edi-
    tion. Oxford, 1951.

19. W. LEONTIEF:
    Studies in the structure of the American economy. Oxford,
    1953.

20. W. LEONTIEF:
    "Quantitative input and output relations in the economic
    system of the U.S." The Review of economics and statis-
    tics, August 1936.

21. W. LEONTIEF:
    "Structural matrices of national economies." Econo-
    metrica, vol. XVII, supplement, July 1949.

22. P. MAILLET:
    L'analyse des flux physiques entre secteurs (The analysis
    of physical flows between sectors). Cahiers du Séminaire
    d'Econométrie, No. 3, 1955.

23. F. T. MOORE:
    "Regional economic reaction paths." The American
    Economic Review, May 1955.

24. F. T. MOORE and J. W. PETERSEN:
   "Regional analysis: an interindustry model of Utah."
   The Review of economics and statistics, November 1955.

25. National Bureau of Economic Research:
   Input-output analysis: an appraisal. Princeton University
   Press, Princeton, 1955.

26. O. MORGENSTERN:
   Economic activity analysis. Wiley, 1954.

27. R. ROY:
   "La demande dans ses rapports avec la répartition des
   revenus" (Demand in its relations with the allocation of
   income). Metron 8, No. 3, 1930.

28. R. ROY:
   "Etudés econométriques" (Econometric research). Sirey,
   Paris, 1935.

29. R. ROY:
   De la théorie des choix aux budgets de famille (From the
   theory of choice to household budgets). Econometrica,
   Vol. 17, supplement, July 1949.

30. P. A. SAMUELSON:
   Foundations of economic analysis. Cambridge, Harvard
   University Press, 1948.

31. H. SCHULZ:
   The theory and measurement of demand. University
   Press, Chicago, 1938.

32. R. SOLOW:
   "Structure of linear models." Econometrica, January
   1952.

33. R. STONE:
   "The analysis of market demand." Journal of the Royal
   Statistical Society (Series A), 108.

34. R. STONE:
   The measurement of consumers' expenditures and be-
   haviour in the United Kingdom. (1930-1938). Cambridge
   University Press, 1954.

35. F. V. WAUGH:
   "Inversion of the Leontief matrix by powers series."
   Econometrica, April 1950.

36. H. WOLD:
   Demand analysis. Wiley, New York, 1953.

Chapter **5**

Business cycle fluctuations

Analysis of business cycle fluctuations is a subject which is not yet firmly grounded in the science of economics. Numerous inconsistent explanations have been proposed which have created considerable confusion among economists. In the absence of theories which have been clearly verified by facts, the techniques for forecasting business cycles are deprived of an empirical basis and require very delicate handling.

The problem of business cycle fluctuations, to be adequately considered, would require considerably greater coverage in the development of a proper context of fact and economic theory than can be accorded in the following pages. Nevertheless, because economic fluctuations play a major part in the life of a firm, this Chapter will consider business cycles.

Marketing research must take into consideration a business cycle situation and its probable developments. Investment policies, prices, and inventories are closely related to general economic activity.

It will not be necessary to do more than briefly summarize the principal aspects of economic fluctuations as they relate to the status of the firm. A description will be given of the few logical developments which have been isolated by economists which constitute the common basis of the various theories*.

This chapter develops the following considerations:

1. The first section provides a general outline of economic fluctuations and discusses the standard statistical methods of prediction.

2. The second section is devoted to the forces, and their cumulative nature, which are at work in the economy during periods of prosperity and depression. Here is where many economists meet on common ground.

3. The theories advanced to account for the "turning points," i.e., change from prosperity to depression and vice versa, constitute

---

* For further elaboration, we refer the reader to G. Haberler's classical book: "Prosperity and Depression" [16].

the subject material of the third section. This is where divergences of opinion are most keen, and discussions most contentious.

4. A final section relates to the problem of inflation, since this, unfortunately, plays an important role in modern European economies.

I

CHARACTERISTICS OF ECONOMIC FLUCTUATIONS AND PURELY STATISTICAL ATTEMPTS AT PREDICTION

An examination of available statistical data led economists, since Clement Juglar (circa. 1860), to observe, in the development and expansion of western economies, "economic cycles" characterized by alternating periods of prosperity and of depression.

A careful analysis of these fluctuations reveals great similarities as well as significant differences.

When adjusted for the influence of trends and seasonal variations, some statistical series correlate very significantly with one another. For example, with few exceptions, the prices of various industrial products increase or decrease simultaneously. Unemployment tends to decrease when prices rise and to increase when prices decline. Finally, and this is particularly important, prices and consumer demand vary in the same direction. This phenomenon does not contradict the traditional shape of the demand function since demand is influenced here by both changes in income and by other dynamic effects. Because prices and demand vary in the same direction, the overall expenditure, whether expressed in nominal or actual monetary units, increases during periods of prosperity and decreases during periods of depression. The regular alternation of these two phases constitutes the phenomenon of an economic cycle.

In the eyes of certain authors, the business cycle concept implies a pseudomathematical periodicity which does not occur in reality. In fact, "the cycles vary in length, from a minimum of six years to a maximum of twelve years, although, with certain rare exceptions, they occur within an interval of seven to ten years, the average being slightly more than eight years."*

Furthermore, in the midst of these oscillations, fluctuations of shorter duration occur, the characteristics of which vary from one cycle to another. Finally, each economic cycle has its own history and characteristics.

---

* [17], p. 19.

This dual aspect of economic fluctuation underlies the differences between theorists who consider fluctuations to be due to extra-economic causes, such as wars, and those (much more numerous) who see in cycles the effects of purely economic sequences of events. But even among the latter, the type of explanation varies, in large measure, according to the emphasis placed upon regularity.

The 1929 economic crisis and the severe depression which followed gave extraordinary popularity, particularly during the 1930-1940 decade, to theoretical and statistical research on the economic cycle. At the statistical level, all efforts were aimed at attempting to isolate "invariants" which would make it possible to predict—in the absence of theory—the development of the cycle. At the theoretical level, on the other hand, the objective of economic research was to develop analysis of forces at work during the economic cycle with a view to either forecasting their effects, or, more particularly, suppressing them with appropriate policy. The least that can be said is that statistical attempts have been rather fruitless, and for this reason, the economic analyst must be thoroughly convinced that there are no readymade solutions. Unsophisticated methods cannot replace personal judgment based on a thorough knowledge of the forces at work in an economy.

a) The four phases of the cycle.

Four successive phases can be discerned in an economic cycle: the period of prosperity, the crisis, the period of depression, and the upturn. During the first and third phases, cumulative movements occur which are now well known. The real difficulty is to explain the crisis and the upturn; that is to say, the reversal of each trend. A complete cycle has the characteristic traits that are briefly summarized below.

At the beginning of a period of prosperity, there is still considerable unemployment, and equipment is used only part time. Total expenditure is low, or—and this is another way of expressing the same thought—money in circulation (especially cash), is not high. The discount rate is lower than the long-term interest rate on the money market.* Prices (especially those of raw materials) are appreciably lower during the final period of a depression. Debts have been liquidated. Bankruptcies and efforts made by industry to lower costs have resulted in the survival of efficient enterprises, although their equipment may be worn or technically obsolete. There is a potential scarcity of certain goods because replacements have been avoided as much as possible during the depression.

At this point, an upsurge in prosperity occurs first evidenced by a slight recovery in the area of consumer demand. The recovery

---

* [3], p. 359.

spreads to the sector of production goods and investment prospects appear to be more favorable. With the return of confidence, banks advance credit. Total production increases, unemployment decreases, and personal income rises. An increase in real wages is followed by further increases in consumption expenditure. Prices, which have long been stationary because a certain number of production factors had remained unused, indicate a rising trend as production costs increase. Increases in production are paralleled by increasing production costs as hours of overtime increase, workers of lower productivity are added to payrolls, industry resumes utilization of old and technically obsolete machinery, and begins to experience diminishing marginal returns. At this point, the demand for goods tends to increase less rapidly than costs, and profits decrease. In order to check the expansion of credit, the banks raise the discount rates which at this point tend to be higher than long-term interest rates.

The limitation of credit, the lessening of investment prospects, the slowdown in the increase of consumer demand, all pose certain marketing problems for some firms. They must accept lower prices in order to sell their products. This decrease in price generates a climate of pessimism. Banks attempt to reduce the quantity of commercial paper in circulation. Industry, anticipating a reduction in prices, decreases investments and inventories. Consumers defer purchases, accentuating still further the decrease in prices and production. Unable to sell their products, firms discharge some of their employees. This results in a decrease in personal income which decreases consumption still further, and accentuates the depression. Bankruptcies multiply. To improve their situation, companies make strenuous efforts to reduce their costs and to increase their productivity. The rate of money in circulation is low. Banks attempt to check the wave of deflation by lowering the discount rate. The cycle is complete and the stages that prevail during the early periods of recovery become evident once again.

This brief description does not presume to be explanatory. The various phenomena of prosperity and depression have merely been related as observed. The logical interaction of these phenomena will be considered later.

The above outline, however, should not be accepted too rigidly. Before the 1920 crisis in the United States, prices had increased considerably, whereas, with the exception of realty prices early in the decade and stock prices throughout, they remained substantially stationary during the entire period which preceded the 1929 crisis.

b) Statistical forecasting of economic cycles.

Short-run forecasts of economic trends are accurate more often than not simply because such trends reverse themselves relatively infrequently. On the basis of such a criterion, the method which consists in extrapolating a current trend for a few months appears to be very satisfactory inasmuch as it would show a high percentage of appreciably accurate predictions. Its occasional failures, however, would be relatively more significant than its frequent successes.

Being aware of the fallacy of a purely statistical prediction, economists have long sought economic factors whose current tendencies anticipate more general trends. Providing there is sufficient lead-time, analyzing the trends of these economic indicators can provide warning of changes in the direction of the business cycle. In this connection, the unfortunate attempt made by the Harvard School of Business at the time of the 1929 crisis will be remembered. More recently, G. Moore and his associates, while examining 801 statistical series available for the United States, found eight containing a characteristic lead [35]. Unfortunately, the nature and extent of this lead varies greatly from one series to another. Despite the fact that these series are pertinent mostly with respect to the United States, it may be profitable to enumerate them as a matter of information:

1. The number of contracts for housing construction: the rise in this series anticipates an increase in the purchase of the raw materials required for the execution of the contracts.

2. The number of contracts for the construction of commercial and industrial buildings: this series provides indications as to the volume of investment decided upon by the enterprise.

3. New orders for durable goods.

4. The price of industrial common stocks: the rise in this series has long been recognized, but the reversal of its trend is not always a forerunner of a reversal of economic trends in general. C. Roos observed, for instance, that in May 1940, despite the increase in economic activity in the United States, the price of shares collapsed because of sales made by Europeans and Americans following the German advance in western Europe [36].

5. The wholesale price of basic goods.

6. The average length of the work week in manufacturing industries.

7. The number of incorporations.

8. The number of judicial settlements and bankruptcies.

Mitchell and Burns, on the other hand, indicated 20 series as representing the best gauges of recovery in the United States [31]. Among them are found practically all of the preceding series plus a few indexes of activity, production, and employment.

1. Number of bankruptcies.

2. Price index of industrial stocks (Dow-Jones Averages).

3. Production of automobiles.

4. Production of trucks.

    5. Production of paper.
    6. Production of inner tubes.
    7. Revenue of railroad operation.
    8. Railroad freight in ton-miles.
    9. Homebuilding contracts.
    10. Average length of work week.
    11. Wholesale price index (Bradstreet).
    12. Clearinghouse operations in banks outside of New York City.
    13. Federal Reserve Board index of industrial production.
    14. Production of pig iron.
    15. Production of steel ingots.
    16. Industrial and commercial building construction contracts.
    17. Activity index (A.T. and Q.).
    18. Industrial production index (Stand. Stat. Co.).
    19. Department store sales.
    20. Total factory employment.

The time lead of these series is always fairly small and variable and extended delays until publication of the figures sometimes reduce their usefulness insofar as predictions are concerned.

A slightly different method of forecasting consists in developing indexes whose variations can indicate the future level of total demand. Among such indexes are the ratio of bank deposits to loans, and the relationship between the level of raw material inventories and the volume of new orders for consumer goods. These indexes can, without question, play a part in the development of a general prognosis.

Another method, which was tremendously popular, if not always very successful, in the United States, was that of opinion polls taken among manufacturers. During recent years, Fortune magazine has conducted semi-annual surveys which, with few exceptions have produced good results. The disadvantage inherent in this procedure is that forecasts made by many American firms are frequently derived from identical, rather than independent, sources. Furthermore, there is no reason to believe that average opinion is the best basis for forecasting. This difficulty can be overcome by using the test of Munich, which is based upon the correlation, provided by experience, between the established development of the business cycle and replies given by industrialists to certain questions requiring "yes" or "no" responses.

Under these conditions, the best procedure at present would seem to be a precise market analysis for the firm combined with an examination of general prospects based upon an understanding of the development of the cycle.

II

THE CUMULATIVE MECHANISMS OF PROSPERITY
AND DEPRESSION

Once prosperity or depression has begun, the mechanisms for market equilibrium that had been contributing to economic stability now give way to new forces of instability that tend to perpetuate and accelerate themselves. Many economists have a similar conception of the nature and the action of such forces. We shall attempt to examine them briefly here.

a) The monetary mechanisms are linked to the volume of hoarded cash and to the level of demand deposits. Let us briefly analyze these two phenomena.

1. Consumers use the income they receive in three different ways: they can spend it in the purchase of consumer goods, invest it by purchasing shares or bonds on the money market, or hoard it by saving it at home or in demand deposits. On the basis of income and economic behavior with respect to that income, households in the aggregate have a certain amount of cash on hand. The alternatives available to enterprises for the utilization of their profits are substantially similar: they can distribute them, use them for the financing of internal or external investments, or conserve them with a view to increasing their working capital.

Since interest rates are positive, "the decision to conserve money instead of offering it for loan apparently remains a disadvantageous decision,"* but it is quite easily seen why an economical man decides to hold cash; cash presents the advantage of ready availability. Ready cash makes it possible to avoid constant liquidation of assets (which can become very costly as a result of high service charges), facilitates a normal balance of receipts and expenditures over a period of time, helps to meet unforeseen needs, and allows one to take advantage of possible opportunities.

In a balanced economy, it is reasonable to believe that the actual value of cash balances required by economy-minded individuals is accurately determined. In other words, given the quantity of currency existing in the economy, the price level—or, what amounts to the same thing, the nominal national income—will adjust itself in order that economic units may possess the actual volume of cash balances desired. But this adjustment does not take place simply because price level variations have dynamic consequences.

Assume that at the beginning of a period of recovery, when actual cash balances are high, prices or income tend to grow.

---

* [2] p. 235, vol. 1.

An economical man has a tendency to assume that this movement will continue. His income will increase although, as a result of price increases, the actual value of his cash balances will decrease. Consequently, he will tend to "diminish his cash balances by amounts equal to sums previously set aside either as a hedge against an uncertain future or in postponement of purchases with a view of taking advantage of a decreasing price trend."* This "dishoarding" results in an increase in both consumption and investment. In summation, the increase in income results in a dishoarding which leads to price increases and increased industrial activity and income.

The dynamic forces contributing to prosperity reverse themselves during depression. Lower incomes are conducive to a climate of insecurity. Even consumers with adequate income tend to decrease current expenditures in anticipation of further price decreases, and increase savings as a means of coping with future uncertainty. Producers reduce inventories and investments in order to increase their cash balances. This behavior tends to further decreases in prices, industrial activity, and income.

The effect of the mechanism described above is cumulative in that the economic factors tend to interact with increasing intensity. This cumulative force should be distinguished from the forces described by the Keynesian multiplier. To briefly describe the multiplier and its effect, let us assume that an economic person, whose revenue increases by dr, increases his expenditure by qdr (q less than 1) and hoards the rest. This qdr expenditure will be an additional source of revenue for another person, and, consequently, will generate a flow of q^2dr expenditures. By repeating this process, it can be observed that a flow of initial revenue dr finally corresponds to a flow of revenue:

$$dr\,(1 + q + q^2 + \cdots\cdots) = \frac{dr}{1-q}$$

The quantity $\frac{1}{1-q}$, designated as the multiplier, is the numerical coefficient expressing the extent of increased income that is generated by an initial expenditure. As such, the multiplier is a function of the amount spent rather than the amount hoarded.

2. The banking system can vary the quantity of currency in circulation by modifying its reserve ratios. This phenomenon is linked to the creation of deposit money which should be briefly examined before attempting to explain the cumulative effects of banking policy and practice.

---

* [2], p. 360, vol. 1.

Assume that, at a given moment, an individual deposits a sum a in a bank. The bank will lend xa, retaining in cash a(1 — x) with a rate of 1 — x. The individual to whom xa has been loaned, will spend this amount, and those who receive it may deposit it in another bank. This other bank, therefore, will see its deposits increase by xa, which, in turn, will make it possible to increase by x^2a the amount of its loans. By repeating this reasoning, and assuming, for the sake of simplicity, that all sums received are deposited in a bank and that the reserve rate is the same for all banks, it will be observed that starting with the initial deposit a, a total volume of bank deposits will be generated which is equal to:

$$a \left(1 + x + x^2 + \cdots \right) = \frac{a}{1 - x}$$

All this happens as though the banking system had created a quantity of money: $a/(1 - x) - a = ax/(1 - x)$. This is the quantity of money which has been given the title of deposit money. Since loan operations are profitable, banks will tend to increase their loans limited only by the minimum reserve requirements. But here, also, dynamic effects can be observed.

At the beginning of a recovery period, the volume of bank deposits is small and bank reserves are high. With increasing income, profits are realized and banks tend to increase their loans. Thanks to this mechanism, the volume of bank deposits increases rapidly. The expansion of credit contributes to an increase in investments and stimulates economic activity, contributing thereby to an increase in income. This, in turn, further encourages banks to reduce their reserves. Here, then, is a second cumulative mechanism at work during periods of prosperity.

This mechanism operates in reverse during periods of depression. When industry can no longer sell all of its output, it runs into difficulties; and, in order to avoid losses, banks then seek to restrict their credits and increase their reserves. With this end in view, they increase the discount rate. A decrease in the volume of bank deposits tends to result in a lowering of prices, industrial activity, and income. This causes further action by the banks*.

Subject to one or two additional hypotheses to be considered later, an understanding of the mechanisms reviewed above can help explain the sequence of events leading to reversals in economic trends. This can serve as a basis for a theory of economic cycles.

b) The relationships among the various sectors of production strongly affect the structure of economic cycles. The existence of

---

* For purposes of simplification, no attempt has been made here to isolate the role of a central banking structure.

industrial relationships tends to generate local waves of prosperity and depression. However, linear models, such as Leontief's, do not account for the very important force of acceleration.

This force, isolated by A. Aftalion, analyzes a well-recognized fact, i.e., the magnitude of changes in demand for hard goods is greater than for soft goods. Let us take the classical example of a company which produces 100,000 shirts per month, using 10 machines each having a ten-year useful life, and replacing one machine each year. If, following an expansion of its markets, the company increases its monthly production schedule to 110,000 shirts, it will find it necessary that year to order two machines, one as a replacement and the other for the additional production. If, on the other hand, production decreases from 100,000 to 90,000, it probably won't be necessary to replace the oldest machine that year. A 10% change in shirt production causes a 100% variation in demand for shirt-producing equipment. This is an extreme example but it is representative (in kind if not in degree) of the relative changes in related demands for consumer goods and producer equipment. A minor change in demand for consumer goods has, in many instances, an accelerated effect on the market of firms producing hard goods. This acceleration phenomenon is found when one considers the relationship existing between demand for services provided by durable consumer goods and demand for the durable goods themselves. In practice, the acceleration phenomenon does not operate with the rigidity described above because by advancing or delaying equipment replacement, the relationship between the production of consumer goods and the demand for production equipment can be modified.

The fact remains, however, that during periods of prosperity, the acceleration force creates a vertical imbalance of the economic structure which manifests itself by an excessive development of industries producing hard goods. A relatively minor decrease in final demand can affect these industries adversely.

In addition to the vertical imbalance described above, horizontal imbalance occurs when manufacturers of consumer goods fail to gauge the future markets accurately and, as a consequence, develop their productive capacities so that their output potential does not correspond to the distribution of demand.

Both vertical and horizontal imbalance are followed by bottle-necks; namely sectors appear in which productive capacity cannot satisfy current demand. This is a result of either the physical impossibility of developing additional capacity with sufficient speed, or the industries' anticipation of future decreases in demand.

States of imbalance in the production sector do not disappear entirely during periods of depression. Although bankruptcies, closing of factories, and the maintenance of minimum inventories help wash out these imbalances, they persist in varying degrees.

At the beginning of an economic upturn, the volume of idle productive capacity varies considerably from one industry to another. These states of imbalance, however, tend to disappear during the succeeding cycle as a result of the general upward trend of economic activity.

The foregoing is a simplified explanation of the various functions and relationships that are basic to all theories of business cycles. One important difference among the various business cycle theories stems from the varying manner in which the turning points of the cycle are considered.

III

THEORIES PROPOSED FOR THE TURNING POINTS

Traditionally, these are presented in two groups: exogenous theories, which assign the existence of economic fluctuations to causes external to the economic system, and endogenous theories which explain them by formal economic relationships. Only the more significant theories will be set forth.

1. Exogenous theories.

The first exogenous theory is attributable to Jevons who linked economic cycles to the occurrence of sunspots. This is now primarily an object of historical curiosity. Since that time, authors have sought to explain the causes of economic cycles in terms of wars or innovations by manufacturers.

The theory that wars are the mainsprings of economic cycles, denies, of course, the periodic character of economic cycles. During a war, the production of consumer goods is reduced while the quantity of money in circulation increases. This quantity of money, much of it hoarded, is used after the end of the war to satisfy the accumulated demand. Once the backlog of demand has been satisfied, industry has only the "normal" demand for the marketing of the output from its expanded productive capacity. The drop in demand creates horizontal imbalances, unemployment and depression. The weakness of this theory is that it is not complete. It ignores the endogenous factors which can either reinforce or diminish the effects of the satisfaction of the post-war backlogs in demand. Furthermore, in a general theory, wars cannot be used to explain cyclical fluctuations occurring during periods between wars.

Nevertheless, this theory is interesting in that it correctly stresses the fact that wars do cause periods of prosperity or of inflation and, therefore, do exert an influence upon the economic cycle.

b) Innovations by manufacturers.

This theory, which was evolved by Professor Schumpeter, assumes that a period of prosperity is started by "innovations" introduced by entrepreneurs. Some businessmen launch new products, or initiate new methods, resulting in the creation of new capacities of production and increases in employment and income. The cumulative forces described earlier then go into action and amplify the wave of prosperity. Industries, where innovations are made, become very prosperous and attract other entrepreneurs in great numbers. However, there comes a time when supply exceeds demand, causing prices to decrease. The resulting lowering of activity in these industries transmits itself to supplying industries, diminishes income, affects expenditures, and finally extends to the entire economy. In such a theory, an economic cycle is always characterized by the history of a few leading industries. Thus, one of the cycles of the 19th century can be associated with the development of railroads; another with that of streetcars; and in the 20th century, the advent of automobiles can be related to several cycles.

Product and production innovations, like wars, influence the economy and relate to many fluctuations. However, as a unique answer to the general problem, it fails to explain the occurrence of fluctuations and cycles during periods when innovations are not felt. Although technology produces innovations at a fairly constant rate, the use of innovations by industry is more erratic. Apparently the timing of entrepreneurs in introducing innovations is affected by the business cycle more than the business cycle is affected by the innovations. Here too, the endogenous factors affecting cycles of economic activity should be explored.

2. Endogenous theories.

a) The influence of credit and currency.

Some authors believe that monetary phenomena—more specifically, the hoarding of money and the issuing of credit—are the mainsprings of economic fluctuations. An outline of this theory, as developed by M. Allais [4], follows.

Let us assume, that desired cash balances and the volume of deposits are functions of the rate of fluctuation in income—cash and deposits descending and income ascending—and, furthermore, that they have maximum and minimum limits. In the case of deposits, this means that the bank reserve ratios can vary only between minima and maxima. The minimum reserve is a reflection of the maximum risks that banks are willing to accept. In the case of cash balances desired, the minimum refers to the level considered by economic persons as strictly necessary working capital for the balancing of their receipts and expenditures. Whatever the state of incomes and prices, a growing cash balance maximizes at that point where the propensity to invest begins to exceed the propensity to hold cash.

In other words, if r represents revenue and t time, the curves indicating the volume of deposits and the cash balance required appear as shown in Figs. 1 and 2 in relation to $\frac{1}{r}\frac{dr}{dt}$.

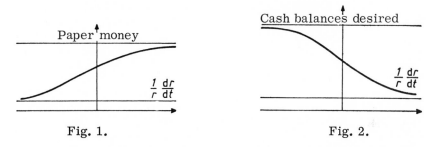

Fig. 1.   Fig. 2.

The above hypotheses lead to an explanation of economic cycles. When, for the higher values of $\frac{1}{r}\frac{dr}{dt}$, the inflation of credit and hoarding cease, and the growth of consumption and of investment slackens, $\frac{1}{r}\frac{dr}{dt}$ becomes weaker which results in a reduction in the the volume of deposits and an increase in desired cash balances which again reduce $\frac{1}{r}\frac{dr}{dt}$. The direction of variation of r finally reverses itself whereupon the depression begins. A somewhat similar description would cover the turning point*.

Naturally, the deflationary effect of credit and hoarding limitations can be counteracted by an increase in the federal budgetary deficit which increases the quantity of money in circulation.

b) The influence of the supply of the factors of production.

Numerous economic theories have emphasized the importance of "real" factors, independent of all monetary phenomena. Since these

---

* In the latest version of M. Allais' theory, it is not the observed rate of expansion which intervenes, but the rate of psychological expansion, equal to an average (with decreasing exponential coefficients) of expansion rates actually observed. Furthermore, it has been noted that it is not necessary, for the existence of a limit to the cycle, that deposits and required cash balances be given a ceiling limit. The shape of the curves is the only determining factor.

theories abound in subtleties and in variants, we shall merely follow the outline given by G. Haberler regarding the influence of the supply of factors of production [16].

During periods of prosperity, a certain imbalance occurs in the production apparatus. The flow of goods does not correspond exactly to the monetary flow; the demand for certain goods may be weaker than production, and a lowering of prices is possible in certain sectors. But these local decreases in prices are likely to be compensated for by increases in prices in other sectors. The imbalance will therefore manifest itself by modifications in the price system, and there will tend to be a readjustment in production. Although this possibility should by no means be excluded, it is very unlikely that this would be sufficient to entail a decrease in total demand as long as factors of production are not fully utilized. When expanded output requires the full utilization of the available factors of production (especially labor), production can only increase at a rate which will be compatible with the growth of population and of technical progress. If, during peak utilization of capacity, the level of activity of machine tool producers, for example, is dependent upon the rate of growth of production in consumer product industries, a slackening in the increase in general demand will be sufficient to cause a sudden and sharp drop in the production of machine tools which could ultimately, if extended, lead to a depression. Prosperity is difficult to sustain largely because of the under-utilization of the factors of production at the beginning of the period of prosperity. This under-utilization creates a certain rhythm of growth which cannot be sustained upon attainment of a full-utilization situation.

On the other hand, no similar phenomenon occurs at the turning-point. This can be explained in various ways. Most economists (especially Haberler) recognize that there is an upper limit for desired cash balances and a lower limit with respect to the volume of deposits. At a certain point, therefore, price decreases stop. The investment possibilities, which had disappeared during the depression because of anticipation of further decreases in prices, reappear. Innovations resulting from technical progress are now introduced and the economic turning point is at hand.

c) "Underconsumption."

In connection with Keynes' book, The General Theory of Employment, Interest, and Money, theories have evolved which view underconsumption as a cause of an economic cycle. In other words, the total demand, toward the end of a period of prosperity, does not increase with sufficient speed to remain in harmony with the development of the apparatus of production. Overproduction occurs; this causes a lowering of prices which leads to a depression. A detailed outline of this thesis would require the introduction of a specialized vocabulary and would extend far beyond the scope of these few notes. However, this theory agrees much more closely with the theory presented in section (a) than is at first apparent. This can be demonstrated by a brief presentation of the popular form this analysis has assumed in the United States.

We have described the monetary phenomena by treating economic individuals as belonging to a homogeneous group. But if the behavior of various socio-economic groups is different, the distribution of income can exert an appreciable influence. Let us imagine for a moment an economy composed only of two groups: the wage class on one hand, and potential investors on the other. Let us assume also that the wage earners always spend all of their income. This is certainly not completely true; but if the situation were so, no economic growth could occur as a result of the wage earners' behavior. If there were only wage earners, the economy would evolve into an unexpanding state of constant balance that might have difficulty maintaining its capital assets. Economic expansion develops as a result of the behavior of the potential investors. The extent of their dishoarding will influence the volume of expansion proportionate to the share of national income they represent.

This phenomenon serves as a basis for a theory which, for obvious reasons, enjoys a certain popularity. According to this theory, the growth of profits in relation to salaries, during prosperity, increases toward the end of the economic cycle; and so does the volume of cash balances desired which indirectly limits the market of industries producing consumer goods. This, in turn, precipitates a crisis. It follows, accordingly, that a wage increase put into effect at the time when productivity is contributing an increasing share to profits would be a sufficient protection against economic cycles. There is no doubt that, within the range where the cash balances held by wage earners remain independent of variations in their income, such a policy can play a part in avoiding violent fluctuations in the cycle providing such policy is complemented by action affecting the volume of credit and the size of the fiscal deficit. If monetary factors were neutralized, the influence of the supply of the factors of production described in paragraph (b) would be less since the cumulative forces of the economy would lose a large part of their vigor.

On the other hand, the use of a sliding scale linking salaries to the cost of living would tend to perpetuate as well as exaggerate economic trends.

This outline of economic cycles is too brief not to abound in imperfections and lack of precision. It can serve, nevertheless, to provide an idea of the type of "backdrop" the cycle constitutes in market research.

IV

INFLATION*

Inflation must be regarded, in market research, as a disease of the economy. It would be wiser to forego short-term predictions during inflationary crises because the economy undergoes rapid evolutions of a violent nature. The economy is extremely sensitive to factors of a psychological nature and is also greatly influenced by government policy. Under these circumstances, the market analyst should limit himself to considerations of general economic trends, and their probable effects on markets, stemming from a priori hypotheses concerning government action and individual behavior.

Inflation can be defined as a cumulative and self-perpetuating increase in all prices. It is the outcome of, initially, a situation of economic imbalance where the equilibrium cannot be reestablished except through a general increase in prices. The interplay of cumulative forces continues the pressure and accelerates price increases in price levels.

In connection with these mechanisms, the constant struggle of various social groups toward improving their condition is an important factor.

1. In order to describe the initial situation, we shall resort to the convenient fiction that the economy produces and exchanges one type of goods only. Assume Q to be the quantity of such goods produced during a given period, P their price, and D the total demand expressed in terms of monetary value. When equilibrium is reached; $D = PQ$. Let us assume that, for reasons which will be examined very shortly, D suddenly increases. Balance can be reestablished at the same price level only through an increase in production. If the increase has attained the maximum level compatible with employment availability and the current state of technology, then only an increase in price can restore the balance between demand and total supply. The same phenomenon would occur if D remained constant and Q suddenly decreased. The two cases can be combined in the following definition of a pre-inflationary situation:

A pre-inflationary situation obtains when total demand, expressed in terms of its monetary value, is greater than the product of the real level of prices and the quantity actually offered provided the quantity cannot be increased.

---

* This section is devoted to a study of temporary increases in price. No attempt is made to analyze the structure and factors that give nominal prices a permanently increasing trend.

In order to describe a pre-inflationary situation, one should therefore review the various factors leading to an increase in D or a decrease in Q:

a) D itself can be represented as the quantity of money M in circulation in the economy multiplied by its velocity V. In other words, V is defined by the relation

$$D = MV$$

In the case of a constant acceleration in the circulation of money, total demand grows in relation to the quantity of money in circulation in the economy. The issuance of money by the State, (the creation of public debt as a result of budget deficits), appears then as one of the causes of pre-inflationary situations, but only (a fact which popular version systematically forgets) in cases where total demand has attained a maximum and where the growth of M does not offset a decrease in V. Thanks to the phenomenon of credit, and with the possibility of increasing deposit money in circulation within the economy, banks can also contribute to the establishment of a pre-inflationary situation.

A sudden acceleration in the circulation of money, which can be observed when owners of cash reserves anticipate a future increase in prices, is generally due, in a pre-inflationary situation, to impacts of outside events. For instance, at the time of the opening of hostilities in Korea, consumers and firms, fearful of shortages, began to dishoard their cash balances and increase their purchases. A decrease in cash balances effectively increases the velocity of money in circulation. A general increase in wages likewise engenders a pre-inflationary situation if the total demand Q has attained a maximum and if the other social groups have succeeded in preventing a modification in real income distribution. An increase in D is then accompanied — at least in the immediate present — by an increase in M and V, since, in order to pay the additional salaries, enterprises must call upon credit and their capital resources.

b) A decrease in the total supply Q, which is a decrease in available production for consumption needs, can be due to levies by a victorious enemy during occupation, an increase in the portion of production which is absorbed by national defense, uncompensated excess exports, and an increase in investments.

As a matter of fact, increased investments eventually lead to an increase in output, but, their initial effect is to absorb capacity without corresponding increases in output for final demand. An increase in investments can be non-inflationary only if it is accompanied by a corresponding decrease in final demand.

2. A pre-inflationary situation degenerates into inflation as a result of the presence of cumulative forces which impede a reestablishment of balance at the new price level. In a brief analysis it can be helpful to distinguish two mechanisms.

The first mechanism is linked to variation in the level of desired cash balances. In an inflationary situation, where the eyes of owners of cash reserves are fixed on price levels, it is to be expected that the desired balances will decrease as the rate of price growth increases. This phenomenon assumes a particularly acute form in phases of rapid inflation. We have only to recall a few well-known accounts of German inflation between the two wars.

The second mechanism is linked to the constant struggle waged by various socio-economic groups with respect to the distribution of income. Let us assume that there is, initially, an increase in wages. If total demand cannot grow, the nominal increase in wages can find expression in an actual increase only if other groups accept a reduction in their real income. It is obvious that the latter will seek to prevent such a situation by every means in their power. On the same day that an increase in wages is announced, and even before it is put into effect, industry will immediately anticipate future increases in production costs by increasing selling prices. This increase in price will become generalized and, before very long, will cancel out the initial advantages granted to the wage earners. In the course of this phenomenon, the other groups probably will have succeeded in securing for themselves a slightly larger share of the national income. Thereupon the wage earners will militate for, and finally obtain, a new increase in wage rates whereby they regain a temporary advantage.

It is unnecessary to underline the element of social dissolution contributed by this inflationary force.

When the two mechanisms and their related sequences of events as mentioned above are set in motion, the quantity of currency, properly speaking, no longer plays an active part in the inflation. The issuance of new money compensates for the budgetary deficit which is itself due to delays in the recovery of taxes and to increases in federal expenditures resulting from increased prices.

In order to halt inflation, prices must be at a level which will balance demand and total supply with respect to a distribution of income that is acceptable to all socio-economic groups. Success is attainable if the purely psychological chain reaction stemming from continued anticipation of higher prices can be broken. There is nothing which is at the same time more obvious to comprehend and yet more difficult to achieve.

With this observation, we will close this chapter on business cycle problems. These few pages do not, to be sure, constitute more than a limited and summary outline of some of the most difficult questions which have been considered by economists. We hope, nevertheless, that they may have contributed to placing market research, with respect to the firm, in a proper perspective. This is an essential viewpoint for an economist if he truly desires to make profitable use of the methods that statistics have placed at the disposal of econometricians.

BIBLIOGRAPHY

1. A. AFTALION:
   "The theory of economic cycles based on capitalistic technique of production." Review of Economic Statistics, Vol. IX (October 1927), pp. 165-170.

2. M. ALLAIS:
   Economie et intérêt (Economy and interest). Paris, Imprimerie Nationale, 1947.

3. M. ALLAIS:
   Il n'y aura plus de cycles économiques (There will be no more economic cycles):
   1. Théorie des cycles économiques (Theory of economic cycles);
   2. Application à l'évolution prochaine des sociétés contemporaines (Application to the impending evolution of contemporary societies).
   Lecture delivered before the Recherches Economiques et Sociales group.

4. M. ALLAIS:
   Explication des cycles économiques par un modèle non-linéaire à régulation retardée (Explanation of economic cycles by a non-linear, delayed-control model). May 1955 Colloquium on dynamics. C.N.R.S. Editions, 1956.

5. E. AMES:
   "A theoretical and statistical dilemma. The contributions of Burns, Mitchell and Frickey to business cycle theory." Econometrics, October, 1948.

6. H. AUJAC:
   Les modèles mathématiques macrodynamiques et le cycle (Macrodynamic mathematical models and the cycle). Economie appliquée, Vol. II, 1949, Nos. 3-4, July-December.

7. H. AUJAC:
   Une hypothèse de travail: L'inflation, conséquence monétaire du comportement des groupes sociaux (A working hypothesis: Inflation, a monetary consequence of the behavior of social groups). Economie appliquée, Vol. III, No. 2.

8. L. BARNES:
   Handbook for business forecasting. New York, Prentice-Hall, 1948.

9. E. C. BRATT:
   Business cycles and forecasting. Irwin, Homewood, Illinois, 1953.

10. Committee of American Economic Association:
    Readings in business cycle theory. Philadelphia, Blakiston
    Co., 1944.

11. R. M. GOODWIN:
    Le problème de la tendance et du cycle (The trend and cycle
    problem). Economie appliquée, Vol. VII, 1954, Nos. 1-2,
    January-June.

12. R. M. GOODWIN:
    "Econometrics in business-cycle analysis" in the book by
    A. HANSEN: Business cycles and national income. New York,
    W. W. Norton & Co., 1951.

13. R. M. GOODWIN:
    "The non-linear accelerator and the persistence of business
    cycles." Econometrica, XIX, January 1951, pp. 1-17.

14. R. M. GOODWIN:
    "A non-linear theory of the cycle." Review of economics
    and statistics, XXXII, November 1956, pp. 316-20.

15. H. GUITTON:
    "Oscillation et croissance" (Fluctuation and growth). Econo-
    mie appliquée, Vol. VII, 1954, Nos. 1-2, January-June.

16. G. HABERLER:
    Prospérité et dépression. (Prosperity and depression).

17. A. H. HANSEN:
    Fiscal policy and business cycles. New York, W. W. Norton
    & Co., 1941.

18. A. H. HANSEN:
    Business cycles and national income. New York, W. W.
    Norton & Co., 1951.

19. R. F. HARROD:
    The trade cycle. London, Oxford University Press, 1936.

20. R. C. HAWTREY:
    Capital and employment. London, Longmans, Green & Co.,
    1937.

21. F. A. HAYEK:
    Monetary theory and the trade cycle. New York, Harcourt,
    Brace & Co., 1932.

22. J. R. HICKS:
    A contribution to the theory of the trade cycle. London,
    Oxford University Press, 1950.

23. W. S. JEVONS:
The sun's heat and trade activity. London, P. S. King & Son,
Ltd., 1910.

24. N. KALDOR:
"Hicks on the trade-cycle." Economic Journal, LXI, December 1951, pp. 833-847.

25. N. KALDOR:
Relations entre la croissansance économique et les fluctuations cycliques (Relationships between economic growth and
cyclical fluctuations). Economie appliquée, Vol. VII, 1954,
Nos. 1-2, January-June.

26. M. KALECKI:
Essays in the theory of economic fluctuations. London,
G. Allen & Unwin, Ltd., 1939.

27. L. R. KLEIN:
Economic fluctuations in the United States, 1921-1941.
New York, John Wiley & Sons, Inc., 1950.

28. J. M. KEYNES:
A treatise on money. New York, Harcourt, Brace & Co., 1930.

29. J. M. KEYNES:
La théorie générale de l'emploi, de l'intérêt, et de la monnaie
(The general theory of employment, interest, and money).
Paris, Payot.

30. L. LeBOURVA:
L'inflation française d'après-guerre (French postwar inflation). Paris, Armand Colin.

31. W. C. MITCHELL, A. F. BURNS:
"Statistical indicators of cyclical revivals." Bulletin 69,
National Bureau of Economic Research, 1938.

32. W. C. MITCHELL, A. F. BURNS:
Measuring business cycles. New York, National Bureau of
Economic Research, 1946.

33. W. C. MITCHELL:
Business cycles and their causes. Berkeley, University of
California Press, 1941.

34. W. C. MITCHELL:
What happens during business cycles. New York, National
Bureau of Economic Research, 1951.

35. G. H. MOORE:
    Statistical indicators of cyclical periods and recessions.
    New York, 1950, National Bureau of Economic Research,
    Occasional paper 31, 1950.

36. C. F. ROOS:
    "Business planning and statistical analysis." Econometrica,
    Vol. XVII, Supplement, July 1949.

37. C. F. ROOS:
    "Survey of economic forecasting techniques." Econometrica,
    October 1955, Vol. XXIII, pp. 363-395.

38. E. SCHNEIDER:
    Einführung in die Wirtschafts theorie (Introduction to the
    theory of economics).
    Vol. 1: Theorie der wirtschafts kreislaufs (Theory of eco-
    nomic cycles).
    Vol. 2: Wirtschafts pläne und wirtschaftsliche Gleichgewicht
    in der Verkehrswirtschaft (Economic planning and economic
    equilibrium in traffic economics). Tübingen. Verlag Mohr
    (1947-1949).

39. J. A. SCHUMPETER:
    Business cycles, 2 volumes. New York, McGraw-Hill Book
    Co., 1939.

40. J. A. SCHUMPETER:
    "The explanation of the business cycle." Economica, Vol. VII
    (December 1927), pp. 286-311.

41. J. TINBERGEN:
    Business cycles in the United States of America, 1819-1932.
    Geneva, League of Nations, 1939.

42. J. TINBERGEN:
    Le mécanisme des cycles vu par un économètre (The cycle
    mechanism as seen by an econometrician). Economie appli-
    quée, Vol. II, 1949, Nos. 3-4, July-December.

Chapter 6

The statistical discussion
of quantitative data

In this chapter we attempt to avoid two dangers. The first is the danger of limiting ourselves to an outline of very simple properties for which little knowledge of statistical methodology is required. At such a level, however, none of the interesting econometric problems could be introduced and the usefulness of the following exposition would be greatly curtailed. At the other extreme is the danger of attempting to present too rigorous a development of statistical methods as applied to econometrics. Since few theoretical details are pertinent in a book of this sort (and statisticians can call upon much better qualified sources), we would fall far short of our objective were we to devote time and space to such considerations.

We have endeavored, therefore, to follow a middle-of-the-road policy.

1. We have adopted, as a starting point, the definitions and the principal results of the calculus of probabilities and of elementary mathematical statistics. For those readers who may wish to refresh their memory, the bibliography contains a list of excellent statistical works including a few that do not require any mathematical sophistication [72] [73].

2. Long or complicated demonstrations have been omitted. However, footnotes refer to the names of publications which contain complete verifications.

3. Methods which are not in current usage or which pose very difficult questions are not covered, since there is little occasion to use them in industrial economics.

4. Our particular objective is to acertain how problems appear and to determine the applicability of available methods. From this standpoint, econometrics can provide either research tools or a framework of thought which will permit better comprehension of the limitations of "naive" methods.

This chapter is divided into three sections. The first section, which is very brief, is devoted to a study of statistical distributions and enumerates those which are in common usage in econometrics.

The second section outlines the econometric methods which are of greatest interest and which are valid when the observations are independent. Unfortunately, this is not characteristic of most economic data, which usually appear as a series of figures related to consecutive periods of time. It is difficult to suppose that the observed values appear at random, independently of each other. For instance, the price of automobiles in 1955 depends on the price of automobiles in 1954. There is a stochastic relationship between them. Although the hypothesis of independence is never perfectly realized, the methods just alluded are currently applicable nevertheless, mainly for reasons of convenience. The third part deals with the problems of time series but is limited to their simplest and most useful aspects, since many questions in this field are very difficult or still unresolved.

I

PROBABILITY DISTRIBUTIONS

The first type of information needed in statistical analysis is usually the probability distribution of certain variables. The general nature of the distribution is of interest per se, but the result is much more profitable if the observed distribution can be related to a known distribution. The properties of the known distribution cast some light on the conditions affecting the form of the phenomenon, and the integration of empirical data into a mathematical model becomes much easier.

The following are the more important probability distributions encountered in industrial economics.

The normal distribution. This is a symmetrical distribution characterized by two parameters, its mean m and its standard deviation s. Its probability density is:

$$\frac{1}{\sqrt{2\pi}\,s}\, e^{-\frac{(x-m)^2}{2s^2}}. \tag{I. 1}$$

It is well known that, under certain conditions, the sum of a large number of random variables is normally distributed.

The log-normal or Gibrat distribution. This is the distribution of a random variable whose logarithm obeys the normal law, and which depends on three parameters: the two parameters m and s of the related normal distribution and the parameter a which determines the lower limit of the variable. The density is expressed as:

$$\frac{1}{\sqrt{2\pi}\,s\,(x-a)}\, e^{-\frac{(\log\,(x-a)\,-\,m)^2}{2s^2}}. \tag{I. 2}$$

Under certain conditions, the product of a large number of random variables is distributed according to the frequently encountered lognormal law. In addition to income distribution—which has already been mentioned—it can adequately represent urban population distributions, the distribution of the surface of emerging islands, the distribution of the value of mineral deposits existing in geographical areas of given surface dimensions, etc. [38]. Many of the variables utilized in econometrics have lower limits—usually positive—and this is one of the reasons why the log-normal law is better adapted to them than the normal law.

The Pareto distribution. This is an empirical distribution which is closely related to the log-normal distribution. It has the advantage of being easily adaptable to very simple calculations. Its probability density is expressed as 0 for $x \leq b$ and as: $\dfrac{(a - 1) \, b^{a-1}}{x^a}$ for $x > b$ (a being a constant greater than 1).

Its average is equal to:

$$\frac{b \, (a - 1)}{a - 2}. \tag{I. 3}$$

The exponential distribution. This is introduced when one can assume that the probability of the occurrence of an event E is constant during any time interval dt and equal to pdt. The probability that E will occur for the first time between t and t + dt is:

$$u_t - u_{t+dt} = p u_t dt. \tag{I. 4}$$

In this relation, u_t is the probability that E will not occur between 0 and t, and u_{t+dt} is the probability that E will not occur between 0 and t + dt.

$u_t - u_{t+dt}$ therefore represents the probability that E will occur for the first time between t and t + dt. This probability is equal to the product of the probability that E will not occur before t, u_t and the probability that E will occur between t and t + dt, pdt.

By noting that $u_0 = 1$, the integration of the preceding relationship demonstrates that the probability that event E will not occur before time t is the decreasing exponential:

$$u_t = e^{-pt}. \tag{I. 5}$$

The probability that event E will occur for the first time before time t is consequently:

$$1 - e^{-pt} \tag{I. 6}$$

and the corresponding probability density:

$$pu_t = pe^{-pt}. \tag{I. 7}$$

Exponential distributions are encountered notably in studies of equipment failure, of the intervals of time between the arrival of vehicles at points of intersection or of customers in a store, and, generally, in many queueing problems.

The Poisson distribution, which can be related to the exponential distribution. Let us consider the probability that this same event E will occur exactly n times during a period of time chosen as unity.

The probability that the event will occur only once during the interval (0,1), and that this occurrence will take place between t and t + dt, is the product of the probability of occurrence for the first time between t and t + dt and the probability of nonoccurrence from t to 1, i.e.,

$$pu_t \, dt \cdot u_{1-t} = pe^{-pt} \, dt \cdot e^{-p \, (1-t)} = pe^{-p} \, dt. \tag{I. 8}$$

The probability P_1 that the event will occur once during the interval (0,1) is obtained by integrating the preceding expression over this interval. Therefore:

$$P_1 = pe^{-p}. \tag{I. 9}$$

The probability P_2 of the event's occurring exactly twice during the interval (0,1) is likewise the integral of the product of the probability of occurrence for the first time between t and t + dt and the probability of occurrence exactly once from t to 1.

This last probability is calculated like P. It therefore equals:

$$\int_t^1 pe^{-p(\tau - t)} \, d\tau . e^{-p(1-\tau)} = (1-t) \, pe^{-p \, (1-t)} \tag{I. 10}$$

Thus:

$$P_2 = \int_0^1 pe^{-pt} \, dt \cdot (1-t) \, pe^{-p \, (1-t)} \frac{p^2 \, e^{-2p}}{2 \, !} . \tag{I. 11}$$

The same reasoning permits the computation of the subsequent probabilities, and the law of recurrence appears easily:

$$P_n = \frac{p^n \, e^{-p}}{n \, !} . \tag{I. 12}$$

The P_n sequence constitutes a distribution known as the Poisson distribution. It can be shown that the average value—the number of times an event occurs on the average within a unit of time—and the variance are both equal to p.

The Poisson distribution, under certain conditions, may describe the distribution of the number of telephone calls received within a unit of time over one line, the number of vehicles arriving at an intersection within a given time, the monthly volume of orders received from a customer ordering an average of p units per month, the number of a newsdealer's daily customers, the number of items requisitioned daily from a stockroom, etc. For this reason it is certainly one of the most frequently used distributions in econometrics.

II

STATISTICAL ESTIMATION IN ECONOMETRICS

It is possible to understand the econometric methods available to a firm only if one is aware of the basic and logical connection existing between these methods and the decision criteria covered in Chapter 2.

Stated simply, the principal objective of econometrics is to estimate parameters. We do not know their true values, but we seek to develop hypotheses about them by studying samples of the total population. On the basis of these observations and of certain criteria, we then select those we consider to be the true values, subsequently proceeding as though these values were accurate.

In order to clarify the above, we will consider this method by presenting two cases where only one parameter is to be estimated. In the first case, the number of observations available is given. In the second case, it is possible to choose the number and size of the samples observed.

a) Let us designate as r the true value (unknown) of the parameter. More specifically, let us assume that r is the average value of a random variable that is normally distributed, and that n observations x_1, x_2, ..., x_n are available. To estimate r requires choosing a function $t(x_1, ..., x_n)$ with the following meaning: If our observations are x_1, x_2, ..., x_n, we decide that $t(x_1, x_2, ..., x_n)$, is the best estimate of r and we proceed as though r were equal to t.

How should the decision function t be selected? In the case of a firm, account must be taken of the loss of profit which results from a faulty estimate of r. Specifically, we must consider the loss $P(r,t)$ realized by the firm if the estimate of the true value is t when actually it is r.

In an example of an evaluation of $P(r,t)$, a firm produces certain goods at a constant cost K and sells a quantity q at the market price p. Then p and q are linked by the relationship of demand: $p = a - bq$.

Assuming a is known, the object is to estimate the true value of b by econometric methods. Let us calculate the loss incurred by the firm if the estimate is b', whereas the true value is b.

The firm will produce a quantity q that will maximize its anticipated income. This revenue is expressed by:

$$R = (a - b'q) q - Kq.$$

This gives a production:

$$q = \frac{a - K}{2b'}$$

and a real revenue:

$$R'' = (a - bq) q - Kq = \frac{(a - K)^2}{2 b'} - \frac{b (a - K)^2}{4 b'^2}.$$

If the firm had estimated b correctly, its returns would have been (as demonstrated by substituting b for b' in the preceding expression:

$$R = \frac{(a - K)^2}{4 b}.$$

Therefore, the loss occasioned by a bad estimate is:

$$R - R'' = \frac{(a - K)^2}{4} \frac{(b - b')^2}{bb'^2}.$$

It is a function of r = b and of t = b'.

Once $P(r,t)$ is known, one is faced with a fourth type of decision in the sense described in Chapter 2: Each decision corresponding to the various values of b' is associated with several possible consequences, differing among themselves by the value of b. The problem is to determine the respective probabilities of each of these various consequences. This may be solved by assuming, a priori, a probability distribution $p(r)$ for r, account being taken of x_1, x_2, ..., x_n, and then by minimizing the function of t which is the mathematical expectation $E(t)$ of the loss:

$$E(t) = \int P(r, t) p(r) \, dr.$$

b) In the second case, where it is possible to select the number and size of the samples observed, the decision function will be more complex, because it will apply not only to the value of t, but also to the size of the sample and to the continuance of observations.

Let d be a decision function. Based on d, we must decide either that t is the true value of r (prior to any observation) or that we must proceed to observing a sample of a certain size from which we must decide either that t′ is the true value of r or that we must proceed to the examination of a new sample, and so forth.

For each decision function d and for each sample there is a corresponding cost to the firm, i.e., a function of d and of the true value r*; these costs are random. The mathematical expectation, calculated by using the joint probability density of possible observations, is a function $P(r,d)$. It indicates the degree to which the firm loses money by selecting a decision function d when the true value is r. Knowing $P(r,d)$, one is once more forced to a choice of the fourth type, with its inherent difficulties.

All of the foregoing, of course, is quite theoretical, but it presents an important fundamental methodology:

1. The estimation of the parameters of an econometric relationship is not independent of its intended use by the firm. There is no better estimate in an absolute sense; there are only estimates that are acceptable in terms of the decisions that a firm intends to make. Thus, the superficial difference between the decisions of a firm and the interpretation of data available to it disappears.

2. Unfortunately, the above theory is quite new. It has not yet had its anticipated influence on econometrics. Furthermore, it is likely that it may lead to complex methodologies and tedious calculations. Its application to business has, therefore, been delayed. It may never arrive if the complexities of utilization overshadow the improvement in estimation.

For these reasons, this chapter adheres to the traditional theory, which corresponds substantially to an expression of loss: $(t-r)^2$, and deals with the search for better estimates independently of their utilization. Although their underlying theories may not be above reproach, the present methods are of considerable practical interest. The above introduction simply places them in their proper perspective.

Econometrics deals with two distinct problems which will be considered separately at the outset to avoid possible confusion [68].

a) The first problem is that of determining the best estimate of a variable when the values of a certain number of other variables are known.

Let us assume p, for example, to be the average annual price of a product and q the quantity exchanged during the same year. A problem of this type will have to be solved if one seeks to predict the quantity q when the price assumes a given value P. In considering this problem, n observations of prices and quantities in previous

---

*This loss naturally takes into account the cost of observations.

years are generally available: p_1, q_1; p_2, q_2; ...p_n, q_n. p and q are considered to be random variables with a joint probability distribution on the p, q plane, so that paired (p_1, q_1) ... (p_n, q_n) values result from n observations with respect to random variables p and q.

If we now select a definition of the best estimate Q of q when p is equal to P, this definition enables us to calculate Q for P, (p_1, q_1) ... (p_n, q_n) being given. Q then appears as a random variable whose numerical values depend on the results of the sample.

This random variable is a better linear estimate if it has the following properties:

1. It is linear; that is, Q has the form aP + b.

2. It is corrected for systematic error; that is, the mathematical expectation of the estimate Q is equal to the mathematical expectation of the variable q for a given P.

3. It has a minimum variance among all other linear estimates corrected for any systematic error [53].

b) The second problem is to determine the best estimate of parameters connected with one or more econometric relationships.*

Let us return to the preceding example. We state the hypothesis that there exists an approximately linear relationship between q and p, and we pose:

$$Q = ap + b + u$$

where a and b are constant parameters, identical for all observations, and u is a random variable. From a knowledge of the probability distribution of p, q in their plane, it is possible to deduce the probability distribution of u for the various possible values of a and b, i.e., F(u,a,b). The problem to be solved is that of finding the best estimates of parameters a and b on the basis of observations p_1q_1, ..., p_nq_n.

Before defining what is meant by the best estimates, it must be specified that this second problem, which may seem similar to the first, has, in fact, a very different significance. For a given P, a valid estimate Q of the form aP + b can be found without necessarily having 'good' estimates of a and b. This distinction is illustrated in paragraph 2 below.

A best estimate can be defined as containing all or part of the following properties [53]:

1. Consistency. An estimate a' of a parameter a is said to be consistent if a' converges in probability toward a when the number of observations n increases indefinitely. This means that the probability that (a-a') is greater than ϵ (no matter how small) tends toward 0 when n increases indefinitely.

---

*During the remainder of this chapter, the word "parameter" is used in a more restricted sense than that used in the preceding pages.

2. Efficiency. An estimate a' of a parameter a is efficient if, when n increases indefinitely, $\sqrt{n}$ $(a' - a)$ is normally distributed with a finite variance s and a zero mean, and if, among all estimates possessing that property, s is here a minimum.

Although it would be advantageous to use efficient estimates, complexities of calculation frequently restrict one to seeking consistency alone.

3. Sufficiency. An estimate of a parameter a is considered to be sufficient if it "exhausts" all of the data that can be gathered from the observations.

The first two properties outlined above are relevant when n approaches infinity. They have their approximate equivalents for a given n:

1. Correction for systematic error. An estimate a' of a parameter a is corrected for systematic error if its mathematical expectation over all samples of size n is equal to a.

2. Efficiency—n. An estimate a' of a parameter a is considered to be efficient for samples of size n when the variance of $a'-a$ is minimum.

The last two properties are rare.

The traditional method of determining the "best estimates" of parameters is the method known as maximum likelihood.

For a given a and b, observations p_1, q_1, ..., p_n, q_n of values u_1, u_2, ..., u_n of u can be deduced. Based on a knowledge of the probability density of (p,q), a and b being given, the probability P can be deduced that u will assume values u_1, u_2, ..., u_n with a sample size n. The maximum likelihood method consists of selecting a and b in such a manner as to yield a maximum P. For reasons of convenience which will be clear later, the logarithm of P, LP, is considered, and a and b are determined by the following two equations:

$$\frac{\partial LP}{\partial a} = 0 \qquad \frac{\partial LP}{\partial b} = 0.$$

The method of maximum likelihood therefore consists of a supposition that the sample which was most likely to occur has been observed. Obviously, it presupposes a knowledge of the function P, initially the functional form of the probability distribution of p and q.

Although the principle on which the method of maximum likelihood is based may seem reasonable intuitively, this method is justified only on the basis of the properties possessed by the estimates reached.

It can in fact be demonstrated that in the important particular case where all observations $(p_1, q_1) ... (p_n, q_n)$ are independent, the estimates arrived at by the method of maximum likelihood are consistent and efficient. Furthermore, all sufficient estimates, if such exist, are a function of estimates obtained by the method of maximum likelihood.

In cases where the various observations are not independent, there are no such general results. This section deals only with cases of independent observations.

1. The best estimate of a variable.

The problem which has been outlined on the basis of a simple model can obviously be generalized to apply to an instance with any number of variables. Let us assume, therefore, that we have observed x_1, x_2, ..., x_n variables, and that there are p observations available for each of these variables. The p observations may relate to p intervals of time, for example, p consecutive years. What is the best estimate that can be made of the value of x_1, when x_2, ...x_n are known? To answer this question, we must select a model which expresses the estimate x_1' of x_1 as a function of x_2, ..., x_n.

A linear relation such as the following one is most frequently used:

$$x_1' = a_0 + a_2 x_2 + \cdots + a_n x_n \qquad \text{(II. 1)}$$

and the best linear estimate is sought, i.e., a linear estimate of minimum variance corrected for any systematic error. Under very general conditions which do not require the independence of the p observations, coefficients a_0, a_2, ..., a_n permitting the computation of x_1' are obtained by minimizing the sum of the squares of the differences between x_1 and x_1':

$$S = \sum_{k=1}^{k=p} (x_{1k} - x_{1k}')^2 = \sum_{k=1}^{k=p} (x_{1k} - a_0 - a_2 x_{2k} - \cdots - a_n x_{nk})^2. \qquad \text{(II. 2)}$$

In effect, when S is a minimum the variance of $x_1 - x_1'$ is minimum and, furthermore, the mathematical expectation of x_1' is equal to that of x_1, as will be seen clearly by considering the equation:

$$\frac{\partial S}{\partial a_0} = 0.$$

Let

$$x_i = \frac{1}{p} \sum_{k=1}^{k=p} x_{ik}$$ be the average value of x_i. Consider the products:

$$A_{ij} = \sum_{ik} (x_{ik} - \bar{x}_i)(x_{jk} - \bar{x}_j). \tag{II. 3}$$

The system of equations for the calculation of $a_2, \ldots, a_n$ is obtained by equating the partial derivatives of S with respect to $a_2, \ldots, a_n$. It can be easily demonstrated that this leads to the following system of linear equations, known as the normal system:

$$A_{22}a_2 + A_{23}a_3 + \cdots\cdots\cdots + A_{2n}a_n = A_{12}$$
$$\cdots\cdots\cdots\cdots\cdots\cdots\cdots\cdots\cdots\cdots\cdots\cdots\cdots$$
$$A_{n2}a_2 + A_{n3}a_3 + \cdots\cdots\cdots + A_{nn}a_n = A_{1n}$$

which, written in condensed form, is

$$\sum_{j=2}^{n} A_{ij}a_j = A_{1i} \qquad i = 2, \ldots, n. \tag{II. 4}$$

When $a_2, \ldots, a_n$ are determined, it is possible to calculate a_0 by stipulating that x_1 and x_1' must have the same average value:

$$x_1 = a_0 + a_2 x_2 + \cdots + a_n \bar{x}_n. \tag{II. 5}$$

The method of least squares therefore makes it possible to arrive at the best linear relation which expresses x_1 as a function of $x_2, \ldots, x_n$, or (which amounts to the same thing) to determine the surface equation of (II. 1) or regression surface of x_1 in $x_2, \ldots, x_n$. In the future, x_1' will be used to forecast x_1. But x_1' depends on the observed sample. The following question must accordingly be posed: Does the correlation found between x_1 and x_1' based on the sample observations have less than a 5% or less than a 1% probability of being due to chance? To solve this problem, it will be necessary to make additional hypotheses as to the probability distribution of $x_1, x_2, \ldots, x_n$.

a) For given $a_0, a_2, \ldots, a_n$, $(x_{1k}-x_{1k}')$ is a random variable of the kth observation. We will assume that this random variable is normal. It follows from the definition of x_{1k}' that its average value is zero.

b) We will suppose that the random variables $(x_{11}-x_{11}')$, ..., $(x_{1p}-x_{1p}')$ are independent.

In other words, we will assume that these differences are distributed normally and independently. The following results are approximated if the errors are not quite normally distributed, but they can be inaccurate if the differences are not independent, as is often the case in economic research.

To test the existence of a correlation between x_1 and x_1', the correlation coefficient r^2 between these variables can be calculated:

$$r^2 = \frac{\left(\sum\limits_{k} (x_{1k} - \bar{x}_1)(x_{1k}' - \bar{x}_1') \right)^2}{\sum\limits_{k}(x_{1k} - \bar{x}_1)^2 \; \sum\limits_{k}(x_{1k}' - \bar{x}_1')^2}$$

Naturally, $x_1' = x_1$. r^2 can be computed more easily from the system of normal equations.

$$r^2 = \frac{a_2 A_{12} + \cdots + a_n A_{1n}}{A_{11}}. \tag{II. 6}$$

Finally, it can be demonstrated that the ratio $\dfrac{r^2}{1 - r^2}$, which is a true random variable since it is dependent on the sample, is distributed as Snedecor's F statistic with n-1 and p-n degrees of freedom. $r^2/1-r^2$ is therefore calculated. If this value is greater than the given value on the 5% level (with n-1 and p-n degrees of freedom) in the Snedecor table, there is a 95% probability that a correlation exists between x_1 and x_1' [63].

It may also be of interest to calculate the variance s^2 of x_1-x_1'. It is demonstrated by the following formula:

$$s^2 = \frac{A_{11} - a_2 A_{12} - \cdots - a_n A_{1n}}{p - n} \tag{II. 7}$$

Note: In the particular instance where the regression of x_1 on x_2 (time, for example) is studied, it is often very useful to draw not only the line of regression of x_1 on x_2, but the two lines D_1 and D_2 which run parallel to this line at a distance of ±2s. If the hypotheses above are verified, there are 95 chances out of 100 that an observation is located between D_2 and D_1 (Fig. 1).

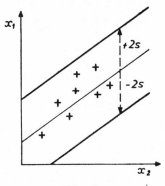

Fig. 1.

2. The best estimate of parameters.

In approaching the problem of finding the best estimate of parameters, it is preferable to adopt the context of an econometric model composed of a certain number of linear relationships. These linear relationships, however, are not verified precisely by the values taken by the variables for the various observations. This can result in two very distinct types of error.

The first type corresponds to errors in the equations. Let us assume, for instance, that we are studying the correlation between a quantity of meat sold, x_1, and the price of meat, x_2, and that we are able to measure these two variables perfectly. The simplest method of representing this correlation is to write:

$$x_1 = a_0 + a_2 x_2 + u$$

where u represents action upon x_1 of certain variables which we have neglected, such as income. We find it necessary to introduce u because the $x_1 = a_0 + a_2 x_2$ relationship is not accurate: u is an error which occurs in the equation.

The second type of error corresponds to errors in the variables. Let us refer to the previous example, but assume that we have reason to believe that there is an exact linear relationship between the quantity of meat sold y_1 and the price of meat y_2, yet the available figures x_1 and x_2 are not accurate values of y_1 and y_2 because these two magnitudes are measured with observation errors u and v. This time we obtain:

$$\begin{cases} x_1 = y_1 + u \\ x_2 = y_2 + u \\ y_1 = a_0 + a_2 y_2 \end{cases}$$

u and v represent errors in the variables which result from errors of observation. In the particular instance where v equals zero (assume that we are measuring y_2 perfectly), the following can be written:

$$x_1 = a_0 + a_2 x_2 + u$$

and the analytical form is the same whether u represents an equation error or a variable error.

For reasons which will be apparent later, the case of errors in the variables is much more difficult than the case of errors in the equations. We shall therefore begin by outlining the latter. A subsequent section will be devoted to the problem of errors in the variables.

Before seeking the best estimates of parameters, the following question should be raised. Taking into account the analytical form of a model, is there a method which will enable us to evaluate the parameters? This is known as the identification problem. It will be outlined in cases of equation errors, but it is obvious that it arises in the other cases as well.

The identification problem arises from the fact that the available figures are the result of the interaction of many economic phenomena. E.J. Working is undoubtedly the first to have raised this issue in his famous article, "What do statistical demand curves show?" [83]. But its precise significance has been identified by T.J. Koopmans and other researchers of the Cowles Foundation [54]. In presenting this problem we shall borrow the following, now classical, example from Koopmans. Let the competitive market for a certain item be such that the price p and the quantity q are determined by the intersection of two lines of supply and demand. Let us assume that the various observations relate to successive time intervals and that the position of the two straight lines remains invariant during that time. The supply and demand equations can therefore assume the form:

$$\begin{cases} q + ap + e = u \text{ (demand)} \\ q + cp + f = v \text{ (supply)} \end{cases}$$

where u and v represent errors in the equations. Their average value is zero. The problem is to estimate a, c, e, f. A moment's thought will reveal that, regardless of the number of observations, it is impossible to determine either the line of demand or the line of supply. In fact, if a scatter of observed points is shown in a figure, it will be observed that the only fact known is that the lines of supply and demand must pass through the midpoint of the scatter. Values a and c can be selected arbitrarily and e and f deduced therefrom. In other words, the figures available to us do not enable us to "identify" a and c. Figs. 2 and 3 represent two possible pairs of demand and supply curves.

The complexity of the identification problem now being apparent, we must study the question rigorously with respect to a general case.

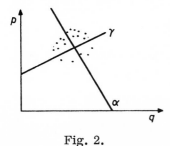

Fig. 2.

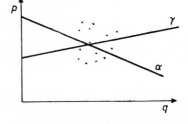

Fig. 3.

Endogenous and exogenous variables, as well as latent variables, can be distinguished in a model constituted by a certain system of equations between variables.

Exogenous variables are variables which are determined external to the relationships represented by the equations of the model. For example, in the study of a model composed of a demand equation and a supply equation, consumer income, if it explicitly enters into the demand equation, is an exogenous variation.

Endogenous variables are variables which are assumed to be determined by the relationships represented by the equations of the model once the exogenous variables are known. Price and quantity are the endogenous variables in a system of supply and demand.

A model is complete when it incorporates as many equations as there are endogenous variables.

Finally, we call latent those variables which are not directly observed and which are the cause of errors in equations.

The parameters to be estimated are the independent coefficients of the variables which enter into the equations. A complete linear model will have the form:

$$a_{i_0} + \sum_{j=1}^{n} a_{ij}x_j + \sum_{j=1}^{p} b_{ij}y_j = u_i \ (i = 1, 2, \cdots, n) \tag{II. 8}$$

in which: the n variables x_j are the endogenous variables,
the p variables y_j the exogenous variables,
the n variables u_j the errors in the equations, and
the a_{i0}, a_{ij}, and b_{ij} the parameters.

The endogenous and exogenous variables are assumed to have been measured without errors.

Example:

$$ap + bq + cr \quad + d = u$$
$$a'p + b'q \quad + c't + e' = v$$

The first relationship represents a function of demand where p is price, q quantity, and r consumer income.

The second relationship is a supply curve where t is a downpour.

In this model, the exogenous variables are r and t, the endogenous variables p and q, and the parameters a, b, c, d and a', b', c', e'. The model is complete.

A parameter is said to be identifiable when it can be estimated from observations; i.e., its probability distribution can be uniquely determined.

An equation is identifiable when all its parameters are identifiable.

A model is identifiable when all its equations are identifiable.

For example, a model of supply and demand in which there is no exogenous variable and where the endogenous variables are price and quantity is not identifiable.

The following two theorems provide the conditions of identification:

1. For an equation to be identified, there must be at least (n-1) variables (endogenous or exogenous) which do not appear in the equation.

2. For an equation to be identified, it is necessary and sufficient that there exist a non-zero determinant of (n-1) order with parameters associated in the (n-1) other equations of the model whose variables do not enter into the equation.

Referring to the preceding examples for the demand equation to be identified where supply and demand have no exogenous variables, it would be necessary to have a 2-1 = 1 endogenous variable which does not appear in this equation. It cannot be identified, therefore, unless we assume, for example, that demand is independent of price. It could be seen in the same manner that the supply equation is not identified.

However, in the case of the model of supply and demand with two exogenous variables r and t, the necessary condition for the identification of the demand equation is fulfilled, since there is a 2-1 = 1 variable which does not enter into this equation; this is the downpour. The necessary and sufficient condition is satisfied if the determinant of the order 1 formed with the coefficient of t in the supply equation is different from 0, i.e., if:

$$c' \neq 0$$

It likewise can be observed that the necessary condition is fulfilled for the supply equation and that the necessary and sufficient condition is fulfilled if $c' = 0$.

Let us now modify the supply equation and introduce the price p' of a type of good whose market is linked to that of the product under study. The supply equation becomes:

$$a'p + b'q + c't + d'p' + e' = v$$

The equation of demand is identified, since there are two variables t and p' which do not enter into this equation. The necessary and sufficient condition of identification is met if one of the two coefficients c' or d' is different from 0. Nothing is changed in regard to the identification of the supply equation.

Before attempting to estimate parameters, it is necessary to ascertain whether this question is meaningful and whether these parameters are identifiable. It is only under such conditions that the above methods can be applied.

3. Estimation of parameters with errors in the equations.

Two cases can be conveniently distinguished:
a) the model containing only one equation;
b) the model containing several equations.

a) A single equation.

When it appears very likely that there is a single and appreciably linear relationship between the variables x_1, x_2, ..., x_n, the best estimates of the parameters of this relationship can be found:

$$x_1 = a_0 + a_2 x_2 + ... + a_n x_n + u \qquad (II. 9)$$

where u represents the error in the equation. We will assume that there are p observations and that for these p observations $(k = 1, 2, ..., p)$ the errors u_k are independently and normally distributed. It is known that, subject to these hypotheses, the method of maximum likelihood leads to estimates with very interesting properties.*

Let s be the variance of u. The probability that u is equal to u_k** in the kth observation*** is:

$$p_k = \frac{I}{\sqrt{2\pi}\, s} \cdot \exp\left[-\frac{I}{2s^2} (x_{1k} - a_0 - a_2 x_{2k} - \cdots - a_n x_{nk})^2 \right] \quad k = I, \cdots, p$$

Since the observations are independent, the probability of observing the values u_1, u_2, ..., u_n is: $P = p_1, p_2, ..., p_n$, or:***

$$P = \frac{I}{(2\pi)^{p/2} s^p} \exp\left(-\frac{I}{2s^2} S\right)$$

where S is the sum of the squares of differences as in paragraph 1. In order to maximize P, it can be demonstrated that it is sufficient to minimize S.

In other words, in a case where errors are independently and normally distributed, the method of maximum likelihood leads to the

---

*Cf. Introduction to Part II.
**This expression is not absolutely correct. It should be termed the probability density of u between u_k and $u_k + du_k$.
***The symbol "exp u" means e^u.

method of least squares. The estimates obtained by the latter method are then consistent and efficient. It is demonstrated that they are also corrected for systematic error if, in addition, each u_k is distributed independently of all x_{ik}' $(i = 2, ..., n; k' = 1, 2, ..., p)$. When u_k errors are independently but not normally distributed, the method of least squares provides only consistent estimates.

Therefore, in an important particular case, the method of least squares provides, at the same time, the best estimate of x_1 and the best estimate of the parameters a_0, a_2, ..., a_n. It will be noted, however, that in order to obtain the best estimates of parameters, more restrictive conditions must be ascertained.

As in the case of the estimate of x_1, the point must now be raised as to whether the results obtained are significant.

1. Are the parameters a_0, a_2, ..., a_n significantly different from 0?

2. The true value of a parameter is certainly not equal to its estimate, since the latter depends on the sample. In which interval, therefore, is there a 95% or 99% chance of its being found?

3. As to the values found for a_0, a_2, ..., a_n, are they in agreement or disagreement with the values assumed a priori for other reasons?

The first question relates to tests of significance, the second to confidence intervals, and the third to tests of hypotheses. The results will be indicated without demonstration. The notations are those of paragraph 1.

1. Significance tests.

In order to test whether one of the coefficients a_2, ..., a_n-a_i for example—is significantly different from 0, the quantity s is considered which is the standard deviation of x_1-x_1', and the minor m_{ii} of A_{ii} is considered in the determinant D of the normal system of equations. For example, m_{22} is the determinant:

$$m_{22} = \begin{vmatrix} A_{33} & \cdots & A_{3n} \\ \cdot & & \cdot \\ \cdot & & \cdot \\ A_{n3} & & A_{nn} \end{vmatrix}$$

It has been demonstrated that the variable: $t = \dfrac{a_i}{s\sqrt{\dfrac{m_{ii}}{D}}}$ is distributed in accordance with Student's t distribution with p-n degrees of freedom. This statistic is computed and the value of the variable corresponding to a 95% level is checked in the Student table. If the absolute value of t is higher than this level, then there are 95 chances out of 100 that the true value of a_i is not 0 [48].

In order to test whether the value of coefficient a_0 is significantly different from 0, the following variable is used:

$$t = a_0 \sqrt{\frac{p-n}{s}}$$

which is also distributed in the same manner as the Student's t with p-n degrees of freedom.

2. Confidence intervals.

In the case of a_2, ..., a_n, and if a_i' is a constant, it follows from elementary properties of the calculus of probabilities that:

$$t = \frac{a_i - a_i'}{s \sqrt{\frac{m_{ii}}{D}}} \qquad \text{(II. 10)}$$

which is distributed in the same manner as the variable introduced in the preceding paragraph, i.e., as Student's t with p-n degrees of freedom. Student's table therefore makes it possible to calculate the two values of a_i' for which t is equal to the corresponding value at the 5% level. These two values are as follows:

$$a_i' = a_i \pm r.$$

There are 95 chances out of 100 that the true value will be covered by the interval a_i-r to a_i+r.

In the case of a_0, the procedure is the same starting from the variable

$$t = (a_0 - a_0') \sqrt{\frac{p-n}{s}}. \qquad \text{(II. 11)}$$

3. Tests of hypotheses.

We wish to ascertain whether experience accepts or rejects the hypothesis that the true value of a_i is a_i'. For this a_i' value, equations (II. 10) or (II. 11), as the case may be, lead to a specified value of t. In Student's table, this t value corresponds to a level of probability p. There are p chances out of 100 of finding a_i if the true value of this parameter is a_i'. According to the value of p, it can then be determined whether the hypothesis is to be accepted or rejected.

Two points remain to be discussed before proceeding to the case of several equations.

1. The first is an observation which will prove useful later in considering the case of errors in the variables. It can be demonstrated

that the method of least squares states that the best estimate of a_0, a_2, ..., a_n is such that the linear relation between x_1 and x_1' is verified by the first two moments of x_1, x_2, ..., x_n. We will demonstrate this in the case of two variables.

$$x_1 = a_0 + a_2 x_2 + u \tag{II. 12}$$

The error in the equation, u, is assumed to be normally distributed. Its mathematical expectation is zero. u and x_2 are independent random variables. Using a horizontal bar to designate the mathematical expectation of a variable, let us write that:

$$\bar{x}_1, \overline{(x_1^2)}, \overline{(x_1 x_2)}$$

verify (II. 12).

We obtain, since u = 0:

$$\begin{cases} \overline{x}_1) = a_0 + a_2 \bar{x}_2 \\ \overline{(x_1^2)} = a_0^2 + 2a_0 a_2 \bar{x}_2 + a_2^2 \overline{(x_2^2)} + \overline{(u^2)} \\ \overline{(x_1 x_2)} = a_0 \bar{x}_2 + a_2 \overline{(x_2^2)}. \end{cases} \tag{II. 13}$$

All of the above moments can be estimated, with the exception of $\overline{(u^2)}$. The three equations above now make it possible to calculate the three unknowns a_0, a_2, $\overline{(u^2)}$. By substituting in the third equation (II. 13) the value of a_0 from the first equation, the following equation is arrived at:

$$\overline{((x_1 - \bar{x}_1)(x_2 - \bar{x}_2))} = a_2 \overline{((x_2 - \bar{x}_2)^2)}$$

which is the equation to which, in this case, the normal system of paragraph 1 is reduced. The same estimates are therefore obtained as with the method of least squares.

2. The second point relates to multicollinearity. It is said that this exists when there is a close stochastic relationship between certain of the x_2, ..., x_n variables. Let us assume for a moment that there is an exact linear relation between these variables. The system of equations permitting the calculation of a_0, a_2, ..., a_n then becomes indeterminate, since any one of the x_2, ..., x_n variables of the relation can be selected and then eliminated from the linear form (II.1). If there should exist a stochastic instead of a functional relationship between variables, the result would be approximately the same and the parameters of (II. 1) would be practically indeterminate. Problems of this nature have been studied by the Norwegian economist R. Frisch [31].

A common example of multicollinearity in demand studies is the correlation found between prices and income throughout the business cycle. Multicollinearity can be considered as a particular instance of absence of identification.

b) Several equations.

Estimating parameters of identified equations of a model is a delicate matter. For the purpose of simplification, we will limit ourselves to equations of exact identification, i.e., to equations in which exactly n-1 variables are absent from the equation.

At first, one would think that the direct application of the method of least squares in determining an equation of best fit would provide consistent estimates. However, in order to apply the method of least squares it is necessary to select one variable which will be expressed as a function of the others. When there are several relationships, there is no reason to select one variable rather than another. It is therefore probable a priori that the direct application of the method of least squares does not lead to satisfactory estimates.

This question will be analyzed on the basis of the second example of paragraph 2, simplified by taking c = 0, a = 1 and b = 1.

$$p + bq \qquad + d = u \qquad\qquad \text{(II. 14)}$$

$$a'p + q + c't + e' = v \qquad\qquad \text{(II. 15)}$$

where u and v are errors in the equations assumed to be independent as well as normally and independently distributed for the various observations. s_1 is the standard deviation of u and s the standard deviation of v. The covariance of u and v is zero.

For u = 0, equation (II. 14) represents a straight line DD' on the pq plane (Fig. 4). For v = 0 and for each t value, the equation (II. 15) represents a straight line $S_t S_t'$. The intersection of these two lines gives the point A (p, q) which, for a given value of t, exactly satifies the system with u = v = 0. For the same value of t point B, which always corresponds to v = 0, is slightly different at the actual observed value of u. B is found on the straight line $D_1 D_1'$ displaced from DD' by a translation equal to u parallel to the p axis. Except in the very special instance where $S_t S_t'$ is vertical, A and B have neither the same abscissa nor the same ordinate.

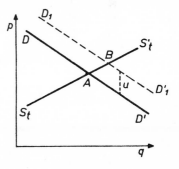

Fig. 4.

If there were only equation (II. 14) in the model, the observed point B and the theoretical point A would have the same abscissa, since the one is defined by: p = -bq-d+u and the other by: p = -bq-d. It would be reasonable to minimize the sum of squares of differences of the ordinates but, owing to the presence of the second equation, p and q both depend on u, just as they both depend on v. To apply the method of least squares to (II. 14) with p as a dependent variable would presuppose that p is independent of u, which is incorrect.

This result can be arrived at analytically. Assume b_1 to be the "estimate" which would be obtained for b if the method of least squares were applied to (II. 14) with p as a dependent variable. Let us seek the relationship which exists between b and b_1. For this, let us begin by reducing the system (II. 14 and 15) to p and q. We obtain the equations:

$$p = \frac{1}{1 - a'b} (bc't + be' - d + u - bv) \qquad \text{(II. 16)}$$

$$q = \frac{1}{1 - a'b} (- c't + a'd - e' - a' u + v). \qquad \text{(II. 17)}$$

In these new equations, t is independent of u-bv or v-a'u. The conditions for the application of the method of least squares are fulfilled and thus it is possible to find valid estimates of the coefficients of these equations. Consequently it is possible to utilize (II. 16 and 17) to determine the covariance of p and q and the variance of q. Designating z as the standard deviation of t, the following relationships are easily obtained:

$$p - \bar{p} = \frac{1}{1 - a'b} (bc' (t - \bar{t}) + u - bv) \qquad ,$$

$$q - \bar{q} = \frac{1}{1 - a'b} (- c' (t - \bar{t}) - a' u + v)$$

$$\overline{((q - \bar{q})^2)} = \frac{1}{(1 - a'b)^2} (c'^2 z^2 + a'^2 s_1^2 + s_2^2) \qquad ,$$

$$\overline{((p - \bar{p}) (q - \bar{q}))} = \frac{1}{(1 - a'b)^2} (- bc'^2 z^2 - a' s_1^2 - bs_2^2)$$

Now:

$$b_1 = - \frac{\overline{((p - \bar{p}) (q - \bar{q}))}}{\overline{((q - \bar{q})^2)}}$$

b can therefore be calculated with respect to z, s_1, s_2 and the parameters of these equations.

$$b_1 = \frac{a' s_1^2 + bs_2^2 + bc'^2 z^2}{a'^2 s_1^2 + s_2^2 + c'^2 z^2}$$

Thus it is observed that b_1 is not equal to b—i.e., it is not a consistent estimate — unless a' is zero (then the line S_t/S_t' is perpendicular) or $s_{\underline{i}}$ is zero (then the error in (II. 14) is zero). The foregoing discussion is of prime importance, as it will be used in Chapter 7 to demonstrate the inadequacy of traditional studies of demand.

Having explained why one cannot apply the method of least squares directly, we will now outline the correct method in the general case of an exactly identified equation.

The model is complete and comprises n endogenous variables and p exogenous variables. The endogenous and exogenous variables which actually enter into the equation under study are respectively numbered from 1 to N and from 1 to P. The equation can be written, dropping the subscript i which characterizes it in the model:

$$a_0 + \sum_1^N a_j v_j + \sum_1^P b_j y_j = u. \qquad \text{(II. 18)}$$

The parameter a_0 can be estimated directly by indicating that the best estimate "passes" through the observed averages of all the variables. We will consider the simplified model where the variables x_j and y_j are replaced by their X_j and Y_j differences for their average value. The equation under study becomes:

$$\sum_1^N a_j X_j + \sum_1^P b_j Y_j = u. \qquad \text{(II. 19)}$$

Since, according to hypothesis, the model is complete, the n endogenous variables can be expressed with respect to the p exogenous variables, and relationships of the following form can be obtained:

$$X_j = \sum_{m=1}^P A_{jm} Y_m + \sum_{m=P+1}^{v} B_{jm} Y_m + V_j \quad j = 1,2,\cdots N. \qquad \text{(II. 20)}$$

The (II. 20) system is the equivalent, in the general case, of equations (II. 16) and (II. 17). The V_j's are linear combinations of the u_j's, and thus possess the same properties. Consequently, if the u errors are:

1) distributed independently of one another,

2) distributed independently and normally for the various observations, the method of maximum likelihood will lead to an estimate of the A_{jm} and the B_{jm} by the method of least squares.

Once the parameters of the equations of system (II. 20) have been determined, the a_j's and b_j's must be calculated. In order to do this, the following grouping is formed:

$$\sum_j a_j X_j$$

$$\sum_{j=1}^{N} a_j X_j = \sum_{j=1}^{N} \sum_{m=1}^{P} a_j A_{jm} Y_m + \sum_{j=1}^{N} \sum_{m=P+1}^{p} a_j B_{jm} Y_m + \sum_{j=1}^{N} a_j V_j. \tag{II. 21}$$

This relationship must necessarily be identical to the (II. 19) relationship. Consequently, the exogenous variables p-P which do not enter into (II. 19) must have zero coefficients in (II. 21):

$$\sum_{j=1}^{N} a_j B_{jm} = 0 \qquad (m = P + 1, \cdots, p). \tag{II. 22}$$

In the same manner, exogenous variables which enter into (II. 19) must have the same coefficients in (II. 21):

$$b_m = -\sum_{j=1}^{N} a_j A_{jm} \qquad (m = 1, 2, \cdots, p). \tag{II. 23}$$

There are exactly n-1 variables which, although present in the model, do not enter into the equation, as can be noted from:

$$(n - N) + (p - P) = n - 1 \quad \text{or} \quad p - P = N - 1$$

The a_j coefficients can be determined uniquely (by an approximation coefficient since the initial equation is homogeneous in the first degree). In other words, the matrix $[B_{jm}]$ which includes N rows and p-P = N-1 columns, is of rank N-1. Once a_1 has been fixed, the (II. 22) system permits the computation of parameters a_j and the (II. 23) relationships then determine the b_j coefficients. It can be demonstrated that the estimates obtained for a_j and b_j are consistent and efficient.

When the (II. 19) equation is overidentified, i.e., if there are more than n-1 variables which do not enter into the equation, it is possible to demonstrate that the matrix $[B_{jm}]$ is of higher rank than N-1. In other words, the (II. 22) system states that there are more than (N-1) independent linear relationships between the N-1 coefficients a_j/a_1 (j = 2, ...n). A solution is therefore impossible. There are two ways, however, of eliminating this difficulty. An arbitrary selection can be made of N-1 equations (II. 22) with a view to deducing therefrom consistent estimates of the parameters of the equation; we thus neglect, however, part of the available information and the result depends on the choice that has been made. Another way is to develop new methods of estimating the

A_{jm}'s and B_{jm}'s which insure that the matrix $[B_{jm}]$ will be of rank N-1. But these methods are extremely complex.*

4. Estimation of parameters when the variables are in error.

We now come to the second problem which is to determine the best estimates of coefficients when there is an exact relationship between variables (i.e., when, contrary to the previous case, all important factors are identified) but where these variables can only be observed with errors, which is generally the case in any attempt at measurement. The coefficients of the exact relationship will be those which will enable us to determine, for example, the extent to which the quantity sold will vary for a given and known variation in the price set by a firm or by the government.

Frisch, Geary, Wald, and Koopmans are the economists and statisticians who have contributed most to the progress of econometrics in this area. In the appendix to this chapter is an outline of the method of considered regression developed by Koopmans; we shall limit ourselves in this text to a determination of its significance on the basis of a simple example.

Let us assume two x and y variables observed p times. The index k (k = 1, ., p) as usual, will indicate the kth observation. x_k and y_k are the measures with errors of observation u_k and v_k of the true values X_k and Y_k of the variables. An exact linear relationship is assumed to exist between X_k and Y_k:

$$\begin{cases} x_k = X_k + u_k \\ y_k = Y_k + v_k \\ Y_k = a + bX_k \end{cases} \tag{II. 24}$$

We will assume that u_k and v_k have a mathematical expectation of zero and, furthermore, are independent random variables whose distribution are normal and independent of k. Under these conditions the system (II. 24) will be completely determined if we know the coefficients a and b.

Let us attempt to apply the method of least squares to this problem, but only by stating that $\overline{y}$ $(\overline{y^2})$, $(\overline{xy})$ satisfy the (II. 24) system.

It will be observed at once that:

$$\begin{cases} \overline{x} = X \quad \overline{y} = Y \quad (\overline{xy}) = XY \\ (\overline{x^2}) = X^2 + (\overline{u^2}) \qquad (\overline{y^2}) = Y^2 + (\overline{v^2}) \end{cases}$$

---

*The reader will find these methods outlined in Tintner's book, "Econometrics", and in Monograph No. 14 of the Cowles Commission.

Thereafter, one may state that the average values of y, y^2, and xy satisfy the last equation of (II. 24), and the following equations will be arrived at:

$$\begin{cases} \bar{y} = a + b\bar{x} \\ \overline{(y^2)} = a^2 + 2ab\,\bar{x} + b^2\,((\overline{x^2}) - (\overline{u^2})) + (\overline{v^2}) \\ \overline{(xy)} = a\bar{x} + b\,((\overline{x^2}) - (\overline{u^2})) \end{cases} \qquad \text{(II. 25)}$$

All of the above moments can be estimated directly from observations, with the exception of $(\overline{u^2})$ and $(\overline{v^2})$. Therefore, we have only three equations available to evaluate the four quantities a, b, $(\overline{u^2})$, and $(\overline{v^2})$. Here are some special cases in regard to the foregoing:

1st special case. x is measured without error, y alone is measured with an error v:

$$y = a + bx + v.$$

This problem can be solved as though there were an error in the equation. The method of least squares is applicable under the same circumstances and leads to consistent and efficient estimates. (II.25) then possesses exactly the same form as (II. 13) (Fig. 5).

2nd special case. y is measured without error. It can be easily verified that the (II. 25) system determines the linear regression of x on y obtained by applying the method of least squares to the relationship:

$$x = -\frac{a}{b} + \frac{1}{b}y + u \quad \text{(Figure 6)}.$$

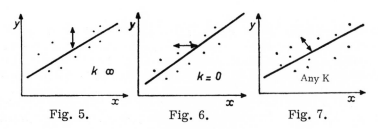

Fig. 5.   Fig. 6.   Fig. 7.

More generally, one can seek to evaluate the relative importance of errors of measurement for y and x and to fix the ratio k:

$$k = (\overline{u^2})/(\overline{v^2}) \quad \text{(Figure 7)}.$$

The first special case corresponds to k = ∞, the second to k = o. Once k is selected, the linear regression is determined so as to minimize the sum of the squares of the differences in a -k direction (see Figure 7).

In the more complex case of n variables observed p times ($i = 1, 2, ..., n; k = 1, 2, ..., p$) with errors of measurement u_{ik}, in which the true values are functionally related, the model to be analyzed is the following:

$$a_0 + \sum_i a_i X_{ik} = 0. \tag{II. 26}$$

$$x_{ik} = X_{ik} + u_{ik}. \tag{II. 27}$$

The u_{ik}'s are assumed to be distributed normally, independently of one another (for the different values of k and i), with a zero mean and variance of k.

The application of the method of maximum likelihood to this problem will be found in the appendix.

III

TIME-SERIES ANALYSIS

Up to the present, we have assumed that the values taken by each variable for the various observations were independent random variables. Such a hypothesis is certainly rarely realized in econometrics, especially when the observations relate to different moments in time. There is generally a stochastic relationship between the values taken by a variable for observations made in a time sequence. This is the phenomenon which renders a strict statistical analysis of economic series so difficult; we will attempt to take this aspect into consideration in this section.

For the purpose of reducing complexity, we are limiting the following discussion to three salient points.

The first point is devoted to trend analysis. The term "trend" is more easily illustrated than defined, and so we will resort to an example. If one considers the annual output of steel since 1830, it will be observed that output tends to grow in an irregular manner. It appears that the irregular pattern constitutes a series of short-term fluctuations superimposed on a steady, long-term growth. It is this regular, long-term tendency which is generally identified as the trend.

The second point deals with fluctuations which are superimposed on the trend. These fluctuations may be seasonal, or functionally related to the business cycle or to other causes specifically related to the series under analysis.

The third point relates to the difficulties created by the existence of stochastic relationships between the values of variables at different moments in time.

In the following exposition, a time series will always designate the entire group of x_{it} observations of a variable x_1 over a period of time including T consecutive intervals ($t = 1, 2, ..., T$).

1. The trend.

Numerous methods have been proposed for the analysis of the trend. The five methods which follow are used currently and are easy to apply; for each problem, at least one of the methods provides satisfactory results. The first four methods assume, a priori, that the trend has a specific analytic form, and seek to determine those parameter values that most satisfactorily relate to a time series expressed in the particular analytic form. The fifth method makes no a priori hypothesis as to the form of the trend. The following will be discussed successively:

a) Analysis of linear trends.
b) Analysis of trends which can be represented by polynomials.
c) Analysis of exponential trends.
d) Analysis of logistic trends.
e) The method of moving averages.

Finally, a last paragraph will discuss relationships between the trend and multiple correlation analysis.

a) Linear trends.

Let us study the x_t time series. This series can be represented by an expression of the form:

$$x_t = a + bt + u_t$$

where $a + bt$ represents the trend and u_t the other elements. The method of least squares permits a determination of the linear form $a + bt$ which, in turn, permits the best prediction of the variable x_t.

The assumption of linearity is justified only on the grounds of simplicity and because, over a short period, any trend can be considered linear. However, the extrapolation of short-term linear trends must be adjusted for possible "turning points" of the business cycle.

b) Trends which can be represented by polynomials.

One of the first approaches to empirical data is to seek trends in the form of: $a + bt + ct^2 + \ldots$. However, such a procedure presents a major disadvantage. If, after having tried a polynomial of degree p, one wishes to use a polynomial of degree $p + 1$, all of the coefficients a, b, etc., must be recalculated. For this reason, the use of orthogonal polynomials is preferred (Laguerre, Lagrange, Hermite polynomials, etc.). Two polynomials of degrees i and j, $P_i(t)$ and $P_j(t)$, are orthogonal over the interval T if:

$$\sum_{t=1}^{T} P_i(t) = \sum_{t=1}^{T} P_j(t) = 0$$

$$\sum_{t=1}^{T} P_i(t) P_j(t) = 0. \qquad\qquad i \neq j$$

These polynomials have been tabulated and, therefore, their use presents no calculation difficulty [7]. Let us attempt to represent x_t, with the aid of a trend which includes n orthogonal polynomials:

$$x_t = a_0 + \sum_{i=1}^{n} a_i P_i(t) + u_t. \qquad \text{(III. 1)}$$

The application of the method of least squares leads to the normal system of equations given earlier, which we shall write here with slightly different notations (the variable x is associated with index o):

$$\sum_{i=1}^{r} A_{ij} a_i = A_{0j}.$$

However: $A_{ij} = \sum_{t=1}^{T} P_i(t) P_j(t) = 0$ for i different from j. The normal system is therefore reduced, because of orthogonality, to a very simple system:

$$a_j = \frac{A_{0j}}{A_{jj}} = \frac{\sum\limits_{t} x_t P_j(t)}{\sum P_j^2(t)}. \qquad \text{(III. 2)}$$

As to a_0, it may be deduced from the relation:

$$a_0 = \frac{1}{T} \sum x_t.$$

The real difficulty of the method lies in selecting the degree n in the polynomial of the highest degree. If a large n is taken, equal to T-1 for instance, the equation (III. 1) constitutes for $u_t = 0$ and t = 1, 2, ..., T a system of T equations with T unknowns (a_0, a_1, ..., a_{T-1}). The polynomials now represent the time series accurately, but such a representation is not instructive and no longer corresponds to the notion of a trend. For this reason, n must be small with respect to T.

The criticisms directed at the use of linear trends remain valid here. They must be emphasized even more, because the use of a more subtle method might lead to an unwarranted increase in confidence in the results.

c) Exponential trends.

Exponential trends have a more basic economic justification because they are equivalent to the hypothesis of constancy in the rate of growth of a variable with respect to a unit of time. Experience indicates that exponential trends are very frequently encountered early in the development of most new processes. Currently, the trend in the production of electricity is still increasing exponentially at a rate of approximately 7% per year.

In order to find an exponential trend, it is merely necessary to determine the most satisfactory linear trend representing the logarithm of the variable. The relation:

$$\log x_t = a + bt + u_t$$

is, indeed, equivalent to:

$$x_t = e^{u_t}\, e^{a + bt}.$$

Special care should nevertheless be taken in the use of exponential trends for the purpose of forecasting. After initial growth at an exponential rate, many production series develop thereafter at increasingly slower rates. By extrapolating exponential growth trends, one runs the risk of overestimating future values of the variable. This danger does not exist in the use of logistic trends.

d) Logistic trends.

A study of animal populations has demonstrated that their rate of growth frequently follows the curve described by the logistic equation:

$$x_t = \frac{a}{1 + be^{-kt}} \qquad\qquad \text{(III. 3)}$$

where a, b, k are positive constants. Many economic time series follow trends of this form. The logistic curve is represented in Fig. 8. It possesses an ordinate asymptote a. For $t = 0$, $x_0 = a/1 + b$. The corresponding tangent has a positive slope: $abk/(1 + b)^2$. The concavity is toward the origin if $b < 1$, and away from the origin if $b > 1$. When b is large with respect to 1, the increase is approximately exponential for a small t. To apply the method of least squares to logistic trends, as in the case of exponential trends a transformation must be found which will permit a linear introduction of parameters. Hotelling [45] has solved this difficulty by differentiating (III. 3). The following is obtained:

$$\frac{1}{x_t}\frac{dx_t}{dt} = k - \frac{k}{a}x_t.$$

As a first approximation, the first member can be replaced by

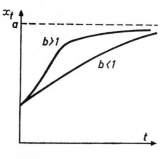

Fig. 8.

$D_i = \dfrac{x_{t+1} - x_t}{x_t}$ and the method of least squares applied to the relationship:

$$D_t = m + nx_t + u_t.$$

Once m and n have been determined, it will be merely necessary to take:

$$m = k \quad a = -\frac{m}{n}.$$

The parameter b is estimated by taking the logistic curve through the point whose coordinates are the average values of t and x_t. Considerable care must be exercised in the use of logistic trends since the ordinate of the asymptote is not precisely determined, and this results in a similar imprecision for extrapolated values of x_t.

e) The method of moving averages.

This very simple method requires no a priori hypotheses as to the form of the trend. But, aside from simple cases, its use is not without difficulties.

If we assume that a time series x_t is composed of a trend y_t and a periodic movement z_t with a known period 2p+1 (a seasonal movement, for instance), then:

$$x_t = y_t + z_t \quad (t = 1, 2, ..., T).$$

Let us calculate the variable:

$$x'_t = \sum_{i=-p}^{i=p} \frac{y_{t+i}}{2p+1} + \sum_{i=-p}^{i=p} \frac{z_{t+i}}{2p+1} \quad (t = p, p+1, \cdots, T-p).$$

Because the average value of z_t over a certain period is zero, the time series x_t is independent of the periodic movement and depends only on the trend. However, the periodic movements in time series which we have to consider in practice are not restricted to known fluctuations possessing constant amplitudes. Seasonal fluctuations may be compounded by the business cycle. In this instance, the method of moving averages can be applied twice, first to eliminate the seasonal component, and again to eliminate business cycle fluctuations. In order to effect this, the periods are evaluated by measuring the distances between the maxima and the minima of the time series. In the case of intermediate points, periods determined by linear interpolation are used. Let us take the example of the time series described in Fig. 9. For the point $\dfrac{t_1 + t_3}{2}$, the period

t_3-t_1 will be adopted. For the point $\dfrac{t_2 + t_4}{2}$, we use the period t_4-t_2, and for the point $\dfrac{t_3 + t_5}{2}$, the period t_5-t_3. These periods are described graphically with respect to time in Fig. 10. For the intermediate moments, the periods indicated by the line of interpolation L are adopted.

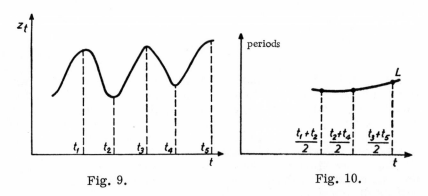

Fig. 9.   Fig. 10.

The moving averages method does not give precise results in attempting to eliminate a fluctuation of variable period. It has the additional disadvantage of causing the loss of 2p observations, p at the beginning and p at the end of the series.

f) Trend and multiple regression.

For n time series x_{1t}, x_{2t}, ..., x_{nt}, let us assume that, in order to analyze the relationships between these time series, we begin by eliminating a linear trend from each of them:

$$x'_{it} = m_i + n_i t$$

Then we seek the multiple regression of the deviations with respect to the trend:

$$\Delta x_{it} = x'_{it} - x_{it}$$
$$\Delta x_{1t} = a_2 \Delta x_{2t} + \cdots + a_n \Delta x_{nt}.$$

A theorem by R. Frisch and F. V. Waugh [32] demonstrates that this is equivalent to seeking a multiple regression between x_{1t}, x_{2t}, ..., x_{nt} and the time t.

$$x_{1t} = a_0 + a_2 x_{2t} + ... + a_n x_{nt} + bt.$$

This second method has the advantage of being much shorter. The preceding theorem is valid for nonlinear trends as well, provided they are linear forms of orthogonal functions (in particular, trigonometric functions or orthogonal polynomials). Therefore, by preserving the notations used earlier in connection with orthogonal polynomials, a direct study can be made of the correlations of the form:

$$x_{1t} = a_0 + a_2 x_{2t} + \cdots \cdots + a_n x_{nt} + \sum_i b_i P_i(t).$$

2. Oscillatory movements.

These have always posed greater difficulties for economists than have trends, and the ineffectiveness of methodology that is not solidly supported by theory is especially apparent in their analysis. These fluctuations are first considered as seasonal movements with a known and fixed period, and next as more complex movements linked or not to the economic cycle and of a variable period.

a) Computation and elimination of seasonal fluctuations.

The simplest method is that of moving averages, but it does not lead to an accurate result if the amplitude of the seasonal fluctuations varies for, under such conditions, the average, over time, of the seasonal component is no longer zero.

A. Wald has developed a method which solves this difficulty [74]. We shall outline it without proof. It presupposes that the seasonal movement has an amplitude which varies slowly with time and that, once the seasonal component has been eliminated, the difference between the "true value" of the time series and the moving average centered on a period of 12 months is negligible.

Let x_{tk} be the observation corresponding to the kth month of the year t ($t = 1, 2, \ldots, T$; $k = 1, 2, \ldots, 12$). Let us consider a period of 12 months centered on the observation x_{tk}, and let us number the months of this period with respect to x_{tk}: -6, -5, -4, -3, -2, -1, 0, 1, 2, 3, 4, 5, 6. Let us form the arithmetic mean x'_{tk} from the following 24 numbers:

1) the observed values of x_t for the months -6 and +6,
2) the observed values of x_t for the remaining months, counted twice. Now let us calculate the quantities:

$$m_k = \sum_{t=1}^{T} \frac{(x_{tk} - x'_{tk})}{T} \quad (k = 1, 2, \cdots, 12)$$

m_k is the average deviation for the month k between the observed time series and the moving average x'_{tk}. If too large deviations $x_{tk} - x'_{tk}$ appear, they are probably due to exceptional events and it is advisable to eliminate them from the calculation of m_k. The coefficients m_k are thereafter corrected by the following equation, which makes their sum equal to zero:

$$m_k' = m_k - \frac{|m_k| \left(\overset{12}{\underset{1}{\Sigma}} m_k\right)}{\overset{12}{\underset{1}{\Sigma}} |m_k|}.$$

Once the m_k''s are obtained, we must determine the seasonal component $s_{t_1k_1}$ of the month k_1 of the year t_1. In order to accomplish this, the following differences are considered:

$$\Delta x_{tk} = x_{tk} - x_{tk}'$$

calculated for each of the 12 months of the period centered on x_{tk_1}, and the quantity $S_{t_1k_1}$ is formed which is the weighted sum of the Δx_{tk} with balancing coefficients:

$1/2\ m_k'$ for the months -6 and +6,

m_k' for the remaining months (from -5 to +5).

Wald has demonstrated that $s_{t_1k_1}$ is then given by the formula:

$$s_{t_1k_1} = \frac{m_{k_1}'}{\overset{12}{\underset{1}{\Sigma}} (m_k'^2)}\ S_{t_1k_1}$$

x_{tk}-s_{tk} can be taken as the value of the time series, once the seasonal component has been eliminated.

Example: The seasonal component of the French industrial production index for the years 1949-1954, construction included, is to be eliminated.

	1949	1950	1951	1952	1953	1954
January	119	125	135	148	139	144
February	125	125	138	149	142	143
March	127	112	136	151	144	151
April.	128	122	140	150	145	155
May	131	128	144	148	147	159
June	129	125	142	147	147	157
July	117	117	133	138	132	147
August.	102	101	113	116	105	122
September.	122	125	137	142	138	156
October	123	132	143	149	143	159
November	123	136	147	147	147	164
December	123	130	144	143	150	—*

*Figure not available at the time of the above calculation.

The differences $x_{tk} - x'_{tk}$ are as follows:

	1949	1950	1951	1952	1953	1954
January		+ 4.5	+ 3.0	+ 5.3	− 2.3	− 0.2
February . . .		+ 4.5	+ 4.9	+ 6.0	+ 1.4	− 2.6
March		− 8.6	− 1.9	+ 7.8	+ 4.0	+ 4.0
April		+ 0.9	+ 4.9	+ 6.2	+ 5.5	+ 6.5
May		+ 5.5	+ 8.0	+ 4.0	+ 7.7	+ 9.2
June		+ 2.2	+ 5.0	+ 3.0	+ 7.4	
July	− 5.6	− 6.5	− 5.2	− 5.6	− 8.1	
August	− 20.9	− 23.5	− 26.2	− 26.9	− 35.3	
September . . .	− 0.1	− 1.0	− 3.2	− 0.3	− 2.7	
October	+ 1.6	− 4.2	+ 1.7	+ 7.2	+ 1.6	
November . . .	+ 2.0	+ 6.9	+ 5.3	+ 5.2	+ 5.7	
December . . .	+ 2.3	+ 0.6	+ 1.8	+ 1.5	+ 6.8	

By arriving at an average for each month of the x_{tk} and x'_{tk}, two extreme deviations will be eliminated, - 8.6 for March 1950, and - 35.3 for August 1953.

The m_k's and the m'_k's are given in the table at the right:

Once the m'_k's have been obtained, the seasonal components $s_{t_1 k_1}$ are easily obtained:

$$s_{t_1 k_1}.$$

	m_k	m'_k
January	2.06	1.963
February	2.84	2.707
March	3.47	3.307
April	4.80	4.575
May	6.98	6.651
June	4.40	4.194
July	− 6.20	− 6.491
August	− 24.36	− 25.504
September	− 1.46	− 1.528
October	+ 3.26	+ 3.107
November	+ 5.02	+ 4.784
December	+ 2.36	+ 2.250

	1950	1951	1952	1953
January	+ 1.59	+ 1.60	+ 2.04	+ 2.11
February	+ 2.17	+ 2.65	+ 2.85	+ 3.29
March	+ 2.37	+ 3.39	+ 3.51	+ 4.44
April	+ 3.29	+ 4.68	+ 4.89	+ 6.11
May	+ 4.91	+ 6.74	+ 7.10	+ 8.82
June	+ 3.14	+ 4.29	+ 4.47	+ 5.60
July	− 4.83	− 6.68	− 6.87	− 8.73
August	− 18.92	− 26.37	− 26.57	− 34.20
September	− 1.15	− 1.61	− 1.57	− 2.04
October	+ 2.42	+ 3.35	+ 3.16	− 4.15
November	+ 3.82	+ 5.10	+ 6.22	+ 6.44
December	+ 1.83	+ 2.35	+ 2.37	−

One of the drawbacks of this method is apparent. We no longer have any information for the years 1949 and 1954.

It will also be observed that there is an appreciable difference between the x_{tk}-x'_{tk}'s (which would constitute the seasonal component if the method of moving averages alone were applied) and the seasonal components finally retained.

Once stripped of the seasonal component, the time series of industrial production indices becomes:

	1950	1951	1952	1953
January	123	133	146	137
February	123	135	146	139
March	110	133	147	140
April.	119	135	145	139
May	123	137	141	138
June	122	138	143	141
July	122	140	145	141
August	120	139	143	139
September	126	139	144	140
October	130	140	146	147
November	132	142	141	141
December	128	142	141	—

b) Nonseasonal oscillatory movements.

If the time series x_t — once the trend and the seasonal component have been eliminated — has a length τ, one can seek to represent it by a Fourier series. If x_t is a periodic function of period τ, a knowledge of τ consecutive observations determines it completely. Consequently, if we seek to represent x_t by a Fourier series, it will suffice that this series include τ terms, since we will be able to select these terms so that the Fourier series will have the same value as x_t for τ consecutive observations. We shall therefore represent x_t by a finite series, a sum of τ trigonometric terms, the periods of which are submultiples of τ.

$$x_t = \sum_{n=1}^{\tau/2} A_n \cos \frac{2\pi\, nt}{\tau} + B_n \sin \frac{2\pi\, nt}{\tau}.$$

However, the x_t time series which are encountered in practice are not quite periodic. They are, therefore, considered as the sum of the previous Fourier series and with random term u_t. The τ coefficients A_n and B_n are calculated according to the method of least

squares.   The formulas obtained are very simple because of the
orthogonality of trigonometric functions:*

$$A_n = \frac{2}{T} \sum_1^T x_t \cos \frac{2\pi \, nt}{\tau}$$

$$B_n = \frac{2}{T} \sum_1^T x_t \sin \frac{2\pi \, nt}{\tau}.$$

However, we can obtain the best estimate of A_n and B_n only if the
u_t's are distributed independently of time and are independent among
themselves. These conditions rarely occur.

As so far outlined, the method utilizing the Fourier series permits the calculation of A_n and B_n after selection of the period τ.
But except in the case of seasonal variations we do not know τ a
priori. The problem is, therefore, one of determining the periods
τ of x_t.

It will be observed that A_1 and B_1 correspond, in the above
notations, to the term of the Fourier series of period τ. It is,
therefore, preferable to modify the notations and to indicate them
by A_τ and B_τ.

In the physical study of wave transmission, it is known that the
quantity $R_\tau^2 = A_\tau^2 + B_\tau^2$ represents the quantity of energy transported
by waves of period τ. The greater A_τ and B_τ (i.e., the greater the
component of period τ), the greater R_τ^2 will be. The quantity R_τ^2 can
be calculated for all possible periods and plotted on a diagram with
respect to τ. The maxima of R_τ^2 will correspond to the possible
periods of x_t.

Several tests make it possible to determine whether the periods
obtained can be attributed to chance. The simplest is the Schuster
test, which does not require any particular tables (this is not
applicable to autocorrelated series). The following is calculated:

$$R_M^2 = \frac{4s^2}{T}$$

where s is the variance of time series x_t. The probability that $\dfrac{R_\tau^2}{R_M^2}$
will be greater than k is: e^{-k}. The probability that a period τ is due
to chance is tested by calculating: $e^{-R_\tau^2 / R_M^2}$.

An evaluation of 1% means there is only 1 chance out of 100 that
the hypothetical period is due to chance. Other similar tests will be
found in Davis' book [21].

---

*The detailed outline is identical with the one used in the analysis
of trends represented by linear forms of orthogonal polynomials.

M. Allais recently generalized the Schuster test in the case of autocorrelated series [4].

It should never be forgotten, in applying harmonic analysis to economic time series, that, under very broad circumstances, a specific function within an interval can always be represented by a Fourier series. Considerable prudence should be exercised, therefore, in arriving at the conclusions one may be led to draw from harmonic analysis.

3. The interdependence of different observations and random time series.

a) Notion of random time series [82].

The notion of random time series generalizes that of random variables. Let us consider the time series:

$$..... , x_{t-1}, x_t, x_{t+1}, x_{t+2}, ...$$

which is a continuation of the values assumed by an x dimension at equidistant moments in time t. The time can assume all values from $-\infty$ to $+\infty$ (this hypothesis, which is not actually necessary, simplifies the discussion). Let us suppose that the values assumed by x result from a random sampling. Each of the variables x_{t-1}, x_t, etc., is then a random variable and the above time series is an infinite series of random variables. For that reason it is given the name of random time series.

This time series can be defined if we know the probability — or the probability density — associated with each event, i.e., the probability that each of the variables in the time series has a given value or lies within a given infinitely short period of time.

Among the most interesting random time series are those that can be classed as stationary time series. A random time series is said to be stationary if the joint probability density of the variables is the same for t and t + T, whatever t may be.

In other words, a stationary time series has no trend. The coefficient of correlation ρ_T between x_t and x_{t+T} is then independent of t; it is dependent only on T. The aggregate of the correlations between the random variables which constitute the stationary time series can then be represented by a series of numbers:

$$\rho_0, \rho_1 \cdots \cdots, \rho_T, \cdots \cdots \quad (\rho_0 = 1)$$

ρ_T being the coefficient of correlation between any two random variables of the time series separated by time T. The ρ_T coefficients have been given the name of autocorrelation coefficients. A series of autocorrelation coefficients constitutes a correlogram.

The following provides two examples of stationary time series:

1. Pure random time series. The different random variables which constitute a time series are independent, and all have the same probability distribution. For example, such a time series is obtained by tossing a coin repeatedly over an interval of time, the result being indicated by x_t ($x_t = 0$ for heads and 1 for tails). In the case of pure random time series:

$$\rho_0 = 1 \quad \rho_1 = \rho_2 = \cdots\cdots = \rho_T = \cdots\cdots = 0$$

2. Moving averages time series. Let x_t be a pure random time series of zero mean value. Let us observe this time series:

$$y_t = a_0 x_t + a_1 x_{t-1} + \cdots\cdots + a_p x_{t-p}. \qquad \text{(for fixed p)}$$

This is a stationary time series known as a "time series of moving averages", and is analogous to the case where y_t is the average of the (p+1) observations. The average value of y_t is zero; its variance — if the variance of x_t is indicated by s^2 — is:

$$(a_0^2 + a_1^2 + \cdots\cdots + a_p^2)\, s^2.$$

It can readily be verified that ρ_T is zero for $T > p + 1$, but not for $T \leq p + 1$. In the case of $T > p + 1$, y_t and y_{t+T} are substituted for the terms of the different and independent x_t time series because this time series is purely random. The method of moving averages described above then introduces — even when applied to a pure random time series — an autocorrelation between values in which the time interval is less than p.

b) Stochastic relationships between random time series.

Just as the notion of random time series generalizes that of random variables, so it is possible to introduce the notion of stochastic relationships between random time series which generalizes that of stochastic relationships between random variables.

In particular, two random time series are referred to as independent if the probability distribution of the variables in one time series does not depend on the values assumed by the variables in the other.

When time series x_t and y_t are stationary, the coefficient of correlation between x_t and y_{t+T} is independent of t and depends only on T. These correlation coefficients have been given the name of mutual correlation coefficients.

The statistical analysis of random time series presents many difficulties. This is a field in which many questions have yet to be answered and in which many of the proposed solutions are crude, imperfect, and laborious. We shall consider here only three important points:

1) The Von Neumann test for autocorrelation of a time series.

2) The application of the method of least squares in the case of correlations between errors,

3) The equations for stochastic differences.

c) The Von Neumann test for autocorrelation of a time series [62].

By means of this test, it can be ascertained whether a time series can be considered as purely random. For instance, for the time series x_t (t = 1, 2, ..., T), we designate by s^2 the variance of x_t:

$$s^2 = \frac{\sum_1^T (x_t - \bar{x})^2}{T} \qquad (x \text{ is the average of } x_t)$$

and by δ^2 the expression:

$$\delta^2 = \frac{\sum_1^T (x_{t+1} - x_t)^2}{T - 1}.$$

Von Neumann has determined the probability distribution of $\frac{\delta^2}{s^2}$ when the x_t's are distributed normally and independently of each other. Through the use of tables which have been set up in this connection, it is possible to ascertain whether the observed ratio is attributable to chance and, consequently, whether the time series is purely random.

When T is large, the distribution of $\frac{\delta^2}{s^2}$ is substantially normal, having an average value of $\frac{2T}{T-1}$ and a variance:

$$\frac{4T^2 (T - 2)}{(T - 1)^3 (T + 1)}.$$

Thereafter, the normal table can be used to ascertain whether or not the time series should be considered as normal.

d) The method of least squares in the case of correlation between errors.

It has been mentioned previously that the method of least squares does not provide the best estimates of parameters unless the errors in the equation are independently and normally distributed for the various observations.

Several results have emerged in the case of correlations between errors and where various observations relate to consecutive time intervals.

Wold has demonstrated that:*

---

*Cf. Chapter 4, reference [36].

1) if time series $x_2, ..., x_n$ are stationary,

2) if time series u is stationary, independent of time series $x_1, ..., x_n$, and of zero mathematical expectation,

3) if time series u can be represented in the form (which does not mean freedom from errors):

$$u_t = e_t + m_1 e_{t-1} + m_2 e_{t-2} + ...$$

the sum $\sum_1^\infty m_i^2$ being limited, and the e_t's constituting a pure random time series with zero mean, the traditional method of least squares provides estimates of the coefficients $a_0, a_2, ..., a_n$ which are consistent and corrected for systematic errors but which are not efficient.

Aitken [1] has evolved, in cases of correlation between errors, a modification of the method of least squares making it possible to obtain the best estimates of parameters. This method has been used to improve the determination of certain demand curves.

The Aitken method presupposes:

1) that the u_t's form a stationary time series of zero mean but do not, however, constitute a pure random time series;

2) that a coefficient of the variance and autocovariances of time series u_t is known (covariances between u_t and u_{t+T} for the various values of T). This constant coefficient, for example, can be the variance s^2 of the time series. Inasmuch as an outline of this method is rather complex, we refer the reader to the original sources.

e) Equations of stochastic differences.

An equation of differences is obtained by expressing that the value assumed by a variable at a certain instant is a function of values assumed by this variable at various previous instances. An equation of stochastic differences is obtained by expressing that the value assumed by a variable at a particular moment is stochasticly related to the values assumed by this variable at various previous moments.

Equations of stochastic differences, therefore, are simply correlations where the variables $x_1, x_2, ..., x_n$ are values assumed by the same variable at different moments in time.

Thus, it is possible to study the correlation between the quantity of steel produced during the year t+1 and the quantity of steel produced during the years t, t-1, etc.

This paragraph is limited to equations of linear stochastic differences of the first and second order.

The equation of the first order can be written:

$$x_{t+1} = ax_t + b + u_{t+1}$$

u_{t+1} being a pure random time series of mean value o and of s^2 variance; a and b are constants.

Knowing the initial value of the variable, for example $x_0 = 0$, the preceding equation allows us to calculate x_t:

$$x_t = a^{t-1} b + \sum_{i=1}^{t} a^{t-i} u_i$$

x_t is a random variable normally distributed as the u_i's. Its mathematical expectation is equal to the solution of the equation of non-stochastic differences of the first order, obtained by setting all the u_i's equal to 0.

Parameters a and b can be determined by the method of least squares.

If a is equal to 1, the mathematical expectation of x_t is constant.

If a is greater than 1, it increases indefinitely.

If a is less than 1, it tends toward 0, and the value of x_t at infinity depends only upon the errors. In other words, at infinity, x_t will behave like a stationary time series.

These results can be pinpointed further by calculating the coefficients of autocorrelation between x_t and x_{t+T}:

$$x_t - \bar{x}_t = \sum_{i=1} a^{t-i} u_i$$

$$\overline{(x_t - \bar{x}_t)^2} = s^2 \sum_{=1} a^{2(t-i)} = s^2 \frac{1 - a^{2t}}{1 - a^2}$$

$$\overline{(x_t - \bar{x}_t)(x_{t+T} - \bar{x}_{t+T}))} = \sum_{i=1} a^{t-i} u_i \sum_{j=1}^{t+\tau} a^{t+T-j} u_j = \sum_{i=1} a^{2t+T-2i} u_i^2$$

$$= s^2 a^T \frac{1 - a^{2t}}{1 - a^2}.$$

From this is derived the coefficient of autocorrelation $\rho_{t,t+T}$ between x_t and x_{t+T}:

$$\rho_{t,t+T} = \frac{a^T (1 - a^{2T})}{\sqrt{(1 - a^{2t})(1 - a^{2t+2T})}}.$$

It will be observed that for $|a| < 1$, the correlogram of the stationary time series toward which x_t approaches for large t is a decreasing exponential ratio of T for $0 < a < 1$ and a dampened oscillation for $-1 < a < 0$. In other words, if a is positive, the stochastic relationship between x_t and x_{t+T} is as "loose" as T is large. If a is negative, the stochastic relationship does, on the average, become looser and looser, but the covariation between

x_t and x_{t+T} is in the opposite direction for even T and odd T. In practice, a time series can reasonably be represented by the solution of a linear equation of stochastic differences of the first order with $|a| < 1$ although this phenomenon may not appear very clearly on the correlogram which may be determined directly from the observations.

The equation of linear stochastic differences of the second order can be set down in the same way:

$$x_{t+2} = ax_{t+1} + bx_t + c + u_{t+2}.$$

The time series u_t possessing the same properties as previously, a, b, c can be determined by the method of least squares. The general solution of this equation is as follows:

$$x_t = \sum_{i=0}^{t} ck_i + \sum_{i=0}^{t} k_i u_{t-i}.$$

The parameters k_i are obtained from the characteristic equation:*

$$z^2 - az - b = 0.$$

A distinction should also be made with respect to differences rising out of this equation's having either real or imaginary roots.
1) $a^2 + 4b \geq 0$. The characteristic equation has two real roots, m and n. The function k_i is therefore the function:

$$k_i = \frac{m^{i+1} - n^{i+1}}{m - n}.$$

For a very large t, the variance of x_t is finite if m and n are both less than 1 and equal to:

$$\frac{(1 + mn) s^2}{(1 - m^2)(1 - n^2)(1 - mn)}.$$

The time series x_t is then substantially stationary and has, as a correlogram, the function:

$$\rho_T = \frac{m(1 - n^2) m^T}{(m - n)(1 + mn)} + \frac{n(1 - m^2) n^T}{(n - m)(1 + mn)}$$

The stochastic relationship between x_t and x_{t+T} is as loose as T is large.

---

*The term "characteristic equation" is used analogously with its use in linear differential equations.

2) $a^2 + 4b < 0$. The characteristic equation has two imaginary conjugate roots:

$$m = r (\cos p + j \sin p)$$
$$n = r (\cos p - j \sin p)$$

with: $\cos p \dfrac{a}{\sqrt{-b}}$ $r = \sqrt{-b}$.

The function k_i remains:

$$\frac{m^{i+1} - n^{i+1}}{m - n},$$

but its expression, by including only real symbols, is:

$$k_i = \frac{r^i \sin (i + 1) p}{\sin p}.$$

When the two roots have an absolute value less than 1, the x_t time series always approaches, for large t, a stationary time series for which the correlogram is the function:

$$\rho_T = \frac{r^T \sin (Tp + q)}{\sin q}.$$

The variable q is defined by the relation:

$$\operatorname{tg} q = \frac{1 - b}{1 + b} \operatorname{tg} p.$$

The stochastic relationship between x_t and x_{t+T} weakens, on the average, as T increases, but this weakening combines with an oscillatory variation of the intensity of the correlation.

Equations of linear stochastic differences of a higher order or systems of several equations of stochastic differences can also be used. These equations can be presumed to be accurate while hypothesizing that the variables are measured with errors of observation.

The introduction of equations of differences makes it possible, at times, to identify a model's equations. For instance, a model of supply and demand, where only the price and quantity sold at moment t are introduced, is not identified, but it becomes so if it is assumed that the demand at moment t is a function of the price at that moment and the supply at moment t a function of the price at moment t-T (where T is the necessary time interval for producers to modify their level of production).

At the close of this rather tedious chapter (which, at times, may have seemed remote from real problems), it may be useful, by way of conclusion, to recapitulate briefly what has been covered above.

The preceding pages have attempted primarily to examine the broad aspects of econometric problems apart from methods of calculation. With this in mind, we have examined concepts of variables and the estimation of parameters, errors in the variables and errors in the equations, identification, independence, correlation between errors, random time series, etc. Without using sophisticated statistical methods, these concepts nevertheless facilitate the comprehension of the problems which are being faced, and the very real and substantial difficulties which are met in econometrics. They constitute a rationale through which analysis of specific problems can be more readily performed.

However, we have not limited this chapter merely to an introduction of these general concepts. We have also attempted the description of the simpler and more practical econometric methods (method of least squares, estimation of parameters of limited information equations, regression, trend determination, harmonic analysis, equations of stochastic differences, etc.). These methods are currently applied and provide profitable results if one does not lose sight of the hypotheses which condition their validity.

For those who may wish to devote further study to econometrics, this chapter may constitute an introduction to specialized publications and to original articles listed in the bibliography. It is with this in mind that we have alluded to somewhat complex methods, such as the Aitken method in the case of correlation between errors.

The adoption of extreme views concerning econometrics should be avoided. The success of an economic analyst depends on a sensible selection of the method best suited to the problem under study. The requirement for complexity and absolute precision is no more sensible than is that of unsophisticated methodology and approximation. Econometrics is a technique and an art, and it is up to the economic analyst to seek the optimum equilibrium of the methods that theory makes available to him.

APPENDIX

Estimating Parameters in the Event of Errors in the Variables

Applied to this problem, the method of maximum likelihood leads to minimizing the expression:

$$S = \sum_{i=1}^{n} \frac{s_1^2}{s_i^2} \sum_{k=1}^{p} (x_{ik} - X_{ik})^2 \tag{II.28}$$

where s_i^2 indicates the unknown variance of u_i and where s_1^2 is the variance of any error arbitrarily taken as being the first.

The above minimization must be made taking the restraint (II. 26) into consideration. Mathematical deductions being long and intricate, we shall adopt their results without prior development.

By the introduction of a Lagrange multiplier m, it can be demonstrated that coefficients a_1, a_2, ..., a_n must represent the solution of the system:

$$\begin{cases} \left(A_{11} - m\,\frac{s_1^2}{s_1^2} \right) a_1 + A_{12}a_2 + \cdots + A_{1n}a_n = 0 \\ A_{12}a_1 + \left(A_{22} - m\,\frac{s_2^2}{s_1^2} \right) a_2 + \cdots + A_{2n}a_n = 0 \\ \cdots\cdots\cdots\cdots\cdots\cdots\cdots\cdots\cdots\cdots\cdots\cdots \\ A_{1n}a_1 + A_{2n}a_2 + \cdots + \left(A_{nn} - m\,\frac{s_n^2}{s_1^2} \right) a_n = 0 \end{cases} \qquad (II.29)$$

where A_{ij} has the same significance as in paragraph 1.

The example of two variables has demonstrated that the problem is indeterminate as long as the ratios of the variances of different errors are not fixed. We shall therefore assume:

$$s_1^2 = k_i\, s_1^2. \qquad (II.30)$$

The system of homogeneous equations (II. 29) is solved by numbers not all of which are zero, if the determinant:

$$f(m) = \begin{vmatrix} A_{11} - m & A_{12} \cdots\cdots\cdots A_{1n} \\ k_2 A_{12} & k_2 A_{22} - m \cdots A_{3n} \\ \cdots\cdots\cdots\cdots\cdots\cdots \\ k_n A_{1n} & k_n A_{2n} \cdot k_n A_{nn} - m \end{vmatrix} \text{ is zero.}$$

To each root of f(m) there corresponds an S value. It can be demonstrated that it is the smallest root of f(m) which leads to the minimum S. Having obtained this root, system (II. 29) permits a determination of the a_i's once one of these has been conventionally taken as being equal to 1. a_0 is obtained by making use of the relation:

$$a_0 + \sum_i a_i\, \bar{x}_i = 0.$$

Let us take the more complex instance where r identified relations (v = 1, 2, ..., r) are presumed to exist between the variables X_j. The problem remains of minimizing (II. 28) but under the restraints:

$$a_{v0} + \sum_i a_{vi}\, X_{ik} = 0 \qquad v = 1, 2, \cdots, r. \qquad (II. 31)$$

We shall merely state the results:

1. All (II. 31) equations contain all the variables. In this case, the r smallest roots of the $f(m) = 0$ equation are sought. To each v root is associated a group of value a_{vi}/a_{v1} which determines a linear relationship.

2. A (II. 31) equation, the vth, for example, contains only n variables $(n_v < n)$. In this case, the smallest root of the following equation is associated therewith:

$$\begin{vmatrix} A_{11} - m & A_{12} & \cdots & A_{1n_\bullet} \\ k_2 A_{12} & k_2 A_{22} - m & \cdots & A_{2n_\bullet} \\ \cdots & \cdots & \cdots, & \cdots \\ k_{n_\bullet} A_{1n_\bullet} & k_{n_\bullet} A_{2n_\bullet} & \cdots k_{n_\bullet} A_{n_\bullet n_\bullet} - m \end{vmatrix} = 0$$

3. In a general case, if q equations include the same variables, the same determinant is associated therewith and their coefficients are determined by the selection of the q smallest roots of this determinant.

The above method can be used in testing the multicollinearity between the X_i variables. The N variables m_i being the N smallest roots of the equation $f(m) = 0$, the following variable is formed:

$$M_N = (p - 1) \sum_{i=1}^{N} m_i.$$

Anderson has demonstrated [5] that for large values of p the random variable:

$$\frac{M_N - pN}{\sqrt{2pN}}$$

is distributed normally with a zero mean and a unit variance. However, the problem of multicollinearity occurs in the course of studies of relationships between variables and when these variables are connected by other relationships (exact or approximate). Multicollinearity can be approximated by seeking the number of independent linear relationships which probably exist among the true values of the variables. The following procedure is used: $M_1, \ldots, M_i, M_{i+1}$ is calculated and a level of probability is chosen (5%, for example). If the values observed for the i first variables are significant (i.e., if they have 95 chances out of 100 of not being due to chance) but if the value observed for the (i + 1)th is not, one may conclude that there are probably i relationships among the true values of the variables. The same test may be used to arrive at the probable number of linear relationships between the true values of any sub-group of n variables. It is merely necessary to adopt for m the smallest roots of the determinant associated with this sub-group of variables.

There remains one last problem. In what manner should variances s_i^2 of the errors, or at least their k_i ratios, be evaluated? Following is a broad outline of a method which is frequently employed and which is known under the name of the method of variate differences [71].

The different observations frequently relate to consecutive intervals of time. Since the true value of X_k, x_k is probably a "regular" function of time, this excludes "zigzags" (in order to apply the method of variate differences, it will therefore be necessary first to eliminate seasonal variations from x_k). If X_k is a "regular" function of k, it can be represented locally by a polynomial.

It is relatively easy to demonstrate that the difference of order n of a polynomial of degree n is a constant, and that the difference of order n+1 is zero.* The differences of $x_k = X_k + y_k$ beginning from a certain order will therefore be solely due to a measurement error u_k. The problem consists in determining this order.

The hypotheses are as follows:

$$\begin{cases} \overline{u_k} = 0 & k = 1, 2, \cdots, p & \overline{u_k u_{k'}} = 0 & k \neq k' \\ \overline{(u_k^2)} = s^2 & & \overline{X_k u_k'} = 0 \end{cases}$$

The x_k differences are random variables, such as x_k, whose variances can be calculated in accordance with formulas admitted without demonstration:

$$x_0 = \frac{\overset{p}{\underset{1}{\Sigma}} (x_k - \overline{x})^2}{p - 1} \quad \text{(variance of } x_k)$$

$$v_r = \frac{\overset{p-r}{\underset{1}{\Sigma}} (\Delta_{rk})^2}{p - r} \cdot \frac{(r\,!)^2}{(2r)!} \quad \begin{array}{l}\text{(variance of the difference of order} \\ \quad\quad r\, \Delta_{rk} \text{ of } x_k). \end{array}$$

It can be demonstrated that for a purely random variable, v_r is a constant independent of v.

From the moment that the calculated values of v become fairly constant, they will constitute a good estimate of the s^2 variance of the error of measurement u_k, since at that moment the differences of X_k will have been eliminated. Tests have been devised to

---

*If P is the value assumed by the polynomial for the k value, the difference of order 1 is defined by the relationship: $\Delta_{1K} = P_{K+1} - P_K$ and the difference of order n by the relationship:

$$\Delta_{nk} = \Delta_{(n-1)(k+1)} - \Delta_{(n-1)K}$$

determine whether the difference between two successive variances $v_r - v_{r+1}$ are significant [71]. Once the variances of errors are known, their ratios can be introduced into the system of equations (II. 29).

Note. In fact, there is a certain incompatibility between the method of variate differences and the estimation of parameters of exact relations by the method of least squares. If one keeps in mind the system of equations (II. 25), it will be discovered that this system is impossible if the variances of u and of v are both known, since there are then three equations for the determination of the two quantities a and b. It is merely necessary to determine the ratio of variances so that the variances may be ascertained as a consequence of the estimate of parameters.

Variances calculated in accordance with the method of variate differences are, therefore, not used, although their ratios are useful. The variances obtained, once the parameters have been estimated, could be different from those originally calculated. One should resort to the method of variate differences only in the absence of any other means of estimating the ratios of the variances in possible errors of the different variables.

BIBLIOGRAPHY

1. A. C. AITKEN:
   "On the least squares and linear combinations of observations." Proceedings of the Royal Society of Edinburgh, Vol. 55.

2. A. C. AITKEN:
   Statistical mathematics. Oliver and Boyd, 1949.

3. M. ALLAIS:
   "Methods of appraising economic prospects of mining exploration over large territories: Algerian Sahara case study." Management Science, Vol. 3, No. 4, July 1957.

4. M. ALLAIS:
   "Test de périodicité — Généralisation du test de Schuster au cas de séries temporelles autocorrellées" (Periodicity test. Generalization of the Schuster test to cases of autocorrelated temporal series). 1957.

5. T. W. ANDERSON:
   "The asymptotic distribution of the roots of a certain determinant equation." Journal of the Royal Statistical Society. Supplement, Vol. 10, 1948, p. 132 et seq.

6. T. W. ANDERSON and H. RUBIN:
   "Estimation of the parameters of a single equation in a complete system of stochastic equations." Annals of mathematical statistics, Vol. 20, 1949.

7. R. L. ANDERSON and E. E. HOUSMAN:
   "Tables of orthogonal polynomial values extended to N = 140." Agricultural Experiment Station, Iowa State College, Research Bulletin 227, Ames, Iowa, 1942.

8. M. S. BARTLETT:
   "Fitting a straight line when both variables are subject to error." Biometrics, Vol. 4, 1949.

9. M. S. BARTLETT:
   Stochastic processes. Raleigh, North Carolina, 1946.

10. D. BLACKWELL and M. A. GIRSCHICK:
    Theory of games and statistical decisions. New York, Wiley, 1954.

11. J. BRONFENBRENNER:
    Sources and size of least squares bias in a two-equation model. Studies in econometric method. The Cowles Commission, Monograph No. 14. John Wiley and Sons.

12. G. D. CHAMPERNOWNE:
    "Sampling theory applied to autoregressive sequences." Journal of the Royal Statistical Society (B), 1948, 10, 204-42.

13. H. CHERNOFF and N. DIVINSKY:
    The computation of maximum likelihood estimates of linear structural equations. Studies in econometric method. The Cowles Commission, Monograph No. 14. John Wiley and Sons.

14. H. CHERNOFF, H. RUBIN:
    Asymptotic properties of limited-information estimates under generalized conditions. Studies in econometric method. The Cowles Commission, Monograph No. 14. John Wiley and Sons.

15. D. COCHRANE and G. H. ORCUTT:
    "Application of least squares regression to relationships containing autocorrelated error terms." Journal of the American Statistical Association, 1949, 44, 32-61.

16. G. COOPER:
"The role of econometric models in economic research."
Journal of Farm Economics, 1948, 30, 101-16.

17. H. CRAMER:
Mathematical methods of statistics. Princeton University
Press, 1946.

18. G. DARMOIS:
"L'emploi des observations statistiques: méthodes d'estimation" (Utilization of statistical observations: methods of
estimating). Actualités scientifiques et industrielles, 356,
Paris, 1936.

19. G. DARMOIS:
Statistique mathématique (Mathematical statistics). Paris,
Doin, 1928.

20. H. T. DAVIS:
Analysis of economic time-series. Cowles Commission
Monograph No. 6. Wiley and Sons, New York.

21. H. T. DAVIS:
Theory of econometrics. Bloomington, Indiana, 1941.

22. DODGE ROMIG:
Simple sampling and double sampling inspection tables.
New York, Wiley and Sons, 1944.

23. R. DUMAS:
L'entreprise et la statistique (The firm and statistics).
Dunod, 2nd edition, 1959.

24. M. EZEKIEL:
"Choice of the dependent variable in regression anaysis.
Comments." Journal of the American Statistical Association,
1943, 38, 214-16.

25. M. EZEKIEL:
Methods of correlation analysis. 2nd edition, New York, 1941.

26. W. FELLER:
An introduction to probability theory and its applications.
Vol. 1, New York.

27. FISHER and YATES:
Statistical tables for biological, agricultural, and medical
research. London, Oliver and Boyd, 1949.

28. F. G. FOSTER and D. TEICHROEW:
"A sampling experiment on the powers of the records tests for trend in a time series." Journal of the Royal Statistical Society, Series B, vol. 17, No. 1, 1955.

29. M. FRECHET:
"Nouveaux essais d'explication de la répartition des revenus" (New attempts at explaining the distribution of income). Rev. Inst. Int. Stat. 1945, 13, 16-32.

30. FREEMAN, FREDMAN, MOSTELLER and WALLIS:
Sampling inspection. New York and London, McGraw-Hill, 1948.

31. R. FRISCH:
Pitfalls in the statistical construction of demand and supply curves. Leipzig, 1933.

32. R. FRISCH and F. V. WAUGH:
"Partial time regression as compared with individual trends." Econometrica, vol. 1.

33. R. FRISCH:
Statistical confluence analysis by means of complete regression systems. Oslo, 1934.

34. J. GARNIER and M. BRICHLER:
Études de la demande (Studies of demand). Direction de la statistique générale. Ministère de l'économie nationale. Études théoriques, 1956, No. 2, 5, 61.

35. R. C. GEARY:
"Determination of linear relations between the systematic parts of variables with errors of observations the variances of which are unknown."

36. R. C. GEARY:
"Sampling aspects of the problem of relationship from the error in variable approach." Econometrica, Vol. 17, supplement, July 1949.

37. R. C. GEARY:
"Studies in relations between economic time series." Journal of the Royal Statistical Society (B), 1948, 10, 140-58.

38. R. GIBRAT:
Les inégalités économiques (Economic inequalities). Librairie du receuil Sirey, Paris, 1932.

39. G. Th. GUILBAUD:
"L'étude statistique des oscillations économiques" (Statistical analysis of economic oscillations). Economie appliquée, Vol. II, 1949, Nos. 3-4, July-December.

40. G. Th. GUILBAUD:
"Note sur l'économétrie des fluctuations" (Remark on the econometrics of fluctuations). Cahiers Séminaire d' Econométrie, No. 1, 1951.

41. T. HAAVELMO:
"The probability approach in econometrics." Econometrica, Vol. 12, 1944.

42. T. HAAVELMO:
Methods of measuring the marginal propensity to consume. Studies in econometric method. The Cowles Commission, Monograph No. 14. John Wiley and Sons.

43. T. HAAVELMO:
"The statistical implications of a system of simultaneous equations." Econometrica, 1943, II, 1-12.

44. B. I. HART:
"Significance levels for the ratio of the mean square successive difference to the variance." Annals of mathematical statistics, Vol. 13, 1942.

45. H. HOTELLING:
"Differential equations subject to error and population estimates." Journal of the American Statistical Association, Vol. 22, 1927.

46. L. HURWICZ:
"Some problems arising in estimating economic relations." Econometrica, 1947, 15, 236-40.

47. M. KALECKI:
"On the Gibrat distribution." Econometrica, 1945, 13, 161-70.

48. M. G. KENDALL:
The advanced theory of statistics (2 vols.). London, Charles Griffin and Co., 1946.

49. M. G. KENDALL:
Contribution to the study of oscillatory time series. Cambridge, 1946.

50. KENDALL and BABINGTON SMITH:
Tables of random sampling numbers. Tract for computers No. 24. Cambridge University Press, 1946.

51. L. R. KLEIN:
A textbook of econometrics. Row, Peterson and Company, 1953.

52. T. J. KOOPMANS:
"Statistical estimation of simultaneous economic relations." Journal of the American Statistical Association, Vol. 40, 1945.

53. Etudes réunies par T. J. KOOPMANS (Collected studies of T. J. Koopmans: Statistical inference in dynamic models). The Cowles Commission, Monograph No. 10. John Wiley and Sons, 1950.

54. T. J. KOOPMANS:
Identification problems in economic model construction. Studies in econometric method. The Cowles Commission, Monograph No. 14. John Wiley and Sons.

55. T. J. KOOPMANS and W. C. HOOD:
The estimations of simultaneous linear economic relationships. Studies in econometric method. The Cowles Commission, Monograph No. 14. John Wiley and Sons.

56. T. J. KOOPMANS:
"Identification in economic model construction." Econometrica, 1949, p. 125.

57. T. J. KOOPMANS:
"Linear regression analysis in economic time series." Haarlem, 1937.

58. P. MAILLET:
"Introduction à l'étude des modèles économétriques" (Introduction to a study of econometric models). Cahiers du Séminaire d'économétrie, No. 3, 1955.

59. J. MARSCHAK:
Economic measurements for policy and prediction. Studies in econometric method. The Cowles Commission, Monograph No. 14. John Wiley and Sons.

60. A. MONJALLON:
Introduction à la méthode statistique (Introduction to the statistical method). Vuibert, 1954.

61. MORICE and CHARTIER:
Méthode statistique (Statistical method). Paris, Imprimerie Nationale, 1954.

62. J. von NEUMANN:
"Distribution of ratio of the mean successive difference to the variance." Annals of mathematical statistics, Vol. 12, 1941.

63. K. PEARSON:
Tables for statisticians and biometricians; table of the incomplete B function; table of the incomplete Γ function. Cambridge University Press, 1946-1948.

64. H. A. SIMON:
Causal ordering and identifiability. Studies in econometric method. The Cowles Commission, Monograph No. 14. John Wiley and Sons.

65. G. W. SNEDECOR:
Statistical methods. Ames, Iowa, 1946.

66. J. TINBERGEN:
Econometrics. New York, 1951. (English translation of Econometrics, Groninghen, 1941).

67. G. TINTNER:
"An application of the variate difference method to multiple regression." Econometrica. Vol. 12, 1944.

68. G. TINTNER:
Econometrics. Wiley, New York, 1952.

69. G. TINTNER:
"The teaching of econometrics." Econometrica, Vol. 22, No. 1, January 1954.

70. G. TINTNER:
"A test for linear relations between weighted regression coefficients." Journal of the Royal Statistical Society, Series B, Vol. 12 (1950).

71. G. TINTNER:
The variate difference method. Bloomington, Indiana, 1940.

72. A. VESSEREAU:
La statistique (Statistics). Paris, "Que sais-je?" series.

73. A. VESSEREAU:
Méthodes statistiques en biologie et en agronomie (Statistical methods in biology and in agronomy). Paris, Baillière et Fils, 1948.

74. A. WALD:
Berechnung und ausschaltung von Saisonschwankungen (Calculation and elimination of seasonal fluctuations). Vienna, 1936.

75. A. WALD:
"The fitting of straight line when both variables are subject to error." Annals of mathematical statistics, Vol. XI, 1940.

76. A. WALD:
Notes on the theory of statistical estimation and of testing hypotheses. Columbia University, 1941.

77. A. WALD:
Statistical decision functions. Wiley and Sons, New York, 1950.

78. A. M. WALKER, PKS. BARTLETT and P. H. DIANANDRA:
"Note on a generalization of the large sample goodness of fit test for linear autoregressive schemes. Extensions of Quenouille's test of autoregressive schemes." Journal of the Royal Statistical Society, Series B, Vol. XII, No. 1, 1950.

79. S. S. WILKS:
Mathematical statistics. Princeton, 1950.

80. W. WINKLER:
Grundfragen der ökonometrie (Basic problems in econometrics). Vienna, 1951.

81. H. WOLD:
"Possibilités et limitations des systèmes à chaîne causale" (Possibilities and limitations of causal sequence systems). Cahiers du Séminaire d'économétrie, No. 3.

82. H. WOLD:
A study in the analysis of auto-regression time series. Uppsala, 1938.

83. E. J. WORKING:
"What do statistical demand curves show?" Quarterly Journal of Economics, Vol. 1, 1927.

84. "Recherches de relations à forme linéaire dans un système économique" (Research on linear form relations within an economic system). Cahiers du Séminaire d'économétrie, No. 1.

85. Statistical analysis of the demand for food: Examples of simultaneous estimation of structural equations. Studies in econometric method. The Cowles Commission, Monograph No. 14. John Wiley and Sons.

Chapter 7

Examples of applied econometrics

An outline of abstract methodology does not fully convey the usefulness of a technique. The preceding chapter is hardly satisfactory for those who view econometrics with scepticism, because it merely describes tools which statistics make available to the economic analyst. This situation could have been avoided by including among the theoretical developments a greater number of examples, but that would have lessened the interest of this chapter which describes specific econometric studies by grouping them by areas of application. It seemed to us that the persuasiveness of such examples would be greater if we took, as a starting point, actual problems which confront executives, instead of limiting ourselves to illustrations of statistical methods.

The illustrative problems set forth in this chapter will relate to the following areas of application which, it should be noted, parallel, with minor modifications, the development of the second part of Chapter 3.

I. Long-term forecasting.
II. The influence of prices and income.
III. Household budgets.
IV. Market dynamics.
V. Management policy.
VI. Ecological conditions of demand.

I

LONG-TERM FORECASTING

Since it is our purpose here to consider the various forecasting methods available rather than the variety of economic areas in which these methods can be applied, we will limit the discussion to one sector of the economy.

The sector we have selected, the production of energy, has an extremely complex structure. The objective is to predict, within the framework of a plan of modernization of plant and equipment, the evolution of the country's demand for energy. Consequently, the predictions are complicated by the fact that they must reflect both the growth of national income and the industrial production envisaged by the plan. A summary of the work described by the third plan of the Commission de l'Énergie du Commissariat Général au Plan [6] is given below.

The following diagram outlines the structure of energy production and consumption.

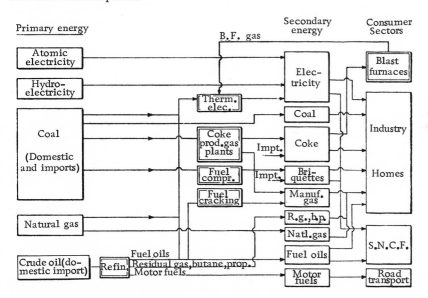

In the column at the left are found the various sources of primary energy; in the center column, those of secondary energy; and in the one at the right, the sectors of utilization. The transformation of primary energy into secondary energy is effected in thermal plants — coke manufacturing plants, gas plants, compressed fuel plants, refineries, cracking installations for fuel oils, and, as a byproduct, in blast furnaces. The diagram, naturally, has been simplified, since it neglects such primary sources of energy as wood and certain subsidiary sources of secondary energy which constitute byproducts of many industrial activities.

In a context of such complexity, empirical measurement is the basis for analysis. We first derive the magnitudes which can be predicted without difficulty; the study then proceeds to those measurements which present greater problems. This line of reasoning leads to the following sequence:

1) study of the correlation between national income and consumption of primary energy;

2) study of electrical power demand;
3) study of the blast furnace demand for coke;
4) study of industrial energy requirements (excluding electricity);
5) study of household energy requirements (excluding electricity);
6) study of the energy requirements of the S.N.C.F. (French National Railways) and road transport;
7) examination of the distribution of total consumption among the various sources of primary and secondary energy.

The above is the sequence which will be followed here; the extent to which the various parts will be developed will vary in accordance with the significance of each with respect to its contribution to analytical methodology.

1. National income and primary energy consumption.

In 1950, M. Prévot developed an excellent study of the correlation between energy consumption and national income during the two periods 1920-1948 and 1850-1910 [25]. The results of the 1920-1948 analysis have been brilliantly confirmed by reports for the years 1949 to 1956. Only the portion of the analysis bearing on the 1920-1948 period is summarized below.

The period 1920-1948 was selected because of the availability of comparable data for energy consumption and for the "net national product".

"An estimate of the net national product under strictly comparable conditions is one of the most difficult points to solve. The series which was adopted is the result of studies by the Commissariat au Plan, and was elaborated in the following manner. The Commissariat au Plan calculated in 1938 francs the theoretical net value, by economic sector, for the year 1938. This computation was made by determining separately the net values of agricultural production, industrial production, transportation, commercial activity, services, and housing revenue during the year 1938. Indices of variation of each of these six activities were then applied to the corresponding values in 1938; the net values produced for each of the years 1920 to 1948 were thereby derived" [25].

The consumption of energy was estimated in terms of millions of tons of coal. It was necessary to select conversion coefficients in order to be able to transform measures of consumption from all sources of primary energy into coal. M. Prévot used the following coefficients:

1 ton of crude petroleum = 1.15 tons of coal.
1 ton of gasoline = 1.46 tons of coal.
1 cubic meter of natural gas = 1.33 kilograms of coal.

1 ton of fuel oil = 1.35 tons of coal.
1 ton of gas oil = 1.40 tons of coal.
1 kw.-hr. of electricity = 1 kilogram of coal.*

The selection of these coefficients is, of course, open to debate, as is generally true of all conversion coefficients, but it can be demonstrated that their use exercises very little influence upon the results.

Included among the sources of primary energy were domestic crude petroleum and the refined products derived from imported crude petroleum. Variations in user inventories were not taken into account in estimating energy consumption inasmuch as the magnitude of error in national product estimates more than compensates for the relatively minor effect of these variations.

Table I reproduces the two series obtained for the total energy consumption and the net national production at cost of the various factors.

Table I

Year	Energy consump-tion (1)	Net produc-tion (2)	Year	Energy consump-tion	Net produc-tion
1920	59.60	233	1935	84.40	324
1921	54.30	216	1936	87.90	320
1922	65.80	262	1937	95.10	331
1923	74.80	283	1938	87.00	328
1924	82.30	329	1939	88.30	351
1925	82.40	331	1940	66.30	290
1926	87.10	346	1941	59.05	230
1927	86.40	334	1942	57.17	205
1928	88.50	354	1943	58.45	195
1929	99.60	391	1944	39.40	165
1930	98.50	386	1945	53.80	180
1931	91.10	369	1946	76.40	275
1932	83.50	344	1947	84.14	286
1933	86.10	345	1948	83.38	335
1934	86.00	338			

(1) In millions of tons of equivalent coal.
(2) In billions of 1938 francs.

---

*The conversion coefficient selected for electricity relates to utilization and not to production. The coefficient for the latter would be on the order of 0.5.

The coefficient of correlation between the two variables was found to be as high as 0.95, a very significant value considering the eventful history of that period. The slope of the line of regression was 0.25 million tons of coal per billion francs of net product.

Figure 1 shows the indices of net product and of primary energy consumption from 1920 to 1956 (1938 = 100), and demonstrates that the ratio of national product to primary energy consumption can be utilized in a study of energy demand.

The predictions of the growth of national income made by the Commissariat au Plan make it possible to estimate total primary energy requirements. Furthermore, because it is possible to estimate future availability of natural gas and of atomic electricity and hydroelectricity, the sum of coal and petroleum requirements can be deduced as a residual.

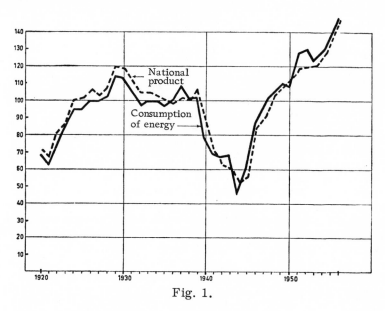

Fig. 1.

2. Electric power demand.

As has been mentioned previously, the consumption of electricity C_t during the year t can be represented by the relationship:

$$C_t = C_0 \left(\frac{I_t}{100} \right)^{0.4} (1.05)^t$$

in which C_0 represents the consumption during the year 0 and I_t the index of industrial production for the year t (the year 0 = 100) [2].

Beginning with the consumption of electricity and its production (hydro and atomic origins), it is relatively easy to calculate the requirement for thermal electricity provided by coal, fuel oil, and natural gas.

3. Blast furnace demand for coke.

The demand for coke generated by blast furnace operations is linked to the production of pig iron and is governed by the amount of ore delivered to blast furnaces for processing. An estimate of these two quantities is basic to a forecast of blast furnace requirements for coke.

An analysis covering the period 1932-1955 indicates a fairly clear relationship between the industrial production index and pig iron production. F_t representing the pig iron production in tons and I_t the industrial production index (1938 = 100), F_t and I_t can be related by the equation:

$$F_t = 56,500\, I_t$$

the standard deviation of the error being of the order of 500,000 tons of pig iron.

The development of coke use per ton of pig iron in processing depends — barring a technical revolution — upon such factors as the nature of the ores used, the blast furnace feed preparation (screening of the coke, crushing and sifting of the ore, agglomeration of coal fines), the availability of scrap iron, and the characteristics of new blast furnaces. It is difficult to assess the effects of these factors quantitatively. It has been observed over a long period in France that the annual use of coke has been decreasing an average of 2 kg. per ton of pig iron per year (approximately 0.2%). It is expected that this decrease may possibly reach 0.5% to 1% per year within the next few years.

Inasmuch as coke consumption in homes and by industry is relatively easy to predict, the knowledge of blast furnace demand for coke permits a statistical determination of coke production as a whole and a calculation of the available quantities of coke gas.

4. Industrial energy demand (excluding electricity).

In order to complete the general determination of French energy demand, it is necessary to study the power consumption of industry, on the one hand, and of households on the other. This dual analysis has been made by E. Ventura [38][39].

Ventura defines the industrial sector by deducting the producers of energy, siderurgy, transportation, and households from the aggregate of consumers.

The consumption of electricity obeys its own laws, so it was logically excluded from the scope of the study. However, it was not possible to exclude the consumption of primary fuels by central power stations owned by large companies. Furthermore, it was necessary to make a great number of corrections in the consumption statistics for the various fuels in order to make them approximately comparable. These modifications, as well as the problems of selecting conversion coefficients and accounting for inventory variations, will be ignored.

This analysis made it possible to prepare Table II, which presents energy consumption (excluding electricity) in thousands of tons of coal and the industrial production index (1954 = 100).

Table II

Industrial energy consumption (excluding electricity)
and industrial production index (1954 = 100)

	1949	1950	1951	1952	1953	1954	1955
Solid fuels	18,006	18,060	19,280	17,320	16,760	17,486	17,762
Fuel oils	3,069	3,990	4,782	5,044	5,388	6,120	6,716
Liquified petroleum gases	6	8	12	18	26	36	50
Other petroleum products	217	238	228	298	309	323	389
Gas	865	926	1,055	1,121	1,058	1,155	1,302
Total energy	22,163	23,222	25,357	23,801	23,541	25,120	26,219
Industrial production index	79.5	80.1	90.1	93.4	91.4	100	109.3

In order to determine whether there is a correlation between energy consumption and the industrial production index, it was assumed that a relationship in the following form existed between these quantities:

$$C = C_0 \left(\frac{I}{I_0}\right)^a e^{-r(t-t_0)}$$

where C, I, t, a, and r represent, respectively, energy consumption, industrial production index, time, elasticity of energy consumption with respect to industrial production, and the relatively slower increase in annual energy consumption as compared with the annual changes in the industrial production index.

In posing: log C = x_1 log I = x_2, the problem consisted of studying the correlation:

$$x_1 = k + ax_2 - rx_3$$

Inasmuch as the data for the years 1949 to 1951 were somewhat questionable, the study was conducted for the two periods 1949–1955 and 1952–1955. Table III summarizes the results.

Table III

	Correlation				Multiple correlation		
	Between x_1 and x_2		Between x_1 and x_3		Corre-lation coeffi-cient	a	r
	Correl. coeff.	a' (*)	Correl. coeff.	r'			
1949–1955 period	0.92	0.367	0.83	0.017	0.94	0.710	+ 0.0179
1952–1955 period	0.99	0.617	0.92	0.036	0.99	0.551	−0.0046

The correlation coefficients between x_1 and x_2 and between x_1 and x_3 indicate that this is most probably a case of multicollinearity. A statistical analysis will confirm this hypothesis. Indeed, a calculation gives the following values for the elements **

$$s\sqrt{\frac{m_{22}}{D}} \quad \text{and} \quad s\sqrt{\frac{m_{33}}{D}}$$

$s\sqrt{\frac{m_{22}}{D}} = $ 0.29 and 0.14 for the periods 1949–1955 and 1952–1955

$s\sqrt{\frac{m_{33}}{D}} = $ 0.015 and 0.009 for the periods 1949–1955 and 1952–1955.

---

*a' and r' are the slopes of the lines of regression of x_1 on x_2 and x_1 on x_3.
**Cf. Chapter 6, p. 138.

The variables

$$\frac{\overline{a}}{s\sqrt{\dfrac{m_{22}}{D}}} \quad \text{and} \quad \frac{\overline{r}}{s\sqrt{\dfrac{m_{33}}{D}}}$$

follow Student's distribution with four degrees of freedom for the 1949-1955 period and one degree of freedom for the 1952-1955 period.

Student's table, which is valid only for nonautocorrelated series, indicates that the probability of a difference greater than

$$s\sqrt{\dfrac{m_{ii}}{D}}$$

is 0.35 for four degrees of freedom and 0.50 for one degree of freedom.

Hence, it follows that the following areas of acceptance can be assumed, with probabilities complementary to the preceding (0.65 and 0.50):

For a: 7-year period: 0.71 ± 0.29 or 0.42 to 1.00
        4-year period: 0.55 ± 0.14 or 0.41 to 0.69.
For r: 7-year period: 0.018 ± 0.015 or 0.003 to 0.033
        4-year period: -0.005 ± 0.009 or -0.014 to + 0.004.

These intervals are very large and the value $r = 0$ for the 4-year period is found to be within the area of acceptance. A simple correlation is therefore as fully justified as a multiple correlation.

By letting $r = 0$ and limiting oneself to the correlation between x_1 and x_2, the same statistical analysis based on Student's distribution indicates that a has about 6 chances out of 10 of being found between:

0.295 and 0.439 for the 1949-1955 period.
0.568 and 0.666 for the 1952-1955 period.

It was decided to retain the correlations established over the 1952-1955 period since these statistics were less questionable.

Once the general projection was established, an analysis remained to be made of the distribution of consumption among the various forms of energy. With regard to gas one was reduced to hypotheses, because the coming years will be characterized by the availability of Lacq gas and because the quantity of gas consumed by industry will depend to a certain extent upon the capacity of thermal power stations equipped for gas operation. The ratio of fuel oil to coal consumption was also rather difficult to evaluate since it is closely connected to the relative level of the prices of these two fuels. It was nevertheless assumed that the price relationship would vary only slightly and, consequently, that the ratio h of fuel oil consumption to fuel oil plus coal consumption (all in equivalent coal units) would tend toward limit L at a rate proportional to L-h. The adjustment of the series to a law of the form:

$$\frac{dh}{dt} = k(L - h) \quad \text{ou} \quad h = Ae^{-kt} + L$$

appeared to be satisfactory and permitted an evaluation of h for the years 1961 and 1965. One should be cautioned, however, against attaching too much significance to this result since the hypothesis of the invariance of the price ratio is somewhat gratuitous.

5. Household energy demand (excluding electricity).

A study of the energy demand of households presented difficulties of a greater magnitude than that of industrial energy demand. First, this sector had to be defined very specifically. It was agreed to include:

"a) private homes (for heating, including that of water, and cooking purposes);

"b) public establishments: national, regional, communal establishments; schools, hospitals, museums, prisons, army, police, etc. (for heating and cooking purposes);

"c) stores and commercial and professional offices (heating)" [31].

It was then decided to study the consumption of the following sources of energy: fuel oils, city gas, liquefied petroleum gas (butane, propane), electricity for thermal uses, firewood, and solid fuels (coal, coke, briquettes). It will be observed that in this phase of the study, electricity for thermal uses was introduced. On the other hand, electricity for lighting and for the operation of household appliances was excluded. This distinction is consistent because only thermal electricity is in direct competition with other sources of energy.

Consumption figures were corrected in order to account for variations resulting from winter severity and inventory fluctuations. Only the figures for the 1949-1955 period were usable; distribution data were too unreliable to permit the use of statistics for previous years. The years under study are not calendar years but "heating" years, beginning with the 1st of April and ending on the 31st of March of the following year (following the tradition of the coal trade in France).

Table IV reproduces the numerical data obtained, after correction, in millions of metric tons of equivalent coal, as well as the gross national product at market prices (in billions of 1952 francs).

Table IV

Energy consumption of the household sector

	1949	1950	1951	1952	1953	1954	1955
Coal	14.35	15.60	16.24	16.71	16.96	17.37	17.42
Fuel oils	0.64	0.80	1.04	1.12	1.57	2.00	2.36
Liquefied pe- troleum gases	0.21	0.30	0.42	0.52	0.68	0.82	0.95
City gas	1.63	1.64	1.66	1.71	1.76	1.82	1.90
Firewood	5.13	4.63	4.19	4.16	3.94	3.68	3.65
Electricity (thermal)	0.19	0.20	0.24	0.27	0.29	0.32	0.34
Total (10^6 metric tons equiv. coal)	22.15	23.17	23.79	24.49	25.20	26.01	26.62
Gross domestic product at market prices	12.33	13.22	13.71	14.14	14.50	15.25	16.06

In order to predict the future development of energy consumption in the household sector, two methods seemed most promising:

The first consisted of extrapolating the trend observed over the 1949-1955 period. Energy consumption C, as a matter of fact, is well represented for this period by the equation:

$$\text{Log } C = 3.1965 + 0.0300\, t \ (t = 0 \text{ in } 1952)$$

where Log C indicates the Napierian logarithm of C. This exponential trend corresponds to a growth of approximately 3% per year.

The second method emanated from an analysis of the correlation between the gross domestic product R and energy consumption. It resulted in a 0.78 value for the elasticity of C with respect to R. This method was advantageous because resultant predictions were compatible with the total data of the plan.

The extrapolation of the two correlations above was certainly reasonable for a period of a few years. However, it would have been dangerous to extend them as far forward as 1975 because this would have required a systematic neglect of ceiling and saturation phenomena.

Following is a mathematical model which, on the contrary, emphasizes this aspect of the problem. We reproduce it here in order to demonstrate the variety of econometric models [13].

The premise can be accepted that, when the income of an individual (or of a family) increases, energy consumption for thermal uses rises rather rapidly toward a ceiling. This phenomenon is certainly more likely in the case of the production of heat than in the case of energy for mechanical use (household appliances), for which new applications will continue to be available almost without end.

By assuming graphically that the consumption a of an individual depends solely upon his income r, it can be imagined that a varies according to log r following a Galton S curve.

$$a = KF(r)$$

where K is the individual maximum consumption and F(r) the function:

$$F(r) = \int_0^r \frac{I}{\sqrt{2\pi \, su}} \, e^{-\frac{\text{Log}^2 u/r_0}{s^2}} \, du$$

(r_0 and s are parameters which define the curve).

The plausibility of this hypothesis is enhanced by systematic studies of household budgets.

On the other hand, individual incomes are distributed in accordance with a logarithmic-normal law of probability density:

$$g(r) = \frac{I}{\sqrt{2\pi \, vr}} \, e^{-\frac{\text{Log}^2 r/r_m}{v^2}}$$

(v is the standard deviation of the related normal distribution).

If P represents the population figure, the total home consumption is therefore:

$$A = KP \int_0^{+\infty} F(r) \, g(r) \, dr$$

Calculation produces:

$$A = KP \; H \left[\frac{\text{Log} \, r_m/r_0}{\sqrt{v^2 + s^2}} \right]$$

H being a total distribution function of the reduced normal law.

From the standpoint of expansion, it can be presumed that population increases exponentially at an annual rate m and that per capita income increases exponentially at a rate n. Furthermore, it is not unreasonable to believe that the relative dispersion of individual incomes will not be modified.

Consequently, if the following is posed:

$$P = P_1 \, e^{mt} \quad \text{(t represents time)}$$
$$r_m = r_1 \, e^{nt}$$
$$v = cste,$$

it becomes:

$$A(t) = KP_1 \, e^{mt} \, H\left(\frac{nt + \log r_1/r_0}{\sqrt{v^2 + s^2}}\right)$$

or:

$$A(t) = KP_1 \, e^{mt} \quad H(h(t - t_0))$$

with:

$$h = \frac{n}{\sqrt{v^2 + s^2}} \qquad t_0 = \frac{\log r_1/r_0}{n\sqrt{v^2 + s^2}}.$$

It will be observed that the curve $A(t)$ which is a function of time admits as an asymptote an exponential ratio m. Because of the term $H(h(t-t_0))$ the growth may appear to be much more rapid during a certain period, but a ceiling phenomenon necessarily occurs.

From the statistical data available, it is difficult to structure the model so that it conforms with the facts. Nevertheless, for purposes of illustration we present a numerical application. A brief calculation of income distribution indicates that v is close to 0.7 and r to 400,000 francs. Furthermore, the average consumption is, at present, approximately two tons per household. Let us tentatively assume K to be three tons per household, and let us also assume that v is substantially equal to s. $\sqrt{v^2 + s^2}$ is close to unity. One can then deduce from $A(O)/KP_1$, which is equal to 2/3, the value of $\log r_1/r_0$. One finds: $\log r_1/r_0 = 0.40$.

In assuming, for the sake of simplicity, that the population is constant (m = 0), $A(t)$ is equal to:

$$KP_1 H \, (nt - 0.40)$$

The calculations no longer present any difficulty. They are reproduced in Table V, where are found:

a) in the first column, the values of t (t = 0 in 1955);

b) in the second, the values of the household incomes R(t) (in billions of 1952 francs);

c) in the third, the values of nt calculated by the formula: $R(t) = R(o)e^{nt}$;

d) in the fourth, those of nt_0;

e) in the fifth, the difference $d = n(t-t_0)$;

f) in the sixth, the corresponding values of H;

g) in the seventh, consumption calculated theoretically (assuming that theoretical and actual consumption are equal in 1955);

h) in the eighth, actual consumption.

Table V

1	2	3	4	5	6	7	8
— 6	10.1	— 0.29	— 0.40	0.11	0.543	22	22.1
— 5	10.7	— 0.23	— 0.40	0.17	0.565	22.9	23.2
— 4	11	— 0.20	— 0.40	0.20	0.580	23.6	23.8
— 3	11.1	— 0.18	— 0.40	0.22	0.587	23.8	24.5
— 2	11.4	— 0.16	0.40	0.24	0.595	24.2	25.2
— 1	12.4	— 0.08	0.40	0.32	0.625	25.4	26.0
0	13.5	0	0.40	0.40	0.655	26.6	26.6

The use of this model covering extended periods of time naturally yields predictions of substantially lower consumption than those obtained by extrapolating correlations. It is not our intention here to dwell upon the validity of the hypotheses or upon results, but to present realistic examples of econometric models.

Once total demand had been predicted it remained, as in the case of industry, to be apportioned in accordance with the sources of energy. At this stage of the analysis, it was fairly easy to estimate the share of electricity, of liquefied petroleum gases, of city gas, and of firewood, and to determine as a residual the total share of fuel oil plus coal. The determination of the respective shares of the two latter fuels gave rise to interesting studies, an outline of which can be found in the original reports [12].

6. The energy demand of the S.N.C.F. (French National Railways) and of road transport.

These sectors of energy utilization do not require detailed studies. Demand for motor fuel can be readily estimated. The S.N.C.F., on the other hand, makes its own estimates of electricity, coal, fuel oil, and gas oil consumption within the framework of the plan. All of these figures are obviously a function of hypotheses regarding the development of railroad competition.

7. Examination of total demand.

Upon completing the determination of each demand category, the economic analyst must compare his results by substituting them within the model of total demand for energy. A comparison between the sum of energy requirements of all utilization sectors and the estimated total consumption of primary energy is the first to be made. Next, the demands of the various sources of primary and secondary energy must be determined; this may necessitate additional hypotheses (particularly with respect to the consumption of thermal power stations).

When the foregoing has been accomplished, the task of the economist is far from completed. Within those sectors where several sources of energy are in direct competition, the sources and quantities of energy supplied are derived only as a function of implicit hypotheses regarding prices. An examination must now be made of the effects which price variations would have upon energy demand in these sectors and an analysis made of probable prices and estimated costs.

This invokes the necessity for considering a whole new spectrum of problems as follows:

a) the competition between fuel oils and coal in the industrial and household sectors;

b) the supply of coal, fuel oils, and natural gas to thermal power stations;

c) the distribution of coal between domestic production and imports;

d) the distribution of primary energy supply between coal and petroleum products.

The above demonstrates very clearly that the development of projections leads to studies both on the structure of markets (in the sense given this term in Chapter 3) and on cost structure.*

The example of projections in a sector of national activity as complex as that of energy has the merit of highlighting the infinite variety of possible econometric models as well as the qualifications required of the research analyst: imagination, care, and commonsense.

II

THE INFLUENCE OF PRICES AND INCOME

This research can be conducted on the basis of time series analysis or on the basis of cross-section analysis.

1. Time series analysis of market statistics.

This is the area in which econometric analysis was first attempted; in the 17th century the English economist Gregory King

---

*Cf. Chapter 10.

attempted to demonstrate a relationship between the price of wheat and the size of the crop. H. Schulz in the United States [32], R. Stone in England [34], H. Wold in Sweden [43], and R. Roy in France [31] are some of the analysts who are most noted in this branch of econometrics.

All of these economists have attempted to determine the demand curves for certain products via the implicit hypothesis that the demand curve is either invariable or shifts regularly with respect to time, whereas the supply curves vary from one year to another. Under these conditions, the points observed for the intersection of a fixed curve and a variable curve permit a determination of the fixed curve.

The demand curve is obtained in practice by applying the least squares method to a correlation between quantities sold and market prices. It was shown in Chapter 6 that this procedure is correct only insofar as the demand curve is identified (i.e., if the supply curve depends upon variables which do not occur in the demand curve) and the error occurring in the demand equation is zero.*

R. Stone has attempted to justify this approach by stressing the practical advantages of avoiding the introduction of several equations to determine the demand curve. His arguments are summarized below [34].

1. Economic theory provides a detailed analysis of demand. However, a system of equations expressing the demand function in context has not yet been formalized. There are various possibilities available, each corresponding to different values of regression coefficients.

2. Multiple time series introduce, at best, complications and, at worst, conflicts which are not always resolved in developing estimates.

3. The estimation of parameters of the demand curve would be a function of the estimates of parameters of the other relationships, which would present considerable variations.

4. Studies which call upon a system of equations have led to results which are similar in large measure to those based on a single equation.

Of these various arguments only the last one is convincing, although the relatively few studies made on the basis of a system of equations prevent this argument from being decisive.

Despite theoretical weaknesses, traditional studies of demand are extremely useful; three examples are given below.

a) The first has been borrowed from H. Schulz and relates to sugar demand in the United States of America.

---

*Cf. Chapter 6, pages 132 and 139.

b) The second is a summary of an analysis of the butter-margarine complex in Sweden by H. Wold.

c) The third presents some of the results obtained in Great Britain by R. Stone.

a) The demand for sugar in the United States [32]. H. Schulz analyzed sugar demand in the United States during the period 1875-1929. He made use of the following two time series:

1) "Total consumption" defined as the sum of American production (beet and cane sugar) and imports (cane sugar, sugar produced from foreign molasses, etc.). This time series differs slightly from actual consumption; however, the statistics did not permit an evaluation of variations in inventories.

2) "Annual prices" which are annual averages of daily quotations (f.o.b. and c.o.d.) in New York for refined sugar in 100-pound bags. (During this period, New York was the dominant market and prices in the United States were fixed according to New York prices).

Three periods were isolated in order to pinpoint the changes which occurred in the elasticity of demand with respect to price: 1875-95, 1896-1914, 1915-29 (the years from 1917 to 1921 were excluded).

For each period, H. Schulz introduced the total consumption of sugar per capita y, the actual price of sugar x, and time t. He tried, successively, the following two models:

$$y = a + bx + ct$$
$$\log y = a' + b'x + c't$$

As a result of an analysis of trends, he amended these two models for the third period by respectively substituting $c(1-0.5^t)$ for ct, and $c'(1-(2/3)^t)$ for $c't$.

In Table VI will be found the numerical results obtained; y is expressed in pounds, x in cents per pound, and t in years.

It will be noted that the variances in elasticity are permissible despite a correlation between time and actual price (the latter decreasing on the average with respect to time).

In his analysis in 1938, H. Schulz arrived at the following conclusions [32]:

"Probably the most important findings of this chapter are: (1) that the demand for sugar is quite inelastic, and (2) that by 1929 the demand curve reached its ceiling, so that the sugar industry can no longer count on a rising per-capita consumption even when the real price of sugar remains fixed — a condition to which it got accustomed during the last century. If these findings are valid, they have a significant bearing on the problems which are confronting the sugar industry today."

"Writers on the subject have been unanimous in attributing the recent ills of the sugar industry to changes in supply conditions.

Table VI

Sugar demand in the United States

Period	a	b	c	Elasticity of demand	Variance in elasticity	Correlation coefficient
1875-95	70.6200	− 2.2588	+ 0.8371	0.3622	0.1553	0.9500
1896-1914	92.8952	− 3,3408	+ 0.9197	0.2578	0.0930	0.9735
1915-29	134.5059	− 7.8031	+ 0.0900*	0.3388	0.1130	0.9321
	a'	b'	c'			
1875-95	2,0559	− 0.3828	+ 0.0156	0.3828	0.1224	0.9493
1896-1914	2.0701	− 0.2717	+ 0.0142	0.2717	0.0844	0.9703
1915-29	2.1980	− 0.3118	+ 0.0090**	0.3118	0.0775	0.9478

*Coefficient of $(1-0.5\underline{t})$.
**Coefficient of $(1-(2/3)\underline{t})$.

Thus, the former chief of the sugar section of the Agricultural Adjustment Administration attributes the present crisis in sugar to three factors — the disruption of the industry by the World War, the rise in agrarian nationalism, and the technical revolution in sugar production — and refers to the prewar conditions as normal and stable. That these are fundamental factors, no one will deny. But he and other students of the problem will make a serious error if they continue to take for granted the prewar demand for sugar. The sugar industry has always been characterized by a secular fall in real prices. What differentiates the prewar situation from the present is that throughout the period from 1875 to 1914, while the price of sugar was falling, per capita demand was rising higher and higher. This situation no longer obtains. With the per capita demand shifting downward with respect to constant real price, any secular increase in consumption must come from an increase in population."

We do not know whether recent economic history has fully confirmed Schulz's analysis, but few texts have expressed as clearly the benefit which an industry might be able to derive from a better knowledge of its demand.

b) The demand for butter and margarine in Sweden [43]. H. Wold and L. Juréen analyzed the demand for various consumer goods in

Sweden from 1921 to 1939. With regard to the butter-margarine complex, H. Wold assumes that the demand d_t is dependent upon the actual average price p_t and on the actual income r_t for the year t, with constant elasticities with respect to price and income:

$$d_t = c p_t^{-e} r_t^E$$

He determines, by the method of least squares, the parameters of the linear relation which links the logarithms of the preceding quantities:

$$\log d_t = \log c - e \log p_t + E \log r_t$$

which can be written:

$$x_1 = a_0 - e x_2 + E x_3 + u_t$$

e and E are solutions to the system:

$$- A_{22} e + A_{23} E = A_{12}$$
$$- A_{32} e + A_{33} E = A_{13}$$

where the A_{ij}'s have the same significance as in the preceding chapter. The solution of this system gives:

$$e = 0.56 \qquad E = 0.70$$

The standard deviation of u_t is approximately 18% of the mean value of x_1. However, with regard to the analyzed figures, there is a significant correlation between prices and income (the correlation coefficient between x_2 and x_3 is -0.61).

Consequently, two additional hypotheses are considered:

1. Having demonstrated in an analysis of household budgets that the elasticity of agricultural products with respect to income is of the order of 0.4, Wold calculates the e value for E values located, a priori, within the range 0.40-0.55. When $E = E_0$, e is given by the relation:

$$- A_{22} e + A_{23} E_0 = A_{12}$$

It is thus observed that for $E_0 = 0.55$, $e = 0.67$ and the standard deviation of u_t rises to 22% of the mean value of x_1.

2. Theoretical considerations (based upon properties of indifference curves not shown here) having indicated that there was reason to expect that $e > E$, Wold then proceeds to an analysis in which he assumes the existence of a constant relationship between E and e.

$$E = ke$$

The method of least squares is applied to the relation:

$$x_1 = a_0 - ez + u_t \quad \text{with} \quad z = x_2 - kx_3$$

This hypothesis led approximately to the same results as the previous one and the values:

$$E = 0.6 \quad e = 0.7$$

were finally adopted.

A study of the u_t correlogram indicated that the u_t time series was not purely random and that, consequently, the estimates obtained were not efficient.

c) The demand for food products in Great Britain [34]. Identifying by q_i the per-capita demand for product i, by p_j the price of product j, and by r the actual per capita income, R. Stone seeks to explain q_i by an equation of the form:

$$\log q_i = a_i + b_i \log r + \sum_{j \neq k} c_{ij} \log p_j / p_k + d_i t + u_i$$

In this formula, all prices are expressed with respect to that of commodity k. Naturally, for a given commodity i, only those prices of commodities j whose demand is linked to that of i are used. In order to avoid the likelihood of autocorrelation which might occur in time series u, Stone applies the method of least squares to the first difference of the following relationship:

$$\Delta \log q_i = b_i \Delta \log r + \sum_{j \neq k} c_{ij} \Delta \log p_j / p_k + d_i + \Delta u_i$$

Furthermore, elasticities b_i with respect to income are estimated by studies of household budgets. Market statistics serve merely as a basis for estimating elasticities with respect to price. This makes it possible to reduce the number of parameters to be estimated on the basis of time series of prices and quantities. Some of Stone's results will be found in Table VII.

Not so much the results as the methods used in previous studies are of interest. The results are influenced by hypotheses which are open to criticism. For example, there is no justification for considering only total consumption and the average price without attempting to analyze various components of consumption. For instance, sugar is consumed both in households and in industry for preserving fruit, the preparation of preserves, chocolate, candy, etc. There does not appear to be a valid reason why these two sectors of consumption should develop in a parallel manner, and by analyzing them separately much better results might be obtained. These studies have

Table VII

Demand for food products in Great Britain

Product	Elasticity with respect to income	Elasticity with respect to price	Elasticity in relation to prices of other commodities	
Beef and veal (domestic production)	0.34	0.41	Imported mutton and lamb.	− 0.50
Pork.	0.58	0.88	Mutton and lamb . .	− 0.85
Fresh fish. .	0.92	0.57	Fresh milk	− 0.21
Butter	0.37	0.41	Margarine	− 0.56
			Tea	− 0.63
Margarine. .	0.16	0.01	Butter.	− 1.01
Potatoes (dom.			Chocolate and con- fectionery	− 1.02
prod.) . . .	0.21	0.56	Cakes and biscuits .	+ 0.46
Apples. . . .	1.33	1.67		
Coffee and coffee			Other fresh fruit . .	− 2.77
extracts . .	1.42	0.55	Tea	− 0.54

also failed to give sufficient consideration to the effect of varying qualities, prices, and geographical locations. But their methods have satisfactory applicability in more restricted areas and when better statistics are available than those in the examples cited.

2. Cross-section analyses.

Quite frequently, the absence of statistics covering a sufficiently extended period precludes the use of time series analysis as a means of determining the demand curve. A cross-section analysis may then be used. This should not be considered, however, merely as a substitute method. It is of equal interest though with different advantages and different difficulties.

The rapid development of fuel oil sales both to industrial sectors and to households has led the coal mining companies to investigate whether the geographical differentiation of delivered prices would not facilitate an evaluation of the influence of the price factor [40].

A calculation was made, for each of the 89 French metropolitan departments, of the average delivered price of a fuel oil unit and of a coal thermal unit as well as of the total consumption of fuel oil therms and of coal therms, for industry and for households respectively during 1952. An attempt was then made to determine whether the percentage of fuel oil therms in the aggregate of fuel oil and coal therm consumption in each department correlated with the price difference between fuel oil and coal. The correlation coefficients were 0.70 for industry and 0.73 for households, which is highly significant in view of the considerable number of tests (89). The study was then resumed by retaining the same abscissa and using the logarithm of the ratio of coal therms to fuel therms as an ordinate. Figure 2 reproduces the scatter obtained for the household sector. These results must be analyzed with considerable care.

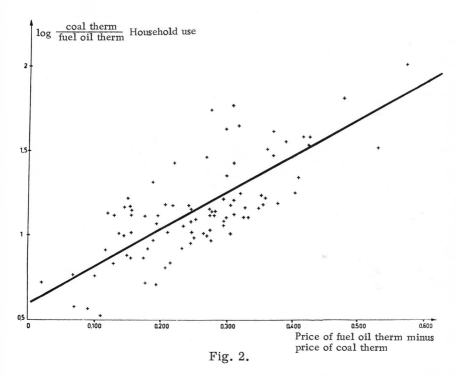

Fig. 2.

1. Designate A as the number of fuel oil therms and B as the number of coal therms consumed within a department where the prices are a and b respectively. The analysis presupposes that A and B are of the form:

$$A = Kf(a - b)$$
$$B = Kg(a - b)$$

where K depends only upon the department. However, the demands assuredly do not depend only upon actual prices. In the field of energy, they depend upon current equipment which, in turn, is a function of past prices. In this connection, time series and geographical analyses of demand are considerably different. Within a geographical framework, differences in price are mainly due to more or less permanent differences in transportation costs. The substitution elasticities obtained will, therefore, measure the effect on demand of differences in price maintained over long periods of time. On the other hand, a time series analysis studies the reactions of demand to a virtually simultaneous variation in prices. In general, elasticities obtained by the cross section analysis method are greater than those obtained by time series analyses.

2. Consumer demand can be a function of prices and of other factors which are stochastically linked to them, such as a consumer's propensity to obtain his supplies from sources close at hand (disregarding the price factor) and the seller's commercial efforts (which are not homogeneously related to consumer distance). From this standpoint, one can understand commercial efforts to develop sales in areas close to the production center (the natural market), as well as the desire to develop additional outlets in more remote areas. Both of these actions are simultaneously possible; the point is that the nature of commercial effort will very likely be influenced by consumer distance. It is now apparent that distance is stochastically, if not causally, related to price. The effects of this phenomenon must be analyzed. For the sake of clarity and simplicity, the reasoning will be developed on the basis of linear relationships.*
For example:

$$y = \log \frac{\text{coal therms consumed}}{\text{fuel oil therms consumed}};$$

x = delivered price per fuel oil therm minus delivered price per coal therm;

z = a proximity factor causally influencing y.

z, for example, can be the difference in distances between the point of consumption and the nearest refinery or coalfield.

a) On the basis of a balanced market: If x and z are the sole factors exercising a causal influence over y, this relationship is expressed by

$$y = ax + bz + d \tag{1}$$

On the other hand, the price factor x depends upon time t and upon z according to a relationship also assumed to be linear:

$$x = pz + qt + r \tag{2}$$

---

*This analysis is the work of P. Gardent, Director of General Research for the Marché Commun aux Charbonnages de France.

If an analysis is made, for a specific department, of the correlation between time series y and x when z is constant, a linear variation will be found represented by a straight line D of slope a and of equation (1). The representative straight lines for each department will all be a slopes; the same will be true for France treated as an aggregate.

If an analysis is now made for a specific year (t constant) of the relationship between y and x by the cross section analysis method, the result is obtained by eliminating z between (1) and (2):

$$y = \left(a + \frac{b}{p}\right) x + d - b\frac{qt + r}{p}.$$

The straight lines will have a slope a $+\frac{b}{p}$ different from a; a and p are necessarily positive. Let us assume, for example:

b > 0 (unfavorable influence of distance upon consumption).
q < 0 (tendency to proportionately reduce fuel price).

A study by the method of cross section analysis will indicate too strong an a + b/p value of elasticity and will create the impression, if followed through for several successive years, that the market is in imbalance with expansion of coal despite a constant price (because of the positive term $-\frac{b\ qt}{p}$).

b) Let us now assume the market to be out of equilibrium. To causal factors x and z is added the factor t, and equation (1) becomes:

$$y = ax + bz + ct + d \qquad (1')$$

An analysis of the y variations as a function of x for a specified department is effected by the elimination of t between (1') and (2):

$$y = \left(a + \frac{c}{q}\right) x + bz + d - c\frac{pz + r}{q}.$$

An analysis of the variations of y as a function of x by the cross section analysis method is obtained by eliminating z between (1) and (2):

$$y = \left(a + \frac{b}{p}\right) x + ct + d - b\frac{qt + r}{p}.$$

The two methods lead to straight lines with differing slopes but neither slope adequately characterizing elasticity a. On the other hand, the shifting of the straight lines as a function of time (c-bq/p shift) does not adequately reflect the market disequilibrium (characterized by c).

It should be clear by this point that great care must be exercised in interpreting studies relating to cross section analysis or to time series.

III

HOUSEHOLD BUDGETS

Econometric studies on the subject of household budgets are numerous, but the most interesting from the methodological standpoint are certainly those of Allen, Stone, Houthakker, and Nicholson in Great Britain [3] [34] [15] [22], and of Wold and Juréen in Sweden [43]. French research is done principally by the I.N.S.E.E. (National Institute of Statistics and Economic Studies) and, in recent years, by the C.R.E.D.O.C.*

Economic analysts in the employ of private companies rarely have the means available for such investigations and they have little choice but to utilize the results of research by other specialists. They must therefore be cognizant of the main problems raised by such studies.

a) In most surveys, selected householders are requested to record their daily expenditures. Some householders refuse at the outset and others drop out before the study is completed. Under these circumstances, even were the initial sampling representative, the final respondents are not necessarily so; the economic analyst must evaluate this possible source of error. Wold estimates total consumption of various goods in Sweden on the basis of household budget surveys and compares them with related statistics as a means of validating the estimates.

b) Once this first verification of the validity of the sampling has been effected, the next step is to develop an econometric model and to test it. Household consumption depends upon many parameters including income, prices, family composition, and social strata.

Income, usually the most significant variant, is difficult to define. For this reason, Houthakker substitutes for income the total expenditures reported in the survey. Because total expenditures are approximately proportionate to income (though at decreasing rates as income reaches high levels), the elasticities with respect to total expenditures will be approximately equal to elasticities with respect to income, but with a tendency to be slightly lower.

---

*Centre de Recherche et de Documentation sur la consommation (Consumption Research and Documentation Center).

As to prices, the hypothesis is usually made that they are the same for all consumers. This hypothesis is questionable because, as has been noted, prices often vary with varying quality. Wold notes that the elasticity of quantity is frequently less than the elasticity of expenditures for the following reasons:

1) Where there are many qualities, an increase in income or a decrease in price encourages consumers to buy better quality products.

2) The price discrimination practised by some firms has resulted in the sale of the same article at a higher price in areas where incomes are higher.

3) In the case of goods whose prices vary seasonally (e.g., fruits, vegetables, etc.), low income households are more likely to pattern their consumption in accordance with price levels.

Houthakker has analyzed the correlation between per capita expenditure e and the average price p_i of commodity i. He found that relationships such as

$$p_i = a_i + b_i \log e$$

represented the phenomenon adequately, and he introduced "quality elasticities" defined as "the relative unit price increase associated with a small relative increase in income."

The effect of family composition is more difficult to isolate and measure. It cannot be assumed that the composition of the average household is independent of income, for income generally increases with age and the same is the case for both the number and the age of the children. Families must therefore be classified according to the dual criterion of income and composition. The usual method of accounting for the composition of the family is to establish a basic unit of consumption — the consumption of an adult male, for example. Each member of the family is then considered as consuming a fraction (less than, equal to, or greater than one) of the selected unit. For example, Wold establishes a structure consisting of various subgroups of household composition, classifies each household in accordance with this structure, and then measures each subgroup with respect to a scale indicating the number of consumption units as a function of age and sex. This enables him to calculate for each subgroup the consumption elasticities with respect to income and to derive a weighted average of these elasticities for all households. Inasmuch as the scale of consumption units applies only to each subgroup, its imperfection entails a relatively small number of errors in the final result. The quality of such a scale can moreover be verified by applying it directly to households as a whole and by comparing the elasticities thus obtained with those previously computed.

Consumption differences between social classes are readily demonstrated. To bring these out, Wold develops independent analyses of working-and middle-class households. Stone and Houthakker utilize the following model:

$$\log d_i = a_i + b_i \log d + c_i x$$

where d and d_i represent, respectively, total expenditures and the expenditures for goods i per unit of consumption, and in which x is a variable of 0 value for working households and 1 for middle-class households. Such a model presupposes that, on the basis of equal income, only average consumptions differ.

c) All of the foregoing considerations affect the econometric model finally decided upon, but the alternatives are reduced to two types of relations between d_i and d: a linear and a logarithmic relation. Logarithmic relationships have the advantage of remaining valid over a large range of incomes, but they verify only approximately the additivity condition which is rigorously satisfied by linear relationships. In effect, if:

$$d_i = a_i + b_i d$$

the condition $\Sigma d_i = d$ is fulfilled, whatever d may be, for $\sum_i a_i = 0$, $\sum_i b_i = 1$.

d) There now remains the problem of the selection of the regression line. It can be assumed that income has been measured without error, and that as a result of errors in the equation (i.e., a random variation in the family choices) expenditures are only stochastically equated to income. But one can also make an inverse hypothesis and study the regression of income in relation to expenditures. Wold has found a very simple test which makes it possible to choose between these two solutions. He calculates the elasticity of total expenditures with respect to income in two different ways:

1) The first method consists of determining the elasticity of total expenditures in the same manner as for each component expenditure.

2) The second method consists of determining the elasticity of total expenditures by calculating a weighted average of the elasticities of the component expenditures.

To each line of regression there correspond, therefore, two measures of elasticity of total expenditures. The line of regression to be retained is that which provides the two closest values. Wold has thus been able to demonstrate that, in the case of the Swedish surveys, the standard method of regression analysis of expenditures with respect to income is justified.

e) For purposes of illustration, a few of the results obtained by Houthakker and Stone will be found in Table VIII.

Table VIII

Expenditure elasticities in relation to total expenditure
in Great Britain in 1938 (Households of civil servants
and industrial workers) *, **

Bread . . .	− 0.01	(−0.06)	Housing	0.62
Meat	0.46	(−0.53)	Clothing and shoes.	1.16
Fish	1.04	(0.98)	Coal	0.48
Fresh milk.	0.66	(0.54)	Gas.	0.41
Butter . . .	0.54	(0.41)	Electricity	1.31
Margarine .	− 0.23	(−0.17)	Heat and light	0.58
Eggs	0.63	(0.60)	Furniture	2.42
Coffee . . .	1.17	(1.58)	Rugs	3.33
Sugar. . . .	0.20	(0.10)	Tobacco and cigarettes . . .	0.85
Vegetables .	1.10	(0.86)	Newspapers and periodicals.	0.70
Fruit. . . .	1.53	(1.34)	Books	1.59
Meals in			Motion pictures	1.31
restau-			Theater and ballet.	2.61
rants . . .	2.36	(2.66)	Physician, dentist.	2.91
Total:			Domestic help	3.36
Food	0.60	(0.59)	Vacation expenditures	3.32
Beverages .	2.52			

* The figures were derived from two investigations, the first
undertaken in 1937-38 by the Ministry of Labour among 10,000
industrial-worker households, the second undertaken in 1938-39
by the "Civil Service Statistical and Research Bureau" covering
civil service households.

**The results are those of Houthakker. With respect to food,
the results indicated by parentheses were obtained by Stone, who
used the same sample but another statistical model.

French firms should follow with great attention similar attempts
made in France, and they should not hesitate to provide financial
assistance in this regard. Any conclusive research in this field is
of considerable importance in the determination of an expansion
policy on an industrial or national scale.

IV

MARKET DYNAMICS

With the exception of the model with which a forecast of the
energy demand of households relative to income was attempted, all

analyses offered to date use, as a starting point, a very brief examination of the phenomenon under study without attempting to consider the entire dynamic complexity of the problem. Yet it is along this road that the future of applied econometrics lies.

An analysis by Roos and Von Szeliski [14] in 1939, so much ahead of its time that it is still considered revolutionary, demonstrates what can be accomplished by the creative imagination of analysts who are not bound by preestablished models. The fact that this analysis was undertaken in close collaboration with automobile industry circles perhaps explains the liberties taken with tradition.

The study was based on an analysis of the volume of sales of private passenger cars in the United States from 1919 to 1938. In his introduction to the study, S.L. Horner begins by mentioning the factors which determine the long-term demand for automobiles:

1) technical improvements and a decrease in the real price,
2) a decrease in the cost of operation,
3) an increase in the average lifespan of the cars,
4) an improvement in highway networks (today, one would have to mention traffic problems),
5) an increase in living standards.

On a short-term basis, the following should be added:

6) economic activity and national income (more accurately, their level and direction of variation),
7) the distribution of national income,
8) the psychological atmosphere,
9) the age of cars owned by new-car buyers,
10) the number of cars sold for scrap,
11) the number and price of secondhand cars owned by used car dealers,
12) credit facilities offered to buyers.

The main considerations among these factors are those which the authors attempted to integrate in their model. With this in mind, they established a distinction between sales to new owners and replacement sales.

a) With regard to sales to new owners, the originality of their study derives from their assumption that the market is not in equilibrium but that each year the total number of cars in circulation approaches a maximum, a condition which derives both from economic factors and from psychological feedback. Their model is an economic adaptation of the differential equation of autocatalysis reactions in chemistry:

$$\frac{dy}{dt} = ry\left(1 - \frac{y}{u}\right)$$

where t represents time, y the quantity obtained in the reaction, u the limit of the reaction, and r the initial rate of increase. This analogy will make it easier to comprehend what follows.

The number S_N of cars sold to new owners is considered to be the product of the maximum potential number of new owners and the probability P that one of these may purchase a car. If M is the maximum potential number of cars in circulation, and C the number of cars actually in circulation during the year, then:

$$S_N = P\,(M - C). \tag{1}$$

P's increase is related to the rate of change in public appreciation of the indispensability of cars. Furthermore, the greater the number of cars in circulation, the greater the possibility that potential buyers will consider it necessary to have one. P is therefore a function of C as well as of the available per capita income I for the purchase of cars and of the price of the product p. As a first approximation, one can write:

$$P = Ap^{-a}\,I^b\,C. \tag{2}$$

M is proportionate to population, or rather to the number of families $f(t)$. It is also related to income I, to price p, and to the average lifespan of the cars v. As a matter of fact, buyer decision is predicated to a large extent on the quotient of the purchase price p divided by the average life v, i.e.,

$$M = Bf\,(t)\,(p/v)^{-c}\,I^{d.} \tag{3}$$

b) Replacement sales are a function of I and of p as well as of the X number of cars sold for scrap (see below), which can be stated as follows:

$$S_R = A'p^{-a'}\,I^{b'}\,X. \tag{4}$$

In order to simplify the foregoing, it can be assumed that the psychology of new and past owners is quite similar with respect to their speed of reaction, i.e.,

$$a = a',\, b = b'.$$

Finally, total sales S are provided by the following expression:

$$S = S_N + S_R = A_1\,p^{-a}\,I^b\,[C\,[f\,(t)\,B\,(p/v)^{-c}\,I^d - C] + A_2\,X]. \tag{5}$$

This formula implicitly presupposes that sales are a function both of income and of its variation, since the number of cars in circulation C is a function of income in the preceding year.

A word should be said concerning the manner in which the principal magnitudes were defined.

With regard to the price of cars, the authors had a choice of several very different indices. They finally agreed upon the average price, including financing charges, of lower priced cars which were readily available on the market.

They defined the income available for the purchase of cars as the difference between the total available income and a minimum subsistence expenditure depending upon the cost of living. This hypothesis did not prove to be very satisfactory.

C could be evaluated on the basis of the number of cars registered (in the United States, registrations are renewed each year).

In order to calculate X, the authors undertook a study of the age distribution of an inventory of cars. This study revealed a steady increase in v from 6 to 9 years during the period. They also traced disposal curves indicating a probability q(x) that a car of age x would be scrapped during the course of the year. The number of cars X thus disposed of was then supplied by the integral:

$$X = \int_0^{+\infty} q(x)\, n(x)\, dx$$

where n(x) is the number of cars of age x.

One of the difficulties encountered in the study was that of measuring M. This number, which is only a limit, is not directly measurable. But it is a well-known fact that autocatalysis equations, of which (5) is a part, lead to "logistic" increases, the $\frac{1}{y}\frac{dy}{dt}$ rate of increase being a linear function of y. The maximum u value is the abscissa of the point of intersection of the representative straight line with the axis of the abscissa. The authors were inspired by this observation to elaborate an econometric method for deriving M. They found two possible expressions for M, slightly different, moreover, from that of the relationship (3):

$$M_1 = f(t)\,(0.378 + 0.000681\,(p/v)^{-0.3}) \tag{6}$$

$$M_2 = f(t)\,(0.500 + 0.0005441\,v^{-0.3}) \tag{7}$$

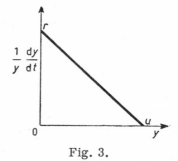

Fig. 3.

Once M had been measured, it was possible to study the correlation between S, C, M, p, I, X. On the basis of the expression M_2, the following was obtained:

$$S = i^{1.20} p^{0.65} (0.0254 \, C \, (M_2 - C) + 0.65 \, X) \tag{8}$$

(i is the ratio of I to its average value of $333).

The adjustment obtained over the period 1919-38 was excellent. However, inasmuch as only 19 observations were used in determining 7 parameters, too great a reliance should not be placed on these conclusions.

The annual development of the elasticity of demand with respect to income can be deduced from the equation (8). It is merely necessary to calculate $\dfrac{I}{S}\dfrac{\partial S}{\partial I}$ taking into account the presence of I in M_2. A table of the values obtained follows:

1919	1.55	1926	2.08	1932	2.44
1920	1.55	1927	2.20	1933	2.19
1921	1.56	1928	2.25	1934	2.19
1922	1.61	1929	2.39	1935	2.20
1923	1.69	1930	2.62	1936	2.25
1924	1.80	1931	2.57	1937	2.40
1925	1.94			1938	2.58

It will be observed that elasticity with respect to income has increased during the period under study. The actual price of cars varied within limits which were too narrow for the determination of elasticity with respect to price to be satisfactory, but the most probable area seemed to be the interval 1.0-1.5.

From this analysis, it would appear that the model should be retained but not the methods employed in the determination of the parameters, for the latter contain aspects which are open to criticism although they are easily explained in terms of the period in which the study was made.

V

BUSINESS POLICY

Any effort made to present a systematic analysis of work undertaken in this area is bound to fail. The sales policies of firms are far too complex, and comprehensive analyses of such are too scarce. A selection has been made of the few examples that are significant contributions and are most likely to encourage thought.

The three studies which are to be summarized relate to:
1) The checking of tickets in a public transportation company.
2) The canvassing policy for sales representatives.
3) The determination of an optimum sales "promotion" policy. The emphasis here will be placed on concepts and method rather than on statistical verification.

1. The checking of tickets in a public transportation company [42].

In public transportation, tickets are checked essentially for the purpose of decreasing the number of passengers who travel without tickets. Let N be the total number of trips taken by travelers. These runs can be separated into a certain number of classes, the cost of a ticket being v_i and the number of trips n_i for class i. The probability p_i that a passenger in class i will travel without a ticket is a certain function of the fraction f_i of tickets which are checked.
If F is the checked fraction of the total number of tickets:

$$NF = \sum_i n_i f_i \qquad 0 \leqslant f_i \leqslant 1 \tag{1}$$

The mathematical expectation of the value of unpaid tickets is obviously:

$$E = \sum n_i p_i v_i (1 - f_i). \tag{2}$$

The maximization of the mathematical expectation of revenue consists of minimizing the sum of E and the cost of checking which is a certain function g(NF), i.e., the expression:

$$\sum n_i p_i v_i (1 - f_i) + g (\sum n_i f_i)$$

where the f_i's are the independent variables and where the p_i's are decreasing functions of the f_i's (Fig. 4).* There is reason to

Fig. 4.

---

*Account will eventually have to be taken of receipts derived from fines.

believe that p_i decreases as f_i grows large, and a function in the following form can be tried as a first approximation:

$$p_i = A + Be^{-C/i}$$

where the A, B, C constants are determined by statistical analysis.

2. The canvassing policy for sales representatives [18].

The celebrated analysis by J. F. Magee demonstrates very clearly the power of scientific method, for the problem with which he is concerned seems at first sight to be too difficult to rationalize.

A coffee company sold its products to a large number of retail groceries throughout the United States. In order to increase the volume of its sales, it arranged to have its customers visited by sales representatives who gave them merchandising materials and extolled the merits of the company products.

The company cost of sales representation, studied over a long period, was such that it proved to be unprofitable to have all the customers visited. In connection with these studies, the percentage of clients visited had varied in the past from 0 to 100%; the percentage of clients visited each month was determined by those who had made the largest purchases during the two preceding months. At the time the studies were undertaken, 40% of the clients were visited by sales representatives.

The directors of the firm and the author undertook to develop a method for determining the percentage of accounts to be visited and the basis for their selection.

During a preliminary stage, an attempt was made to classify the behavior of the various customers. The analysis of a large body of data indicated that actual monthly demand deviated from the monthly average demand randomly. The hypothesis was made that actual monthly demand was distributed according to the Poisson law. Then, c being the average number of cases of coffee ordered monthly by a client, it was assumed that the probability of this client's ordering n cases during a particular month was:

$$p(n, c) = \frac{e^{-c} c^n}{n!}.$$

In order to test this hypothesis, it was merely verified that the average value and the variance in orders were substantially equal for several hundred different accounts.

The next step was to examine all accounts as a class. It was necessary to characterize them only by the frequency $Y(c)$ of accounts with an average demand c. The frequency $f(n)$ of accounts who ordered n cases was then calculated by the relationship:

$$f(n) = \int_0^{+\infty} p(n, c) Y(c) \, dc.$$

Upon completion of this preliminary study, the next stage was to analyze the effect of specific policies on Y(c) and f(n):

a) Existing data made it possible to establish f(n) when all accounts were visited by sales representatives. The various observations were represented by:

$$Y(c) = \frac{1}{s} e^{-c/s} \qquad f(n) = \frac{s^n}{(s+1)^{n+1}}$$

where s is the ratio of the total number of cases ordered to the number of clients.

b) Let us assume that only those accounts, a fraction a of all accounts, who placed the largest number of orders were visited. The distribution of those accounts who represented an average demand c is a certain function $Z(c,a)$ and the fraction of orders for n cases received from these clients a function $g(n,a)$.

By trial and error, it was determined that an excellent adjustment could be derived by taking:

$$Z(c, a) = \frac{1}{as} (1 - e^{-rc/s}) e^{-c/s} \quad \text{where} \quad r = a/1 - a$$

and consequently:

$$g(n, a) = \int_0^{+\infty} p(n, c) Z(c, a) \, dc = \frac{s^n}{(s+1)^{n+1}} - \frac{s^n}{(s+r+1)^{n+1}}.$$

It will be observed that these formulas go back to the preceding equation used when all accounts were visited (r infinite, a = 1).

c) The difference f(n)-g(n,a) provides the distribution of orders of the fraction (1-a) of those who purchased the least when they were visited:

$$f(n) - g(n, a) = \frac{s^n}{(s+r+1)^{n+1}}.$$

By comparing this expression with the actual distribution of orders when these accounts were not visited, it then became possible to estimate the effects of visits by sales representatives. The conclusion reached was that in the absence of visits the number of clients ordering n cases decreased by half, regardless of the size of n.

Therefore, where N represents the total number of accounts and a the fraction of N visited by sales representatives, the average number of orders to be expected is recorded:

$$D(a) = N \left[a \int_0^{+\infty} c Z(c, a) \, dc + \frac{1}{2} (1 - a) \int^s c(Y(c) - Z(c, a)) \, dc \right]$$

and, after calculation:

$$D(a) = \frac{Ns}{2}(1 + 2a - a^2).$$

The completion of the study then becomes very simple: the sales price having been fixed, the receipts are proportional to $D(a)$; on the other hand, the total cost of sales representation is proportional to a, which must be chosen in such manner as to maximize income.

The various improvements available to management through a study of this type can be readily imagined.

3. The determination of an optimum sales promotion policy.

Market reaction to a sales policy always assumes the form of a curve of response with respect to the intensity of the means utilized. For example, in considering an advertising policy a firm is faced with the necessity of making two decisions. First, the firm must select the most efficient type of advertising, i.e., that which will maximize the quantity sold by the firm for a given volume of advertising expenditure. Second, the firm must determine the optimum volume of advertising costs. Now, it is probable that the curve representing the quantity sold with respect to advertising costs — assumed to have been utilized in an optimum manner — has the shape of the curve in Fig. 5. In the absence of advertising, the quantity sold is q_0. Within limits, advertising increases sales considerably. Beyond these limits, sales become practically independent of advertising [26].

If D indicates advertising costs and q the quantity sold, an elasticity $\frac{Ddq}{qdD}$ of the quantity sold with respect to advertising costs can be defined, such elasticity being related to advertising costs already incurred, the products in question, the percentage of the market covered by the firm, and the advertising policy of competitors and their reactions to a modification in the firm's advertising policy.

When an advertising budget is established in order to promote the sales of several products, a knowledge, even approximate, of the curves of response makes it possible to determine the optimum allocation of promotional effort.

This type of analysis can be applied with little or no change to many aspects of sales policy. The operations research group at the Case Institute of Technology analyzed the problem of allocation of sales ef°ort at the Lamps Division of the General Electric Company, using such techniques as have been considered above [1]. The initial approach was to develop a curve (having the appearance of that in Fig. 5) expressing the volume in dollars of sales to consumers (intermediaries, in this instance) per unit of time spent in sales representation.

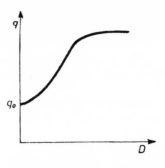

Fig. 5.

In order to derive this curve statistically, the authors grouped the accounts of the General Electric Company into homogeneous classes, i.e., into class intervals with respect to the amount of time spent by sales representatives. They then proceeded to analyze, for each class, the cluster of points having as an ordinate the value of sales and as abscissa the time spent. No significant correlation was observed.

Among the possible explanations, the most likely was that the time spent upon the majority of accounts during the years 1953 and 1954 exceeded the saturation points of the curves of response. But this remained to be proven. In order to accomplish this, one began by studying whether there existed a correlation between the variations of sales in each account from 1952 to 1953 and corresponding variations of sales in these accounts during prior years.

The answer was again negative. The accounts in each class were then separated into four groups characterized as follows:

	1953			1952		1954			1953	
1.	Time spent	>	Time spent			Time spent	>	Time spent		
2.	"	"	>	"	"	"	"	>	"	"
3.	"	"	<	"	"	"	"	<	"	"
4.	"	"	<	"	"	"	"	<	"	"

A statistical analysis indicated that there was no significant difference in the distribution of sales variations from 1953 to 1954 in these four groups. There was therefore every reason to believe that the saturation point had been exceeded. Although the volume of sales of the division was expected to rise during the following years, it was decided not to increase — at least temporarily — the number of sales representatives.

The three foregoing studies are in the forefront of applied economic analysis, and are among the earliest to have entered a field of rich commercial application.

VI

ECOLOGICAL CONDITIONS OF DEMAND

Demand analysis in ecological terms refers to research into the relationships between demand and the natural environment. Here again the field is very wide, since it ranges from a study of the influence of climate to a geographical analysis of economic relationships. In order to provide an idea of its extent, we have selected four entirely different examples, the first two relating to the correlation between the volume of sales and meteorological conditions, the third relating to areas of retail sales, and the fourth concerning a geographical-economic description of the cement industry.

1. Volume of demand and meteorological conditions.

The first example of this type is derived from an American article by A.T. Steele [33]. In an analysis of a store's daily sales, Steele began by correcting for the long-term trends and the seasonal and weekly variations. He then proceeded to test for a statistical association between the corrected sales data and concurrent meteorological conditions.

The latter were represented by the following five parameters: the amount P of precipitation from 6 o'clock in the morning until 6 o'clock in the evening, the thickness of snow N at 6 o'clock in the evening, the temperature T at noon, the wind velocity V between noon and 1 o'clock, and an index U characterizing the quantity of sunlight received during the day.

The analysis demonstrated that it was preferable to replace P by its logarithm and to substitute for T and V a factor C referred to as a cooling factor. This takes the following form:

$$C = V^{1/2} (80 - T)$$

(T is expressed in degrees Fahrenheit). The period analyzed consisted of the seven weeks preceding Easter during each of the six years 1943-1948. Two multiple regressions were determined, one for the years 1945, 1947, 1948 when Easter was early (I) and the other relating to the years 1943, 1944, and 1946 when Easter was late (II). There are 126 observations for each regression. S being the corrected level of sales:

$$S = 104.73 - 0.0228\ C - 0.0219 \log P - 0.2635\ N + 0.0675\ U \qquad \text{(I)}$$
$$S = 109.51 - 0.0361\ C - 0.0429 \log P - 0.2596\ N + 0.0189\ U \qquad \text{(II)}$$

The influence of sunlight U is negligible except at the 5% level. The coefficient of correlation between actual sales and "corrected" sales, once short-term variations and long-term trends have been reintroduced, reaches 0.98. Forty-two percent of the variance in sales is explained by meteorological conditions and 46% by the short-term variations and long-term trends.

Unfortunately, this analysis has very limited application. The second example, however, concerns a more fruitful analysis. This example relates to an analysis of gas consumed in the Paris area [20].

Table IX indicates, for the year 1952, the values of gas consumed (on a 30-day basis) in the Paris area, and the monthly average temperatures observed at the Châtelet.

Table IX

Paris area: Monthly Temperatures and Volume
of Gas Consumption *

Month	Temperatures observed at the Châtelet (° C)	Gas consumption on a 30-day basis (millions of cubic meters)
January	3.5	139.6
February.	3.5	141.0
March	8.6	124.3
April	13.0	106.0
May	16.2	100.3
October	10.7	112.7
November	5.6	135.2
December	3.6	143.7

* The figures for the months of June through September are not indicated since there is no gas heat during this period and, consequently, temperature exercises no influence on gas consumption.

Figure 6 clearly pinpoints the correlation between the two variables, gas consumption being the ordinate and temperature the abscissa, a correlation which can be represented by the linear relationship:

$$Y = 154.3 - 3.6\,X$$

where Y is gas consumption and X the temperature. This relationship indicates that a decrease in the mean temperature of 1°C caused an increase in gas consumption on the order of 3.6 million cubic meters.

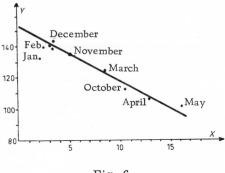

Fig. 6.

Naturally, the linear representation is satisfactory only with respect to the colder temperatures (below 16°C) when heating is required. Furthermore, in using this linear equation account should be taken of the effect of new installations of gas heating equipment during the observed period.

These supplemental studies have been made by the Services de Gaz de France which has similarly analyzed the distribution of cold waves and their effect on daily gas consumption.

Because it is possible statistically to isolate consumption for heating purposes from all other gas consumption and to predict its development in the near future, these analyses provide the means of forecasting the influence of temperature upon gas consumption and of calculating the productive capacity which must be available in order to meet peak demand with a given probability of failure.

2. Retail sales.

It is of interest to the retail trade to know the geographical distribution of its customers. Such knowledge enables it to make better use of its promotion budget as well as to locate its branch outlets better [8][10][27].

Research on this subject has been under way for a considerable period of time in the United States. In 1930, W.J. Reilly indicated that, in the case of furniture, household equipment, wearing apparel, etc., Newton's law of gravitation could apply to the distribution of retail trade between two towns. He called this phenomenon the law of retail gravitation. For instance, there are two towns A and B and an intermediate town of lesser importance, whose inhabitants make their purchases either in A or in B. P_A and P_B being the populations of the two towns and D_A and D_B their distances from the intermediate town, the volumes V_A and V_B of purchases by the customers of the intermediate town from the retail outlets in A and B are:

$$\frac{V_A}{V_B} = \frac{P_A}{P_B}\left(\frac{D_B}{D_A}\right)^2. \tag{1}$$

The population of the towns is analagous to the physical concept of mass and the ratio of sales is proportionate to the ratio of the population and inversely proportionate to the ratios of the distances.

By identifying the point at which $V_A = V_B$ as the separation point, and by designating d_B as the distance of the point of separation from town B and D as the distance from A to B, one can deduce the following from relationship (1):

$$d_B = \frac{D}{1 + \sqrt{P_A/P_B}}. \tag{2}$$

In numerous instances in the United States, knowledge of this relationship has made it possible to identify the area and practical limits of a sales district without prior investigation, thereby achieving substantial savings in time and money.

Relationship (1) has been tested a number of times. In 1949, research devoted to this subject covered certain counties of southwest Iowa. In the case of the points of separation, relationship (1) assumes the form of:

$$\log \frac{D_A}{D_B} = u \quad \log \frac{P_A}{P_B} \tag{3}$$

with u = 1/2.

Many statistics and investigations being available for the direct determination of the points of separation, an effort was made to determine the slope of the line of regression of $\log D_A/D_B$ as a function of $\log P_A/P_B$. Here are a few of the results [28].

	u	square of the coeff. of correl.
Groceries	0.46	0.71
Motion picture theaters	0.38	0.48
Agricultural equipment	0.51	0.63
Physicians	0.27	0.24
Women's wear	0.51	0.90
Men's footwear	0.50	0.75

Aside from the truly special case of physicians, u never varies much from 0.5 and the coefficient of correlation is high.

Relationship (1) does not indicate how the purchases made by the inhabitants of town B are distributed between the retail trade in B and in the larger neighboring town A, but it can be adjusted to provide an answer as follows:

$$\frac{V_A}{V_B} = \frac{P_A}{P_B}\left(\frac{x}{D}\right)^2$$

x is a moving factor or, if preferred, the "distance equivalent" to the preference sometimes indicated by customers who make their purchases in a larger city. (In the United States, x varies between 5 and 10 km. except in the environs of very large populations such as Chicago, where it drops to 3 or 4 km. because of parking and traffic difficulties, and as a consequence of the decentralization of retail trade).

3. Description of the cement industry.

For large producers of intermediate goods, analysis of the consuming industries constitutes one of the main chapters of market research. We will consider here the cement industry, which consumes large quantities of energy-producing coal and fuel oil. Following some general information relating to the industry, an outline of its economic characteristics is presented [16].*

a) General Information. Technical structure: Cement is a binder obtained by baking a mineral paste in a special oven. At the present time, 99% of the production of cement is provided by rotating ovens which permit large and continuous production runs. The process uses low grade coal at the rate of 220 to 360 kilograms per ton of pure product, depending upon whether it is produced by the dry process (paste containing less than 10% water) or the moist process (paste containing 30-40% water). The use of one or the other of these processes is recommended according to the characteristics of the mineral matter to be processed. In fact, the average consumption by French cement manufacturing plants runs to 280 kilograms of coal per ton of pure product. Cement delivered for consumption contains quantities of clinker, the product of the cement kiln, mixed with quantities of blast furnace slag. According to the proportions of slag and clinker, the following qualities are distinguished:

	Clinker, %	Slag, %
Portland	> 90%	< 10%
Iron cement	70–80%	30–20%
Mixed metallurgical cement	50%	50%
Blast furnace cement	30%	70%
Slag cement with clinker	≤ 20%	≥80%

*The objective of the following pages is to provide useful rather than precise information.

Production and production capacities: Production in 1953 amounted to 9.05 million tons, of which 6.15 million tons were Portland cement.

If the French production capacity is expressed in terms of the average quality of material (80% clinker cement), it will be found that capacity has increased since 1938 as follows:

1938		5	million tons
1939	(beginning)	8	million tons
1953		11	million tons
1954		12	million tons
1955		12.5	million tons

The actual capacity is lower than this nominal capacity by approximately 15%.

Productive capacity is largely concentrated in about 75 plants employing approximately 15,000 persons. The distribution of plants by capacity is approximately as follows:

from 350,000 to 550,000 tons per year : 5
from 200,000 to 350,000 tons per year : 12-15
from 100,000 to 200,000 tons per year : 25-30
from 50,000 to 100,000 tons per year : 12-15
        less than 50,000 tons per year : about 15.

The geographical distribution of the cement manufacturing plants is as follows:

Regions	Capacity, %
North	18 %
Paris area.	18 %
West.	5 %
East	18 %
Center.	5 %
Southeast (Lyon)	6 %
Mediterranean coastal area and Rhône valley	18 %
Southwest.	12 %

This distribution is fairly similar to the geographic distribution of the internal consumption of cement. Since 1938, this industry has shifted southward; 41% of the industry is now located south of the Loire as compared with a little more than a third in 1938. This pattern can be related to requirements of the export trade as well as to the location of the large plants of Electricité de France and of the Compagnie Nationale du Rhône.

A regional analysis of 1953 production indicates that utilization at that time was high in Paris, in the east, and in the southwest; somewhat lower in the west and in the north; and much lower in the southeast.

Product distribution consisted of 70% for construction, 15% for public works, and 10% to 12% for export. However, from 1949 to 1953 the cement production index increased much more rapidly (40%) than the index of building construction (8%). This phenomenon is explained by the ever-increasing uses of cement.

b) Economic Data. Cost price structure of cement: This structure emphasizes the importance of energy expenditures in the production of cement.

Labor   20%
Energy   50% of which: Electrical energy 10%
                            Thermal energy   40% (coal, fuel
                                oil, or gas)
Other materials 10%
Amortization   12% of which: 1/3 for capital equipment and
                            2/3 for materials
Financing costs 4%
General manage-
    ment costs   4%

The electrical energy is used mainly for the production of motive power.

Fuel oil and coal price equivalence: Three sources of thermal energy can be used, coal, fuel oil, and gas. We will limit ourselves to a discussion of the competitive conditions of the first two.

Fuel oil requires storage tanks and reheating equipment. Its sulphur content may have disadvantages but, on the whole, its use is nearly as convenient as that of gas.

On the other hand, the use of coal requires a vast storage area, large stocks, grading facilities in order to standardize the fuel feed, crushing equipment to obtain pulverized coal, and, finally, drying equipment. These require an investment corresponding to the size of the stock of coal, to the cost of equipment (dryers, crushers), and to the supplemental production costs (power for the crushers, heating for the dryers, freight charges for this machinery, ash removal operations, etc.). In some cases, there is a byproduct advantage derived from mixing ashes with the product.

By assigning values to these various elements, it becomes possible to determine the coal equivalence price, that is, the price level of factory delivered coal at which the cement maker is indifferent as to whether he uses fuel oil or coal. Naturally, the figures given below merely constitute orders of magnitude because specific values can vary considerably from one cement-making plant to another. Furthermore, they are already somewhat out of date.

1. Basis of computation for the production of one ton of Portland cement.

Following are the various factors entering into cost:

a) Interest rate: 8%.

b) Additional investments attributable to coal heating (storage areas, etc., minus the tanks and reheating equipment in the case of fuel oil heat): approximately 800 francs per ton/year capacity, i.e., for an average life expectancy of 15 years, a total annuity of the order of 12%.

c) Investment in coal inventories (an average of one month's operation), i.e., at the rate of 1,600 therms per ton of product, at 80 centimes per therm and for a ton-year capacity:

$$(1,600) \times (0.8/12) = \text{approximately 100 francs.}$$

d) Additional labor costs attributable to coal heat: approximately 40 francs per ton produced.

e) Drying: (coal at 6,500 calories per kilogram requiring approximately 200 therms per ton processed and a consumption of 250 kilograms of coal per ton of product, of which approximately 200 must be dried):

$$(200) \times (0.22) \times (0.8) = \text{approximately 35 francs.}$$

f) Motive power for clinker crushing: (it is assumed that 30 kw.-hr. at 6 francs per crushed ton are required):

$$(30) \times (6) \times (0.22) = \text{approximately 40 francs.}$$

g) Miscellaneous upkeep and repair costs for the supplemental equipment required for coal heat, losses attributable to irregularities in operation and manufacture, etc.: approximately 15 francs per ton of product.

2. Computation of equivalence prices under various hypotheses.

The basis used in the calculation of therm variation is the cost per ton with respect to a consumption of 1,600 therms.

New installations. The additional costs attributable to coal heat amount to:

a) Financing costs and amortization:

$$800 \times 0.12 + 100 \times 0.08 = 104 \text{ francs;}$$

b) Direct costs:

$$40 + 35 + 40 + 15 = 130 \text{ francs;}$$

or a total of 15 centimes per therm. If two new installations are compared, the equivalence price of coal is lower by about 15 centimes per therm than the price of fuel oil.

Other cases. Conversion to fuel oil from a new coal heat plant will make it possible to save 130 francs in direct costs, subject to financing costs and amortization of the fuel oil installation, i.e., approximately $400 \times 0.12 = 48$ francs. The net saving drops to 80 francs per ton of product, i.e., about 6 centimes per therm.

On the other hand, conversion to coal heat from a new fuel oil installation will incur corresponding charges, i.e., $1,200 \times 0.12 = 144$ francs per ton. The net saving amounts to: $234 + 144 = 378$ francs per ton of product, i.e., about 18 centimes per therm.

Naturally, the equivalence spread is a function of the age of existing installations and may assume all of the values between 6 and 18 centimes per therm. This phenomenon is described in Fig. 7.

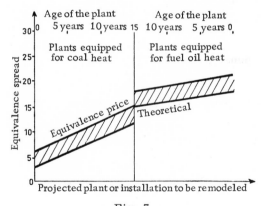

Fig. 7.

Decisions to convert from coal to fuel oil or from fuel oil to coal are not dependent solely upon the concurrence between actual equivalence price spreads, since decisions are reached on the basis of forecasts as to price spreads during the life of the installation. This phenomenon, linked understandably to psychological reluctance to convert the installation constantly, helps explain why only very few conversions are recorded as long as the actual price spread does not exceed the equivalence price spread by more than a few centimes. This produces a zone of indifference with respect to price spread which is indicated by the shaded area in Fig. 7.

Equivalence prices are a valuable guide for the establishment of commercial policy but they must be used with great care, since their computation is based on a considerable number of hypotheses.

The above description of the cement industry is obviously very superficial; it should be complemented by the specific geographic location of the plants, by an enumeration of their energy-producing equipment, by a detailed analysis of the origin and nature of the fuels consumed, by an examination of forecasts of future cement production and planned investments, etc. This should probably be sufficient, however, to demonstrate the potential usefulness of monographs on various branches of industry.

This chapter brings to a close Part I of this volume. The way has now been cleared for an analysis of cost structure.

BIBLIOGRAPHY

1. L. Russell ACKOFF:
   Allocations of sales effort. Case Institute of Technology, April 5-7, 1955.

2. AILLERET:
   "Estimation des besoins énergétiques" (Estimate of energy requirements). Revue Française de l'Energie, No. 76, September 1955.

3. R. G. D. ALLEN and A. L. BOWLEY:
   Family expenditure. London, 1935.

4. E. CHAMLEY:
   "La dépense des biens d'alimentation dans les grandes villes de France, par catégories socio-professionnelles" (Expenditure for food products in the large cities of France, by socio-professional categories). Economie appliquée, Vol. VII, 1954, No. 4, October-December.

5. G. CHOW:
   The demand for automobiles in the U.S. Paper presented at a meeting of the Econometrics Society, New York 28-30 December 1955.

6. COMMISSARIAT GÉNÉRAL AU PLAN:
   "Troisième plan de modernisation et d'équipement" (Third Plan for Modernization and for Equipment). Report by the Commission de l'Énergie.

7. R. P. CONGARD:
   Étude économétrique de la demande de tabac (Econometric analysis of the tobacco demand). Armand Colin, Paris, 1955.

8. P. D. CONVERSE:
   "New laws of retail gravitation." The Journal of Marketing, Volume XVI, No. 2, October 1949.

9. W. E. DAVIDSON:
   Operations research in the Lamps Division of General Electric Company. Case Institute of Technology, April 5-7, 1955.

10. E. DOUGLAS:
    "Measuring the general retail trading area. A case study." The Journal of Marketing, April 1949 and July 1949, Vol. XIII and XIV.

11. RAGNAR FRISCH:
    "Some basic principles of price of living measurements." Econometrica, No. 4, October 1954.

12. P. GARDENT:
    Prévisions de consommation de fuel et de charbon dans le secteur des foyers domestiques (Forecasting the consumption of fuel oil and coal in the household sector). House document of the Charbonnages de France, 1956.

13. P. GARDENT:
    Consommation d'énergie à usage thermique des foyers domestiques (Household consumption of energy for thermal uses). House document of the Charbonnages de France, 1956.

14. GENERAL MOTORS CORPORATION:
    The dynamics of automobile demand. New York, 1939.

15. H. S. HOUTHAKKER:
    "The econometrics of family budgets." Journal of the Royal Statistical Society, pp. 1-21, 1952, Series A.

16. J. LAIGROZ:
    Analyse des ventes de charbon à l'industrie (Analysis of the sale of coal to industry). House document of the Charbonnages de France, 1955.

17. H. C. LEVINSON:
    "Experiences in commercial operations research." Journal of the Operations Research Society of America, 1953, No. 4.

18. J. F. MAGEE:
    "The effect of promotional effort on sales." Journal of the Operations Research Society of America, 1953, No. 2.

19. J. F. MAGEE:
Operations research at the General Electric Lamps Division.
Case Institute of Technology, April 5-7, 1955.

20. Y. MAINGUY and J. MOTHES:
"L'analyse et l'exploitation des séries chronologiques.
Application sommaire à la prévision des émissions hebdoma-
daires de gas, en 1961, dans la région parisienne" (Analysis
and utilization of time series. Brief application to the forecasting of weekly gas use in the Paris area in 1961). Revue
de Statistique appliquée, Vol. 1, Nos. 3-4.

21. Y. MAINGUY and G. NAHON:
"Prévisions à long terme des ventes de gaz en France"
(Long-term forecast of gas sales in France). Revue Française
de l'Énergie, No. 72, February 1956.

22. J. L. NICHOLSON:
"Variations in working-class family expenditures." Journal
of the Royal Statistical Society, Vol. CXII, 359.

23. G. P. O'DONNEL:
The marketing of a petroleum product by probabilities.
Proceedings of the Conference on Operations Research.
Society for the Advancement of Management, New York,
1954.

24. Y. PARER and M. McCLINTOCK:
Traffic and trade. New York, McGraw-Hill, 1935.

25. M. PREVOT:
"Les variations concomitantes de l'énergie consommée et du
produit national" (Concomitant variations in energy consumption and in national product). Journal de la Société de
Statistique de Paris, January-February-March, 1951.

26. A. RASMUSSEN:
"The determination of advertising expenditure." The Journal
of Marketing, April 1952.

27. W. J. REILLY:
Law of retail gravitation. New York, W. J. Reilly Co., 1931.

28. R. B. REYNOLDS:
"A test of the law of retail gravitation." The Journal of
Marketing, January 1953, Vol. XVII.

29. V. ROUQUET la GARRIGUE:
"Les problèmes de la corrélation et de l'élasticité. Etude théorique autour de la loi de King (Problems of correlation and elasticity. Theoretical analysis based on King's law). Volumes I, II. Actualités scientifiques et industrielles 1039, 1043, Paris, 1948.

30. R. ROY:
"Contributions aux recherches économétriques" (Contributions to econometric research). Actualités scientifiques et industrielles, 412, Paris, 1936.

31. R. ROY:
Études économétriques (Econometric analyses). Sirey, Paris, 1935.

32. H. SCHULZ:
The theory and measurement of demand. University Press, Chicago, 1938.

33. A. T. STEELE:
"Weather's effect on the sales of a department store." The Journal of Marketing, April 1951.

34. R. STONE:
The measurement of consumers' expenditure and behaviour in the United Kingdom (1920-1938). Cambridge University Press, 1954.

35. G. STUVEL and S. F. JAMES:
"Household expenditures on food in Holland." Journal of the Royal Statistical Society, Series A, Vol. XCIII, 1949.

36. J. TOBIN:
"A statistical demand function for food in the United States." Journal of the Royal Statistical Society, Series A, Vol. XCIII, 1949.

37. E. VENTURA:
"Prévisions de consommation d'énergie dans les foyers domestiques (Forecasting household energy consumption). Annales des Mines, January 1957.

38. E. VENTURA:
"Prévisions de consommation d'énergie de l'industrie française" (Forecasting French industrial energy consumption). Annales des Mines, February 1957.

39. E. VENTURA:
   "Essai de prévision à moyen terme des cours des métaux non ferreux" (Attempt at medium-term forecasting of prices of nonferrous metals). Annales des Mines, May 1956 and April 1957.

40. J. WALCH:
   Étude de l'élasticité relative des marchés du charbon et des fuel-oils (Analysis of the relative elasticity of coal and fuel oil markets). House document of the Houillères du Bassin du Nord-Pas-de-Calais, 1953.

41. R. H. WHITMAN:
   "The statistical law of demand for a producer's good, as illustrated by the demand for steel." Econometrica, Vol. IV, 1936.

42. P. WHITTLE:
   "Optimum preventive sampling." Journal of the Operations Research Society of America, May 1954, No. 2.

43. H. WOLD:
   Demand analysis. Wiley, New York, 1953.

PART II

COST STRUCTURE

Chapter 8

The concept of cost:
from bookkeeping to economics

The first part of this book was devoted to methods of analysis available to business management for the purpose of acquiring a better understanding of its environment. Throughout that part, the emphasis was on the identification of phenomena rather than on the utilization of such knowledge for action (despite the strong relationship existing between econometric analysis of demand and the decisions inspired by it—a link which reveals statistical decision functions very clearly). This second part is devoted to an analysis of the firm itself (i.e., at the economic level) and to a study of its cost structure. It introduces a different perspective which will be utilized when problems of synthesis are examined in the third part of the book. We are now ready to deal with problems in which the relationship between knowledge and action becomes increasingly close. If desired, one can study the elasticity of demand without having any particular application in mind, but consideration of marginal cost without any knowledge of the nature of the decision to be made can only be illusory; it is impossible to consider the search for an optimum program independently of a related specific decision. Extending the analytical approach from the cost concept to marginal costs, we logically proceed to questions relating to management policy as a whole: production control, management of inventories, determination of operating and investment programs, and the establishment of price.

The word "cost" possesses many shades of meaning, each linked to some particular use. For example:

a) Costs can be studied for the purpose of determining a firm's income during a past period, from which the firm calculates its tax liability and dividend policy. This accounting notion of cost is important to the firm because of its statutory and fiduciary obligations, but has little economic significance.

b) On the other hand, cost analysis is generally basic to management's decision-making process in the determination of prices, inventory levels, current production, and future productive capacity requirements. In comparing various alternatives, only expenditures pertinent to decision-making are relevant; past or inevitable future expenditures are not taken into consideration.

c) Finally, we come to an analytical study of costs as a means of evaluating management effectiveness as well as of deducing operational objectives and controlling their execution. These notions of cost derive from industrial accounting. They are midway between the two previous concepts. An analysis of the development of these costs from one period to another is linked to the study of the influences exercised upon expenditures by such elements as hourly or daily production, the cost of factors of production, productivity, level of inventories, etc.; this implies a certain familiarity with the economic notions of cost envisaged in the preceding paragraph.

If we omit this third point of view, we are left with two groups of cost concepts, an accounting group and an economic group, and we find there is a considerable difference between these two. It is because of this that the use of accounting records for economic studies possess such delicate problems throughout industry that it is frequently necessary to ignore existing figures and develop new data. The cost of obtaining additional data can be minimized when bookkeeping is organized in a manner facilitating economic investigations without, at the same time, neglecting its own role.

One should never lose sight of the fact that relationships between accounting and economics are governed by three propositions:

a) In seeking to report the condition of a firm, bookkeepers record past expenditures.

b) Economists, in the pursuit of quantitative data which can serve as a basis for decisions, analyze the degree to which choices can influence future expenditures.

c) Economics borrows its documentation from bookkeeping to the extent that past costs can provide an indication of future expenditures.

When the relationships between accounting and economics are examined from this standpoint, many questions can be resolved with respect to the conditions which must be fulfilled by bookkeeping to ease the problems of management. This chapter and the following one are devoted to these questions. The problem of amortization will be dealt with separately in Chapter 9, because it is of sufficient importance and complexity to warrant separate treatment. This chapter is devoted essentially to:

a) a few accounting problems which are really pseudoproblems from an economist's point of view;

b) conditions of a rational utilization of accounting in econometrics.

I

ECONOMIC PSEUDOPROBLEMS IN ACCOUNTING

This title requires some explanation. The problems referred to here are pseudo only with respect to their relevance to economic analysis; they are quite real, however, if limited to the accounting field. In calculating average costs, for example, an accountant is compelled to adopt a method for the allocation of expenditures and because, as everyone is aware, there are no satisfactory solutions, he must decide somewhat arbitrarily in favor of one of them. On the other hand, in considering alternative decisions an economist need not be concerned with average costs or the allocation of expenditures.

An analysis of the bookkeeping for related products in one plant will be used to demonstrate the difference in approach. For a simple illustration we will limit our consideration to the concurrent production of several products in the same section of a factory. These commodities are ready for external sale on leaving this section of the factory.

What does the accountant tell us? The allocation of common expenditures "is one of the major accounting problems in the case of related products. Various methods indicate different costs. The important principle to be remembered is that the method must be reasonable, reliable, and able to provide sufficiently accurate costs for each product. Otherwise, management would not be in a position to measure with any precision the profitable character of the various products it produces and sells" [3].

In any case, an attempt must be made to identify for each product those expenditures directly connected with its production. Thereafter, the common expenditures can be allocated according to multiple rules which take into account the value of the product, or the type of labor employed, or the material utilized, etc.

The economist considers the same area in terms of certain decisions of which the following is typical. Is it in the interest of the firm to change the production level of certain products? For the sake of simplicity we will limit ourselves to the case of two products, 1 and 2, and to a market in which the prices p_1 and p_2 of these products are given. Let D be the expenditures of the firm during a given period and q_1, q_2 the corresponding production. The profit of the firm is expressed as:

$$R = p_1 q_1 + p_2 q_2 - D \qquad (I.1)$$

The accountant calculates cost c_1 and c_2 such that:

$$c_1 q_1 + c_2 q_2 = D \qquad (I.2)$$

He then evaluates quantities p_1-c_1 and p_2-c_2. On the other hand, the economist wonders what would happen if q_1 or q_2 were modified. Technically, two cases are possible:

a) the ratio of productions q_1 and q_2 in a coke-making plant is given as the ratio of the quantities of coke to gas as they leave the coke ovens.

b) the ratio of production q_1 to q_2 in a coke-making plant varies as one takes into account the additional possibility of using coke to fire gas-producing equipment.

Let us examine these two cases:

a) In the first instance, $q_2 = aq_1$ can be assumed, a being a constant. D, consequently, is solely a function of q_1 and the only possible decision is whether to modify the level of q_1. If this level is varied by dq_1, the variation of R will be:

$$dR = [(p_1 + p_2 a) - D'(q_1)]\, dq_1 \qquad (I.3)$$

This demonstrates that, in order to reach a decision, it is not necessary to allocate expenditures between products 1 and 2. It is sufficient to determine to what extent expenditures D would be affected by a variation in the production level and then to compare the variation in expenditure with the variation in income.

b) In the second case, expenditures D are contingent upon q_1 and q_2. Possible decisions relate to various levels of production of q_1 and q_2. Should these levels be modified by dq_1 and dq_2 the profit varies by:

$$dR = \left(p_1 - \frac{\partial D}{\partial q_1}\right) dq_1 + \left(p_2 - \frac{\partial D}{\partial q_2}\right) dq_2. \qquad (I.4)$$

In this case it is also unnecessary to allocate expenditures between products 1 and 2 in order to reach a decision. It is merely necessary to evaluate expenditure variations linked to the respective variations of productions 1 and 2. Therefore, no attempt will be made to increase q_1 unless

$$p_1 - \frac{\partial D}{\partial q_1} \geqslant 0.$$

For the economist, therefore, the problem of allocating expenditures between related products is a pseudoproblem which occurs only when an attempt is made to calculate production costs. If the answer to the problem posed by the accountant is arbitrary, the answer to the problem posed by the economist is perfectly definite, once the technical process for production modification is specified. [1]. The determination of a method of allocating expenditures does not lead to a correct solution; in the absence of any additional analysis, knowing the level D of expenditures does not permit the calculation of

$$\frac{\partial D}{\partial q_1} \text{ and } \frac{\partial D}{\partial q_2}.$$

Nevertheless, industrial accounting must be conceived in such manner as to determine the values of $\frac{\partial D}{\partial q_1}$ and $\frac{\partial D}{\partial q_2}$, which correspond to a firm's routine decisions.

Note. Accounting suggests special methods when one of the products, say product 2, is a byproduct of the other.

When the ratio of the production of q_1 to q_2 is fixed, the approach which has the greatest economic significance is to consider byproduct sales as a reduction in the cost of the main product. The coefficient of dq_1 in (I.3) can be expressed as:

$$p_1 - [D'(q_1) - p_2 a]$$

where $p_2 a$ represents the returns on q_2 calculated in q_1 units.

When the ratio of production q_1 to q_2 is variable, none of the methods suggested by the accountant is truly satisfactory; and if the value of the production of 2 constitutes a substantial percentage of the production value of 1, it is preferable to give the same analytical treatment to both products.

The allocation of overhead among the different sections of a factory poses problems similar to those which have been considered above.

The foregoing discussion demonstrates that where, in the case of a certain class of decisions, expenditures are fixed, their allocation among different departments is arbitrary and useless from the economic standpoint since the decisions to be taken are independent of these expenditures. In other words, the level of fixed charges has no influence on the decision as to how to maximize profits. It merely affects the value of this maximum.

Later, in Chapter 9, the problem of allocating fixed charges among various years will be considered as part of the amortization problem. Here again the problem of allocation will not bear on the problem of decision-making, but determining the value of equipment at the end of each year will at least permit reaching a solution which is satisfactory on the accounting level.

II

CONDITIONS FOR A RATIONAL ECONOMIC UTILIZATION
OF ACCOUNTING

In the foregoing pages, we have attempted to indicate why direct utilization of accounting figures without a close analysis of their significance is generally devoid of economic value and cannot serve as a basis for sound decisions. To reduce the risk of error and to derive maximum benefit from accounting, it is advisable to keep the following observations always in mind:

1. Allocations made by an accountant are often arbitrary and frequently useless. The phase in the development of accounting data of most interest to the economist is not the final phase, where details are somewhat obscured, but the preliminary stages where allocations are still minimal. It is, in effect, much easier during these stages to obtain an idea of the nature of the expenditures and consequently to dissect and rearrange them for the purpose of economic analysis.

Without entering into any technical details, we can envisage the form in which accounting can contribute to the process of developing its data. This brings us to a recapitulation of the stages of industrial accounting.

First, the factory is divided into specific departments and the expenditures incurred within each department are attributed to that department. This information can be presented along the lines of the traditional rectangular table in which each line represents a department and each column an expenditure of a specific type (Table I). The departments will include, of course, production and support services (production of power, maintenance, sales service, general management, etc.). Furthermore, since no allocation has yet been made, there will be other general expense departments such as rentals whose cost will be carried in a separate column.

Table I

	Wages	Super-vision	Supplies	. . .	Rentals	Total
Production department 1	x	x	x			x
Production department 2	x	x	x			x
Production of power	x	x	x			.
Rentals.					x	x
TOTAL. . . .	x	x	x	. . .	x	x

Some of the overhead costs in Table I can, at times, be very reasonably allocated among the different departments. For example, the 5% tax on wages and other similar charges can be assigned to various departments in proportion to the wages paid.

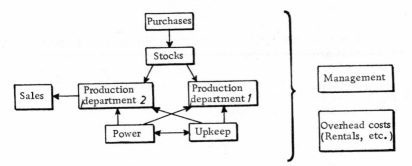

Fig. 1

Upon completion of this first allocation, certain lines in Table I are cancelled.

To define the production costs of the various departments, the accountant must then prorate upon a more arbitrary basis. To accomplish this without vitiating prospective economic analyses, he must visualize clearly the plan of the factory's various departments. Consider, for example, a factory comprising the departments represented in Figure 1. Arrows indicate the flow of services performed by one department for another.

As a general rule, it is advisable to minimize the amount to be allocated and to proscribe the sequence of allocations.

It is unnecessary to allocate to each production department:

a) expenditures of the sales department and, in general, those of all departments which are below the level of production units; and

b) overhead expenditures which can be considered to be independent of management decision.

The next step is to prorate the expenditures for power, maintenance, and stock acquisition between the two production departments. It might be helpful to develop the proration in accordance with the outline presented in Table II, in which the colums correspond to the departments whose expenditures are distributed pro rata to the department on each line.

Table II

Department	Stock purchase	Power	Maintenance
Production department 1 . .	x	x	x
Production department 2			
Repairs.	x	x	
TOTAL.	–	x	–

Tables I and II, together with the factory flow chart (Fig. 1), constitute an excellent working tool for the economist and enable him to know the extent to which he can make use of accounting for the specific problem facing him.

It would also be helpful to develop, for each unit of production, a table along the lines of Table III, in which expenditures are grouped by type and by origin. This grouping leads to a breakdown of business and technical costs.

Table III

Origin \ Type	Wages	Super-vision	Supplies	. . .	Amortization and financing costs	Total
Direct salaries .	x					x
Direct supervision		x				x
Direct supplies .			x			
Direct amortization and financing costs.					x	x
Power expenditures*	x	x	x		x	x
Maintenance expenditures*. . .	x	x	x		x	x
TOTAL	x	x	x		x	x

*For the production department under consideration.

The "total" column on the right provides a breakdown of expenditures by origin and the "total" line across the bottom of the table provides a breakdown of expenditures by type. It is emphasized that it is impossible to undertake a serious economic analysis unless both distributions—rather than simply the totals—are known.

Consequently, and precisely because accounting and economic analysis do not have the same objective, the economic analyst is required to have a sound knowledge of the accounting structure of his company. He must direct his attention beyond the aggregate and summary tables to the intermediate analytical tables containing specific details which provide a more reliable account of the flow of values.

2. To make sound use of accounting, it is not merely sufficient to know the total volume of expenditures. It is also necessary to

know the quantities of the different products consumed and the past development of their prices. Accounting costs are of interest to the economist only insofar as they permit a good estimate of future costs. To achieve this, the economist must be in a position to determine the influence of:

a) predictable future price changes;

b) variations in consumption linked to technical development.

Where past costs have been influenced by price inflation to the extent that the accounting returns are no longer based on comparable costs, it is generally impossible to use accounting data to predict costs. Economic analysis is then restricted to the consideration of consumed quantities and anticipated prices.

3. Experience shows that it is essential to develop tables which indicate both unit and total costs. The accounting practice of reasoning on the basis of average costs and of presenting statements based on these averages is a source of wasted time and of errors in interpretation. What is vital in a decision is not the variation in average cost but the variation in total profit; the total volume of expenditures is what actually affects total profit. If expenditures are fixed, they do not affect profit variation. This phenomenon is obscured when reasoning is based on average costs, because the unit charge of fixed expenditures then varies with production.

An excellent practice for economists and accountants is to base their reasoning on the total volume of expenditures. It familiarizes them with marginal analysis and leads them to make use of a good criterion, i.e., maximization of profits. In analyses relating to average costs, on the contrary, there is always a tendency to seek the minimum cost, which is in no sense an objective of the firm. One allows oneself to become hypnotized by unit increases or decreases in fixed charges.

The preferable method is to use both total costs and unit costs for the past and to establish for the future the single measure of total costs. Usually, future fixed charges can thus be derived immediately, which permits the determination of proportionate future expenditures by means of a simple multiplication. The simultaneous use of previous total and unit costs serves to help guard against human fallibility which, in a rapid analysis, tends to overestimate fixed charges when a table of total costs is available, and variable charges when a table of unit costs is available.

The foregoing discussion demonstrates that in economic analyses it is of utmost importance that the intermediate stages in the development of accounting figures be available. Prorations should be postponed as long as possible and developed according to rules which are well known; the different departments and positions should be defined very specifically, and one should have both quantities and prices available. Finally, the tables should include both unit and total costs. Under such conditions, an economist will be more likely to utilize accounting data successfully in his cost analyses as a basis for helping executives to arrive at decisions.

BIBLIOGRAPHY

1. M. ALLAIS:
   La gestion des houillères nationalisées et la théorie économique (Management of nationalized coal mines and economic theory). Imprimerie Nationale, Paris, 1953.

2. P. COUTURE:
   Cours de Comptabilité (Course in accounting). École Nationale Supérieure des Mines de Saint-Etienne, 1937.

3. NEUNER:
   Cost accounting; principles and practice. Irwin, Inc., Homewood, Illinois.

4. A. VEYRENC:
   Cours de comptabilité (Course in accounting). Durassié.

Chapter 9

Amortization

With the increasing importance of equipment, amortization costs now represent a substantial percentage of production costs. The method by which these are calculated can, therefore, appreciably influence the determination of costs and management decisions. As a matter of fact, very few firms attempt to arrive at a precise estimate of amortization. Although multiple refinements are used to improve the measurement of operating costs, amortization costs are determined by the application of conventional rules of thumb.

A second reason for this chapter may also be considered: the amortization concept is frequently misunderstood and can be separately identified only with difficulty from concepts which, like replacement values, are basic to the theory of investment. Such confusion is the source of innumerable errors in practical problems; in discussing amortization at this point, we are laying the groundwork for subsequent discussions.

This chapter is divided into three sections, devoted respectively to relationships between present value and amortization theory, to the computation of amortization during periods of monetary stability, and to the computation of amortization during inflation. In writing this chapter, we have derived considerable inspiration from M. Boiteux' remarkable pamphlet, "Comment calculer l'amortissement?" (How should amortization be calculated?) [2].

I

PRESENT VALUE AND AMORTIZATION THEORY

To define the concept of amortization, the simplest method is to consider the case of a firm borrowing a certain amount of money for the purpose of purchasing equipment. Amortization of this equipment consists of putting aside a sum of money each year which permits payment of interest and reimbursement of principal by the end of the life of the equipment. This definition pinpoints two of the essential aspects of the concept of amortization:

1. Amortization represents a problem to management because it owns equipment which is used over several consecutive fiscal periods. If accounting periods lasted one day, a great number of costs currently regarded as operating costs would have to be counted as amortization costs. On the other hand, if the fiscal periods lasted 10 years, the greater portion of amortization costs would be considered as current costs. The problem of amortization is, therefore, a problem of distributing costs over a period of time; as such, it will be observed that it contains aspects similar to related problems touched upon in the preceding chapter.

2. The problem of amortization relates to past expenditures, i.e., equipment already purchased and in use. This is an accounting problem which influences the calculation of annual income and affects management decisions. It is not, strictly speaking, an economic problem, because the decision to purchase a particular piece of equipment is dependent upon the difference between the present value of receipts and future expenditures, and not upon the rules of amortization.

To simplify matters, let us assume a period of monetary stability and, following M. Boiteux' lead, consider the taxicab driver who purchases a new car of value V_0 at the beginning of year 0 with money borrowed at a rate of interest i, and who retains the car during its entire lifetime, i.e., n years. The amortization of this car will require the driver to set aside annual amounts a_1, a_2, . . . , a_n, which enable him at the end of n years to repay his loan, plus interest, completely. To do this, it is merely necessary that the present value of the aggregate of the successive sums a_1, a_2, . . . , a_n be equivalent to V_0, i.e., in accordance with the following relationship:

$$V_0 = \frac{a_1}{1 + i} + \frac{a_2}{(1 + i)}2 + \cdots + \frac{a_n}{(1 + i)}n. \tag{I.1}$$

In fact, if the two members of the relationship (I.1) are multiplied by $(1 + i)^n$, it will be immediately verified that the successive investment of sums a_1, a_2, . . . , a_n makes it possible at the end of n years to liquidate both principal and interest.

It is obvious in relationship (I.1) that n-1 annual costs can be chosen arbitrarily. In other words, the company's situation is dependent only upon V_0 and is not dependent upon the rule selected for the allocation of V_0 among the various years. We might say, as in the preceding chapter, that the problem of allocating amortization costs is a pseudoproblem since:

a) a firm's decision to purchase equipment is dependent only upon the present value of its future income and is in no way contingent upon the manner in which this equipment will be amortized;

b) assuming that the borrowed capital is equal in real value to the aggregate of its costs over the years, a firm will have replaced the borrowed principal at the end of the lifetime of the equipment.

It is considered advisable, however, not to select the a_1, a_2 . . . arbitrarily. Let us suppose that equipment which is to last two years is not amortized the first year and, for the sake of simplicity, that this equipment yields the same revenue R during each of the two years. The present value of the firm's future income at the beginning of the year is:

$$\frac{R}{(1 + i)} + \frac{R}{(1 + i)^2} - V_0$$

a value which is not dependent upon the rate of amortization; however, the first year's income is $R-iV_0$ and that of the second year (in constant dollars), $R-V_0-iV_0$. The first year's income is very high and that of the second year very low (probably negative). In judging the results of the first year, it must be kept in mind that the second year will be a poor one. Such a situation is inconvenient, for it is not possible to rationalize constantly all investment lifespans. This could lead to very serious errors in judgment.

In the case of the taxicab driver, on the other hand, recourse to the market provides a valid basis for the evaluation of annual costs. The taxicab driver can, at the end of one year, resell his taxi at price V_1 (the market value of a one-year-old vehicle of this type) and repay the amount borrowed. The taxicab driver's expenditures for the year amount to:

$$a_1 = (V_0 - V_1) + iV_0. \tag{I.2}$$

They are composed of two terms, the second representing the financing costs and the first the car's depreciation during the year, or industrial amortization. Instead of selling his cab at the end of the first year, the driver could have retained it for another year, repaying the lender the sum V_0 V_1 and selling his cab at the end of the second year at price V_2. His costs during the second year would have been:

$$a_2 = V_1 - V_2 + iV_1. \tag{I.3}$$

This procedure can be generalized so that during the year t the taxicab driver's costs (if he still has his vehicle) will be:

$$a_t = V_{t-1} - V_t + iV_{t-1} \tag{I.4}$$

V_{t-1} and V_t representing the vehicle's market values at the end of the years t-1 and t. The (I.4) relationship can naturally be expressed:

$$V_{t-1} = \frac{a_t + V_t}{(1 + i)}$$

which demonstrates that, by eliminating successively V_1, ..., V_t, ... from the preceding relationships, one again has the relationship (I.1) between V_0, a_1, ..., a_n. Recourse to the market, therefore, provides a means of evaluating annual costs and shows that it is reasonable, to obtain a correct picture of the enterprise, to take the real depreciation of the installations as the annual amortization.

This discussion can be summarized in the following manner. Financially, the allocation of acquisition cost in accordance with an amortization schedule is arbitrary. Industrially, it is necessary to relate amortization to the decrease in the effective value of the equipment. To clarify this distinction, we will borrow the following hypothetical example from M. Boiteux: "The enterprise consists of two departments, the industrial department and the financial department. The first borrows from the second—which in this case plays the part of a bank—the sums required for its new projects (expansion and modernization) and each year repays the amortization of its loans according to conditions to be specified"—related, of course, to the decrease in value of the plant and equipment. "The difference between sales receipts and production costs (amortization and financing costs included) constitutes industrial profit. For its part, the financial department obtains the required capital and undertakes the payment of principal and interest charges at a rate which may not in any way coincide with the amortization schedule effected by the industrial department, thus realizing a certain 'financial profit' deriving from more or less successful speculations. Industrial profits and financial profits are distributed each year to the stockholders; the stockholders eventually reinvest their profits in the business by turning them over to the financial department, which finds therein one of its sources of financing" [2]. The function of the financial department, therefore, consists of converting an industrial amortization rate, related to the actual depreciation of the installation, into a financial amortization rate reflecting the wishes of the lenders.*

---

*Note: In a perfect market, in the absence of risk and management costs, the operations of the financial department would be entirely blank. For readers who may not be familiar with present values, it may be interesting to verify this by a simple example. For instance, take equipment of an initial value V_0 which lasts two years: $V_2 = 0$. At the time of the purchase of this equipment, an amount V_0 has been borrowed which is to be repaid in three years. The sums remaining to be paid respectively V_1' and V_2' at the end of the first two years. It is assumed $V_1' < V_1$. The first year, the production department pays the financing charges iV_0 but owes in principal $(V_0 - V_1')$, whereas it has available only $V_0 - V_1$. The

The foregoing presentation of the theoretical notion of amortization, though brief, nevertheless provides a clear answer to certain questions.

a) The theory indicates that it is absurd to incorporate simultaneously both industrial and financial amortization in the calculations. To do so would imply that, on the basis of a loan C, a firm would have at its disposal, at the end of the lifespan of the equipment and once interest is paid, a sum 2C. It could reimburse the lender and also finance the purchase of an equivalent installation with its own funds. Thus, costs would be artificically inflated in order to permit an increase in the firm's own capital. Under such circumstances, the firm could find itself operating at a loss even as it grew richer.

b) Relations (I.1) to (I.4) indicate that it is necessary to operate on the basis of compound interest in order to avoid ending up in logical contradictions. Computation on the basis of simple interest consists of constantly determining the financing costs on the new value, and, consequently, substituting for relationship (I.4) the following relationship:

$$a_t = V_{t-1} - V_t + iV_0. \tag{I.5}$$

It indicates that this system arbitrarily inflates the financing charges and makes the absurd hypothesis that principal amounts are not reimbursed until the end of an equipment's life and in the interim are locked in a drawer, where they remain unused.

Company accountants, however, implicitly use compound interest because the financial product of available capital is deducted

---

financial department thereupon borrows $V_1 - V_1'$ at an interest rate i. The second year, the production department pays the financial department the financing charges iV_1 and the principal V_1. The financial department must pay: a) iV_1' of financing charges to the first lender, and b) $i(V_1 - V_1')$ of financing charges to the second lender, or a total of iV_1 in financing charges. It must turn over $V_1' - V_2'$ as principal to the first lender. However, it has $V_1 > V_1'$ available. It therefore pays $V_1' - V_2'$ to the first lender and $(V_1 - V_1')$ to the second. Consequently, it has repaid the second lender in full and still retains V_2'. It invests this sum at an i rate of interest, which enables it during the third year to reimburse V_2 to the first lender as well as to pay the financing charges iV_2'.

In practice these operations are never blank, since interest rates may vary from one loan to another, and operating costs of the finance department must be considered part of the cost of financing. The above means simply that the rate of interest used in industrial amortization operations can logically be different from that at which the loans are contracted.

from the financing costs of the loans. The risk involved in the use of simple interest, therefore, does indeed relate to economic analyses made independently of bookkeeping.

c) The manner in which the equipment is initially financed is of no importance whatever; one should not become blinded by the argument which stresses that no interest is involved when a firm invests its own funds. In Chapter 2, we have pointed out the fallacy of this opinion.

d) The difference between amortization and provision for replacement will now become apparent. Amortization relates to past expenditures and is a sum which enables a firm:

1) when it has used its own funds, to maintain its capital constant;

2) when it has borrowed, to reimburse exactly the amounts which have been loaned.

Providing for replacement consists in setting aside sums which will permit the purchase of a new piece of equipment at the expiration of the life of the present one. In the case of a firm which uses its own funds, amortization and provision for replacement would be equal only in the case of a steady state in which money and prices were stable and where equipments would be replaced at the end of their lives by those of identical number and quantity. But, in reality, there is no such thing as a truly steady state. Equipment is replaced by different equipment or not at all, and amortizations which relate to the past no longer constitute a good approximation of future investment costs.

II

CALCULATION OF AMORTIZATION IN A PERIOD
OF MONETARY STABILITY

The foregoing analysis has permitted the elaboration of a satisfactory concept of industrial amortization. In the case of the taxi, the practical application is immediate and easy because a market price exists. But this is not the case for most equipment. Two methods are possible:

a) the application of a systematic rule for determining, at the beginning of the life of a piece of equipment, the entire amortization schedule;

b) an annual determination of the charge which could be made if a third party were given the right from then on to use the equipment in its present location [2].* This second method is intellectually

---

*The value of this right, at the beginning of the life of a piece of equipment, is far greater than the resale value for use in another location.

satisfying but, in order to evaluate better the objection raised in connection with practical difficulties of application, it is well to review the systematic rules which have been suggested.

Naturally, these rules presuppose that a prior estimate has been made of the anticipated lifespan of the equipment. This span, however, is never very accurately known. Many factors may cause a piece of equipment to become unusable. In addition to physical factors deriving from accidents and wear, there is the economic factor represented by obsolescence. Obsolescence can result from technical change, geographical shifts of commercial centers, an inappropriate productive capacity, changes in demand, etc. It is difficult to predict obsolescence, but an attempt must nevertheless be made to determine the probable lifespan of equipment, avoiding gross norms which prescribe it as a function of the type of expenditure or, worse, of the volume of expenditures. Prudence would dictate using a lifespan n slightly below the most probable lifespan, for too rapid an amortization is preferable to an amortization that is a little too slow. Once n has been computed, one may choose between the following methods:

a) The straight line or constant amortization annuity method.

This method consists of calculating an amortization annuity equal to $\frac{V_0}{n}$. Obviously, it has the merit of simplicity and, for this reason enjoys a certain favor. It leads to decreasing costs each year over the life of the equipment because, if the amortization annuity is fixed, the financing costs themselves decrease from year to year.

This rule, however, has no economic justification and may lead to results which are entirely erroneous. In the case of automobiles, for example, it is well known that the loss in value is considerable during the first few years, after which it is progressively reduced. M. Boiteux also cites the example of coal-burning central power stations during the past 30 years: "A modern central power station, with a good output, was operated approximately 5,000 hours per year and necessitated relatively moderate maintenance expenditures. But it was progressively displaced by newer plants with better output to such an extent that its utilization decreased from year to year down to about 100 hours toward the end of its life. The annual value of the service performed therefore decreased very clearly with age. . . The method of constant annuity, under such conditions, leads to costs of the order of the 100 or so francs per kw.-hr. produced for the oldest stations still in operation, a cost which, everyone agrees, is devoid of any significance. However, the cost which was calculated by the same method for the first few years was equally erroneous, because if the annuity today is too high for the latter years, it was too low for the first' [2].

b) The lost-funds or constant total annuity method.

This method presupposes that a constant sum a, representing principal and financing charges, is paid each year to the lender. Since the present value of these sums must be equal to the initial value V_0 of the equipment, one must naturally have:

$$V_0 = a \sum_{}^{n} \frac{1}{(1 + i)^p} \tag{II.1}$$

i.e.,

$$a = \frac{iV_0(1 + i)^n}{(1 + i)^n - 1}. \tag{II.2}$$

To understand the nature of the annual depreciation this hypothesis presupposes, let us split a into its two parts, principal and financing costs. From (I.2) we obtain:

$$V_0 - V_1 = a - iV_0 = \frac{iV_0}{(1 + i)^n - 1} \tag{II.3}$$

then, from (I.3), by letting: $V_0 - V_1 = x$

$$V_1 - V_2 = x(1 + i). \tag{II.4}$$

It can then be demonstrated, by iteration, that the depreciation for the year p has a value equal to $x(1 + i)^{p-1}$. This property also provides a justification for the name of lost-funds method; everything occurs, insofar as the amortization portion is concerned, as though the firm placed a sum x each year in a fund at an interest rate i. The capitalized value of these sums at the end of the life of the equipment is naturally equal to the latter's initial value V_0:

$$V_0 = \sum_{1}^{n} x(1 + i)^{p-1}. \tag{II.5}$$

On the other hand, the financing costs are successively:

$$iV_0, \ i(V_0 - x), \ i(V_0 - x - x(1 + i)), \text{ etc...}$$

The constant annuity method therefore implies greatly increasing depreciations and, for that reason, is even more subject to the criticisms directed at the preceding method. The objection which we raise in this connection, however, is valid only in terms of the evolution of costs over time. There is no objection to the use of this method in attempting simply to determine the profitability of an operation, making the calculation on the basis of one year with the aid of the constant annuity slope.

c) The method of depreciation at a constant rate.

This method attempts to avoid the defects of the preceding methods by leading to a decreasing depreciation over time. The value v of an equipment at the end of its life is generally not zero, for it is at least equal to the value of scrap. This method assumes, therefore, that the equipment loses each year a constant percentage r of its value. r is determined by the relationship:

$$v = V_0 (1 - r)^n. \qquad (II.6)$$

However, r is essentially dependent upon v/V_0 which is not usually known; thus, the amortization rate of the first few years, which corresponds to the highest annuities, is rather arbitrary.

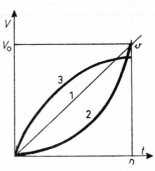

Fig. 1
1. Constant amortization annuity. 2. Constant total annuity. 3. Depreciation at a constant rate.

The three amortization methods which have been described are compared in the foregoing figure, in which the amortized values at the end of year t are shown as ordinates.

d) The method of constant annuity amortization per unit produced.

This method takes as a basis not the lifespan of the equipment, but the probable number of units it will serve to produce. Let this number be p. To each unit produced is assessed an amortization charge $\frac{V_0}{p}$, or a charge of $\frac{gV_0}{p}$ for a year in which the production is q. Despite appearances, this method presents a major disadvantage. It neglects the fact that obsolescence is as important a cause of shelving as actual wear. If, for one reason or another, the equipment is not put to maximum use during the first years, the method postpones amortization to a future period on the assumption that the lifespan will eventually be prolonged. Nothing is less sure, and by the end of the period it may be necessary to reduce p sharply, which may lead to considerable amortization costs.

All of these methods are in large part arbitrary. It would be preferable, if possible, to determine directly the value V_t of the equipment at the end of each year. A few of the theoretical means of attack which have been suggested are described, although as yet they are rarely used:

a) In the case of certain equipment (automobiles, trucks, etc.) for which there is a secondhand market, it is possible to use the market price, corrected up or down depending on the condition of the item.

b) When there is no market price, a proposition in economic theory provides the means of evaluating V_t indirectly. If a perfect competitive market existed, the price of the equipment would be equal to the present value of its future income. An effort could then be made to determine at the end of each year the present value of future services and the sum of future maintenance expenditures.

c) One of the drawbacks of traditional methods is that they create fictitious profit at certain times as well as fictitious deficits at others. From this comes the idea of attempting to determine an amortization rate at the beginning of equipment life such that the operational profit, after deduction of fixed charges, remains constant or, more generally, becomes each year a fraction of the total profit B. If R_i represents profit before deduction of fixed charges for the year i, one should have:

$$R_i - a_i = k_i B \qquad (i = 1, 2, ..., n)$$

coefficients k_i having a present value equal to 1.

This concept is particularly interesting in practice for, in the case of most industrial goods, there is no market value which permits an accurate determination of actual depreciation. A risky estimate is replaced by a calculation of allocation of profits over time.

It is possible to allocate these profits so as to:

a) create a profit each year in a case where the operation as a whole is profitable;

b) create each year a larger profit for a solution A than for a solution B if, in regard to the operation as a whole, solution A is preferable to solution B.

In order to accomplish this, it is merely required that coefficients k_i be selected and that they be positive and constant.

M. Boiteux [5] has demonstrated that economic significance is thus restored to the amortization concept because it is possible through annual computations, taking amortization into account, to arrive at the same results as those obtained by present-value computations.

In a very important article on amortization [6], J. Desrousseaux outlines a similar viewpoint. He suggests the use of equal k_i coefficients, or, alternatively, the defining of theoretical amortizements a', equal to anticipated profits before deduction of fixed costs; the present value of the a'_i-a_i differences restores total B of anticipated profit. The calculation of production units then approaches a state of equilibrium, and managers become anxious to avoid indicated deficits (i.e., actual results which are less than those anticipated).

We have seen the drawbacks which are inherent in traditional methods when they are applied to single items. It is believed by some that these drawbacks are greatly reduced by compensating factors when observed from the standpoint of a firm which operates many pieces of equipment of various ages. To examine this argument we must, still following the trail laid by M. Boiteux, distinguish the cases of static, expanding, or declining organizations.

In the static case, let us consider a firm in a fixed state owning n machines which have a life expectancy of n years whose ages are uniformly distributed. Under such conditions, a machine is replaced each year and, if V_0 is the total value of the plant in its new condition, the annual depreciation is V_0/n; it remains so regardless of any hypothesis which may be made concerning the decrease in value of each machine. On the other hand, this hypothesis has an influence on the value of financing charges:

a) If the value of each machine decreases regularly each year by one nth, the value of the plant at the end of each year is equal to half its new value and the financing charges are $1/2\ iV_0$.

b) If, on the contrary, the value of a machine is practically constant during the first p years of its life, approximately canceling itself out thereafter, the value of the plant is of the order of pV_0/n and the financing costs are ipV_0/n.

Therefore, even in this particular instance, an arbitrary rule cannot be adopted for the computation of amortization because the financing charges are actually dependent upon the hypothesis made with respect to the decrease in value of the different pieces of equipment.

We now come to the case of an expanding firm. The investment expenditures D for one year are used for the purpose of:

a) replacing existing equipment which has reached the end of its usefulness;

b) increasing the size of the plant.

If V is the value of this plant at the beginning of the year and r the rate of expansion of the enterprise, the expansion costs are rV and the industrial amortization cost D-rV. The financing charges being iV, the total fixed charges amount to:

$$F = D + (i - r)\ V.$$

The charges decrease to the amount D of new projects when the rate of expansion of the enterprise is equal to the interest rate. In other words, the financial department makes available, each

year, capital amounts D to the industrial department for its expenditures incurred in connection with new projects, and the
industrial department reimburses charges F = D on the basis of
prior debts. The industrial department, therefore, does not need
the financial department; it finances itself completely. On the
other hand, the financial department must each year obtain capital
in amounts equal to the payments which it has to make on account
of previous debts. Naturally, the situation is no longer such when
i is different from r. If r is less than i, the industrial department
turns over each year to the financial department capital amounts
F greater than those which the industrial department receives
from the financial department for its new projects. An opposite
situation occurs if r is greater than i.

In the case of an expanding firm, the fact that F is dependent
upon (i-r)V (except when i = r) indicates that, in general, the
selection of an amortization rate—a rate upon which V is dependent—also has repercussions upon F. In this case, too, the
amortization rule should not be selected arbitrarily.

Finally, in the case of a declining firm, the annual amount D
of new projects is less than the industrial amortization of a
quantity rV (r, which is positive, represents the rate of decline).
The amount of the industrial amortization becomes D + rV and
the total fixed charges are:

$$F = D + (r + i) V.$$

The industrial department each year returns to the financial department capital amounts that are greater than those which are
allotted to it for its new projects.

III

COMPUTATION OF AMORTIZATION DURING INFLATION

One of the characteristics of inflationary situations is that
these are, in general, periods during which forecasting is difficult.
We will neglect this fundamental aspect for the present, however,
in order to view matters more clearly.

Let us therefore consider a chronic and progressive inflation
such that prices increase each year at a constant rate a. With
regard to the interest rate, the nominal rate i of the market must
be distinguished from the rate i_r which would be established if,
other things being equal, prices remained constant.

Two extreme situations are possible:

a) The money market is fully aware of the inflationary phenomenon and, consequently, investors are not willing to lend their money

except at a rate i equal to the sum of i_r and of the rate a of increase in prices [2]:

$$i = i_r + a.$$

The annual charge becomes, using the notations of equation (I.4):

$$a_t = V_{t-1} - V_t + (i_r + a) V_{t-1}. \tag{III.1}$$

b) The money market does not react before inflation and the rate is is equal to i_r. In this instance, the firm must reevaluate annually the value of its equipment. As a matter of fact, assuming that is has initially purchased its equipment with its own funds, it will only have available at the end of the amortization a sum equivalent to the nominal value of the depreciated equipment and will have lost much money. In the first situation this would not occur, since the firm would have collected higher financing charges which would compensate for the low value of the amortization. This second situation, therefore—if amortization is reevaluated—leads to the same annual charges as the first, but with a different distribution between principal payments and financing charges:

$$a_t = (1 + a) V_{t-1} - V_t + i_r V_{t-1}. \tag{III.2}$$

In practice, the market interest rate is neither i_r nor $i_r + a$. The interest rate is not insensitive to inflation, but its increase does not fully reflect the monetary depreciation. Consequently:

$$i_r < i < i_r + a$$

or:

$$i - a < i_r < i.$$

If the firm knew i_r, it would have the choice of two equivalent policies:

a) to calculate the financing charges at the rate i_r and to reevaluate the value of the equipment;

b) to calculate the financing charges at the rate $i_r + a$ and not to reevaluate the equipment.

These reasonable policies are intermediaries between the two extreme policies which follow.

1. Assume that $i_r = i-a$, and:

a) either calculate the financing charges at the rate i without reevaluation;

b) or calculate the financing charges at the rate i-a with reevaluation.

Since, in fact, i is lower than $i_r + a$, this policy underestimates fixed charges and costs. At the end of the amortization period, the firm has at its disposal a sum less in real value than the initial sum.

2. Assume that $i_r = i$, and:

a) either calculate the financing charges at the rate $i + a$ without reevaluation;

b) or calculate the financing charges at the rate i with reevaluation.

Since i is greater than i_r, this policy inflates fixed charges and costs and enables the firm to have at its disposal, at the end of the amortization period, a sum greater in real value than the initial sum.

From a strictly economic standpoint it would be preferable to attempt to estimate i_r rather than to use blindly one of the extreme policies above. Naturally, in the case of inflation, considerations of general policy can lead a firm to adopt decisions different from those which would be economically correct. In particular, the temptation is very strong to overestimate costs when it is possible to reflect any increase in expenditures in selling prices.

More generally, a firm's amortization rules cannot be determined solely on the basis of economic criteria. Tax legislation, in particular, leads firms to make many adjustments. Here we find again, in a special case, the distinction made earlier between the decision of an executive and the conclusions of economic analysis. It is unnecessary to dwell further on this subject.

On the other hand, it is interesting to note in passing one of the characteristics of accounting analysis which has appeared in the course of the last two chapters. In bookkeeping, one must constantly resist the temptation to end up with precise, but false, figures, rather than with imprecise ones which are approximately exact. The crude application of certain traditional methods, even though having the advantage of simplicity and economy of thought, can lead to arbitrary results and to costs which may be devoid of economic significance. A closer collaboration between accountants and economic analysts may afford the possibility of developing less systematic methods in which reflection will play a more important part. The resulting estimates will make it possible for management to judge the condition of its business more accurately.

BIBLIOGRAPHY

1. M. ALLAIS:
   Traité d'économie pure (Treatise on pure economics). Paris, 1953.

2. M. BOITEUX:
   Comment calculer l'amortissement? (How should amortization be calculated?) Paris, Sirey, 1955, and Revue d'Économie Politique, No. 1, January-February 1956.

3. M. BOITEUX:
   "L'amortissement industriel. Incidence des lois de dépréciation individuelle des installations sur les charges de
   capital d'une grande entreprise" (Industrial amortization.
   Incidence of laws of individual depreciation of installations
   upon the capital charges of a large enterprise). Annales
   des Mines, March 1956.

4. M. BOITEUX:
   "L'amortissement: dépréciation des automobiles" (Amortization: depreciation of automobiles). Revue de statistique
   appliquée, Vol. IV, No. 4, 1956.

5. M. BOITEUX:
   "L'amortissement peut-il jouer un rôle dans le calcul
   économique?" (Can amortization play a part in economic
   calculation?). Revue française de Recherche opérationnelle,
   No. 4, 1957.

6. J. DESROUSSEAUX:
   "Calcul de l'amortissement dans les prix de revient in-
   dustriels" (Calculation of amortization in industrial production costs). Annales des Mines, May 1958.

7. R. HENON:
   "L'amortissement du matériel industriel" (Amortization of
   industrial equipment). Journal Soc. Statist., Paris, 1943,
   84, 119-55.

8. G. RULLIÈRE:
   "Amortissement et décision d'investissement de l'entrepreneur" (Amortization and entrepreneurial investment decision). Revue d'Economie Politique, November-December
   1956.

9. E. A. SALIERS:
   Depreciation. Principles and application. The Ronald Press
   Company, New York, 1939.

Chapter 10

Marginal costs:
theory and applications

In Chapter 8 we have shown that economists seek to develop concepts of cost which may aid business executives in making decisions. Since many decisions relate to modifications in production, marginal costs occupy a central position in economic analysis. Marginal cost is measured by the incremental expenditure incurred in producing the last item in a production run.

In recent years, French economic analysts have attempted to bridge the gap between theorizing about cost and the application of these theories to specific problems in business management. It is this evolution that we shall attempt to trace in this chapter, which, incidentally, is one of the first examples in the field of economics of the interaction between theory and practice.

In the first section we shall summarize the modern theory of production functions and marginal costs [1], [42].

In the second section we shall discuss the concept of marginal cost and the role it assumes in management studies. With this in mind, we plan to introduce the distinction between short- and long-term marginal costs. We shall also discuss certain practical difficulties that occur when marginal costs are used. The latter portion of this section will be devoted to an analysis of the various factors which are likely to modify such costs.

Leading logically from the preceding discussion, we shall present examples of practical problems in the last two sections. In the third section we shall give examples of how marginal costs are calculated and defined in various types of industrial problems. The use of marginal costs in administrative and management problems will be discussed in the fourth section. The marginal cost concept will also be considered in subsequent chapters, especially where price policy is discussed. In the conclusion of this chapter we shall attempt to evaluate the contribution of this concept to applied economics by means of a discussion of the advantages and the inadequacies of the concept of marginal cost.

I

THE THEORY OF MARGINAL COST [1]

1. Production functions.

The concept of production functions has already been introduced toward the end of Chapter 4, but a brief description should be helpful in understanding the concept of marginal costs. Let us consider an enterprise engaged in the production of good (Q). In order to produce a quantity Q of these goods, the firm must utilize raw materials, blue-collar workers, and engineers, and operate its available machinery and equipment. In other words, the firm combines the services of various factors of production in order to obtain a desired level of production. This combination has two characteristics:

a) The quantities of the various factors used are not independent. "It is in this way that a farmer can decrease his acreage under cultivation while maintaining his crop yield by increasing his inputs of labor, fertilizer, and other aids to intensive cultivation" [1].

b) For a given production, such quantities are not determined in a unique manner. Substitutions are possible among the various factors of production. It is evident that a firm must attempt to derive maximum advantage from the factors of production it utilizes. In other words, a firm tends to maximize production for each given set of quantities of factors. When this is achieved, the volume of production Q becomes a function of the quantities of the various factors used, $q_1, \ldots, q_i, \ldots, q_n$, and is expressed as

$$Q = Q\,(q_1, ..., q_i, ..., q_n) \qquad (I.1)$$

This function is called the production function.

In actual practice, one is never certain of making maximum use of available factors. A considerable portion of the efforts of business is directed at this aspect of management, which is purely technical since prices are not taken into account.

When a firm produces several types of goods, (Q) and (Q') for example, the production function can be described as follows:

$$f\,(Q, Q', q_1, ..., q_i, ..., q_n) = 0 \qquad (I.2)$$

provided it is possible to modify the proportions of Q and Q', or it can be split into two functions:

$$Q = Q\,(q_1, ..., q_n) \qquad (I.3)$$

$$Q' = mQ \qquad (I.4)$$

provided there exists a constant ratio m between the quantities of (Q) and (Q') produced. In order to simplify, we will assume in what follows, unless otherwise stated, that the firm manufactures only one product.

Production functions can at times be considered as homogeneous. In other words, if the quantities of the factors of production are multiplied by an integer u, the quantity produced is also multiplied by u. Stated mathematically,

$$uQ = Q \ (uq_1, \ ..., \ uq_n) \tag{I.5}$$

The hypothesis of homogeneity of production functions may be tested by linear programming methods (Chapter 12). But, in general, production functions are not homogeneous and for an integer u the following inequality obtains:

$$uQ \leqslant Q \ (uq_1, \ ..., \ uq_n) \tag{I.6}$$

In fact, when the quantities of factors used are multiplied by u, a choice is offered between u identical installations, using the same production methods, and one or many larger installations. The relationship (I.6) may be verified by noting that larger installations are utilized only if they employ more efficient production techniques.

2. Some properties of production functions.

The quantity produced, Q, is evidently an increasing function of the utilized quantities $q_1, \ldots, q_n$. This relationship can be represented either on a (Q, q_i) plane or on a (q_i, q_j) plane.

From the first method of presentation (Fig. 1), we can observe how the quantity produced varies with the quantity used of the factor of production q_i, while other factors are held constant. It should be noted that at the beginning Q increases very rapidly, slows, and finally approaches a limit as q_i increases indefinitely. The shape of the curve obtained can be justified by considering some general observations. When the factor q_i is used in small quantities, the increase in its consumption permits its better utilization. For instance, when manpower is relatively small with respect to the number of available machines, an increase in manpower permits a more effective distribution of tasks which results in a more than proportionate increase in production. But when there is a sufficient number of workers to operate all the machines, an increase in the number of workers will not appreciably increase production unless they work additional shifts.

Two magnitudes are associated with a factor q_i, its output and its marginal efficiency.

The output of q_i is the ratio Q/q_i. This ratio increases until it reaches M, at which point the tangent to the production curve passes through zero. Beyond M the ratio decreases.

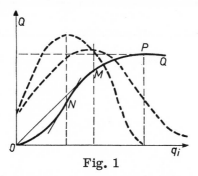

Fig. 1

The marginal efficiency of q_i is the partial derivative $\partial Q_i/\partial q_i$ or, in other terms, the increase in production which results from the use of an incremental unit of q_i. Marginal efficiency increases up to the point N, the inflection point on the Q curve of output, and then decreases until it cancels out the maximum of the Q curve at P. At M it is equal to the output.

In the second method of presentation we shall indicate the substitution possibilities of factors q_i and q_j for a given production and given utilization of the other factors. In fact, once all variables have been fixed except q_i and q_j, the (I.1) relationship traces a curve on the (q_i, q_j) plane. A similar curve is associated with each value of production Q. When it is not possible to substitute factors q_i and q_j, the above curve approaches a right angle whose sides are parallel to the coordinate axes since, in such case, the quantity q_i necessary for the production of Q is independent of q_j and vice versa.

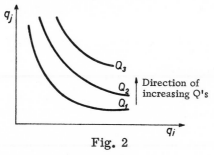

Fig. 2

3. Maximization of a firm's income.

We shall now limit ourselves to a consideration of the case of a hypothetical firm existing for exactly one year. If it sells a quantity of goods Q at a price P and if the various factors of production are purchased at prices p_i, the firm's income is:

$$R = PQ - p_1 q_1 \cdots - p_i q_i \cdots - p_n q_n \qquad (I.7)$$

Management must, at the very outset, select the combination of factors of production which will result in a production Q at the minimum cost. By differentiating (I.1) and (I.7) to maximize R for a given Q, it can be seen that

$$p_1 dq_1 + \cdots + p_i dq_i + \cdots + p_n dq_n = 0 \qquad (I.8)$$
$$Q'_{q1} dq_1 + \cdots + Q'_{qi} dq_i + \cdots + Q'_{qn} dq_n = 0 \qquad (I.9)$$

i.e.,

$$\frac{Q'_{q1}}{p_1} = \cdots\cdots = \frac{Q'_{qi}}{p_i} = \cdots\cdots = \frac{Q''_{qn}}{p_n}. \qquad (I.10)$$

In other words, when the average cost is a minimum (for a given production), the costs of the factors of production are proportional to their marginal efficiency.* Through the use of relationships (I.10) and (I.1) it is possible to calculate q_i with respect to Q. Consequently, when the average cost is minimized for each level of production, production costs are solely a function of the quantity produced. In actual practice, a firm is never certain of finding itself in this situation. Hence, a large portion of its efforts will be spent in determining the optimum combination of factors for each level of production.

Once this result has been obtained, it then remains to determine the level of production itself. This can be illustrated by considering two cases. The first case involves a firm which is in a state of perfect competition and considers price P as given. The second case considers the enterprise faced with a demand curve P(Q); this condition can result from the fact that it occupies a monopolistic position.

We shall now consider these two cases in greater detail.

a) Perfect competition.

When relationship (I.10) holds, the total cost is a function of Q. Let D (Q) be that function:

$$R = PQ - D(Q)$$

---

*At least if the possibility of terminal equilibria is omitted due to the fact that the q_i's are positive or zero.

To maximize R for a given P requires that:

$$P = D'(Q) \qquad (I.11)$$

By definition, $D'(Q)$ is the marginal cost of production. On a producer's market where the price is given, the manufacturer must attempt to set his production at such a level that the marginal cost will be equal to the selling price.

It will be observed that:

$$D'(Q) = \frac{p_1 dq_1 + \cdots + p_i dq_i + \cdots + p_n dq_n}{dQ} = \frac{p_1 dq_1 + \cdots + p_n dq_n}{Q'_{q1} dq_1 + \cdots + Q'_{qn} dq_n} \qquad (I.12)$$

which demonstrates that $D'(Q)$ is equal to the common value of the ratios p_i/Q'_{qi}.

It is important to note that at this point economic analysis has distinguished three types of decisions. The first relates to the optimum technical organization of production (maximization of production for given quantities of factors). The second concerns the minimization of costs (determination of the optimum combination of factors of production) for given levels of production. The third attempts to determine the optimum volume of production. These three types of decisions are frequently inextricably mixed in actual practice, but it is well to remember that they are of very different natures.

A geometric presentation of the foregoing results would be helpful at this point. This is done in Fig. 3.

If it is assumed that the curve representing the production function is of the type shown in Fig. 1, the output of the various factors increases in the beginning, thus allowing a decrease in average cost as production increases. Then the output of the factors of production decreases and the average cost increases with production. This results in an average cost having the traditional U shape. The extent to which practical significance can be attached to these theoretical deductions will be seen later.

If c_m is the marginal cost and c_r the average cost, then:

$$c_m = \frac{d}{dQ}(c_r Q) = c_r + Q \frac{dc_r}{dQ}. \qquad (I.13)$$

The relationship (I.13) indicates that the average cost, when it decreases, is greater than the marginal cost; when it increases, it is less.

Since a firm continues its production only if its income is positive, the selling price and, consequently, the marginal cost must be greater than the average cost.

In Fig. 3, the abscissa is Q and the ordinates are c_m, c_r, and P.

In Fig. 4 the same phenomena are shown, but the ordinates represent total expenditures instead of average and marginal costs. The slope of the tangent at a running point M represents marginal cost, whereas the slope of the straight line OM represents average cost.

There are cases, such as in the railroad industry, where the average cost decreases continually, and consequently the marginal cost is always less than the average cost. For this reason, the markets for these sectors have always been the object of organized efforts to raise prices to the level of average costs (for example, price agreements, formation of public or private monopolies, State control of prices, etc.).

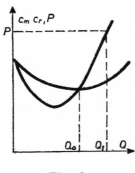

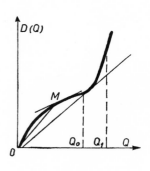

Fig. 3   Fig. 4

b) Existence of a demand curve.

If the price P is a function of the quantity sold Q, the firm's income is:

$$R = P\,(Q)\,Q - D\,(Q).$$

One of the necessary conditions for maximizing income is the existence of the equality:

$$\frac{d\,(PQ)}{dQ} = P\,(Q) + Q\,\frac{dP}{dQ} = D'\,(Q).$$

Consequently, the producer will seek to equalize the marginal cost and the marginal income $d(PQ)/dQ$. The latter is the sum of the receipts for the last unit sold (designated by P) and the variation in receipts for the quantities already sold when the sales are increased by one unit (designated as $Q\,\frac{dP}{dQ}$).

Since this last expression, in accordance with the properties of demand curves, is negative, marginal income is lower than the sales price.

The concept we have just defined is represented in Fig. 5, which is the homologue of Fig. 3. At point A the marginal income equals the marginal cost, whereas at point B selling price equals marginal cost. At point A, however, the sales price is greater than the marginal cost.

The above are the essential facts provided by the economic theory of marginal costs. It must be recognized that, if marginal costs concepts provide a sufficient basis for the development of theories of perfect competition, of general economic equilibrium, and of economic optimum (corporate return: cf. Chapter 14), it constitutes only a starting point for the practitioner of applied economics. However, what the science of economics does provide for management is a certain method of approach to management problems, and it is in that respect that the concept of marginal cost is fruitful, even in its simplest expressions.

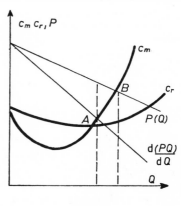

Fig. 5

II

THE CONCEPT OF MARGINAL COST IN ECONOMIC ANALYSIS

Contrary to the hypothesis made by economic theory, a firm finds it difficult to know systematically how to vary its production. According to economic circumstances and the social situation, it can easily consider different processes. For instance, a firm can increase its production by working its available personnel over-time, by hiring additional workers and establishing two shifts instead of one, by purchasing new equipment and creating a new shop, etc.; these possibilities are by no means exhaustive.

For this reason, an economic analyst defines not only one marginal cost, but as many marginal costs as there are possible solutions. Marginal cost has no meaning for an analyst as long as the technical process associated with it is not specified. One should also have the rational limits of production always in mind. Beyond such limits, marginal cost has no meaning.

Workable definitions of marginal costs are therefore contingent upon the industry under consideration, and it would be extremely difficult to adopt a systematic presentation if there were no common problems among the various industries. We shall limit ourselves here to the basic problems, which involve 1) the distinction between short- and long-term marginal costs, 2) the difficulties arising from indivisibility, 3) cases of related production, 4) the estimation of unknown parameters, 5) the effect of technical progress and price factors upon marginal costs.

This entire section (especially pages 263 to 267, 273 to 275, and 278 to 286) has been inspired by the remarkable works of M. Boiteux on the subject. It is to be regretted that these writings have not been published and, consequently, have not had the distribution they deserve beyond a restricted group of specialists.*

1. Short- and long-term marginal costs [6], [3].

In analyzing production functions, we have deliberately refrained from specifying whether it was possible for the producer to vary the quantities of all factors consumed. This possibility is dependent upon the type of decision involved.

In estimating production for the short run, management can expect a variation in the number of man-hours worked and in the consumption of raw materials, but it must generally assume fixed plant capacity. If, on the other hand, management wishes to make plans for the years ahead, it may give thought to the purchase of new equipment and to plant expansion. For instance, an entire range of technical processes exists, from immediate production modifiers to long-range ones. As the time horizon extends, the number of factors of production whose consumption is likely to vary increases. To this range of technical processes can be associated a range of marginal costs.

It is more convenient, however, to reduce the above set of circumstances to two classes: 1) short-term marginal costs, within the framework of a given capacity of production; and 2) long-term marginal costs which presuppose a variable production capacity.

On this basis, short- or long-term marginal costs vary in accordance with the interest rate. If, within the framework of available productive capacity, we increase yearly production, the increase in expenditures is ascribable solely to the increase in production. In a first approximation, the decision taken this year will in no way modify our area of possibilities for the following year. Its effects are exhausted within the year. Short-term marginal cost therefore relates only to a modification in production

---

*We wish to express here our deep appreciation to M. Boiteux, who has been kind enough to authorize us to make use of his studies.

and in expenditures within a specific year, and consequently it may be said that the interest rate does not enter into its calculation.

If, on the other hand, we increase the productive capacity, the expenditures we make will make it possible to increase production not only for the present year, but also for the years following. The effect of our decision extends over the life of the newly created productive capacity. In order to define long-term marginal costs, we must take into consideration both present and future production and expenditures. In order to do this, it will evidently be necessary to utilize the interest rate. For this reason, long-term marginal costs pose more delicate problems than short-term ones. Furthermore, they are closely related to the theory of investment (Chapter 13).

a) Short-term marginal costs.

The simplest procedure is to begin by considering total expenditures. A portion of these expenditures is set at short term and is not affected by a modification in production (for example, the salaries of the director and the nightwatchman, the building rental and maintenance expenses, the portion of amortization and financing costs which represents the depreciation of equipment aside from any use thereof). The remaining expenditures are variable and, once the technical process for modifying production has been determined, an increasing function of the latter. When Q approaches the production capacity Q_m* it becomes increasingly difficult to augment production, and, for even a small increase in the latter, expenditures tend to spiral. Hence the appearance of the function $D(Q)$ in Fig. 6.**

As shown in Fig. 7, the marginal cost increases very slowly in the beginning and then increases very rapidly in the neighborhood

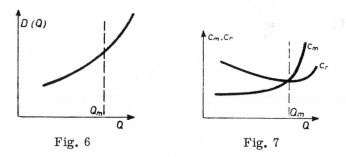

Fig. 6   Fig. 7

---

*Q_m is defined later.

**It will be observed that Fig. 6 reproduces, in fact, the right-hand part of Fig. 4.

of Q_m. The average cost decreases at first, is equal to the marginal cost in a zone close to Q_m, and then, in its turn, increases rapidly.

As a first approximation, it can be taken for granted that it is impossible to exceed Q_m and that no saturation effect is discernible as long as Q_m is not reached. The marginal cost is then practically constant until it reaches Q_m, where it becomes infinite. Figures 6 and 7 become Figs. 8 and 9.

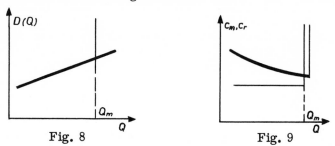

Fig. 8   Fig. 9

In Fig. 8, $D(Q)$ is represented by a straight line with a positive slope until Q_m, and then by a vertical line.

In Fig. 9, the marginal cost is represented by a horizontal line until Q_m, and then by a vertical line. The average cost is a descending hyperbola segment until Q_m, and then it coincides with the vertical line of the marginal cost. It is at the productive capacity Q_m that the equality occurs: $c_m = c_r$.

In the interval where Q is less than Q_m, the short-term marginal cost approximates what is commonly known either as proportional or as partial cost. Proportional cost relates to the expenditures as a whole which, at short term, are proportionate to production, whereas partial cost relates to that portion of expenditures which, at short term, is a function of production.

Figures 8 and 9 show that if the selling price is greater than the marginal cost, the firm will make full use of its productive capacity. If, on the other hand, the price at which Q_m could be sold is less than c_m, the firm will decrease its production and will limit itself to serving customers who are willing to pay a price higher than c_m.

Short-term marginal costs have four general characteristics which should be emphasized:

1. Such costs are not determined in a unique manner, since short-term production can be modified in several ways. The production capacity, furthermore, is not the same for the various technical processes which may be contemplated.

2. In the $Q < Q_m$ interval marginal cost is less than the average cost, but this no longer obtains as one approaches the limit of production capacity.

3. The foregoing presentation is static. It analyzes the variation in expenditures when changing at short term from a stable production level to another production level equally stable. It neglects, however, expenditures which are related to the actual change in the production rate. An analysis of more complex models will be found in the next chapter, which takes into account the dynamic aspects of production.

4. Short-term marginal costs correspond to substantially reversible modifications in the production level. Complete reversibility is reached when the excess expenditure required to increase the production of a unit is exactly equal to the saving brought about by reducing production by one unit. In coal mines, for instance, such a condition approximately obtains when production is changed by regulating the number of workdays in the week. Sometimes reversibility is not complete; for example if, in order to increase production, additional workers are hired, it will be necessary when reducing production to lay off some workers. However, such an operation entails some expenditure. It will be necessary either to grant severance pay, or to wait a certain time before laying off workers, or finally, for social reasons, to abstain from any layoffs and wait for attrition to restore the balance. Under these conditions, the marginal cost of contraction will be greater than that of expansion. But the difference is slight and the relationship between contraction costs and expansion costs is not complex. This is not the case insofar as long-term marginal costs are concerned.

b) Long-term marginal costs.

For the sake of simplification, we shall at first assume that short-term marginal cost is defined without any ambiguity, although we are aware of the fact that this is generally not the case. In order to justify this temporary position, we wish to point out that it is reasonable to assume that, within the framework of a given production capacity, the firm makes use of a production technique which will minimize expenditures for each production level.

We have analyzed how expenditures vary with production Q for a factory which has a capacity Q_m. Such expenditures are characterized by the function $D(Q,Q_m)$, in which Q_m is a parameter. The curves $D(Q,Q_m)$ have an envelope (L) which is shown in Fig. 10. Since we have not yet assigned a specific definition to productive capacity, nothing need prevent us from defining it as the abscissa value of the intersection of the curve of expenditures and its envelope. The latter's function, consequently, is: $D(Q_m,Q_m)$. It remains to be seen what it represents economically.

The immediate result of an envelope's properties is that it is impossible to produce a quantity Q_m by allowing expenditures less

than $D(Q_m,Q_m)$. Furthermore, minimum expenditures are obtained
in the case of a factory of capacity Q_m, i.e., a factory where the
production capacity is exactly ad-
justed to the production level.

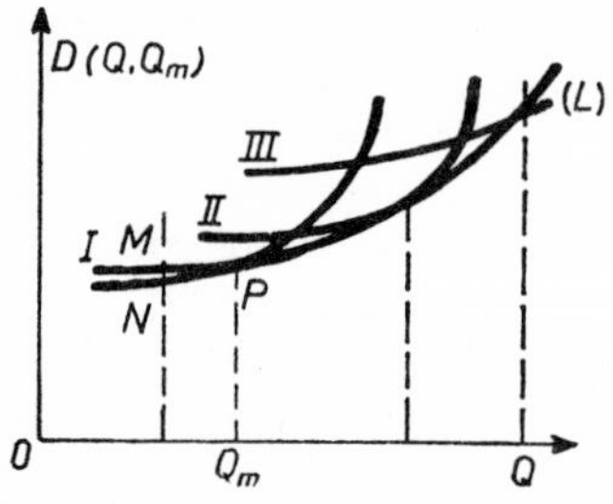

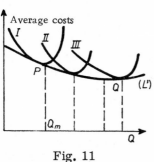

Fig. 10

Curve (L) is therefore the curve
of expenditures when considering factories of variable capacity and whose
production levels are equal to the
capacity.

Let us now select a curve $D(Q,Q_m)$
which is tangent to (L) at a point P of
abscissa Q_m, and two other points
M and N on the same abscissa such
that M is on the curve $D(Q,Q_m)$ and
N on (L). The slopes of the straight
lines OM and ON represent, respectively, the average cost when Q
is produced in a factory of capacity Q_m, and the average cost when
Q is produced in a factory of capacity Q.

The first is the short-term average cost and the second can be
defined as the long-term average cost. By "long-term" we mean
"that which relates to a plant with an adjusted capacity."

The short-term average cost is naturally always higher than
the long-term average cost, except at the intersection P of the curves
$D(Q,Q_m)$ and (L). When a Q value lies in the neighborhood of Q_m,
the difference in the slopes of the lines OM and ON is an infinitesimal of the second order. Curves representing the two average
costs are therefore tangent to each other at a point whose abscissa
value is Q_m. This justifies the presentation in Fig. 11 in which
average costs are indicated as ordinates. Furthermore (L'), which
represents the long-run average cost curve, is the envelope of the
short-term average cost curves.

As a general rule, an increase in
productive capacity results at first
in a decrease in average costs. However, beyond a certain capacity, organizational difficulties become pre-
ponderant and average costs begin to
increase. Thus the curve (L') has a
minimum (denoted as R in Fig. 11)
whose position is dependent upon the
state of technical knowledge.

Fig. 11

Finally, let us deduce from Fig.
10 what we can concerning marginal
costs. It is natural to define long-term marginal cost as the slope of
the curve (L). It is the ratio of the difference in expenditures dD to the
difference in production dQ for production plants of Q and Q+dQ capacity. Figure 10 demonstrates that the long-term marginal cost C_m

is greater than the short-term marginal cost c_m for $Q < Q_m$, but becomes less than c_m for $Q > Q_m$.

When Q is less than Q_m, there are fewer differences between the expenditures of one factory at two similar levels of production than between the expenditures of two factories having similar capacity. In effect, in order to increase the production of the factory whose capacity is Q_m, it is sufficient to increase manpower and materials in "reasonable" quantities, since we are producing below production capacity. However, when one goes from a capacity Q to a capacity $Q + dQ$, it becomes necessary to increase expenditures for supplemental investments.

When Q is greater than Q_m, the plant of capacity Q_m becomes so badly adjusted that the increase in expenditure for manpower and supplies along with production more than compensates the differences of investment between factories whose capacities have been adjusted.

Figure 12 shows various curves of short- and long-term marginal costs.

In the particular case of Figs. 8 and 9, where short-term marginal cost is held constant, Figs. 10 and 12 become Figs. 13 and 14. The curve (L) is the locus of the angular point of curves of short-term expenditure when Q_m varies. The curve of long-term marginal costs intersects the curves of short-term marginal costs on their vertical extension.

At this point, we must realize that geometry can be misleading and is responsible for four types of difficulties in interpretation. They are discussed below.

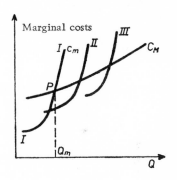

Fig. 12

1. It should be noted that all $D(Q,Q_m)$ curves and curve (L) assume a given level of technology. If certain industrial plants are preferable to others for certain productions, it is not because they make use of more modern techniques but because they call upon a combination of existing techniques better adapted to such production.

2. What do the expenditures indicated by the ordinates actually represent? Let us consider a permanent system where the plants all have the same life expectancy T. The cost of renovating a plant is equal to its construction cost, and consequently the amortization and financing charges can be interpreted as a provision for such renovation.

The $D(Q,Q_m)$ function incorporates, under these conditions, all of the accountable expenditures of a year in which production is Q;

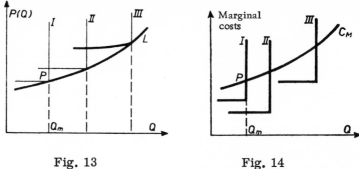

Fig. 13   Fig. 14

these expenditures include past expenditures (or provisions for future expenditures) in the form of amortization and financing charges as well as fixed expenditures (such as maintenance costs) or variable expenditures (such as some wages and material).

Let $D_1(Q_m)$ and $D_2(Q,Q_m)$ respectively represent these two types of expenditure, with $I(Q_m)$ the investment required for the construction of an industrial plant with a capacity Q_m. Let us also assume that the sum of the amortization and financing charges is the same each year. Hence it follows that

$$I(Q_m) = D_1(Q_m) \sum_{p=1}^{T} \frac{1}{(1+i)^p} \quad i\text{: interest rate}$$

$$D(Q, Q_m) = D_1(Q_m) + D_2(Q, Q_m).$$

The short-term marginal cost is the derivative with respect to Q of $D_2(Q,Q_m)$ for a given Q_m. The long-run marginal cost is the derivative with respect to Q_m of $D(Q,Q_m)$ for $Q = Q_m$.

The definition of long-term costs therefore requires an allocation of the costs of investment among the various years. It is assumed, in fact, that if an industrial plant with a capacity Q_m produces Q_m during its entire life, all annual costs are equal. Insofar as long-term marginal cost is concerned, we must therefore represent on a yearly graph a phenomenon which extends over the entire lifetime of an installation. For this reason, a simple consideration of marginal costs does not answer all questions relative to production levels.

3. The curve (L) compares the cost of factories of different capacities constructed on the same technological level. If we start from point P in Fig. 10 and move along the (L) curve, this would imply that we are abandoning the factory with capacity Q_m and that we are constructing a factory with a capacity $Q_m + dQ_m$. However, if the industrial plant with a capacity of Q_m has not yet reached

the end of its economic life and if management wishes to increase
the available capacity of production by dQ_m, it would probably be
preferable to expand the capacity of the existing factory rather than
construct an industrial plant with a capacity $Q_m + dQ_m$. The additional expense will amount to $dD(Q_m)$. It is obvious that:

$$dD\ (Q_m) \geqslant C_M dQ_m$$

This solution obviates the need for renovating the productive
capacity of the existing factory. It is only at the expiration of the
economic life of the plant that another plant with a capacity of
$Q_m + dQ_m$ need be constructed.

4. There is nothing to prevent us, within the above theory, from
replacing a factory by an industrial complex comprising several
factories. It can also happen that the optimum enterprise for a
capacity $Q_m + dQ_m$ will consist of a number of factories forming
the optimum for the capacity Q_m plus an additional plant of capacity dQ_m. For example, in the case of coal mines the optimum
enterprise with a capacity $Q_m + dQ_m$ will be obtained by adding
another branch to those already existing. The optimum enterprise
with a capacity of $Q_m - dQ_m$ may be attained by closing the least
satisfactory shop or plant.

The nature of long-term marginal cost then becomes much more
simple and useful. The long-term marginal cost is the actual additional expense incurred when a new installation of unit capacity is
added to existing installations.

In actual practice, long-term marginal costs can rarely be related to variations in capacity of homogeneous units. Most of the
time, the factories constituting an enterprise are of different ages
and the technological homogeneity called for in the preceding
theory is not realized. In order to increase production, a shop or
a modern factory is created; to reduce production, older installations are closed. The long-term marginal cost for an expanded
system differs from the cost for the contracted system. Finally,
since the best solution is not known a priori, one is led to define
several long-term marginal costs instead of the single marginal
cost associated with the optimum solution provided by the theory.

We therefore must restudy long-term marginal costs from a
slightly different point of view, taking into account the distinction
between expansion costs and contraction costs [33].

The following analysis presents an approximation usable when
the selling price of the goods remains constant over a period of
time.

Expansion costs.

Let us assume that in constructing a shop or a new factory we
increase the future capacity and actual production of an enterprise.

With the help of investments, production can increase from its present level by:

$$\Delta Q_1 \text{ the first year}$$

. . . .

$$\Delta Q_p \text{: the pth year.}$$

But to bring about this increase in production will require two types of expenditure: new projects expenditure: $D_1, D_2, \ldots, D_p$ spread over the first two years, and additional operational expenditures which can be conveniently incorporated each year in the shape of the product of the increased production Q_p multiplied by a properly calculated unit cost c_p. The present value of the future expenditures required by the increase in production is therefore:

$$D_0 = \sum_p \frac{D_p + c_p \, \Delta Q_p}{(1 + i)^p}.$$

There exists then a cost x such that, should each year an additional production unit cost x, future expenditures would be equal in present value to D_0, so that:

$$x \sum \frac{\Delta Q_p}{(1 + i)^p} = D_0.$$

From the above discussion of long-term marginal costs, it is logical to define x as the marginal cost of expansion of an enterprise; x is contingent upon the technological process which is used to increase production.

Contraction costs.

This problem can be posed in similar terms, but here the comparison ends. Let us assume that by closing shops or factories we cause a decrease in the future production of an enterprise—a production which, otherwise, would have been constant—and let us limit ourselves to a simple case in which the reduction in production is effected in a single year.

In order to define contraction cost, we must compare the solution of the immediate closing of marginal units with the other possible solutions such as an indefinite extension of their utilization or their shutdown at various times in the future, possibly at the end of their useful lives.

The first alternative to be considered is either an immediate closing down of marginal units or an indefinite extension of their utilization. In short, now or never.

If ΔQ, the production of marginal units, had not been stopped, the firm's expenditures would have been, for an annual production $Q + \Delta Q$, D_1 the first year, D_2 the second year, etc.

The shutdown will bring expenditures down to D_1', D_2', ..., D_p'. The present value of savings resulting from the closing is therefore:

$$D_0 = \sum_p \frac{D_p - D_p'}{(1 + i)^p}.$$

There is a saving x such that if, each year, the production of one less unit would save x, future savings would be equal in present value to D_0:

$$x \sum \frac{\Delta Q}{(1 + i)^p} = D_0.$$

It is possible to define x as the marginal cost of contraction in the "now or never" alternative. This marginal cost, which compares two permanent systems, is in the neighborhood of the (L) curve.

The consequences of closing down marginal shops will not be felt immediately. The firm may economize immediately on expenditures for raw materials and wages. It will probably avoid laying off certain specialized workers, foremen, or engineers. It will therefore have, within these various categories, a transitory volume of employees over and above its actual needs. Attrition through resignations and retirements will reduce these expenses. On the other hand, as a result of the closing down of marginal shops, the capacity of certain sections of the factory may have become surplus. These margins of capacity can only be reabsorbed progressively as renovations occur.

If, in the event the plant were not shut down, the annual expenditures remained constant, this situation could be represented on a graph in which production is indicated as the abscissa and annual expenditures as the ordinate. The enterprise is initially at P (with production $Q + \Delta Q$ and expenditure d). The first year production decreases from $Q + \Delta Q$ to Q, and the expenditures from d to d_1. The following years production remains constant, but the costs decrease uniformly to levels d_2, d_3, ... and finally to a limit d_L when the firm is completely readjusted to its new productive capacity. Hence:

$$D_0 = HP_1 + \frac{HP_2}{1 + i} + \frac{HP_3}{(1 + i)^2} + \cdots$$

It will be observed that, as a result of transitory expenses, the contraction cost x is less than the average cost of marginal units.

However, alternatives other than that of the immediate shutdown of marginal units or the indefinite extension of their utilization should be considered. Such alternatives are immediate closing or within a year, immediate closing or within two years, etc.

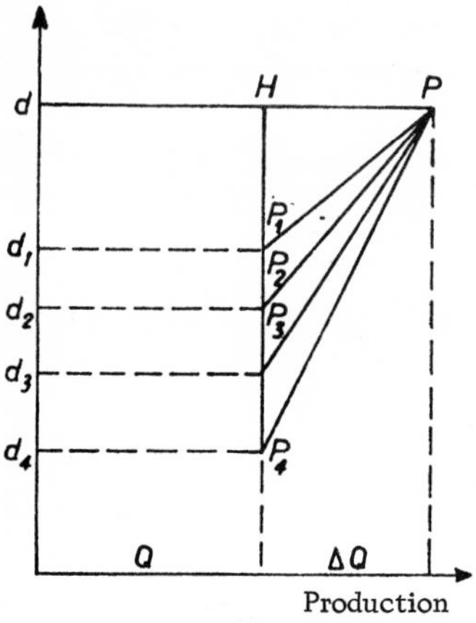

It is possible to ascribe contraction costs to each of these alternatives. We will indicate as x_0^t the contraction cost corresponding to immediate closing or in t years. The contraction cost x defined in the foregoing paragraph becomes, by virtue of this convention, x_0^∞.

D_0 always being the difference in realized expenditures between the two solutions compared, x_0^t is defined by the relationship:

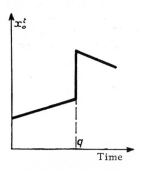

Fig. 15

$$x_0^t \sum_{p=0} \frac{\Delta Q}{(1 + i)^p} = D_0.$$

x_0^t makes it possible to know what the cost would be of continuing production Q for an additional year. It would most likely be small; since the installation will be closed, every effort will be made during that period to avoid purchasing additional material and to reduce maintenance and repair costs, etc. x_0^5 is probably greater because during the interim some maintenance and repair will be necessary. If, during a certain year q, it becomes necessary to renovate all or part of the equipment, x_0^{q+1} would be much greater than x_0^q (cf. Fig. 16).

The new long-run marginal costs which we have defined above do not evolve from a comparison of two permanent systems. For

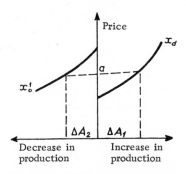

Fig. 16

Fig. 17

this reason, they are only loosely related to marginal cost as defined by the curve (L). Contrary to the latter, they are the result of an effort at adjustment of the concept of marginal cost to a system which evolves over time.

The new plant units which may be created may be very different from those which may be shut down, so there is no reason for contraction and expansion costs to be equal a priori. This is demonstrated by the following very simple model. If the units which can be created are classified in the order of increasing expansion costs x_d and the units which can be shut down are classified in the order of decreasing contraction costs x_0^1, two monotonic curves can be drawn representing contraction and expansion costs. Let a be the sales price of a product manufactured by the firm presumed to be constant over a period of time. The following three cases are then possible:

1) If a is greater—in the present situation—than the values of x_d and x_0^1, it is in the interest of the firm to increase its production capacity until: $x_d = a$.

2) If a is less—in the present situation—than the values of x_d and x_0^1, it is in the interest of the firm to close units until: $x_0^1 = a$.

3) If a is included between x_d and x_0^1, two alternatives are possible:

a) $x_d > x_0^1$ The firm does not change its production.

b) $x_d < x_0^1$ The firm opens new units and immediately closes older units until the following equality is realized:

$$x_0^1 = a = x_d.$$

If the initial production of the enterprise was A, the balanced production is: $A + \Delta A_1 - \Delta A_2$ (Fig. 17).

It is conceivable that there must also exist, as a result of company policy, a functional relationship between x_0^1, x_0^2. . . . But it is unnecessary to dwell further on this analysis. The important thing was to demonstrate the diversity of marginal costs in the real world.

2. Difficulties caused by indivisibility.

Let us begin by recalling the well-known example of the "passenger for Calais." A train is about to start for Calais. A traveler shows up. What does the additional expenditure caused by this traveler amount to? This is a short-term problem and in this discussion we shall utilize a curve similar to that in Fig. 6. The abscissa will represent the number of passengers.

As long as there are seats still available in the train, the cost increases very slowly with the number of passengers. The additional passenger will cause very minor cost increases for some additional wear to the seat covering and a minute increase in the coal consumption by the locomotive. When the number of passengers increases and approaches the limit of the train's capacity, costs tend to rise abruptly. For example, there may be some passengers who are travelling without tickets, or the inside equipment of the railroad cars may be damaged. Furthermore, because of crowded conditions, some passengers may prefer to use their private automobile or the bus next time. Thus an impossible situation is reached. The curve of expenditures I is shown in Fig. 18.

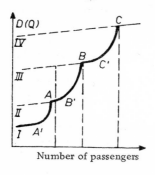

Number of passengers

Fig. 18

If the number of passengers continues to increase, another car is added to the train. In other words, the process of adjustment of production to demand is modified. Costs are then represented by curve II of Fig. 18. This curve does not exist for X values less than A. With an additional car, saturation reappears in the interval B. However, the curve corresponding to the addition of a second car (curve III) is probably farther removed from curve II than curve II is from curve I. This is so because an overloading of cars causes the locomotive to burn coal beyond its capacity.

In the interval C, costs rise to a level where it would be advisable to have the train run in two sections. The cost in such case will be represented by curve IV.

Although the curves which correspond to each technical process can be considered as continuous, the minimum total cost curve presents, in actual practice, discontinuities at A, B, C. The marginal cost is very low throughout except at A, B, C, where it is practically infinite (see Fig. 19). In any case, this marginal cost does not provide any information regarding the general trend of expenditures.

This analysis proves that we have placed ourselves on a level where our hypothesis of continuity no longer is valid and the concepts introduced thereby lose their usefulness. A recognized procedure in physical science is to change the level of observation to make the hypothesis of continuity tenable. Through such points as A′, B′, C′, we can trace a curve representing the costs of running one train relative to the number of cars, or (which amounts to the same thing) relative to the number of passengers if we assume the cars to be completely filled. The slope of the curve, at first constant, will increase rapidly when it becomes difficult to add more cars to the train. The same curve can be drawn for two trains where the abscissa represents the number of passengers transported by the two trains. A curve representing total costs

relative to the number of trains is traced through points I, J, etc.,
where it is preferable to make up an additional train rather than
to add another car (Fig. 20).

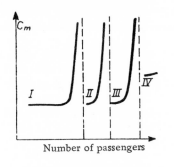

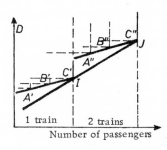

Fig. 19   Fig. 20

The slope at any point of the curve A′B′C′ defines an average
marginal cost corresponding to the increase in the number of cars,
and the slope curve IJ defines an average marginal cost corresponding to the increase in the number of trains.

The curve A′B′C′ serves as a long-term curve relative to
curves I, II, III, IV. It corresponds to the change in capacity represented by the change in the number of cars. Similarly, the curve
IJ serves as a long-term curve relative to curves such as A′B′C′.
It corresponds to the change in capacity represented by the change
in the number of trains.

We started our discussion with examples of discontinuities
connected with operations, but even more important discontinuities
are found in investment problems. In coal mining, for example, it
would not be economical to open a new mine if the coal extracted
were less than 2,000 to 3,000 tons per day, or 600,000 to 900,000
tons per year.

It can be realized intuitively that, if the distance between two
discontinuities is not too great with respect to the zone of production variation, the curves which define average marginal costs are
of some importance. When the discontinuities are "distant" and
small in number, it is preferable to abandon these curves and
reason merely on the basis of discontinuity.

3. Multiple production.

In criticizing certain accounting practices in Chapter 8, we
touched upon the question of multiple products. At this point it
must be reconsidered relative to the concept of marginal cost.

The solution is immediate when there are fixed relationships
between the quantities of the various goods produced. It is only

necessary to identify the marginal cost of the multiple production. Of greater interest is the general case where it is possible to modify the relative proportions of the various products. It is such a case that we plan to examine in two stages. The first stage deals with a firm which produces two distinct types of goods. The second stage concerns a firm which produces the same nonstorable goods at different periods of time.

a) With its production of gas and coke, a coke-making plant is a perfect example of a factory producing two types of goods. Coke is produced in the ovens from which is derived, in a given ratio, both rich gas (G_0) and coke (C_0).

If it is desired to obtain the maximum of coke, the ovens are heated by fires of rich gas and, for a quantity C_0 of coke, the available quantity of gas is G_0' (where $G_0' < G_0$).

But if it is desired to increase the quantity of gas, coke can be burned in gas generators, and the byproduct gas obtained can be used to replace the rich gas used to heat the ovens. This operation can be continued until the ovens are heated only by byproduct gas.

In order to increase the quantity of gas still further, it is necessary to add to the rich gas a blend of byproduct gas and of cracking gas.

Stated geometrically, if the ordinates represent the quantity of coke produced and the abscissa represents the quantity of gas, the area above the straight line whose slope is C_0/G_0' represents impossible technological combinations (Fig. 21).

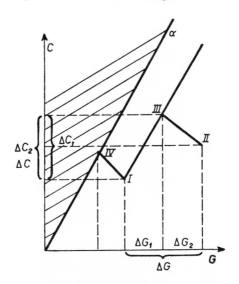

Fig. 21

The total cost of the coke-making plant is a function $D(C,G)$ of quantities C and G of coke and gas produced. Marginal costs of production of coke and gas are therefore defined by the relationships:

$$c_{mC} = \frac{\partial}{\partial C} D(C, G)$$

$$c_{mG} = \frac{\partial}{\partial G} D(C, G).$$

These two marginal costs are obviously dependent upon C, G, and the processes employed in modifying production.

Let us determine, for example, the additional expense entailed by a change of production C_1, G_1 (point I in Fig. 21) to production C_2, G_2 (point II in Fig. 21). The costs are:

$$C_2 = C_1 + \Delta C \qquad G_2 = G_1 + \Delta G.$$

Let us assume that we wish to increase the production of coke. This is accomplished by increasing the production of the ovens, i.e., in shifting from point I to point III on a straight line whose slope is C_0/G_0'. The cost of this operation varies according to whether it is necessary to refire a battery of ovens, construct an additional battery in the coke-making plant, or construct a new plant. Moving from point III to point II implies that a portion of the additional coke produced has been burned.

Let us define the following:

ΔC_1 ΔG_1 are the components of vector I-III.

ΔC_2 ΔG_2 are the components of vector III-II.

α is the ratio of coke produced to gas produced in ovens heated with rich gas $\alpha = \dfrac{C_0}{G_0'}$.

β is the ratio of coke consumed to gas produced when burning coke in gas generators and when by-product gas is substituted for rich gas in the heating of the ovens.

$$\Delta C_1 = \alpha \Delta G_1 \qquad -\Delta C_2 = \beta \Delta G_2$$
$$\Delta C_1 + \Delta C_2 = \Delta C \qquad \Delta G_1 + \Delta G_2 = \Delta G.$$

Finally, let the function $D_1(C)$ represent the cost of coke-making in the ovens with respect to the quantity of coke obtained as output, and let the function $D_2(G)$ represent the expenditure involved in the use of gas generators with respect to the additional quantity of gas obtained when coke is burned to obtain gas. Let C_1' and G_1' be the coordinates of point IV, which represents the situation before the use of gas generators, when it is desired to arrive at point I. When changing from point I to point II, the additional expense is expressed as:

$$D_1'(C_1') \Delta C_1 + D_2'(G_1 - G_1') \Delta G_2$$

ΔC_1 and ΔG_2 can be expressed as a function of ΔC and ΔG. From the four equations previously written between ΔC, ΔG, ΔC_1, ΔG_1, ΔC_2, ΔG_2, one obtains:

$$\Delta C_1 = \frac{\alpha\,(\Delta C + \beta \Delta G)}{\alpha + \beta} \qquad \Delta G_2 = \frac{\alpha \Delta G - \Delta C}{\alpha + \beta}.$$

The coefficients of ΔC and ΔG are, by definition, the marginal costs of an increase in the production of coke and gas, respectively. They are:

$$\text{Coke:} \quad \frac{1}{\alpha + \beta}\,(\alpha D_1'\,(C_1') - D_2'\,(G_1 - G_1'))$$

$$\text{Gas:} \quad \frac{\alpha}{\alpha + \beta}\,(\beta D_1'\,(C_1') + D_2'\,(G_1 - G_1')).$$

In the example provided above, it is possible to vary the proportions of coke and gas by combining two processes each possessing constant ratios of the two products. This case occurs frequently in actual practice, which is why it has been discussed at some length. However, there are, of course, some industries, such as oil refineries, where the same technique can produce variable percentages of different products. This condition does not create any difficulty in the calculation of marginal costs. These result, as above, from a comparison of costs between two similar production methods. It is especially convenient to select these methods in such manner so that they differ only in the production level of a single product.

b) "Multiple products" may very well be physically identical since it suffices that they be economically distinct, that they not be storable, and that they be produced at different periods of time. For instance, a kilowatt-hour in March and a kilowatt-hour in June must be considered as two related products. The same applies to telephone communications at different hours of the day, transportation of passengers by the S.N.C.F. on different days, gas distribution among the various months of the year (in fact, normally the only means of storage is provided by gasometers which can regulate production only on a daily or weekly basis), and all services in general, from haircuts to medical consultations.

Volume of production may be shown on a curve as quantities delivered per unit of time. For example, Electricité de France delivers at each moment t a certain power $q(t)$ based on a curve which, once the rates are given, is selected by the consumers. The total annual cost is now dependent upon curve $q(t)$ as a whole. Under these circumstances, what does the notion of marginal cost become [7] ?

In order to simplify matters, we will consider the particular case of an isolated steam generating station distributing energy to its network according to a given power curve q(t). The station's annual expenditures must be analyzed with respect to q(t). However, researchers have usually tried to avoid considering curves as a whole and have attempted to substitute for curves a finite number of parameters. Thus, instead of dealing with a distribution, they base their deductions on the first and second moments, and, in dealing with probability functions, they concern themselves only with the mean and the variance. The problem here is to substitute for an infinite number of related products represented by q(t) a small number of hypothetical products A, B, . . . These hypothetical products can be considered as simultaneous products, such that a) the demand q(t) is satisfied for given productions of A, B, etc., but is not satisfied when there is any reduction in one of them, and b) the total annual cost is a function of A, B.

Thus the costs of a steam generating plant can be separated into power costs and energy costs, and assume the form:

$$D = D_1(P) + CE$$

in which: P is the plant's power;

E the energy it produces in one year;

C the short-term marginal cost of a kilowatt-hour when the latter is required for power less than P.

Energy costs, in addition to being a function of the hours of use, are also dependent upon the costs of such items as fuel, maintenance, amortization and financing charges, and necessary renovation and replacement. Power costs, on the other hand, are a function of investments related to the size of the station, whose replacement is more or less independent of use.

Within a given year (O,T) the curve q(t) has a maximum at $\hat{q}$ which is the required peak power. The area below the curve represents the supply of energy furnished during the year:

$$Q = \int_0^T q(t)\, dt.$$

If the station has a power P equal to $\hat{q}$ and produces during the year a quantity of energy E equal to Q, it fully meets demand. Any reduction in either P or E will result in a failure to meet the demand. Consequently, peak power and annual energy constitute two related products which can be substituted for the curve q(t).

In order to carry the analysis further, we shall distinguish between the general case of a curve of any load whatsoever and the particular case of a load curve having a peak level.

1. The general curve (Fig. 22). If the load curve is modified in such a way that q remains constant, there is no need of peak energy. With a change dQ in demand, the variation in cost is:

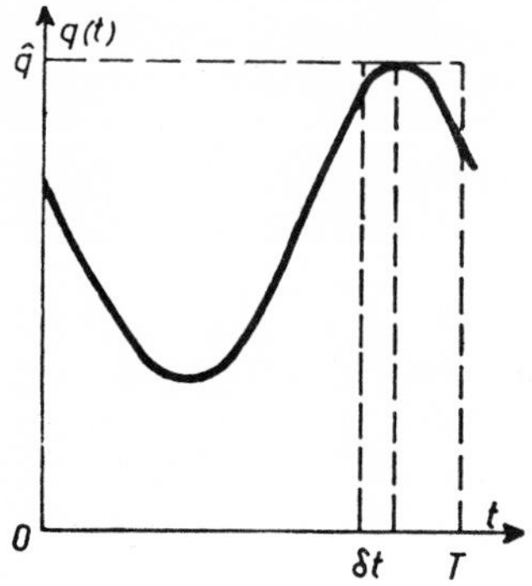

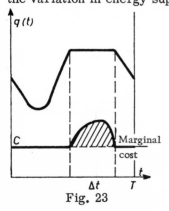

$$dD = CdQ.$$

In other words, the nonpeak marginal cost equals the kw.-hr. energy cost. If, on the other hand, the peak power of the load curve should move from $\hat{q}$ to $q + dq$ during the very short time δt, and if the additional energy required is equally distributed during the peak period δt, the cost variation is:

Fig. 22

$$dD = D_1' \, (\hat{q}) \, \frac{dQ}{\delta t} + C \, dQ$$

since: $dQ = \delta t \cdot d\hat{q}$.

The peak period marginal cost, consequently, is equal to: $\dfrac{D_1' \, (q)}{\delta t} + C$ and since the peak lasts but a brief time, the cost is considerable.

As was pointed out previously, when a firm seeks to maximize its income, it establishes a relationship between its selling prices and its marginal costs. The peak marginal cost being high, a firm producing electricity would find it necessary to fix the peak price at a very high level. This would result in the collapse of the peak and the establishment of a peak level. This second type of load curve will now be analyzed briefly.

2. Load curve with a peak level (Fig. 23). Let Δt be the finite extent of the peak level. For a total displacement of the peak level, the variation in energy supplied is:

$$dQ = \Delta t \cdot d\hat{q}$$

and the marginal cost as a whole for the peak level has the finite value:

$$C + \frac{D_1' \, (q)}{\Delta t}.$$

Within this hypothesis, we are able to calculate only the marginal cost of the peak level as a whole because any call upon peak energy during a very brief period of time would lead as before to an extremely high marginal cost.

Fig. 23

A curve representing the marginal cost in addition to the load curve is shown in Fig. 23. The former, which is equal to C except at the peak level, is unknown for the t values which correspond to the peak level. All that we know is that the shaded area is equal to:

$$C + \frac{D_1' \, (\widehat{q})}{\Delta t}.$$

The marginal cost at each of the peak level points can be determined, however, by calling upon the properties of demand.

In order to demonstrate this, we will assume:

a) that the selling price and the marginal cost are equal at each instant of time t;

b) that the instantaneous demands are independent. This hypothesis, which is obviously inaccurate, amounts to assuming that demand at instant t is dependent only upon the price at that instant, and does not depend upon the prices prevailing at other hours of the day.

When the selling price is equal to C, demand is a well-determined function of time: q(t,C). However, the sales price is not equal to C during the peak level period. This demand function is valid, therefore, only below the horizontal of the ordinate q̂.

To each value of q̂ is associated a peak level, both lengthwise and locationwise. If p(t) represents the selling price, one must find over the whole level that:

$$\int_{\Delta t} p \, (t) \, \mathrm{d}t = C \, \Delta t + D_1' \, (\widehat{q})$$

This relationship expresses the equality of marginal cost and selling price over the entire range of the peak level. However, q(t) is a price which must maintain demand at the level of q̂. This condition defines the prevailing price at each moment, and this relationship can be expressed as:

$$\int_{\Delta t} p \, (t, \widehat{q}) \, \mathrm{d}t = C \, \Delta t + D_1' \, (\widehat{q}).$$

It defines q̂ and, by the same token, the price—and the marginal cost—at each peak moment.

The nature of this demonstration would be in no wise changed if it were assumed that the various instantaneous demands are not independent.

Despite the difference in presentation, the relationship which exists between short- and long-term marginal costs, on the one hand, and peak and extrapeak period marginal costs, on the other, will be easily recognized. The nonpeak period marginal cost is merely a short-term marginal cost when total capacity is not utilized. The peak period marginal cost is a long-term marginal cost since it corresponds to an increase in the capacity of production, but it differs from that defined in paragraph 1. In paragraph 1 we assumed that the productive capacity was fully utilized at each moment. Here, however, we assume that it is only utilized during the peak level period.

In actual practice, it is interesting to note that peak period marginal cost is substantially higher than during a nonpeak period. In the case of the S.N.C.F., for instance, there is no relationship between the cost of transporting one passenger on a weekday in winter and the transportation cost of the same passenger during late July and early August, the peak period of vacation travel. In order to be in a position to provide this summer transportation, the S.N.C.F. must purchase, store, and maintain during the whole year material and equipment which will be put into use for only a few days [3]. In the case of Electricité de France, also, there is no common measure between the cost of producing a kilowatt-hour during the night, when demand is very low, and the cost of production of one kilowatt-hour during a peak hour of a winter day. The production of electricity to meet peak demand requires the use of additional standby power sources such as older steam generating plants.

This is why the price-setting of nonstorable goods must make a distinction between peak and nonpeak delivery. These problems will also be considered in the chapter on price policy.

4. Taking uncertainty into account.

Until now we have assumed that demand and production were known. But either one or the other can be uncertain. In this section we shall attempt to state and develop the problem when either demand or production is not known [9], [32].

a) Random demand.

Let us consider the case of a firm which produces nonstorable goods (Q) and must meet the demand at the very moment it occurs. Such a demand very frequently includes a random component.

Before we proceed we shall assume that the firm has set its selling price at a value P which cannot be adjusted to meet variations in demand; we shall further assume that demand is a random variable and that Q is distributed according to the normal law with a mean value $\bar{Q}(P)$ and a standard deviation s.

As demonstrated in Chapter 2, one of the means available to a firm for the determination of its behavior is to attribute to itself a likelihood of stockout p, i.e., the likelihood that at price P it will be unable to meet the demand. Once p has been selected it becomes possible to determine the necessary productive capacity Q_m. This capacity is related to p by the equation:

$$p = \int_{Q_m}^{\infty} \frac{1}{\sqrt{2\pi s}} e^{\frac{-(x-\overline{Q})^2}{2s^2}} \, dx. \qquad (\text{II.}1)$$

The relationship (II.1) can be written as follows:

$$\frac{Q_m - \overline{Q}}{s} = k(p) \qquad (\text{II.}2)$$

since the integral (II.1) makes use only of the transformed variable:

$$\frac{x - \overline{Q}}{s}$$

k(p) is a diminishing function of the likelihood of stockout, positive infinite for p = 0, equal to for p = 1/2, and negative infinite for p = 1.

If C represents the marginal cost of the short-term production of a unit of Q within the limits of productive capacity, and $D_1(Q_m)$ is the cost with respect to the capacity Q_m, the mathematical expectation of the expenditures of the firm, assuming that the likelihood of stockout is small, will be:

$$D = C\overline{Q} + D_1(Q_m). \qquad (\text{II.}3)$$

Some interesting observations may be deduced from the above relationship:

Marginal cost of average demand. If, for a given p, Q increases slightly, the relationship (II.2) implies that $dQ_m = dQ$. The marginal cost of average demand is therefore:

$$\frac{dD}{d\overline{Q}} = C + D_1'(Q_m). \qquad (\text{II.}4)$$

Marginal cost of random demand. One may seek to determine for given p to what extent an increase in s causes an increase in costs. In other words, the following question is raised: What would be the cost of maintaining the same guarantee if demand became more erratic? Relationship (II.2) sets:

$$dQ_m = k(p) \, ds.$$

From which is derived the marginal cost of random demand:

$$\frac{dD}{ds} = k(p) D_1'(Q_m). \qquad (\text{II.}5)$$

If a firm sells to a certain number of customers i whose demands are independent random variables with a standard deviation s_i, the total variance is:

$$s^2 = \Sigma s_i^2.$$

The differential of s is then:

$$ds = s_i \frac{ds_i}{s}$$

which enables us to define the marginal cost when the demand of customer i fluctuates:

$$\frac{s_i}{s} k(p) D_1'(Q_m).$$

Marginal cost of stockout. We have indicated in Chapter 2 the desirability of analyzing cost variations with respect to the likelihood of stockout. This analysis gives some idea of the saving which could be realized by allowing a certain flexibility in the guarantee.

When p takes on an increment dp, the differential of the necessary productive capacity Q_m becomes:

$$dQ_m = sk'(p) dp.$$

Consequently, when p is small, the marginal cost of stockout is:

$$- D_1'(Q_m) sk'(p).$$

It is negative since k'(p) is negative, and it is the diminution of the probability of stockout that is expressed by an increase in costs.

The consequences of stockout can be very different from the customer's standpoint. There is no common ground between an electric power failure which interrupts an operation in a hospital and a power failure which prevents a six-year-old child from doing his homework. It would therefore be entirely logical for an enterprise such as Electricité de France to offer different types of contracts to its customers with variable guarantees and the price scaled to the guarantee.

b) Random production [13].

We could deal in the same manner with the case of a random production which is normally distributed about its mean value Q with a standard deviation s, and destined to meet a constant demand Q. Such a case would correspond quite well to that of a hydroelectric power station supplying a network, because the production of electricity is then a function of the random variable represented by the water flow (with p still representing the likelihood of failure), and we obtain the relationship:

$$\bar{Q} - Q_m = sk\,(p)$$

and the marginal cost would then be $D_1'\,(Q) + C$.

However, it will be noted that all portions of production are not offered with the same guarantee. The demand Q_m is well supplied with a "1-p" guarantee, but it is possible to meet a greater demand with a lower guarantee, or a lower demand with a greater guarantee. Thus, we can consider that the plant supplies a range of energy of various qualities. "The lowest portions are available 100 or 99 years out of 100; they correspond to guaranteed energy. The next portion is produced 98 years out of 100; its value is that of energy guaranteed at 98% and the average income over 100 years represents 98% of the product of the height of the portion multiplied by its value (since during 2 years out of 100 the portion is not sold through lack of production). Toward the last portions, finally, levels of practically no guarantee are reached, and, as a result, a zero price, a zero annual revenue, and a zero average revenue over 100 years" [13].

In order to simplify the above, the seasonal character of hydraulic flows is disregarded. Furthermore, we shall change the notations slightly.

The annual expenditure for a hydroelectric plant consists, in actual practice, merely of amortization and financing charges. It is a function of the installed power $\hat{q}$ which defines the maximum volume of water capable of being put through the turbines and of the volume of deposits during an average year Q which serves as an index of the production of electrical energy during an average year.

Consequently: $\qquad D = D\,(\hat{q}, Q)$.

The quantity q which is capable of being produced a particular year is expressed as:

$$q = rQ$$

where r is a random variable indicating the water level. To each $\hat{q}$ there corresponds an r value which will be designated as $\hat{r}$.

The portion included between q and q + dq can be supplied with a likelihood of delivery P(r) which is a diminishing function of r and, consequently, of q (Fig. 24). We can designate either by c(r) or c(q) the marginal cost which we are attempting to associate with the portion q, q + dq, when such portion is produced.

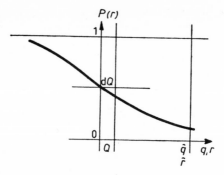

Fig. 24

Let us consider what relationships the function c(r) obeys.

If the installed power is increased by $d\hat{q}$, it will be possible to turbinate an additional portion $d\hat{q}$ with a guarantee $P(\hat{r})$.

The additional cost is, on the one hand:

$$D'_{\hat{q}}\,d\hat{q};$$

and on the other: $c(\hat{r})P(\hat{r})d\hat{q}$ (since the portion is delivered only with the guarantee $P(\hat{r})$).

Therefore:

$$c\left(\hat{r}\right) P\left(\hat{r}\right) = D'_{\hat{q}} \tag{II.6}$$

If the volume of average deposits is increased by δQ, and the installed power is increased by $r\delta Q$, the production of the infinitesimal portion of the guarantee r is increased by $dr\delta Q$.

The cost increase is expressed on the one hand by:

$$(D'_Q + \hat{r}\, D'_{\hat{q}})\, \delta Q$$

and on the other by

$$\int_0^{\hat{r}} c\left(r\right) P\left(r\right) dr\, \delta Q.$$

The function c(r) must therefore verify the relationship:

$$D'_Q + \frac{\hat{q}}{Q}\, D'_{\hat{q}} = \int_0^{\hat{r}} c\left(r\right) P\left(r\right) dr. \tag{II.7}$$

In order to complete the determination of the function c(r), it is necessary to consider the properties of demand, as in the case of the determination of the allocation of marginal costs along a peak level. Let us outline the reasoning involved: If, in order to simplify, it is assumed that the demands of the portions of different guarantee are independent, the density of demand associated with the guarantee r—when selling at marginal cost—is a function of the marginal cost c and of r. This relationship can be inverted and it can be written that the selling price c is a function of r and of the density of demand delivered with a guarantee r. In order to establish an equilibrium, the density of demand must be equal to a corresponding density of production. In this case the density of production is a function of r and of the available equipment, i.e., of Q and $\hat{q}$. All told, the unknown function c(r) of relationships (II.6) and (II.7) can be replaced by a known function of r, Q, $\hat{q}$. Relationships (II.6) and (II.7) then determine Q, $\hat{q}$ and, consequently, the function c(r) of marginal costs.

In actual practice, Electricité de France does not count on a great number of portions of different guarantees. It limits itself to making a distinction between two or three types of deliveries such as: totally guaranteed deliveries when P(r) is included between P_0 and 1, partially guaranteed deliveries when P(r) is included between P_1 and P_0, and deliveries without any guarantee when P(r) is less than P_1. With regard to the latter type, the marginal cost c(r) is assumed to be zero.

These interesting applications of the notion of marginal cost to random savings will be encountered again in connection with price policy.

5. The influence of technical progress and of the price of factors upon marginal cost.

It has been assumed up to the present that the level of production is known, and that the cost of the various factors of production is constant. As a matter of fact, these two assumptions are necessary to define accurately the function D(Q) of the minimum costs for each level of production. However, any technical progress and any variation in the price of factors which changes the function D(Q) also modify the value of marginal costs.

a) Technical progress: In theory, the definition of technical progress is simple. Technical progress obtains when the production function changes and when production can be increased through the utilization of given quantities of factors. But such a definition is of little interest since not much is known concerning production functions.

In order to make the above definition useful, the conference on research on price matters of the United States National Bureau of Economic Research states that technical progress must be credited with "any change in the relationship between production and the quantity of factors used that can be attributed neither to a change in price of such factors nor to variations in the rate or scale of production of the enterprise in question" [36].

This definition emphasizes the economic aspect of the problem and does not consider technical progress synonymous either with inventions or with mechanization.

The measurement of technical progress is fairly difficult. During the past few years, there have been many studies dealing with the growth of productivity as measured by hours of work. But technical progress cannot be measured exactly in this way, since such progress is not the only factor which can affect a man-hour production index. There are five other factors which are discussed below:

1. A change in the relative productive capacity utilized can increase or reduce productivity. For example, unemployment contributes to an increase in coal mine productivity—miners seek to earn in five days what they formerly earned in six.

2. A change in the relative wages for different kinds of work may, for example, cause management to substitute highly skilled workers for a greater number of unskilled workers and, consequently, obtain an increase in productivity.

3. A decrease in the cost of energy or of capital may replace manpower by machines and thus increase productivity.

4. Any variation in the productive capacity of an industrial plant may modify the combination of factors of production and hence alter productivity.

5. Finally, on an industrial level, productivity is a function of the distribution of production among the different firms.

Productivity indices not only have the defect of incorporating too many factors, but also have the shortcoming of not being affected by technical improvements. For example, a technical improvement which makes it possible to replace rare and expensive raw material by abundant and inexpensive raw material may have no repercussion on productivity.

Productivity and technical progress must therefore be considered as two related but distinct notions. In fact, technical progress can be measured only by comparing the difference in cost from one period to another after all other causes of variation have been eliminated.

b) The price of factors of production.

The price of the factors of production affects the cost of production in two ways:

1. With a given combination of the quantities of factors, a variation in the price of a factor has an immediate and proportionate repercussion upon the total production cost.

2. By modifying the relative prices of the various factors, this price variation entails substitutions among factors. The extent and

the importance of these substitutions is dependent upon such items as the branch of the industry involved, the factors considered, and the time. Such substitutions are immediate, such as that of fuel oil for coal in a dual boiler. Others are possible only at the time of the construction of a new factory.

By means of its repercussions upon the cost function, a change in the price of a factor can, moreover, lead the firm to modify its level of production.

It is unnecessary to dwell further on the difficulty which is experienced in measuring the price of a factor of production. Manpower, for example, is characteristic in this respect. When a new agreement with a trade union modifies the basic wage rate, it frequently contains numerous clauses affecting seniority benefits, the price of overtime work, paid vacation conditions, health benefits, layoff conditions, promotion rules, the prices of cafeteria meals, and many other stipulations. It is often difficult to distinguish between purely financial clauses and other types.

In this second part, we have retained mainly four sources of variation which may affect the volume of a firm's expenditures. These four sources are:

1) The rate of production, within the framework of a given productive capacity.

2) Productive capacity.

(These two variables lead to notions of short- and long-term marginal costs.)

3) The price of factors of production.

4) The technical level of production.

The degree of variability generated by these four sources may be modified by management's ability to make the best use of existing techniques, or to combine the factors of production to the best advantage in order to minimize costs.

An interesting analysis which could be undertaken by economists and accountants would be to determine to what extent the influence of these variables explains variations in costs from one year to another.

To carry this type of analysis through successfully, it is necessary to start from a model which expresses, for a given state of technique and of prices, the volume of expenditures with respect to parameters such as production and manpower. This model should make it possible to determine the costs for the year $t + 1$ if these parameters have maintained their values of year t, and if, from the year t to the year $t + 1$, neither prices nor technique have changed. The gap between actual costs and the calculated costs for the year $t + 1$ can be ascribed to price changes and modifications in technology. A knowledge of price evolution permits the elimination of the influence of this factor and the isolation, item by item, of variations in cost due to a transformation in technique and in management. Subject to a few precautions and to a considered selection of the initial model, such an analysis may enable the head of a firm to learn why his expenditures have changed, and may provide him with a means for the rational establishment of a budget for the following year.

III

CALCULATION OF MARGINAL COSTS

Calculations of marginal costs can only be made in specific cases. They are dependent upon available information, upon the degree of accuracy required, and upon the marginal cost properties which have been defined. From a practical standpoint, three methods of approach are possible. They are through:
1) accounting,
2) direct technical analysis,
3) statistical analysis.

1. The accounting approach.

In order to calculate marginal costs from accounting data, the various costs should be divided into several homogeneous groups so that the total value for each group may be a simple function of parameters defining the various functions of the factory.

For instance, in the calculation of short-term marginal costs it is customary to classify accounting costs as fixed expenditures or as expenditures proportional to production. The marginal cost sought is, within the limit of available productive capacity, the unit cost of proportional expenditures.

To be valid, such a breakdown of costs must be based upon a detailed analysis of expenditures. The limits of validity of this analysis must also be specified, and the question must be raised constantly as to whether the proportional expenditures are the same for marginal units and the units already produced. Such is not the case, for example, if workers must work overtime, or if older machines with a relatively low output must be brought back into use.

To illustrate the above better, we shall summarize an example which is covered in greater detail in reference [33].

Assume that a coalfield, reduced to inactivity as a result of the commercial situation, starts extraction again. The additional tons will be extracted under the same conditions as the others (same method of exploitation, same means of transportation, same washing, etc.) since all areas of the coalfield will work only a few days more per year. Marginal expenditures should, therefore, as a

In general, however, amortization and financing costs are not calculated correctly and, in the case of installations about to be closed, the part of the investment still left to be amortized is more often than not higher than the sum which could be derived from a sale of the installation.

Amortization and financing costs should therefore be divided into two parts, as follows:

1) the portion which corresponds to the actual value of the installation and is immediately avoidable;

2) the portion which corresponds to the difference between the book value and the actual value of the installation and is avoidable later over the estimated lifetime of the installation.

To emphasize the above, the computation elements of the contraction cost of a French coalfield are shown in Table II.

Table II

Cost elements	Cost per ton	Immediately avoidable	Avoidable later	Unavoidable
Wages	1,850	1,750	—	100*
Salaries.	400		320	80
Related charges.	1,480	840	520	120**
Mine timber	200	200		
Electrical energy, other supplies, contractor statements.	950	850		100
Overhead costs	250	70	80	100
Amortization and financing costs.	1,000	400	500	100***
Coal for the personnel .	150	80	70	
	6,280	4,190	1,490	600

Notes: *In the above calculation, it is assumed that the workers are laid off as soon as the mine is shut down but the salaried employees are retained. During a transitional period, the coalfield therefore has a larger number of employees than it needs.

For this reason, the larger portion of wages is immediately avoidable, whereas the larger portion of salaries is avoidable only over an extended period of time.

A fraction of the salary and wage costs cannot be avoided because, as seen in the example under consideration, installations such as entrances are common to the marginal mine and to others, and cannot be closed when the marginal mine ceases to extract coal.

**A detailed cost analysis can identify, within related costs, those portions that can be avoided immediately, those that can be avoided over an extended period of time, and those that cannot be avoided.

***The portion of amortization and financing costs that cannot be avoided is related to the common installations that continue to operate. The portion that is avoided over time derives from an overestimation of the value of equipment.

In this example, an analysis of costs that are avoidable over time has demonstrated that they could be grouped into three parts: a) 1,000 francs, avoidable within five years at the rate of approximately 200 francs per year; b) 300 francs, avoidable within 10 years at the rate of about 30 francs per year; c) 190 francs, avoidable within 20 years at the rate of about 8.50 francs per year.

$$x = 4{,}190 + \sum_{1}^{5} \frac{200}{(1 + i)^p} + \sum_{1}^{10} \frac{30}{(1 + i)^p} + \sum_{1}^{20} \frac{8.5}{(1 + i)^p}$$

i.e., at an interest rate of 6%:

$$x = 5{,}420 \text{ francs.}$$

2. Direct technical analysis.

Marginal cost can be obtained by direct technical analysis when evaluating—with the help of technical considerations—the quantities of production factors brought into play. Expenditures are calculated later by multiplying quantities by estimated prices.

This method has many advantages, and a few drawbacks. The first advantage is that it poses the question directly, in terms of future costs, and consequently the economist is not tempted to utilize past prices or present specific consumption inputs. The second advantage derives from consideration of the technical procedure to be retained at the time the calculation is made. A technical analysis automatically distinguishes between the minimization of expenditures for a given output and the cost of production expansion. For example, in the case of the extension of a power line, a technical analysis begins with the determination of the optimum distance between poles and the optimum thickness of the cables, and ends with the calculation of the marginal costs.

For these two reasons, marginal costs derived from technical analyses are less unreasoned than those derived from other approaches.

The method presents a few drawbacks, however. The first is that the computations are lengthier than those involved in an accounting approach. When both methods are possible, the choice depends in part upon the amount of time available. The second drawback is that the technical method does not necessarily take all expenditure items into account. In contrast to the accounting method, it is not automatically exhaustive. Pure and simple omission is exceptional, but there are more subtle forms of omission. For example, one lies in the assumption that an expansion program will proceed as planned, requiring no additional costs, changes in the project, etc. In order to guard against this, estimates of future costs should be increased by an amount to cover such contingencies.

Another form of omission occurs in studies involving plant expansion, where too many accountable expenditures may be considered as independent of the decision. For example, although the cost of coal for the production of steam would invariably be considered in the decision process, other accountable expenditure requirements, such as warehouse expansion or increased requirements for materials handling equipment, might be overlooked. The underestimate of the expenditures incurred as a result of the decision is natural, but it unfortunately reinforces a natural difficulty in envisaging long-range decision effects [29].

In actual practice, the distinction between technical analyses and accounting studies is more apparent than real. However, certain items of expenditure are difficult to estimate directly on the basis of technical considerations. The usual and fully justified practice is to estimate such items on the basis of bookkeeping or statistical elements obtained elsewhere.

Two examples of the computation of marginal costs through technical analysis follow. The first has been borrowed from the aircraft industry, and is taken from Louis Bréguet's book, Détermination et calcul du prix de revient des transports aériens (Determination and computation of net cost of air transportation). Although this document is now fairly old, it is interesting, for it is the work of a true pioneer. The second example relates to the transportation of natural gas over long distances as analyzed by H. B. Chenery [16], [19].

Example 1: Operation of an air transport service [16].

The first part of the analysis is purely technical and consists of determining the payload that can be transported by an aircraft.

The payload F_u is a fraction a of the total freight which could, theoretically, be transported by the aircraft. Such total freight is, by definition, the difference between the total weight P of the equipped and loaded plane, and the respective weights of the fuselage P_p, the engines P_m, the fuel and oil P_c and the equipment and crew P_e.

$$F_u = a \left(P - P_p - P_m - P_c - P_e \right) \tag{III.5}$$

P_p is proportional to P:$P_p = bP$, b being a coefficient of lightness of construction which depends upon the technique used.

P_m is equal to the product of the nominal engine power by the weight q in kilograms for a nominal power unit:

$$P_m = W_0\, q$$

W_0 must be greater than the effective power W_e necessary in horizontal flight, since it is necessary to take into account the lift requirement and a coefficient of safety:

$$W_0 = x\, W_e \text{ (x greater than 1).}$$

The necessary effective power W_e is proportional to the weight P of the plane and to the speed V:

$$W_e = \frac{PV \operatorname{tg} u}{270} \tag{III.6}$$

tg u being an index of aerodynamic performance.

The exact expression of the weight of the fuel is complicated but L. Bréguet has developed a much simpler formula, which is expressed as follows:

$$P_e = \frac{Pm \operatorname{tg} u\, E}{300} \tag{III.7}$$

in which E is the length of the trip in kilometers, and m the consumption in kilograms per horsepower/hour. This formula assumes the headwind velocity to be zero.

P_e in kilos assumes the form: $P_e = 100 + 0.03\, P$ $\qquad$ (III.8)

From relations (III.5 to III.8) it is possible to deduce a formula (III.9) which gives the payload with respect to the plane's characteristics.

$$F_u = aP \left(1 - b - x\, \frac{V \operatorname{tg} u}{270}\, q - \frac{m \operatorname{tg} u}{300}\, E - \frac{100}{P} - 0.03\right). \tag{III.9}$$

If N is the total number of trips per year, the number of kilometer-tons effected by the plane is: $\frac{F_u NE}{1,000}$, the coefficient 1,000 resulting from the fact that F_u has been calculated in kilograms.

In the second part of the analysis—on the basis of formula (III.9)—the total cost of the operation of an air transport service is developed as follows.

Let n', n'', n''' be, respectively, the number of aircraft in service, the number of aircraft in reserve, and the number of aircraft being overhauled. At the time he wrote, L. Bréguet estimated that n'' was at least equal to 2, and n''' could be determined by means of the following formula:

$$n''' = N \frac{J}{365 H} \frac{E}{V} \tag{III.10}$$

E/V is the number of flight-hours per trip, J the number of days required for overhaul of a plane, and H the number of flight-hours of an aircraft between two overhauls. Formula (III.10) is obtained by writing that n'''/n' is equal to the relationship of J to the number of flight-days of a plane between two successive overhauls.

The following cost elements must be taken into consideration:

1. Amortization and overhaul of the planes. If x_p is the purchase price of a plane per kilogram and $1/A$ the fraction of the air fleet replaced each year, the replacement costs are:

$$\frac{1}{A} Px_p (n' + n'' + n'') . \tag{III.11}$$

If each overhaul costs a fraction $1/k$ of the purchase price of a plane, the overhaul cost per flight-hour is: $\frac{1}{H} \frac{1}{k} Px_p$ and the total annual overhaul cost is:

$$\frac{NE}{V} \frac{1}{Hk} Px_p . \tag{III.12}$$

2. Amortization and overhaul of engines. Let us designate as M the lifespan of the engines in hours. The total annual expenditure for the purchase of new engines is the product of the purchase price of the plane's engines by the number of the company's annual flight-hours divided by M:

$$x \frac{PV}{270} \operatorname{tg} u \, x_m \cdot \frac{NE}{VM} \tag{III.13}$$

in which x_m represents the purchase price per unit of power.

On the other hand, it can be verified immediately that if H' represents the number of hours of service of an engine between two overhauls and $\frac{1}{k'} x_m$ is the cost of the overhaul, the annual expenditure for the overhaul of engines is:

$$\frac{1}{k'} \frac{PV \operatorname{tg} u}{270} \frac{NE}{VM'} x_m . \tag{III.14}$$

3. Fuel and oil. If x_c is the cost of fuel per kilogram, the annual cost will be:

$$m \frac{PV \operatorname{tg} u}{270} \frac{NE}{V} x_c. \tag{III.15}$$

4. Crew. L. Bréguet favors the following formula in gold francs:

$$\frac{NE}{V} (18 + 0.04 P). \tag{III.16}$$

5. Overhead. Overhead costs vary linearly with respect to the number of kilometric tons:

$$G + G' \frac{NE F_u}{1,000}. \tag{III.17}$$

The company's annual costs are obtained by adding the expressions III.11, 12, 13, 14, 15, 16, 17. By dividing the expression obtained by $\frac{F_u NE}{1,000}$, one arrives at the average cost per kilometer-ton.

In L. Bréguet's analysis, all parameters introduced are given a numerical value corresponding to the average conditions of the period, Q, n', n'', n''' being given by tables with respect to N.

Service being a kilometer-ton, the cost per unit of service offered is, in gold francs:

$$\frac{G + 12.500 (n' + n'' + n''') + 938.1 N}{497.76 N}.$$

N	n'	n''	n'''	G (in gold francs)
< 1460	4	2	4	200,000
≥ 1461	4	2	5	
≥ 1601	5	2	5	
≥ 1826	5	2	6	
≥ 1971	6	2	6	
≥ 2191	6	2	7	
≥ 2351	7	3	7	250,000
≥ 2556	7	3	8	
≥ 2701	8	3	8	

N, the number of trips per year, is, for given F_u and E, proportional to the number of kilometer-tons offered (with a proportionality coefficient of 1,000 within the framework of the numerical hypotheses retained).

The average cost curve is shown in Fig. 25.

Four marginal costs can be defined:

a) When N is fixed, the number of tons actually transported varies, costs are practically fixed and the marginal cost is essentially zero.

b) When n', n'', n''' are fixed and N varies, the marginal cost is constant and equal to: $938.1/497.76 = 1,885$ F per unit of N, i.e., 1,880 francs per kilometer-ton.

c) At points A, B, C, ... where G, n', n'', or n''' vary, the marginal cost increases abruptly:

by: $12.5 \times 1,000/497.76 = 25$ F in A, B, C, D, F;

by: $(50 + 2 \times 12.5) \times 1,000/497.76 = 150$ F in E.

d) On the basis of points A, B, C, D, E, F only, a curve can be drawn representing long-run average costs when capacity, here represented by the number of planes, varies.

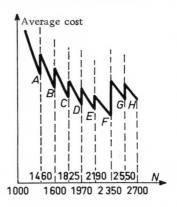

Fig. 25

Example II: Transportation of gas over long distances [19].

The transport of gas from Lorraine to Paris has been the first French attempt to transport gas over a long distance through pipelines. However, to facilitate the consumption of natural gas from the Lacq field, the laying of a great number of additional pipelines is taking place. This is, therefore, a real present-day economic problem.

Costs being proportional to the length of the pipeline, our reasoning will be in terms of a standard length. The capacity X of the pipeline in millions of cubic meters transported per day is a function of the interior diameter D, of the input pressure P_1, and of the output pressure P_2:

$$X = k D^{8/3} P_1 \sqrt{1 - (P_2/P_1)^2} \qquad \text{(III.18)}$$

P_2 can be considered as given. In posing: $R = \dfrac{P_1}{P_2}$, the expression of X becomes:

$$X = k D^{8/3} P_2 \sqrt{1 - 1/R^2}. \qquad \text{(III.19)}$$

1. A well-known formula for the resistance of metals makes it possible to relate P_1 to the thickness e of the pipeline and to the tension t at the end of the pipeline:

$$P_1 = \frac{2et}{D}. \qquad \text{(III.20)}$$

2. On the other hand, a compressor's power is a function of the compression rate R and of the volume of gas pumped X:

$$P = (mR - n) X. \tag{III.21}$$

3. The weight of the pipeline, for a given length, is proportional to De since e is small.

Annual transportation costs T are a function of X, R, D, e and are allocated among operational costs and amortization and financing costs linked to initial investment costs. They can be represented by the following relationship in which:

$$D = (a_1 i + b_1) P + (a_2 + a_4) iq + (b_2 + a_5 i) D + a_3 i + c_1 C \tag{III.22}$$

$a_1 = a_1(P)$ represents the installation and purchase cost of the compression station.

$b_1 = b_1(P)$ represents the annual cost of the operation of the compressor.

$a_2 = a_2(t)$ is the purchase cost per ton of pipe.

a_3 corresponds to the portion of pipeline installation costs which is a function of length.

a_4 corresponds to the portion of pipeline installation costs which is a function of weight.

a_5 corresponds to the portion of pipeline installation costs which is a function of diameter.

$b_2 = b_2(e)$ represents the annual maintenance cost of the pipeline.

c_1 corresponds to other operational costs which are assumed to be a constant percentage of the total cost C.

i represents the relationship of the amortization annuity and financing charges to the initial investment. i depends upon the interest rate and the estimated lifespan of the pipeline.

The first problem is to determine, for a given X, the quantities D, R, e in order to minimize the annual cost C. Since the life of a pipeline is not, in practice, dependent upon these parameters, this criterion is truly compatible with that of a minimization of total costs.

In order to minimize C, it is necessary that:

$$\frac{C'_R}{X'_R} = \frac{C'_D}{X'_D} = \frac{C'_e}{X'_e}. \tag{III.23}$$

The elimination of R, D, E from the relationships (III.19, 22, and 23) modified to take into account (II.20 and 21), provides a long-term cost curve in which C is a function of X. The various calculations will not be shown, but Fig. 26 provides a geometrical presentation of the results.

The average cost C/X (curve I) is a diminishing function of X and, consequently, the same applies to long-run marginal cost (curve II). In the case of a given capacity, short-term costs correspond to a variation in the volume actually transported without a modification of the compression rate.

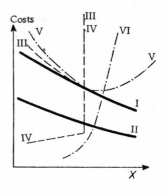

Fig. 26

The costs of the compression station, therefore, are the only variable costs. The average cost is represented by curve III and the marginal cost by curve IV. Finally, "intermediate" average and marginal costs corresponding to a given pipeline can be introduced, but at a variable compression rate R. Curves V and VI represent average cost and variable cost respectively, under this hypothesis.

The two examples which have been briefly discussed are certainly sufficient to demonstrate that technical analyses form an excellent starting point for the definition and calculation of marginal costs.

3. Statistical analysis.

Although very few relatively detailed analyses have been made, statistics provide a means of determining cost curves, subject to the same precautions and the same difficulties as in the case of demand. The advantage offered by statistical analyses, obviously, is that the facts themselves may be used to determine the allocation of expense between fixed and variable costs. For this reason statistical analyses are fruitful, despite the care required, the problems of interpretation they create, and the fact that they relate only to the past.

As in the case of demand analyses, they make use either of time series relating to different levels of production for the same factory, or of comparative analyses grouping the figures of different factories.

Professor Joel Dean is well known for these analyses, since he is practically the only one to have tackled with them with all the required care. And, whether they be short- or long-term analyses, the necessary precautions are unfortunately numerous, and are listed in that order.

a) Short-term analyses.

The statistical measurement of costs, aside from reference to a specific theoretical model, is devoid of significance. The short-term cost curve shown in Fig. 5 presupposes a given capacity of production, a certain state of technology, and constant prices for factors of production. If the series of data used do not verify these three conditions, one does not know what one is measuring. Therefore, the researcher who observes the two points M and N (Fig. 27), but omits capacity differences, will tend to conclude that marginal cost is represented by an MN slope, whereas such a slope represents neither short-term nor long-term cost.

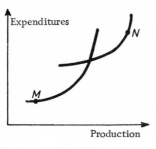

Fig. 27

It is necessary, therefore, to begin by selecting a period for analysis during which the factory's capacity remains constant.

Next, starting from an adequate price series and a breakdown of the total expenditure into a certain number of homogeneous items, it is necessary to calculate the corrected variable costs in the prices of production factors.

The evaluation of technological development is a delicate matter, but an attempt can be made at taking it into consideration by introducing into regression forms a term which is dependent upon time.

A detailed study must analyze total expenditures (and not average cost) with respect to production. In effect, over a broad area expenses vary more or less linearly with production, whereas average cost assumes the form of a decreasing curve. The adjustment is therefore much more delicate and, furthermore, average cost does not directly give the trend of marginal cost.

Care must be exercised that production and costs correspond; that is, some costs are related to current deliveries, and others to preceding or future periods.

Production is sometimes difficult to measure when a factory produces several products. Even if these products are measured by the same standard, their production costs can be very different. The method usually adopted consists of calculating a weighted production in which the coefficients of weighting take production cost differences into account. The drawback of this method is that it artificially introduces a correlation between the two series under analysis.

Finally, the use of the method of least squares can be used statistically (as shown in Chapter 6).

b) Long-term analyses.

The main difficulty here lies in the selection of a sample of comparable factories or stores differing only in capacity; this presupposes a certain homogeneity of geographical location, factor prices, production or sales composition, the age of the establishments, and the techniques employed. It does not appear likely that examples of such homogeneity in manufacturing or distributive industries will be more than scarce. In fact, retail trade alone seems rather promising, and it is significant that one of J. Dean's studies relates to a chain of shoe stores.

The "capacity" concept should also be defined accurately. Three different concepts can be involved, depending upon whether reference is made to the amount of fixed assets, to the available quantities of factors of production (especially manpower, or to production itself.

The amount of fixed assets is easily measurable only when the equipment is standardized and composed of homogeneous units (such as the number of beds in a hospital). Aside from the textile industry, this is seldom the case.

The determination of productive capacity, when several products are produced by a factory, cannot be effected until the various products have been aggregated by some weighting scheme. Furthermore, it will be necessary to specify the definition of production employed.

For these two reasons, and especially the first, a statistical analysis of long-term marginal costs is a delicate undertaking and, it must be admitted, less than promising.

Three examples of statistical analysis will now be given: two for short-term and one for long-term analysis. The first relates to steel production, the second to a plant producing leather belts, and the third to a chain of shoe stores.

Example I. U.S. Steel Corporation cost analysis [51].

An analysis of the costs of the U.S. Steel Corporation was made prior to the war, in the 1927-1938 period, by a group of economists under the direction of Professor Yntema.

An estimate of the total annual costs was made, including costs of operation, costs of maintaining inoperative plants, and interest, less purchase discounts and estimated intraorganization transactions. It was important to subtract the last item, since it artificially inflated the costs and receipts. The cost figures were basically accounting figures and, consequently, were related to tonnage deliveries rather than to tonnage produced. For this reason, the tonnage delivered was retained as a production index.

The problem rising out of a multiplicity of products sold was resolved by weighting the delivered tonnage of each product by its production cost. This method was especially helpful in "translating into steel equivalents" products other than steel sold by affiliates of the company.

During the period under study, the company's capacity remained constant, steel output varied considerably, and capacity utilization fluctuated between 17.7% and 90.4%.

At first, the correlation between gross cost and production was found to be very satisfactory; the regression line (fixed costs) crossed the y axis at 120,530 million dollars with a slope equal to 54.51 dollars per ton (short-term marginal cost).

This correlation could not be maintained, however, since an objective of the study was to determine the short-term marginal cost under 1938 conditions. Consequently, the principal items of expenditure for previous years had to be corrected in order to meet that year's conditions.

Considering interest and pensions as fixed costs, the 1938 figure was adopted for the entire period.

An analysis of the correlation between taxes and production revealed two independent regression lines, one for the 1927-1932 period and the other for the 1932-1938 period. Consequently, the actual figures for the years 1932-1938 were retained, and the amount of taxes which would have been paid if the 1932-1938 correlation had obtained during the earlier period was assigned to the years 1927-1932.

With regard to amortization, after considerable discussion the actual figures were used. Wages were corrected by reference to an index of average hourly increases.

With regard to "other costs," the authors decided to retain 50% of these without modification and to correct the remaining 50% by reference to the index of wholesale prices (excluding food and agricultural products) supplied by the U.S. Bureau of Labor Statistics. They justified this decision by virtue of the fact that the prices of certain goods purchased by the company were much less variable than those shown in the index.

The group next studied the correlation between corrected costs and the volume of production. This correlation proved to be linear. An examination of the relationship: "variation of actual costs from the line of regression" with "costs indicated by the line of regression" demonstrated that the values were truly distributed about zero. This distribution, however, followed a diminishing trend (attributed to improved technology) of 0.39% per year, creating a total variation of +2.17% at the beginning of the period and of -2.15% at the end. By correcting costs to eliminate this effect, the authors found that, under 1938 conditions, U.S. Steel Corporation costs could be considered as the sum of fixed costs amounting to 182 million dollars and variable costs of 55.73 dollars per ton.

The different expenditure items next remained to be analyzed individually. The major problem related to technological improvement. The method used for total costs brought to light a -1.31% trend per year for wages and a +0.95% trend per year for other costs. When the corresponding corrections were made, the correlations resulted in the information contained in the following table:

U.S. STEEL CORPORATION TOTAL COST ELEMENTS
UNDER 1938 CONDITIONS

	Fixed cost	Marginal cost per ton
Interest............	3,300	—
Pensions	7,700	—
Taxes, other than social security and Federal income tax	24,200	1.43
Wages.............	62,100	29.10
Other costs	47,800	21.67
Social security taxes ...	2,500	1.16
Amortization	29,500	2.37
TOTAL.........	182,100	55.73
	millions of dollars	dollars per ton

Without entering into a detailed discussion of this analysis, we may make the following observations from the study:

1. The above analysis relates to a sizable enterprise and not to just one plant. No technical interpretation of the results obtained is possible.

2. Technological improvement has been assumed to be linear over the entire period, which amounts to assuming that technological changes regularly affect costs through all phases of the economic cycle. Nothing is less certain.

3. The influence of wage variations upon wage costs has been eliminated with the aid of an index of average hourly wage increases. This presupposes that both wage variations and wage costs vary according to the same pattern with changes in production.

4. Too much importance should not be attached to the variable portion of amortization which is a function of bookkeeping practices and does not necessarily have economic significance.

Example II. Marginal cost in a plant producing leather belts. [22].

This analysis, undertaken by J. Dean, was made for the purpose of determining the short-term marginal cost in a leather belt shop. Its considerable interest lies in the fact that, by referring specifically to the theoretical model, it deals very lucidly with problems of statistical determination of costs.

The period from January 1, 1935 to June 1, 1938 was selected because it most adequately fulfilled the following conditions:

1) large variety in production;
2) existence of detailed and complete cost information;

3) unchanged capacity and equipment;

4) stability of methods of production.

Overhead costs arbitrarily allocated to the plant were excluded from the total costs. The costs retained were separated into their main components in order to analyze the contribution of each item to the marginal cost. Corrections were effected in the gross figures in order to eliminate the following two sources of distortion:

1. the time lag between production and the recording of related costs (a portion of the recorded expenditures for materiel was, in fact, related to production completed about three months earlier);

2. price variations in factors of production.

To measure the total cost retained as a variable "to be explained," the following variables were selected after discussion:

a) production measured in terms of single-thickness surface treated ("single-ply belting") (in square feet): X_1;

b) the average weight of product according to standard surface unit of single-ply belting surface treated (because raw material costs and the cost of certain operations are dependent thereon) (in pounds

c) variation of output in relation to the previous month: X_3.

A certain number of other possible variables (average width of single-ply belting surface treated, variation in the production rate during the period being accounted for, size of lots, proportion of special orders, personnel turnover rate) were eliminated after analysis.

J. Dean obtained excellent adjustments by the use of linear relations, total cost D, direct costs D_1, and indirect costs D_2 being expressed as:

$$D = -60,178 + 0.770\,X_1 + 70,181.30\,X_2$$

coefficient of correlation: 0.998

$$D_1 = -61,636.9 + 0.760\,X_1 + 69,324.13\,X_2$$

coefficient of correlation: 0.999

$$D_2 = 2,108.72 + 0.0108\,X_1 - 4,828\,X_3$$

coefficient of correlation: 0.842

When X_2 and X_3 are omitted, these relations become:

$$D = 2973.75 + 0.770\,X_1$$
$$D_1 = 662.54 + 0.760\,X_1$$
$$D_2 = 2108.72 + 0.0108\,X_1$$

and the adjustment is still very satisfactory; this very strongly confirms the hypothesis of constant short-term marginal cost, and of costs varying linearly according to production.

The same hypothesis appeared to be very satisfactory in regard to the various elements of cost:

Cost elements: Direct:

Cement	— 0.06	+ 0.0282 X_1
Direct work	0.99	+ 0.0538 X_1
Leather	0.90	+ 0.675 X_1

Indirect:

Fixed charges	0.905	+ 0.00143 X_1
(Taxes, amortization, insurance, power, water)		
Indirect work	0.249	+ 0.00207 X_1
Repairs	0.5016	+ 0.00120 X_1
Supplies	0.098	+ 0.00380 X_1

The above breakdown, when partial marginal costs are added thereto, amounts to a total cost of 0.765 dollars, in excellent agreement with the 0.770 dollar cost obtained directly.

After having obtained the above results, the author proceeded to engage in a searching statistical discussion of their value. He attempted a cubic expression in order to represent the total cost in relation to production. Without recording improvements, he also studied the correlation with production of the relation:

$$\frac{\text{costs during month n—costs during the month n-1}}{\text{production during month n—production during the month n-1}}$$

This relationship appeared to be approximately independent of production.

Example III: Long-term marginal costs in a chain of shoe stores [25]. The objective of this analysis, also by J. Dean, was to determine the influence of size upon a store's costs. The method employed compared the costs of various stores belonging to the same enterprise. A sampling of 55 stores selling men's shoes, and all located in the same large city, formed the basis of the analysis. Although the company owned several chains within that city (each chain carrying a different price range of shoes), only stores of the same chain were chosen. Recently opened stores which had not yet attained their equilibrium were eliminated. Records of annual sales and costs for the years 1937 and 1938 were made available to J. Dean.

Out of three possible methods for the measurement of size (equipment, capacity in terms of factors, capacity in terms of production), the third was adopted; sales volume was also chosen as a variable representing size. In fact, such volume does not accurately represent capacity and makes the interpretation of results a somewhat delicate operation. As an index of annual sales, the number of pairs of shoes sold per year was preferred to receipts in dollars, since the latter gave a weighting to higher priced shoes which bore no relation to store costs. Accounting

homogeneity made it possible, finally, to place costs on comparable
bases. Only two items of expense were excluded from the total;
these resulted from an arbitrary allocation of the company's
general costs among its store.

The statistical analysis brought to light an excellent correlation
between the logarithm of costs and the logarithm of sales, but the
correlation obtained was not linear since the logarithm of costs
increased faster than that of size. In other words, the elasticity of
total costs in relation to production was not constant, but increased
steadily from a value lower to a value higher than 1.

Fig. 28

The average cost curve was parabolic
in shape, with a minimum corresponding
approximately to 32,000 pairs of shoes
in 1937 and 38,000 in 1938. Unfortunately,
the ascending line of average cost was
rather ill-defined, for only three of the
stores in the sample were located in this
zone.

But it is not established—and this will
bring to the fore the difficulty encountered in the statistical determination of
of long-term marginal costs—that the
parabolic aspect of the cost curve obtained by J. Dean is a confirmation of
the general theory. Dean himself indicates that the explanation can
be very different. In fact, assuming, a priori, the long-term marginal
cost to be constant, the long-term cost curve may then be represented by a straight line (Fig. 29). For stores with an A, B, C, D
capacity, short-term cost curves are (below capacity) the straight
lines MA, NB, PC, and QD. However, size has been measured
according to the annual sales which represent a percentage of
capacity equal to the average of daily percentages. The volume of
daily sales can fluctuate more widely in a large store than in a

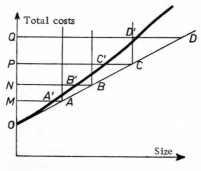

Fig. 29

small store. It is even conceivable that capacity is more frequently reached by a small store than by a large store. If such is the case, the mean point will be relatively farther from capacity in the case of the large store than in the small store. Instead of following a straight line passing through O, we should utilize curve $A'B'C'D'$ whose shape is compatible with Fig. 28.

It is regrettable that J. Dean was unable to pursue his analysis by using a new measurement for production capacity. At least his endeavor has the merit of indicating the care required in statistical analysis of long-term marginal costs.

The above examples provide an idea of the variety of methods which are available for the calculation of marginal costs. It is up to the economist to select the most suitable one, taking into account the amount of time at his disposal, the specificity required, and the application he has in mind.

IV

SPECIFIC APPLICATIONS

The notion of marginal cost will reappear constantly in all the chapters which follow. It will form the basis of most theories and applications. We cannot, at this point, attempt to describe in great detail all possibilities of practical utilization of marginal costs. We must limit ourselves to an enumeration of the main directions and to illustrating these by means of a few briefly discussed examples.

In this context, we will briefly discuss:

1) an analysis of the break-even chart;

2) a determination of price policy;

3) a determination of the production policy of an enterprise;

4) the orientation of production programming of competing enterprises at the governmental level.

It is somewhat arbitrary to distinguish price policy from production policy, since price selection has immediate repercussions upon quantities sold, and, consequently, upon production itself. Nevertheless, we plan to consider these problems separately to clarify certain aspects of marginal costs.

1. Analysis of the "break-even chart" [40].

A break-even chart is one of the most popular management tools in the United States. Although this method of presentation has been rendered obsolete by modern techniques, it can still be of some use by reason of its simplicity. It consists of a diagram on which are indicated short-term relationships between costs and receipts, on the one hand, and production (measured in terms of percentage of capacity, for example) on the other.

The cost curve, which is usually represented as a straight line, is the theoretical short-term curve in which it is assumed that, for a given capacity of production, the prices of factors and the state of technology are static.

The receipts curve is also generally represented as a straight line, which implies the hypotheses of a stable sales price and a fixed allocation of production among the different products.

The diagram derives its name from the intersection at point A of the two curves where profit is zero.

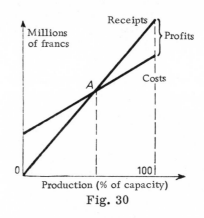

Fig. 30

At times, sales volume in millions of francs is represented in the abscissa instead of production as a percentage of capacity. The receipts curve is then the first bisector and the diagram is contained in a square. The drawback of this second presentation and the reason which will cause us to adopt the first here is that any change in the sales price affects the cost curve.

If the user is not fully aware of the many hypotheses which form the basis of the "break-even chart," he runs the risk of running into considerable frustration and disappointment. The diagram is dangerous by reason of its very simplicity. But it can be a convenient tool for an informed economist in deriving the following information:

a) Above what level of production revenue becomes positive. This is an interesting item of information by reason of the unpredictability of the future.

b) The effect upon income of a change in sales price, fixed costs, or short-term marginal cost.

The break-even chart can, of course, be generalized for all problems in which receipts and expenditures are dependent—linearly or not—upon a single parameter.

Care should be exercised in distinguishing the "break-even chart" as described above from historical "break-even charts" in which are indicated points representative of the condition of a firm during various years in the past. Such diagrams constitute an excellent résumé of the life of an enterprise, but cannot, by themselves, serve as a basis for decisions.

2. Price policy.

In Chapter 2, we indicated that, for firms in a state of perfect competition, maximization of profit conforms to the general interest, and we have seen at the beginning of this chapter that this policy results in equality of sales price and of marginal cost.

Still in connection with Chapter 2, a statement was made, without further justification, that in the case of monopolistic enterprises the policy which corresponded to the general interest was that which brought about equality between sales price and marginal cost—or, which amounts to the same thing mathematically, maximized profits at constant prices.

For this reason, the notion of marginal cost plays an essential part in all price regulation problems where the general interest is concerned. It is also fundamental in the determination of the price policy of an enterprise which seeks profit maximization. This is quite obvious if such an enterprise is in a state of perfect competition. If the firm is a monopoly, the equalization is between marginal cost and marginal revenue to obtain a maximization of profit, as shown at the beginning of this chapter.

We will postpone a discussion of these problems until Chapter 14, and deal here with a much simpler question.

The question we will consider here, in the case of a firm able to increase its production, is the price at which it will accept contracts. Two examples of such a question follow.

Example I. Exports from the coalfields of Lorraine.

In 1954, it was possible to increase the production of the Houillères de Lorraine substantially without additional investments by hiring workmen and opening new veins in the existing mines. Since only the coal dust from the additional tonnage produced could be sold on the domestic market, graded coal had to be sold on the export markets. The problem consisted of determining both the maximum discount which the coalfield could grant for these types of coal and the additional tonnage which could be sold without loss.

The commercial department was able to provide the following table indicating the salable tonnage of graded coal in various countries and the corresponding discount to be granted in relation to the basic scale of prices:

	Tonnage (in 1,000 t)	Discount per ton
Spain	60	500
Austria	70	850
South America	50	1,000
Switzerland	350	1,300
Portugal	50	1,300
Scandinavia	150	1,400
Italy	300	1,400
England	150	1,500
Total	1,180	

Let c_m be the marginal cost of Houillères de Lorraine, a the percentage of graded coal, and R the receipts obtained from the sale of coal dust on the French market per ton of additional coal produced. Any export is profitable if made at a price p such that:

$$ap \geqslant c_m - R.$$

An analysis of the particle size breakdown of production revealed a to have an approximate value of 55%. The calculation of R was very simply made by considering the French markets which would be likely to absorb the additional coal dust produced. A value R = 1,500 francs was taken. Finally, thanks to marginal cost analyses effected separately, c_m was known to be equal to 3,900 francs.

In order for export to be profitable, it was necessary that the coalfield should receive, for each ton of graded coal, minimum receipts amounting to:

$$p = \frac{3,900 - 1,500}{0.55} = 4\,350 \text{ F.}$$

However, at the time graded coal was sold at the average scale price of 5,360 francs. The coalfield could therefore not grant a discount of more than 1,010 francs, which made it possible to distribute 180,000 tons in Spain, Austria, and South America.

Example II. A contract for the sale of gas by a coke-producing plant.

During a certain period, the coke plant of the Houillères du Bassin de la Loire was functioning at 80% capacity. They were then considering signing a contract with Gaz de France for the sale of additional quantities of gas. This contract was to make it possible:

    a) for the coke-making plant to function at 100% capacity;

    b) eventually to increase this capacity by the addition of a further battery of coke ovens.*

Considering both of these hypotheses, what would the minimum sales price of gas be under the new contract, below which it would be preferable for the Houillères de la Loire not to effect a deal?

Definition of the parameters of the problem: An additional ton of coal dust used in the ovens for coke-making supplies k tons of coke at a price K and g cubic meters of gas at a price G, subject to an additional expenditure d. But, in order to obtain coal dust for coke making, it is necessary either to increase the coal field's production or to ship to the coke plant tonnages which had heretofore been sold to other customers. In the situation of the Houillères de la Loire, as it existed at that time, the first hypothesis was the more reasonable.

Let us designate the marginal cost of extraction of an additional marketable ton by C. This ton gives (1-a) cokeable tons, and a noncokeable tons from which receipts s can be obtained per ton.

The sales price G of the additional gas is sought for which the increase in revenue is equal to the increase in expenditures. G is then given by the relationship:

$$(1 - a)(gG + kK - d) + as = C$$

i.e.,

$$gG = d - kK + \frac{C - as}{1 - a}.$$

Numerical expression of the parameters: One ton of dust used in the ovens gave:

    a) 0.765 tons of coke, of which 0.010 ton was utilized for the fabrication of poor gas for dilution;

    b) 175 cubic meters of rich gas, after heating of the ovens, to which 20% of poor gas was added;

or, finally: k = 0.755 tons of coke;

          g = 210 cubic meters of gas.

For each ton of coke, receipts from the sales of coke, tar, sulphate, and benzol amounted to 7,900 francs. But it was to be feared that the additional tons of coke produced could not be disposed of under such favorable conditions. It was advisable to anticipate a loss in receipts of about 200 francs per ton.

---

*For obvious reasons, the numerical values have been modified. They constitute, nevertheless, valid orders of magnitude.

Consequently:

$$K = 7,700 \text{ francs.}$$

The coalfield's marginal cost as determined from the regression line was 4,900 francs per marketable ton. One marketable ton of bituminous coal included approximately:

74.3% coke,

6.0% of unwashed slag sold at 2,330 francs per ton,

3.7% of mixed slag sold at 2,280 francs per ton,

16% of crude coal dust whose cinder content was too high to be sent to the coke-making plant and sold at an average of 3,800 francs per ton.

Under such conditions:

$$as = \frac{1}{100} (6 \times 2530 + 3.7 \times 2280 + 16 \times 3800) = 830 \text{ F}$$

and:

$$\frac{C - as}{1 - a} = \frac{4,900 - 830}{74.3} = 5,470 \text{ F.}$$

Operation at 100% of present capacity.

An accounting study demonstrated that if the coke-making activity of the plant were speeded up without modifying its capacity of production, additional operating costs would rise to 1,228 francs per ton of additional coke produced, to which must be added 300 francs for transportation per ton of oven dust.

Therefore: $d = 0.755 \times 1,228 + 300 = 1,227$ francs.

In other words, it was not in the interest of the coalfield to negotiate for the additional amount of gas allowed by the available capacity below the price:

$$G = \frac{1}{210} (1,227 - 0.755 \times 7,300 + 5,470)$$

$$G = 4.20 \text{ F (approximately) per cubic meter.}$$

Increase in the available capacity of production.

From the same accounting study a marginal cost of operation of 1,710 francs per ton of coke was derived and, consequently, the following value for d:

$$d = 0.755 \times 1710 + 300 = 1,593$$

The price limit for the gas under such conditions was equal to:

$$G = \frac{1}{210} (1\,593 - 0.755 \times 7\,700 + 5\,470)$$

$$G = 6.0 \text{ F (approximately) per cubic meter.}$$

Calculation of errors.

A certain number of the above numerical estimates being very approximate, a calculation of error was effected in order to determine the influence on G of the various parameters. d being relatively well known, the only variables considered were the price of coke K, the marginal cost C, the valuation of varieties not suitable for coke making s, the percentage of the latter a.

$$g \, dG = - k \, dK + \frac{dC}{1 - a} - \frac{a \, ds}{1 - a} + \frac{C - s}{(1 - a)^2} \, da.$$

After all calculations had been made:

$$dG = - 0.0036 \, dK + 0.0064 \, dC - 0.0016 \, ds + 31 \, da.$$

Therefore:

1) a decrease of 500 francs in the price of coke increases the cost of gas by 1.8 F/m^3;

2) an increase of 500 francs in the marginal cost of extraction increases the cost of gas by 3.2 F;

3) a decrease of 500 francs in the valuation per ton not suitable for coke making increases the price of gas by 0.80 F;

4) an increase of 5% in the nonsuitable portion increases the cost of gas by 1.5 F.

The result is extremely sensitive to the values of parameters K and C. Further studies, based on a better knowledge of these parameters, appear warranted.

3. Production policy of an enterprise.

We shall discuss an example very briefly, since this question is to be dealt with at greater length in the next chapter.

Example: the coal-mining situation in France in 1953 and 1954.

At that time, the mining capacity of the Charbonnages Français was found to be—following a drop in demand—in excess of demand. Their coalfields in the Centre-Midi Area were especially affected and experienced unemployment. For social reasons, and with a view to limiting unemployment in these coal-mining areas, management decided to halt the increase in manpower in the Lorraine coalfields and to reserve additional markets for the coalfields of the Centre-Midi, subject to large discounts from the list price. It was interesting to learn whether this policy was economically justified, and, if not, what would be the loss entailed in attempting to avoid a painful social situation. The small amount of time available did not permit consideration of the distribution from French coalfields as a whole. Therefore, it was decided to consider, successively, only coalfields in pairs: Loire-Lorraine,

Cévennes-Lorraine, etc. In the case of Lorraine, information was available as to the marginal cost c of increasing production by increasing manpower, and for the mining areas of the Centre-Midi, the marginal cost c of unemployment. A calculation was also made, for each of these coal-mining areas, of the marginal receipts r, i.e., the receipts per ton for each of the different kinds sold on the least remunerative markets. Assuming that it was possible to compare marginal tons, the differences r - c for each coalfield were compared. The calculation demonstrated that r - c was substantially lower for the Lorraine fields than for the coalfields in the Centre-Midi, which justified, economically, the policy selected. On the other hand, if, for Lorraine, the marginal cost of unemployment were substituted for the marginal cost of an increase in manpower, the result was converse.

In order to relieve the Centre-Midi coalfields it appeared desirable to check the expansion of the Lorraine coalfields, but not to create any unemployment in that area.

4. Government action under conditions of competition.

Here again an example would no doubt be preferable to abstract discussion.
Example: Studies of the Commission de l'Energie du Plan de Modernisation et d'Equipement regarding fuel oil-coal competition.

During recent years, the consumption of fuel oils by industry and by households has increased at an extraordinarily rapid rate which has tended to depress coal sales during certain years.

In order to appreciate the conditions of this competition, it was interesting:

1) to study the respective economic cost related to the use of these two types of fuels;

2) to learn to what extent the maintenance of coal utilization would check the increase of our imports of crude petroleum, save foreign currency, and consequently have a favorable effect upon the balance of payments.

The study group entrusted with an examination of these problems devoted its attention first to the matter of central heating in the Paris area. Accordingly, let us indicate in Fig. 31 the growth of demand in relation to time:

Curve 1 corresponds to the total demand for fuel oils and coal, the ordinate between curves 1 and 2 to the demand for coal, and the ordinate between curve 2 and the axis of the abscissa to the demand for fuel oil.

The answer to the two questions raised above can be obtained by varying curve 2 slightly alternatively in the direction of an increase and toward a decrease in coal demand, and by determining:

1) the variation in the total economic cost on the basis of constant service;

2) the changing quantities of foreign currency required.

The marginal costs to be taken into consideration are not pure development or regression costs (i.e., obtained by a comparison with a hypothesis of constant production), but are development or regression costs beginning from a certain curve of production in time.

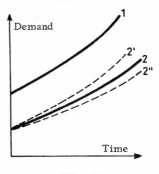

Fig. 31

Let us suppose then, by applying an administrative measure to be defined, that we substitute a ton of fuel oil for a ton of coal in the central heating systems of the Paris area. The costs increase by:

$$px + d + t + f$$

in which: p, expressed in dollars, is the price of the crude petroleum required for the production of one ton of fuel oil;

x is the rate of exchange;

d is the marginal cost of refining the fuel oil;

t is the marginal cost of transportation from the Lower-Seine refineries to Paris;

f is the marginal cost of distribution expenses.

However, this is offset by savings effected to the extent that the quantity of coal consumed decreases. Let us designate as E the number of tons of coal which are able to provide the same service as a ton of fuel oil. E depends both on the caloric properties of the two combustibles and the thermal yield of fuel oil and coal installations. The savings on cost are then:

$$E (C + T + F + S)$$

in which: C is the marginal cost of coal extraction;

T is the marginal cost of transportation from the coal field in question to Paris;

F is the marginal cost of coal distribution;

S is a positive or negative quantity which represents, for each ton of coal, the additional indirect costs which must be allowed when a coal installation is substituted for a fuel oil installation. Let us assume that in constructing a new building we have the alternative of installing either central coal heating or central fuel oil heating. Account should be taken not only of the cost of fuels but also of the differences in investment costs and of future operating and maintenance costs. These are the differences which are incorporated in S. On the other hand, no account is taken in S of nonquantitative elements, such as the psychological preferences of consumers for one or the other of these fuels.*

Let us therefore consider the quantity y:

$$y = px + d + t + f - E(C + T + F + S)$$

If y is positive, it is desirable to develop heating by coal.

If y is negative, then it is desirable to develop heating by fuel oil.

The calculation of y for the true value of x therefore provides an answer to the first question. But we can also calculate the value x_0 of x for which y is zero. This value will provide an answer to the second question. As a matter of fact, in the case of this value, coal and fuel oil are equivalent, and everything occurs—when developing coal at the expense of fuel oil—as though foreign currency were being procured indirectly at the rate x_0. If x_0 is not too high in relation to the official rate of exchange, it is reasonable to check the expansion of fuel oils because the domestic production of coal compensates for the slightly high price of the foreign currency saved. If, on the other hand, x_0 is far greater than the official rate of exchange, it is preferable to allow the development of fuel oil consumption to proceed and to resort to other methods for saving foreign currency.

Depending on the value of x_0, it can be to the government's advantage to intervene or to remain aloof from the fuel oil-coal competition.

*
* *

As we reach the end of this chapter, we are now in a position to evaluate the contribution of the notion of marginal cost to economic method. This notion is derived directly from the criterion of maximization of profit. In fact, when profit is at a maximum, any technically possible variation in production would probably reduce receipts more than it would reduce costs.

The advantage presented by the notion of marginal cost is its extreme utility. Whereas a series of future costs and revenues—even when converted into present value—is not of great significance for the practical man, marginal cost is immediately indicative, even when its definition requires some care as in the instance of contraction and expansion costs. It is this characteristic of simplicity which makes the notion of marginal cost such an attractive one for the technical economist.

-----

*This method has been devised by M. Boiteux in his capacity as chairman of a study group of the Commissariat Général au Plan.

Nevertheless, one must always remain conscious of the variety of marginal costs and their conditions of validity. Nor should the limitations of this concept be overlooked. Marginal costs are the result of a comparison of costs between two stable levels of production. Accordingly, they cannot completely describe the relations which hold between costs and production because variation in the level of production, when not extremely slow, results in additional adjustment costs.

Having mastered the concept of marginal cost, we must now go one step further and take up the subject of models which present in more complex and realistic form the conditions of an enterprise from the point of view of production.

BIBLIOGRAPHY

1. M. ALLAIS:
   A la recherche d'une discipline économique (In search of an economic discipline). Imprimerie Nationale, Paris, 1943. Book published under the title: Traité d'Economie pure (Treatise in pure economics).

2. M. ALLAIS:
   La gestion des Houillères nationalisées et la théorie économique (Management of nationalized coal mines and economic theory). Imprimerie Nationale, 1953.

3. M. ALLAIS:
   "Le problème de la coordination des transports et la théorie économique" (The problem of transportation coordination and economic theory). Revue d'Economie politique, Vol. 58, March-April 1958.

4. ALT and BRADFORD:
   Business economics. Principles and cases. Irwin.

5. L. J. ATKINSON:
   "The marginal feed cost of pork and lard." J. Farm. Econ., 1945, 27, 375-87.

6. M. BOITEUX:
   "La tarification des points" (The pricing of peaks). Revue générale d'Electricité, August 1949.

7. M. BOITEUX:
   Coûts marginaux de l'Energie thermique (Marginal costs of thermal energy). Document d'Electricité de France, 1950.

8. M. BOITEUX:
La tarification au coût marginal et les demandes aléatoires (Pricing at marginal cost and random demand). Cahier du Séminaire d'Econométrie, No. 1, 1951.

9. M. BOITEUX:
Tarification des régimes aléatoires de la demande (Pricing of random systems of demand). Document d'Electricité de France, 1950.

10. M. BOITEUX:
Coûts marginaux de l'énergie hydroélectrique régularisée. (Marginal costs of regularized hydroelectric power). Document d'Electricité de France, 1950.

11. M. BOITEUX:
Coûts marginaux de l'énergie au fil de l'eau (Marginal costs of hydroelectric power). Document d'Electricité de France, 1950.

12. M. BOITEUX:
Note complémentaire à l'étude des coûts marginaux de l'énergie hydroélectrique régularisée (Supplemental note to the analysis of marginal costs of regularized hydroelectric power). Document d'Electricité de France, 1950.

13. M. BOITEUX:
Coûts marginaux de l'énergie au fil de l'eau compte tenu du caractère aléatoire des apports (Marginal costs of hydro-electric power, taking into account the random nature of supply). Document d'Electricité de France, 1950.

14. M. BOITEUX:
Réflexions sur la concurrence du Rail et de la Route. Le déclassement des lignes non rentables et le déficit des chemins de fer (Observations on the competition between rail and road. Abandonment of nonprofitable lines and the railroad deficit). Brochure, 39 pages.

15. F. BRAMBILLA:
"Un'applicazione econometrica della teoria della produzione all'industria del gas" (An economic application of the theory of production to the gas industry). L'industria, 1949, 255-8.

16. L. BREGUET:
Détermination et calcul du prix de revient des transports aériens (Determination and calculation of cost in air transportation). Paris, Librairie aéronautique Etienne Chiron, 1935.

17. BULLINGER:
Engineering economic analysis. McGraw-Hill, New York, 1950.

18. H. B. CHENERY:
Engineering basis of economic analysis. Ph.D. thesis, Harvard.

19. H. B. CHENERY:
"Engineering production functions." Quarterly Journal of Economics, Vol. LXIII, 1949.

20. J. DEAN:
Managerial economics. Prentice-Hall Inc., New York, 1951.

21. J. DEAN:
"Cost structures of enterprises and break-even charts." American Economic Review, Vol. XXXVIII, pp. 153-164, 1948.

22. J. DEAN:
The relation of cost to output for a leather belt shop. New York, National Bureau for Economic Research, 1941.

23. J. DEAN:
Statistical cost functions of a hosiery mill. The University of Chicago Press, 1941.

24. J. DEAN:
Statistical determination of costs with special reference to marginal costs. The University of Chicago Press, 1936.

25. J. DEAN:
The long-run behavior of cost in a chain of shoe-stores, a statistical analysis. The University of Chicago Press, 1942.

26. J. DEAN and R. W. JANES:
The long-run behavior of costs in a chain of shoe-stores: a statistical analysis. Studies in business administration, 1943, 13. 3. Chicago: University of Chicago Press.

27. F. K. EDWARDS:
"Cost analysis in transportation." American Economic Review, 1947, 37, 441-61.

28. A. R. FERGUSON:
"Empirical determination of a multidimensional marginal cost function." Econometrica, July 1950.

29. GIGUET and MORLAT:
"Les causes d'erreurs systématiques dans la prévision des travaux" (Causes of systematic errors in work forecasting). Annales des ponts et chaussées. September-October 1952.

30. E. L. GRANT:
Principles of engineering economy. The Ronald Press Company, New York, 1950.

31. M. R. HUTTER:
"La théorie économique et la gestion commerciale des chemins de fer" (Economic theory and the commercial management of railroads).
I. Qu'est-ce que le coût marginal? (What is marginal cost?) II. Le problème tarifaire (The pricing problem). III. La coordination des transports (The coordination of transportation). Revue générale des Chemins de Fer, February 1950, Dunod, Paris, 1950.

32. J. LESOURNE:
"Le comportement des entreprises et certains aspects de l'imprévisibilité" (Enterprise behavior and certain aspects of unpredictability). Revue d'économie politique, January 1954.

33. J. LESOURNE:
"La notion du coût marginal dans l'industrie houillère" (The notion of marginal cost in the coal-mining industry). Annales des Mines, April 1955.

34. P. LYLE:
Regression analysis of production costs and factory operations. 1946, 2nd ed., revised. Edinburgh and London: Oliver and Boyd, Ltd.

35. J. L. MOSAK:
"Some theoretical implications of the statistical analysis of demand and cost function for steels." Journal of the American Statistical Association, Vol. XXXVI.

36. NATIONAL BUREAU OF ECONOMIC RESEARCH:
Cost behavior and price policy: a study prepared by the Committee on Price Determination for the Conference on Price Research.

37. W. von NORDLING:
"Le prix de revient des transports par chemin de fer" (Cost of rail transportation). Annales des Ponts et Chaussées, 1886.

38. R. C. NOYES:
"Certain problems in the empirical study of costs." American Economic Review, September 1941.

39. E. H. PHELPS BROWN:
"Analyse de l'étude de L. Bréguet" (Analysis of the study by L. Bréguet). Econometrica, 1936.

40. RAUTENSTRAUCH:
The economics of business enterprise. New York, Wiley, 1939.

41. W. RAUTENSTRAUCH and R. VILLERS:
The economics of industrial management. New York, Funk & Wagnalls, 1949.

42. G. ROBERT:
"Le prix du gaz en France" (The price of gas in France). Revue française de l'Energie, No. 1, September 1949.

43. G. ROTTIER:
"Notes sur la maximation du profit" (Notes on maximization of profit). Economie appliquée. Vol. IV, 1951, No. 1, January-March.

44. P. A. SAMUELSON:
Foundations of Economic Analysis. Harvard University Press, 1948.

45. E. SCHNEIDER:
Theorie der Produktion (Theory of production). Vienna, Verlag von Julius Springer, 1934.

46. C. SMITH:
"The cost-output relation for the U.S. Steel Corporation." Review of Economic Studies, November 1942.

47. V. E. SMITH:
"The statistical production function." Quarterly Journal of Economics, 1945, 59, 543-62.

48. G. J. STIGLER:
The theory of price. New York, MacMillan, 1947.

49. E. STRAUSS:
"Cost accounting and statistical cost functions." American Economic Review, June 1945.

50. H. STAEHLE:
"The measurement of statistical cost functions: an appraisal of some recent contributions." American Economic Review, Vol. XXXII, 1942.

51. U.S. STEEL CORPORATION:
TNEC papers. Volume I. Steel prices volume and cost. Controlling limitations on price reductions.

52. M. VERHULST:
"The pure theory of production applied to the French gas industry." Econometrica, October 1948.

52. K. H. WYLIE and M. EZEKIEL:
"The cost curve for steel production." Journal of Political Economy, Vol. XLVIII, 1940.

PART III

PROBLEMS OF SYNTHESIS

Chapter 11

Control of production
and inventory management

The preceding chapter was mainly concerned with the definition of marginal cost and the problem of its measurement. For reasons which are due in part to the limitations of this concept and in part to the viewpoint adopted, we were not able in the foregoing discussion to examine various problems posed by management policy. Having discussed the various cost concepts, we now have available the required material for an analysis of the more complex aspects of this policy.

This analysis will form the subject of the following four chapters, devoted respectively to control of production and inventory management, to the determination of optimum programs, to investment problems, and to price policy. Because the matter now at issue is to take a synthesizing view of company management, one should not be surprised if the sequence of the subjects treated in the various chapters appears somewhat arbitrary. As a matter of fact, we have taken an aspect of a firm's activity as the focal point of interest in each of chapters 11, 13, and 14; and, in chapter 12, a method of analysis.

This lack of symmetry, somewhat illogical in appearance, will make it possible to regroup all the models of similar viewpoint within a single chapter. Furthermore, it is not through pure coincidence that inventory management is discussed at the same time as control of production. Although these two fields may at first appear to be completely independent of one another, all who have some industrial experience know to what extent this impression is doubly incorrect. First, badly managed inventories result in considerable expenditure due to immobilized capital, production irregularities, and delivery failures. Second, inventory problems frequently cannot be dealt with separately from problems of production.

Let us take an example from a manufacturing industry. The machines in a shop, once started, manufacture a series of parts. In order to minimize production costs, large production runs will be scheduled to avoid repetition of adjustment and restarting costs. If, on the other hand, one wishes to reduce storage costs, inventories will be kept at a minimum and the machines will be stopped as soon as this minimum is reached. The production runs are then very short. Neither of these solutions is satisfactory. It is necessary to determine the length of the run and the level of inventory for which total costs are at a minimum, i.e., for which there is "equilibrium" between the advantage of a smaller inventory and the disadvantage of a shorter run. In problems of synthesis, inventory management and production control thus appear as two aspects of a single policy.

There are, however, instances in which questions of stockage and of production are not related. First, there are the extreme cases of firms that either produce nonstorable goods or purchase products only for resale. In the first case there are no inventory costs, and in the second there are no production costs. There is also an entire range of intermediate cases in which independence between production and stockage is sufficient to permit independent treatment of these two areas. This, added to the wish to proceed from the elementary to the complex, explains the plan of this chapter which covers, in succession, production policy, inventory management, and simultaneous control of production and inventories. In all of these problems, and especially in those relating to stockage, risk plays a major role. Risk, however, will not be considered separately. Instead, in each of the three parts of this chapter, the use of the known and then that of the unforeseeable future will be studied successively.

It is unnecessary to repeat at this point the justification of the hypothesis of a perfect forecast, inasmuch as it was discussed within its proper framework when criteria were examined in Chapter 2.

I

PRODUCTION POLICY

An analysis of production policy is a logical sequel to an analysis of marginal costs. As demonstrated in Chapter 10, problems of production can be of three different types relating to: a) maximization of the production obtained with given quantities of factors; b) minimization of costs for a given production; c) determination of the optimum volume of production under certain market conditions.

Because the first type of problem falls outside the framework of this book, and since it is desirable to delay a discussion of the third until the chapter on prices, we will primarily consider the second type of problem here.

This procedure may seem paradoxical because a definition of the marginal cost of a unit of production presupposes, at least in theory, that costs have already been minimized for each level of production. Why, therefore, does this analysis follow a chapter on marginal costs instead of preceding it? It is because in Chapter 10 we did not specify the units of production to which the concept of marginal cost was to be applied. The unit considered could be a firm, single factory, a simple shop, a coal field or a mine, a steam generating plant, or the central power stations of Electricité de France as a whole. In each case, the unit was considered as a complete production unit. If it is now split into component units, however, it is possible to define the marginal cost of each component and to use such marginal costs to allocate production among the units to the greatest economic advantage. In the case of component units taken individually, costs will have been minimized for each level of production; but it is the equalization of the marginal costs of these units which will make it possible to perform the same operation for the whole.

The two paragraphs following (the first stipulating certainty with respect to the future, and the second a future known only as a probability) analyze the manner in which a given production must be allocated among the various units of production so as to minimize total costs.

1. Certainty with respect to the future.

The optimum rule of management rests in an astonishingly simple principle. Given production Q_i and $D_i (Q_i)$ the cost of unit i (i = 1, 2, ..., n), the problem is to produce a given quantity by minimizing the total cost:

$$Q = \Sigma_i \, Q_i \qquad\qquad (I.1)$$

$$D = \Sigma_i \, D_i \, (Q_i). \qquad\qquad (I.2)$$

If, in order to simplify, account is not taken of the limitations which restrict the areas of variation of the Q_i's, and if it is taken for granted that cost functions are continuous and differentiable, a minimum is realized when this equality is verified:

$$D_1' \, (Q_1) = \cdots = D_i' \, (Q_i) = \cdots = D_n' \, (Q_n). \qquad\qquad (I.3)$$

In other words, production must be allocated among the various units until their marginal costs are equal. The common value of these marginal costs can then be defined as the marginal cost of the productive medium as a whole.

If, on the other hand, the area of variation of Q_i's is limited, minimizing conditions are more difficult to express. A minimum is realized if there is a number c independent of i, such that:

$$D'_i(Q_i) = c \tag{I.4}$$

for all Q_i's which are not at the limit of their area of variation,

$$D'_i(Q_i) \geqslant c \tag{I.5}$$

for all Q_i's which are at a lower limit of their area of variation,* and

$$D'_i(Q_i) \leqslant c \tag{I.6}$$

in the case of all Q_i's which are at an upper limit of their area of variation. Such conditions may appear to be quite normal to readers accustomed to extreme problems. As a matter of fact, if (I.4) and (I.5) are respectively verified for the values j and k of i, a reduction in costs would be obtained only by reducing Qk and increasing Qj (which is impossible because Qk is at the lower limit of its area of variation). Similar reasoning in connection with (I.4) and (I.6), (I.5) and (I.6) would make it possible to complete the demonstration.

Number c, of course, can be defined as the marginal cost of the productive medium as a whole.

The following are a few examples of specific applications of the foregoing theory:

Example I. In the manufacturing industry a frequent problem of cost minimization arises from the possibility of manufacturing the same part on different machines. Because several types of parts have to be produced, the problem consists in allocating the various types in accordance with available machine time.

This problem and numerous similar problems will be dealt with in some depth in the next chapter.

Example II. The production of electricity from a group of steam generating plants. In Chapter 10 we studied marginal costs in the production of energy by a steam generating plant built to meet the demand of an isolated area. Let us now analyze the problem of the production of electricity by a group of steam generating plants [14].

"The various plants are considered to be located very close to one another, which amounts to omitting costs inherent in the interconnecting lines which link them (or to ascribe such costs 'appropriately' to the various plants). The area to be served by

---

*The lower limit is very frequently a zero value.

the group under consideration is isolated from any other source of electrical power." Furthermore, each plant's power potential is small in relation to the total power of the group; and a plant, when in operation, operates at full capacity.

Total demand can be represented either by a curve indicating the power q at each moment, or by a curve indicating the timespan h during which a power superior or equal to a given value q is used. Fig. 1 shows the relation between these two curves.

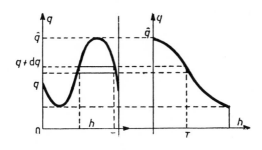

Fig. 1

a) Existing steam generating plants can cope with peak power. The only costs which are a function of the allocation of production among the various plants are therefore costs which are proportionate to the power produced. The condition for cost minimization is then obvious: the plants must be started in the order of their increasing proportional costs. Plants which have a low proportional cost will be fully utilized and will operate around the clock, whereas those which have a high proportional cost will operate for only a small number of hours to meet peak demands. In actual practice, the more modern plants utilizing the latest equipment will be operated around the clock while the older, less efficient plants will fill in to supply peak loads.

b) No equipment exists and an optimum group of steam generating plants must be constructed.* In a given state of technology, each type of plant is characterized by a certain proportional cost C and by a certain volume π of fixed charges per unit of power. The various types of plants can be arrayed in the order of increasing proportional cost. The fixed charges π of the acceptable types are then necessarily decreasing functions of the proportional cost C, since one can exclude a technical solution at once when another exists which leads simultaneously to lower proportional costs

---

*Such a problem would have to be solved, for instance, if it were necessary to reconstruct a group of plants in an area after its destruction through war.

and fixed charges. The most acceptable types of plant, as a group, are therefore represented by the curve π (C) in Fig. 2.

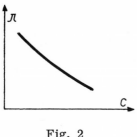

The plant whose period of utilization will be h will supply power dq each time the total power required exceeds q. The total costs will be expressed:

$$D = \int_0^T [Ch + \pi(C)] \frac{dq}{dh}\, dh.$$

C in relation to h remains to be determined.

The integral is at a minimum when the function C(h) being sought fulfills the condition:

Fig. 2

$$\frac{\partial \pi}{\partial C} = - h. \qquad (I.7)$$

In other words, the optimum duration of plant operation of proportional cost C is equal to the slope of the curve π(C) with the sign changed at the point of abscissa C. This condition is sufficient to determine the optimum group as a whole.

We can proceed to analyze the marginal cost of the whole complex of plants as has been done for an isolated steam generating plant. The results obtained are identical, with the exception that "the nonpeak marginal cost is no longer constant but is equal to the proportional cost of the first plant which starts to operate when an additional demand for power occurs and the peak marginal cost is equal to the marginal cost of the peak level of the peak plant" [14].*

c) The foregoing can serve as a basis for the establishment of a program for the retirement of existing plants. By reason of technical improvements, the older plants are generally those with a high proportional cost. But these outmoded plants are likely to be shut down and replaced by modern power stations. Under these conditions, the cost of fixed charges π to be ascribed to an older plant with a proportional cost C must include, over and above the maintenance costs, a reserve for replacement by a new power station with a similar proportional cost (assuming amortization has already been effected). Because the investment costs for a given C are lower for a modern plant, π is as low as the remaining lifetime of the plant is short. Conversely, each older plant has a specific value of π associated with the date of retirement.

However, an optimum utilization of existing plants assigns to the plant with a proportional cost C a period of utilization h(C) (cf. a above). Knowing this function, the curve of the equation can be traced:

*Cf. Chapter 10.

$$\pi = - \int_{C_0}^{C} h\,(C)\,\mathrm{d}C + \pi_0.$$

π_0 representing the fixed charges of the most modern full-time plant with the lowest proportional cost C_0.

Each value of C can therefore be associated with a value of π which will make it possible to determine, for each of the plants with a proportional cost C, the optimum date of retirement.

Example III. The production of electricity of a thermal-hydro-electric network [13]. The objective here is to discuss a problem similar to the preceding one, except that here we consider a mix of steam generating plants and hydroelectric plants. Let us consider, for instance, a region of thermal production 1, a region of hydroelectric production 2, and an intermediate region which consumes both the hydroelectric and the thermal output. If losses are omitted, the total demand at time t, q (t) is equal to the sum of the thermal production q_1(t) and the hydroelectric output q_2(t).

$$q\,(t) = q_1\,(t) + q_2\,(t)$$

It can be immediately deduced from the general theory that the optimum allocation of production between the two areas presupposes: 1) "an equality of hydroelectric and thermal marginal costs when the two production processes are operated simultaneously, and 2) a lower marginal cost when the supply is provided by only one of the sources of power" [13].

The marginal cost of the entire production system is then equal to: 1) the joint value of the marginal costs of the two processes when these are used simultaneously, and 2) the marginal cost of the process actually employed, when only one of the two is used.

Assume that the two processes are always employed simultaneously. The detailed diagram of the aggregate load is shown in Fig. 3. The quantity of hydroelectric production relates to the water supply except for a t_2 period in summer when plant capacity is a limiting factor. To avoid investing in capacity that would not be fully utilized most of the year, the hydroelectric plant is usually not built to accomodate the short-run peaking of water supply.

As we have noted in the preceding chapter, the marginal cost of producing thermal energy is infinite at its peak unless some peak level capacity is present. Consequently, when the selling price and the marginal cost are equal, installed thermal power must be used in full during the entire peak level period of t_1 duration, and the load charge curve then follows, almost as a constant, the shape of the curve of hydroelectric production.

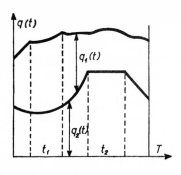

Fig. 3

The year can therefore be divided into three periods:

1. a summer period t_2 during which the hydroelectric equipment operates at capacity;

2. a winter period t_1 during which the steam generating equipment operates at capacity;

3. an intermediate period t_3 during which the two types of equipment operate simultaneously below their maximum capacity.

$$t_1 + t_2 + t_3 = T$$

During the period t_2, marginal cost is equal to the nonpeak thermal cost C, or to the hydroelectric marginal cost. If D represents the total annual costs for hydroelectric equipment when installed power is $\hat{q}_2$, the hydroelectric marginal cost for the total period t_2 during which the hydroelectric equipment operates at capacity is: $\dfrac{\partial D}{\partial \hat{q}_2}$, and the following equality is therefore reached:

$$t_2\, C = \frac{\partial D}{\partial \hat{q}_2}.$$

During the period t_3, the marginal cost is equal to the nonpeak thermal cost C.

During the period t_1, the marginal cost for the entire period is equal to the thermal marginal cost at the peak level, i.e., $Ct_1 + \pi$, if we retain the notations contained in the preceding example. The average value of the marginal cost at each instant is:

$$C + \frac{\pi}{t_1}.$$

With respect to hydroelectric equipment, the period t_1 is a low-water period. If it were desired to increase output from the hydroelectric equipment during that period it would be necessary to tap a greater portion of water from the river basin, which would result in an increase in fixed costs. A development cost of the hydroelectric production potential can be defined for the low-water period as a whole. The average value at each instant of such marginal cost must be equal to: $C + \dfrac{\pi}{t_1}$.

It would be possible to demonstrate that relationships between marginal costs, taking into account conditions of demand, permit a determination of the optimum characteristics of thermal and hydroelectric equipment.

Although the two foregoing examples are derived from the same industry, their range is sufficiently general in character to provide an idea of possible methods of analysis of the allocation of production when the future is a certainty.

2. The future considered as a probability.

The theory contained in the foregoing paragraph is easily modified to relate to cases where the future is known only as a probability. The random character can be due to production, to demand, or to both. A discussion of the first possibility in the case of nonstorable goods should be sufficient to demonstrate the mechanism of the analysis.

Two situations are possible:

1) All output is random, and stockout cannot be avoided with any certainty.

2) Only some output is random, but it is possible to compensate for its variations by adjustment of the production that is certain.

In the first case, the executive can control only the productive capacities which will be identified by the letters $Q_1, ..., Q_n$ (in order not to multiply notations).

If the model contains a stockout cost, and if the mathematical expectation of costs is to be minimized, it will be necessary to determine the minimum of the function:

$$D = D(Q_1, ..., Q_i, ..., Q_n)$$

taking into account the variation limitations imposed upon the Q_i.

If the model contains a stockout probability, and if the same criterion is adopted, the minimum of the same function is determined:

$$D = D(Q_1, ..., Q_i, ..., Q_n) \tag{I.8}$$

subject to the condition:

$$p(Q_1, ..., Q_n) \leqslant p \tag{I.9}$$

which demonstrates that the stockout probability is less than the imposed value p. If, in order to simplify, we transform the (I.9) inequality into an equality and neglect the variation limitations of the Q_i, then the Q_i satisfy, when a minimum is obtained, the relationships:

$$\frac{\partial D}{\partial Q_1} \bigg/ \frac{\partial p}{\partial Q_1} = \cdots = \frac{\partial D}{\partial Q_n} \bigg/ \frac{\partial p}{\partial Q_n} \tag{I.10}$$

$\dfrac{\partial D}{\partial Q_i}$ can be defined as the marginal mathematical expectation of cost for goods i, and $\dfrac{\partial p}{\partial Q_i}$ as the marginal probability of stockout. In other words, at the optimum, the marginal mathematical expectations of cost are proportional to the probabilities of stockout.

In the second case there is no stockout, since assured outputs can compensate for the variations of random outputs. For instance, during a year let Q be total demand, let r_j (j = 1, 2, ..., m) be the values of random output, let q_i (i = 1, 2, ..., n) be the values consequently assumed by assured production, and let R_j and Q_i be the productive capacities for the different techniques. The cost for such year is a function:

$$D(q_1, ..., q_n; r_1 ... r_n; Q_1 ..., Q_n; R_1, ... R_m)$$

If the equipment is given, all variables are determined with the exception of q_i. The first problem therefore consists in selecting these variables in such manner that:

$$q_i \leqslant Q_i$$
$$\Sigma q_i = Q - \Sigma_j r_j.$$

This problem is analogous to those we have discussed in the case where the future is a certainty. When it is solved, the q_i become known functions of the r_j and of the productive capacities. The year's cost is therefore, a priori, a random variable through the intermediary of the r_j. Its mathematical expectation is a function:

$$d = d(Q_1, ..., Q_n; R_1, ..., R_n)$$

and there remains a second problem: that of the determination of productive capacities. These capacities are subject to a relation which states that the sum of the assured productive capacities and the minimum random production permits meeting demand Q.* We are therefore brought back to a problem of minimization related to the type of problem already examined.

The fact should be underscored that choices are made here at two levels:

First, there are tactical choices concerned with decisions taken each year as the near future enters the domain of the known. Next, there are long-term strategic choices which relate essentially to productive capacities. Such choices can be made only after a

---

*Naturally, it is possible to generalize the model by permitting a certain stockout.

determination of the annual rules of optimum management. In other words, to determine equipment needs it must be assumed that optimal decisions will subsequently be made.

This duality between strategic choices and tactical choices will be considered again when a synthesis of problems of production and inventories will be attempted.

Until now, we have considered the case of a firm producing only one type of goods but having several production techniques at its disposal. The problem remains essentially unchanged when the firm produces several types of goods. Following is a brief outline of a theoretical model which demonstrates the latter. This model has the further advantage of starting from a criterion other that that of the minimization of the mathematical expectation of cost.

Example: Allocation of an agricultural program between two types of crops. A farmer owns land covering a surface U which he can sow either with A or with B. The quantity of A harvested is practically independent of meteoreological conditions. On the other hand, rain, a random variable, exerts considerable influence upon the harvest of B. Furthermore, there are world market prices, and the farmer cannot hope for an increase in price b of B if weather conditions are unfavorable. In other words, prices a and b are given. The quantity of work performed by the farmer and his farmhands is Y.

What is the optimum mix of A and B that the farmer should cultivate on his land? If there were no risk attached, the farmer could maximize his profit and cultivate A and B in such proportions that the relationship between the marginal efficiencies of an identical factor of production in the two crops would be equal to the relationship between prices a and b. This is no longer necessarily so when risk is taken into account.

Production relationships can be represented by the four relations:

$$A = f(Y_A, U_A)$$

(production function of A in which Y_A and U_A represent the amount of work performed and the land devoted to the cultivation of A respectively),

$$B = Xg(Y_B, U_B)$$

(production function of B in which rainfall X is a normal ramdon variable of average value 1 with a standard deviation s, and where Y_B and U_B represent the amount of work performed and the land devoted to the cultivation of B respectively),

$$Y = Y_A + Y_B \quad \text{(I.11)}$$
$$U = U_A + U_B \quad \text{(I.12)}$$

(total quantities of work Y and land U are given).

It can easily be verified that the farmer's income is a normal random variable, of average value R and of standard deviation S. A criterion such as the maximization of a function F (R, S) can therefore be adopted.

Now:

$$R = af\,(Y_A, U_A) + bg\,(Y_B, U_B)$$
$$S = sbg\,(Y_B, U_B).$$

In determining the maximum of F (R, S), taking into account relationships (I.11) and (I.12), the following are obtained:

$$\frac{f'_{U_A}}{g'_{U_B}} = \frac{f'_{Y_A}}{g'_{Y_B}} = \frac{b}{a}\left(1 + s\,\frac{F'_S}{F'_R}\right).$$

The rain risk therefore changes the allocation of land between the two crops A and B. Everything takes place as though, for the farmer, the price of product B were:

$$b\left(1 + s\,\frac{F'_S}{F'_R}\right)$$

and as though this product were then produced on an assured basis (F $'$ = 1).

It will be observed that if a farmer does not wish to take a risk, F$'_S$ is negative. The risk attributable to weather conditions leads to a reduction of B in favor of A. If the farmer maximizes his mathematical expectation (F$'_S$ = 0), he behaves as though the average production of B were assured.

Although this model is quite unrealistic, it serves to illustrate the influence risk has with respect to the organization of production.

Unpredictability or uncertainty will play an even more important part in inventory problems.

II

MANAGEMENT OF INVENTORIES

Before considering specific inventory models, it is well to review the main variables as well as the nature of inventory problems.

An inventory is fed by inputs and reduced by outputs. Inputs can be quantities purchased or quantities produced in other parts of the factory.

With respect to in-house production of inputs, the input rate is contingent upon decisions in the area of production and cannot be influenced by the stock department. This rate is frequently predictable even in cases where it must be considered as a random variable linked to failures in production lines. Examples of such a situation are the hydroelectric reservoirs, whose inputs are the natural water supply which is a random variable. Inputs can be continuous or intermittent. They can be regarded as continuous if a large number of units go into inventory within a period of time which is brief in relation to the period of decision. Such is the case in manufacturing, for instance, when units are stocked immediately upon reaching the end of the production line. Discontinuity may result either from the small number of units produced during a basic period of time or from the necessity of grouping deliveries from the production department in the storage areas.

On the other hand, quantities purchased may be contingent upon decisions by the stock department. These quantities usually arrive intermittently because it is preferable to group purchases to avoid costs of repetitive ordering and to benefit from lower transportation rates. One of the fundamental parameters of the system is the delay in delivery, i.e., the interval of time separating the order from its delivery. Depending upon the case, this delay can be considered as fixed or random.

Outputs consist either of deliveries to consumers or deliveries to other areas of the factory. Most of the time their rates are determined by other than stock department decisions. Depending upon the case, it can be assumed that outputs are either definitely known or are known only as probabilities. Under the second hypothesis, there is a possibility of stockout. This stockout, however, arises under very different conditions depending on whether the enterprise is or is not free to delay deliveries to customers. As in the case of inputs, outputs can be continuous or intermittent. If they are intermittent and random, unpredictability applies both to the date of the orders and to their volume.

The type of decision relating to stockage is contingent upon the possibility of modifying inputs and outputs. If neither can be modified, the only variable which can be considered is storage capacity (whose determination constitutes, in the other cases, only one of the significant elements of the policy to be followed). For example, in the case of hydroelectric reservoirs it is not sufficient merely to choose the capacity of the reservoirs; the flow of water must continually be determined. In the case of a retail store whose output is predetermined but whose inputs are subject to determination, the conceivable policies are essentially dependent upon available information. If it is relatively easy to ascertain the inventory status regularly (each day for example), an order can be placed as soon as the inventory of a particular product drops below a certain critical value, the size of the order being either fixed or a function of inventory status plus sales forecasts. If, on the other hand, it is a very costly procedure to ascertain the inventory level regularly, it is preferable to make an inventory of stocks on hand periodically and to order accordingly.

Naturally, the policy to be followed must be determined on the basis of an analysis of inventory costs. Inventory costs can fall into five different categories in addition to information costs:

1. At the very outset, there are costs linked to the creation and maintenance of storage capacity. They are a function of anticipated maximum storage.

2. Next, in cases where goods do not necessarily go through storage, costs are involved in receiving and issuing stock. These can be very low, as in the case of precision parts, or relatively high, as in the case of coal.

3. The variation in value of objects stocked (which is generally negative) constitutes the third item of cost. This can be due to aging or to any variation in the sales price.

4. Financial costs with respect to the immobilized capital are also one of the important elements of storage costs. They occur automatically in calculations of present value.

5. Finally, in cases of inaccurate prediction, there are the consequences of stockout. As explained in Chapter 2, this problem can be resolved by introducing either a probability of stockout or a stockout cost. The two methods are equivalent, but the second has the advantage of taking the extent of the stockout into account.

The above discussion demonstrates that inventory models can be extremely varied. The skill of the researcher is measured by his ability to select that which is best adapted to a specific situation under investigation.

No advantage would be gained in discussing all inventory models here. The models we will consider are some that are used frequently, giving a fairly broad view of the subject. We will assume here, in succession, that: a) the future is definitely known; and b) the future is known as a probability.

1. Certainty.

The simplest model is that of Wilson-Whitin [58]. It considers the case of a firm purchasing storable goods for resale. The sales of the firm are evenly distributed over the year. Since there is an intrinsic cost of ordering (independent of the size of the order), it is to the firm's advantage to order large quantities at relatively infrequent intervals. Following the hypothesis made on sales, the time interval between orders is constant and the volume ordered is also constant. The determination of volume takes the following into account:

y, the annual quantity sold;

a, the unit purchase price, assumed to be independent of the size of the order;

S, the size of an order;

K, the ordering costs, independent of volume, for an order (K includes administrative costs, part of the transportation costs, etc.);

c, annual inventory costs for one unit. c can at times assume the shape of ua, that is to say, the form of a percentage u of the purchase price. c takes into account all costs enumerated above.

If the delay in delivery d is constant and known, an order arrives at exactly the time when the inventory reaches zero. Along the time scale t, the inventory follows (during the year) the broken lines indicated in Fig. 4.

The portion D of costs which is a function of S is the sum of costs of: 1) inventory $\frac{cS}{2}$ since the average annual stock is obviously $\frac{S}{2}$; and 2) ordering: $\frac{Ky}{S}$ since there are y/S orders during the year.

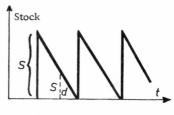

Fig. 4

D is minimal when:

$$\frac{dD}{dS} = \frac{c}{2} - \frac{Ky}{S^2} = 0$$

$$S = \sqrt{\frac{2Ky}{c}}. \tag{II.1}$$

This formula, derived by Wilson in 1916, is extremely convenient for determining both the maximum inventory requirement and the size of each order.

The calculation is not much more complicated if the following hypotheses are substituted for those above:

1) the cost price a of a unit is not constant, but decreases in relation to the size of the order:

$$a\ (S) = a_0 - a_1 S;$$

2) the annual inventory cost of a quantity z is the sum of a constant term c_0 (costs linked to storage capacity) and of a proportional term c_z (financial charges, depreciation, costs involved in receiving and issuing from stock):

$$cz = c_0 + c_1 z.$$

This new hypothesis made with respect to a has the advantage of accounting for the discounts often granted by suppliers for sizable orders and the usual reduction in unit transportation costs depending on the quantities transported.

We leave to the reader the task of demonstrating that it is always advantageous to restock at constant intervals of time, ordering the same amount each time. Variable costs now have the expression:

$$D = c_1 \frac{S}{2} + \frac{Ky}{S} + (a_0 - a_1 S) y$$

which, after cancelling the derivative, leads to the optimum value of S:

$$S = \sqrt{\frac{2Ky}{c_1 - 2a_1 y}}. \tag{II.2}$$

Formula (II.2) actually gives the results which can be anticipated a priori: S increases with the cost of an order K, while the unit inventory cost c_1 decreases. Unit price a_1 drops as the size of the order S and the volume of annual sales y increase.

Note: In all of the foregoing, it is implicitly assumed that the storage duration of a lot is quite short. This hypothesis is generally admissible for problems pertinent to the models outlined above.

When the future is assumed to be accurately known, the determination of optimum storage duration is interesting only because of the fact that this knowledge can help reduce the number of orders. Economic models which postulate accurate forecasting have, therefore, only a limited approach to the storage question and, for that reason, have less utility than those which allow for an unpredictable future.

2. Models in which the future is known only as a probability.

We will analyze successively: a) the definition and the determination of a safety level; b) the choice of the optimum size of orders when taking into account the probability of stockout; and c) the choice of inventory policy when it is possible to estimate the cost of stockout.

a) Definition and determination of the safety level.

Starting at the beginning of a period, let us consider a firm whose sales are a random variable X of average value x. The firm purchases stock for resale but is not in a position to restock after the beginning of the period. The safety level is the difference between the stock which must be available to the firm at the beginning of the month so that its probability of stockout during the month may be lower than p, and the average volume of monthly sales.

Experience demonstrates that the probability distribution of a small number of sales frequently obeys the Poisson law. If the number of sales increases, this law can be generally approximated by a normal distribution of mean x and standard deviation $\sqrt{x}$. In the event of a large number of sales, normal laws are generally observed in which the standard deviation is not related to the average value.

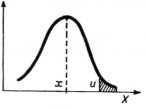

Fig. 5

Since p represents the probability of stockout, the inventory at the beginning of period U is determined by the condition:

$$\text{Probability } (X > U) \leqslant p$$

which means that the shaded area in Fig. 5 is equal to p. In the case of a Poisson distribution assimilated to a normal distribution, this is written:

$$\int_{U}^{+\infty} \frac{1}{\sqrt{2\pi x}} \, e^{-\frac{(X-x)^2}{2x}} \, dX = p.$$

The integral of the first member is contingent only upon the reduced variable $\frac{X - x}{\sqrt{x}}$, making it possible to express the above condition as:

$$U = x + k(p)\sqrt{x}$$

in which k (p) is a known function of the probability of stockout. In the case of p = 1%, for instance, k (p) is equal to 2.326.

Therefore, the safety level U–x is proportionate to the square root of the average volume of monthly sales. It is also a strongly decreasing function of the probability of stockout.

b) Models with a probability of failure [59].

On the basis of the foregoing calculation, it is possible to reexamine the model discussed at the beginning of the first paragraph. The demand during each period is now a normal random variable whose variance is equal to the average value. y represents the average annual demand while c and K have the same meaning as heretofore.

Four cases are possible, depending on whether a knowledge of the inventory level is constant or intermittent and whether the delay in delivery is negligible or not. The four models M_1, M_2, M_3, and M_4 are defined in the following table.

Delay in delivery Knowledge of inventory	Intermittent	Continuous
Negligible.............................	M_1	M_3
Non-negligible........................	M_2	M_4

Model M_1.

One of the simple policies available to a firm is the following: A firm takes inventory periodically; at this time it places an order (if required) to bring the inventory level back to a desired volume V. The level of V is set to limit to p the probability of stockout during the interval between two inventories.

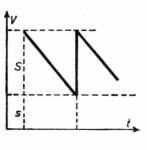

Fig. 6

To determine V, let T be the time measured in years which elapses during the interval between two inventories. An order should normally meet the average demand during the time T. The volume S of the average order is therefore equal to yT. At the time each inventory is taken and before any order is placed, the available stock should normally be equal to the safety level s. Consequently: V = S + s. But we have already calculated s which, for a probability of stockout p, is equal to:

$$s = k\,(p)\,\sqrt{yT} = k\,(p)\,\sqrt{S}$$

in the case of a normal low approximating a Poisson distribution.*

The inventory level normally fluctuates as indicated in Fig. 6, and costs are expressed:

$$D = \frac{Ky}{S} + c\left(\frac{S}{2} + k\,(p)\,\sqrt{S}\right)$$

D is at a minimum when:

$$\frac{c}{2}\,S^2\,\sqrt{S} - 2Ky\,\sqrt{S} + ck\,(p) = 0. \tag{II.3}$$

Fairly often, ck(p) is small in relation to the other terms.

The root of equation (II.3) is therefore close to the root obtained in making k(p) = 0, i.e., in neglecting risk.

In such case the average quantity ordered and the interval between two inventories must therefore be the same as in the absence of risk. The sole consequence of unpredictability is the additional presence of the safety level.

Model M_2.

If the delay in delivery is not negligible, possibilities of stockout between order and delivery must be taken into consideration.

---

*Similar to the reasoning for any normal law.

The risk now applies to the sum of the delivery delay T' and of the period of consumption T covered by one order.

The safety level must be calculated in this case over the period $T + T'$. Nothing is changed in the calculation of T and of the optimum average order.

Model M_3.

The level of stocks is constantly known and the delivery delay is negligible; the firm runs no risk because it is merely necessary to reorder as soon as the stock nears exhaustion. This model has few practical applications.

Model M_4.

The result of the hypotheses of this model is that the safety level must be calculated with respect to the delivery delay and that the order must be placed when the stock reaches a quantity equal to the sum of the safety level and the average demand during the delivery delay.

Model M_4 will be illustrated by examining the problem of reprovisioning an air base.

Example: Reprovisioning an air base. The very interesting example which follows has been borrowed from M. J. Solomon [52]. An air base must have a considerable inventory of parts of different types in order to be in a position to make immediate repairs on the planes assigned to the base. For a given type of plane, there is a definite number n (several thousand) of vital parts, i.e., parts of such a nature that a plane is grounded if one of them is unavailable.

The first problem posed by Solomon was to minimize the total costs for a given probability of grounding a plane. Next, he examined the problem of how this probability was to be determined.

Delivery delays are significant and not necessarily the same for the different parts. The number of parts of each type in stock is always known. The problem, therefore, is to determine for each part the reorder point (i.e., when to reorder) and the volume to be ordered. Each part being characterized by a symbol i, the notations are as follows:

S_i is the volume of the order for part i,

s_i the point at which an order is to be placed,

u_i the average number of units of part i used during the delay in delivery,

r_i the safety level,

a_i the unit purchase price of part i,

c_i the marginal inventory cost per year (c_i takes into account financial charges and obsolescence),

K_i the fixed cost of an order,
y_i the àverage number of parts i used per year.

The annual costs ascribable to part i have as mathematical expectation:

$$D_i = y_i \left(a_i + \frac{K_i}{S_i}\right) + c_i \left(s_i + \frac{S_i}{2}\right).$$

However, by definition of the safety level, $s_i = u_i + r_i$. D_i is therefore dependent upon the two parameters S_i and r_i. S_i is determined as before. It remains to select the r_i so that total costs $\Sigma_i D_i$ may be at a minimum for the predetermined probability of stockout p_0.

Let p_i be the probability of stockout of part i. Stockouts of the different parts as a first approximation can be considered independent. Since the absence of any one part grounds a plane:

$$1 - p_0 = \Pi_{i=1}^n \qquad (1 - p_i). \qquad (\text{II.4})$$

Because the safety level is not dependent upon the periodicity of orders, the following must finally be minimized:

$$\Sigma_i c_i r_i$$

subject to condition (II.4). By the introduction of a Lagrange multiplier m, one returns to a search for the minimum of:

$$c_i r_i + m \left(\Pi_{i=1}^n (1 - p_i) - (1 - p_0)\right)$$

and it can be readily verified that, for the minimum, the following conditions must necessarily be satisfied:

$$c_i \frac{dr_i}{dp_i} (1 - p_i) = \text{Const (independent of i).} \qquad (\text{II.5})$$

The n-1 conditions (II.5) and condition (II.4) permit a determination of the n unknowns p_i.

Conditions (II.5) can be rediscovered directly by a marginal analysis. It is merely necessary to note that variations dp_i and dp_j of any two probabilities of stockout are linked, when condition (II.4) is verified, by the relation

$$\frac{dp_i}{1 - p_i} + \frac{dp_j}{1 - p_j} = 0$$

to prove that (II.5) expresses the equality of the marginal costs of the various probabilities of stockout for variations which are compatible with the relationship.

Solomon next studied the manner in which the probability of stockout p_0 must be chosen. When stockout occurs, it is immediately necessary to call upon a reserve plane. Accordingly, the cost of such an operation must be analyzed. Let:

N   be the total number of hours to be flown per year by all base planes;

C_r the average additional cost of urgently requisitioning a standby plane;

C_a the annual cost of a base plane (amortization, interest, etc.),

H   the average number of flying hours per plane per year if the absence of parts does not ground it,

U   the average number of flying hours lost as a result of a stockout.

Provisioning and inventory costs, having been analyzed, can be written in the form $D(p_0)$. Costs involved in an emergency requisition of planes are p_0NC_r. Finally, plane stockage costs are expressed: $\dfrac{NC_a}{H-p_0 U}$, since $\dfrac{N}{H-p_0 U}$ is the number of planes which must be available at the base. Total costs:

$$D(p_0) + p_0 NC_r + \frac{NC_a}{H - p_0 U}$$

are therefore the sum of a term which is a decreasing function of p_0 and of two terms which are increasing functions of p_0. An optimum is to be sought.

The second part of this example leads us now to consider models in which the cost of stockout is introduced directly.

c) Models with stockout costs.

Two models will be analyzed here:

Model M_5 without any delivery delay and with an intermittent knowledge of stock levels.

Model M_6 with a delivery delay and a continuous knowledge of stock levels.

Model M_5.

The following model is attributable to E. Naddor [46] and is deliberately constructed on different bases from those of the preceding models. It presupposes that a) decisions regarding orders are made periodically, the period being predetermined; b) the demand Y during the interval between two decisions is a random variable of probability density f(y); c) inventory costs are proportionate to time and to the quantity in stock, their amount by unit of quantity and of time being C_1; d) in the event of stockout, delivery of quantities requested can be postponed until such time as new quantities become available and, in addition, the loss per unit is proportional to the delay in delivery with a value c_2 for a delay equal to the time unit.

In order to simplify notations, the period of decision is taken as a unit of time. Under these conditions, the optimum level— of stock on hand at the beginning of a period once the order has been received has to be derived.

Aside from the introduction of cost of stockout, this model can be distinguished from the preceding models in one important respect: The period of decision is predetermined and is not related to a determination of the optimum size of the order. The number of orders being fixed, the cost K of an order no longer appears in the calculation.

It can be assumed, roughly, that random sales are regularly distributed during the period. Depending upon the value y taken by Y, there may or may not be a stockout. These two situations are represented in Figs. 7 and 8.

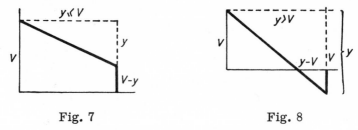

Fig. 7　　　　　　　　　　　Fig. 8

When there is no failure, inventory costs are:

$$c_1 \left(V - \frac{y}{2} \right).$$

When there is a failure, the stock becomes exhausted at the end of time $\frac{V}{y}$ and inventory costs are:

$$c_1 \frac{V}{2} \frac{V}{y} = c_1 \frac{V^2}{2y}.$$

The stockout lasts $1 - \frac{V}{y}$ and the cost of stockout is:

$$c_2 \frac{y - V}{2} \cdot \frac{y - V}{y} = c_2 \frac{(y - V)^2}{2y}$$

The mathematical expectation of the costs associated with an initial stock level V is therefore:

$$D = \int_0^V c_1 \left(V - \frac{y}{2} \right) f(y) \, dy + \int_V^{+\infty} \left(c_1 \frac{V^2}{2y} + c_2 \frac{(y - V)^2}{2y} \right) f(y) \, dy.$$

This mathematical expectation is minimal when the derivative of D with respect to V is zero. Hence the condition:

$$c_1 \int_0^V f(y) \, dy + c_1 \int_V^{+\infty} \frac{V}{y} f(y) \, dy - c_2 \int_0^{+\infty} \frac{y - V}{y} f(y) \, dy = 0. \quad \text{(II.6)}$$

The above condition calls for the integrals of functions f(y) and $\frac{f(y)}{y}$, integrals which are known since f(y) is known. Letting

$$F(V) = \int_0^V f(y) \, dy \qquad G(V) = V \int_V^{+\infty} \frac{f(y)}{y} \, dy$$

(II.6) is then written:

$$c_1 F(V) + c_1 G(V) - c_2 (1 - F(V)) + c_2 G(V) = 0$$

The value of V is therefore determined by the relation:

$$F(V) + G(V) = \frac{c_2}{c_1 + c_2}. \quad \text{(II.7)}$$

Note: As an example of marginal analysis, it is interesting to demonstrate the relation (II.7) directly.

1-F(V), by definition, is the probability of stockout.

G(V) is, a priori, the probable value of the time at which the stockout begins. $\frac{G(V)}{1-F(V)}$ is therefore this same probable value if it is assumed that there has been a stockout.

Under these conditions, if the initial stock V is increased by dV, the costs per additional unit are:

under probability $\quad F(V) : c_1$

under probability $\quad 1 - F(V) : \quad c_1 \dfrac{G(V)}{1 - F(V)} - c_2 \left(1 - \dfrac{G(V)}{1 - F(V)} \right)$

(the first term representing inventory costs and the second, savings on cost of stockout).

By equating the mathematical expectation of these additional costs to zero, relation (II.7) is directly obtained.

The inventory policy in this model can be summarized as follows: At the beginning of each period, a firm places an order to restore its inventory level to the optimum V value. Since inventory is taken only on certain dates, this policy is related to an ''ordering cycle system.'' A final model will now be considered in which the policy is that of the ''two-bin system.''

Model M_6.

Let us assume that: a) the level of stocks is known at all times; b) an order of size S is placed as soon as such level reaches the s value of the reorder point; and c) the delay in delivery is significant.

Contrary to what occurs in the previous model, stockout now occurs only during the delay in delivery.

We will designate: by y the average value of sales during the year; by U the random volume of sales during the delay in delivery, U's average value being u_0 and its probability density $f(u)$; by K the fixed cost of an order; by c_1 the annual cost of stocking one unit; and by c_2 the cost of stockout. For a change, we assume here that it is impossible to postpone deliveries; c_2 is therefore the cost of stockout per unit requested but undelivered.

The question is to determine the reorder point s and the size S of the order. The mathematical expectation of costs is expressed:

$$K\frac{y}{S} + c_1\left(\frac{S}{2} + (s - u_0)\right) + c_2\frac{y}{S}\int_s^{+\infty}(u - s)f(u)\,du. \tag{II.8}$$

The first term represents fixed costs linked to orders; the second, inventory costs; and the third, losses due to stockouts.

By differentiating (II.8) with respect to s and S, two relations (II.9) and (II.10) are obtained whose simultaneous solution by successive approximations permits the determination of the reorder point and the size S of the order.

$$S = \frac{c_2}{c_1}y\int_s^{+\infty}f(u)\,du \tag{II.9}$$

$$S^2 = \frac{2Ky}{c_1} + \frac{2c_2y}{c_1}\int_s^{+\infty}(u - s)f(u)\,du. \tag{II.10}$$

e) Critique of the models discussed.

The models analyzed above do not cover the entire range of possible models since they have the following hypotheses in common: 1) inputs are unrestricted and discontinuous; 2) outputs are random and continuous; and 3) sales during the various periods are independent and have the same probability distribution.

If this last hypothesis were to be abandoned, the models would assume an entirely different character. They are not treated here since they would then be closely related to those which will be studied in the third section.

Finally, it should be noted that all models contained in this paragraph consider solely decisions which are dependent upon a small number of parameters: two for models M_4 and M_6, one for the others. This simplification is necessary for two reasons: first is the simplicity of the hypotheses, especially those relating to the functions of cost and the probability distribution of sales; second is the selection of the optimum policy from a fairly specific group of policies.

Consequently, in our study of model M_5 we have assumed that an order was placed at the time each inventory was taken. This made it possible to omit the costs related to ordering. However, it would have been possible to consider the more general aspect of the policies according to the two following parameters (s, V): no ordering if the level x of stock at the time of taking inventory is greater than a value s, and an order of size V-x if the level x of stock is less than or equal to s.

The better of these policies (s, V) would certainly lead to costs lower than (or at least equal to) those of the best of the V policies.

The (s, V) policies themselves do not exhaust the range of possible policies. The most general policy would be characterized by a V(x) function indicating for each level x of stock available at the end of a period the stock V required at the beginning of a period. However, a determination of the V(x) function is more difficult than the determination of the two numbers (x, V) or of the single number V.

A phenomenon that is common to problems of production and inventory is now encountered. An analyst does not always seek to optimize with respect to all possible policies. To facilitate calculations and to arrive at simple rules of management, he is usually willing to suboptimize with policies depending on a small number of parameters.

Throughout this paragraph, the probability function of sales has been assumed to be known. But there are inventory problems where it is impossible to evaluate a priori the probability of the various sales. Certain stocks are held to meet the threat of strikes, armed conflict, etc., and probabilities cannot be attached to such events. One is therefore brought back to questions which relate to the fourth type of decision (see Chapter 2) and to the theory of statistical decision functions.

III

SIMULTANEOUS REGULATION OF PRODUCTION

AND OF STOCKS

An enlightened inventory policy has a favorable effect on production costs for the following two reasons:

1) The indivisibility of production techniques. This problem relates to the size of production runs. Rather than manufacture an item each time an order is placed, it is often preferable to manufacture a series of such items to avoid a repetition of costs involved in restarting production.

2) The high cost of irregular production. This problem itself may be due to various causes. The production cost curve usually shows a slight concavity upwards. Fig. 9 confirms the fact that the production costs of P_1 and P_2 during one month are greater than the production cost of $\dfrac{P_1 + P_2}{2}$ during two months

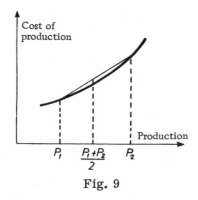

Fig. 9

When production is irregular, a higher than average production capacity must be available. Each modification in the rate of production results in additional costs due to the starting of new lines and to the lowering of productivity during the adjustment period. Finally, manpower is not as fluid as varying production requirements. Workers cannot be hired and fired at frequent intervals without incurring significant inefficiencies, not only because of the social and moral aspects involved but also because of the economic repercussions: severance pay, additional training costs, and a lowering of the average quality of manpower in a firm practicing such a policy. If production is irregular, manpower will at times be in excess and at times insufficient—and, in the latter instance, it will be necessary to incur the cost of overtime pay rates.

The inventory costs heretofore analyzed should be compared to the disadvantages of irregular production.

Any economic model attempting to determine an optimum production and inventory policy must successively analyze the various items of expenditure and the variables of which they are a function. The main variables among these are: a) production during the period, productive capacity, the variation in production from one period to another; b) manpower and its variations from one period to another; c) stock on hand, storage capacity, and variations in stock during the period.

Naturally, not all of these variations are independent. For instance, the difference between production and sales over a period is equal to the variation in stock. The analyst will select one or more independent variables which will serve to characterize the firm's policy and will be of assistance in expressing the total cost for each period. Next, either the aggregate effective income should be maximized or the effective cost minimized (if receipts can be considered as given). Mathematically, there will be a choice between a discontinuous representation in which x_t, for example, will be the production during an interval of time $t, t + 1$ and a continuous representation in which $x(t)dt$ will be the production during an interval of time $t, t + dt$. The first formulation comes closer to reality.

The analysis will be in two parts: a perfectly known future and a future considered as a probability; the latter, requiring considerable development, will form the subject of several paragraphs (2 to 6).

1. Perfectly known future.

A model covering the optimum length of a production run and a model covering regulation of production within a period of time will be sufficient to provide a general idea as to possible methods.

a) Optimum length of a run. The Wilson–Whitin model for the determination of the optimal size of an order, in connection with inventory policy, can be used here without difficulty.

Let y be the volume of annual sales. If sales are evenly distributed throughout the year, and if the costs K of starting production of a run are independent of its length, it is advisable to manufacture runs all of the same length, L. If c is the inventory cost of one unit, the variable costs will be expressed:

$$D = \frac{cL}{2} + K\frac{y}{L}$$

on the hypothesis that the remaining production costs are only a function of the annual volume y. The above relation leads directly (for L) to the expression:

$$L = \sqrt{\frac{Ky}{c}}$$

structurally identical to that which previously indicated the maximum stock S.

Naturally, this model is very succinct, but it can be developed without too much difficulty.

b) Control of production within a period of time. F. Hohn, F. Modigliani [42], F. Morin [44], K. Arrow,* and W. Cooper** are the authors who, during recent years, have presented the most interesting models of production and inventory control in the case of a determinate future.

The F. Modigliani and F. Hohn model will be presented here in the continuous form given to it by F. Morin. This model has the disadvantage of omitting an interest rate, thereby applying only to relatively short periods of time. Furthermore, the hypotheses made regarding costs are far from being valid for all branches of industry. But the structure of the equations and the development of solutions have a very general scope of application.

In all of these analyses, the following should be introduced simultaneously:

a) the rate of production at instant x (t) ((x (t) dt represents the quantity produced between t and t +dt) and the sum $x(t) = \int_0^t x(t)\,dt +$ S_0 of the cumulative production from the initial instant t and of initial stock S_0;

b) the density of demand d(t) at instant t(d(t) dt represents the quantity demanded between t and t + dt) and the cumulative demand:

$$D(t) = \int_0^t d(t)\,dt$$

from the initial instant to instant t.

d (t) and D (t) are functions known to the firm.

Stock at instant t is expressed:

$$S(t) = X(t) - D(t)$$

If it is impossible to postpone delivery of orders, the stock remains constantly positive or zero:

$$X(t) \geqslant D(t)$$

We will proceed on the assumption that the firm desires to meet demand requirements completely by having its stock become exhausted at the final instant T while adhering to a policy which minimizes its costs over the period (o, T):

---

*Communication to the Congress on Econometrics, December 1955.

**See ref. [19] in Chapter 12.

$$X(T) = D(T)$$

The costs are the sum of inventory and production costs. By hypothesis, the inventory cost is a constant a per unit of time, and production costs of x(t)dt are a function f (x) dt such that $f'(x)$ and $f''(x)$ exist and that $f''(x)$ is positive. $f'(x)$ being none other than marginal cost, this latter notation expresses that marginal cost increases as production increases.

Mathematically, the problem consists of determining the function X (t) for which:

$$C = \int_0^T (a(X - D(t)) + f(X')\, \mathrm{d}t$$

is at a minimum, account being taken of the conditions:

$$X(o) = S_0$$
$$X(T) = D(T)$$
$$X(t) \geqslant D(t).$$

The curve X(t) is the solution to such a problem in the calculus of variations, if one designates by F(t, X, X′) the integral function consisting in part of extremal curves and in part of the boundary arcs X (t) = D (t). This property is expressed by the three following conditions:

$$\frac{\partial F}{\partial X} - \frac{\mathrm{d}}{\mathrm{d}t}\frac{\partial F}{\partial X'} = o \qquad \text{for extremal curves;}$$

b) a boundary arc cannot be part of the curve solution unless, in receding, C is increased, i.e., if:

$$\frac{\partial F}{\partial X}(t, D, D') - \frac{\mathrm{d}}{\mathrm{d}t}\frac{\partial F}{\partial X'}(t, D, D') \geqslant o$$

c) at a point X_0 in the curve solution common to both an extremal and a boundary arc, one must obtain

$$F(t_0, X_0, X'_{+0}) - F(t_0, X_0, X'_{-0}) = (X'_{+0} - X'_{-0})\frac{\partial F}{\partial X'}(t_0, X_0, X'_0)$$

X'_{-0} and X'_{+0} designating the derivatives at the left and at the right of X_0, i.e., rates of production before and after t_0. This condition expresses that there is no advantage in changing the position of this boundary point.

By replacing function F (t, X, X′) by its expression in C, the following conditions are arrived at:

a) $x' f''(x) = a$

b) $d' f''(d) \leqslant a$

c) $f(x_{+0}) - f(x_{-0}) = (x_{+0} - x_{-0}) f'(x_{-0})$.

To interpret these conditions as they relate to an example, a particular case in which $d''(x)$ is a positive constant b is naturally the simplest. The foregoing conditions are written:

a) $x' = a/b$ $x = \dfrac{a}{b} t + C^{\text{Const}}$

b) $d' \leqslant a/b$

c) $x_{+0} = x_{-0}$.

In other words, at a common point, the extreme and the boundary arc are tangential.

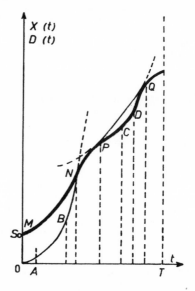

Fig. 10

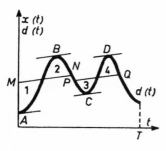

Fig. 11

It is convenient to discuss simultaneously the plane (X or d, t) and the plane (X or D,t) (Figs. 10 and 11). A simultaneous consideration of these two presentations is always very useful in problems of this type.

The limits of possible boundary arcs are points at which $d' = \dfrac{a}{b}$. These are points A, B, C, D, which are localized immediately in Fig. 10 and which can be trans-ferred to Fig. 11.

In Fig. 11, extremes are parabolas whose t^2 coefficient is $\frac{a}{b}$. First, one seeks the parabola of the family which passes through the point $(0, S_0)$ and is tangent to D(t). It is the curve MN of Fig. 11. Then one determines the parabola of the family which is bitangential to curve D(t) between N and R: this is curve PQ in Fig. 11. X (t) is then represented by curve MNPQR in which NP and QR are portions of curve D (t). It can be verified that these portions are well outside the intervals AB and CD in which $d' > \frac{a}{b}$.

In Fig. 10, the curve x (t) consists of: a) the straight line MN, in such a way that the difference in areas 1 and 2 is equal to S_0; b) the NQ portion of curve D(t); c) the straight line PQ, in such a way that areas 3 and 4 are equal; and d) the QR portion of curve d(t).

If inventory cost a were zero, conditions a) and b) would be written x = Const and $d' \leq 0$, regardless of what function f(x) might be. The parabolas in Fig. 11 would be replaced by straight lines and the rates of production would naturally be even more regular. In other words, if one assumes inventory cost to be negligible and marginal cost to be increasing with the rate of production, it is unnecessary to know the cost function in order to determine the optimal policy of production and inventory. It is sufficient merely to trace in Fig. 11 the tangent to D(t) carried from point $(0, S_0)$ and the straight lines bitangent to D(t). In a case of opti-mum policy, time T is divided into periods in which the rate of production is constant, separated by periods of transition in which the rate of production is equal to the density of demand.

2. Future considered as probabilistic.

Herein are broached some of the most difficult problems as well as some of the most specific problems posed by company management. It would seem that for reasons of convenience most analyses have been made on the basis of discontinuous models. These analyses separate time into a sequence of equal periods and assume that decisions can be made only at the beginning of each period. The random nature of these problems can be due to demand, to production, or to both, but in the last analysis the complexity of these problems is hardly resolved by knowing the probabilistic source. There is still a problem of choosing be-tween the utilization of probabilities versus costs for stockout, but in general most writers favor the second possibility, which leads to simpler mathematical developments. As a matter of fact, one final characteristic of these studies results from the mathematical difficulties created by the analysis of a series of decisions relating to a chain of random variables.

The distinction between strategic and tactical choices here reassumes its full significance.

Strategic choices relate to variables which, once fixed, remain fixed for a large number of successive periods; for example, productive capacity, storage capacity, purchases and sales whose volume is determined by long-term contracts, etc.

Tactical choices, on the contrary, relate to variables whose value is fixed at the beginning of each period and for that period only. An excellent illustration of a tactical variable is the output scheduled for one production period.

Strategic variables always complicate models inasmuch as they restrict the domain of possible variation of tactical variables and, consequently, add inequalities to those which express that production and stocks can never become negative. To avoid these bothersome inequalities, some authors forego consideration of strategic variables and allow stocks to become negative by authorizing the delayed delivery of orders which have not been fulfilled. They do not need to take into account the inequality which expresses that production is always positive or zero, because the lower limit is never actually reached in the case of an optimal policy. On the other hand, the failure to consider production capacity restricts the validity of the models to certain branches of industry, and the expression of optimum policy is not always the same for strategic or tactical choices.

In the case of tactical choices, analysis is concentrated upon the determination of a management rule which defines the value of tactical variables in relation to the state of the system at the beginning of a period and to what knowledge may be acquired regarding its evolution during the period. The management rule does not make it possible to know now the values which tactical variables will have during a future period, because such values will be dependent upon events which will occur beforehand. In other words, tactical choices become more and more specific as the future becomes the past and the known, and what one seeks to determine a priori is merely the link between tactical choices and additional information which becomes available by the time of the final decision.

In the case of strategic choices, which for the sake of simplicity can be assumed to have been made at the beginning of the first period, the analysis will attempt to determine the strategic variables. However, the function to be maximized (e.g., the mathematical expectation of income) depends solely upon strategic variables only when the rule which is used in making tactical choices has been defined. One must then begin by determining, for given values of strategic variables, the optimum tactical management rule and then determine the strategic optimum, assuming that such rule is actually followed.

The following models will be considered: 1) a model where strategic choices have been eliminated, deriving from the rules of linear decision of the Pittsburgh school (Holt, Modigliani, Simon) (paragraph 3); 2) a model introducing strategic and tactical choices simultaneously (as developed by P. Massé), containing as a characteristic case an analysis of the propagation of random stoppages in production lines (Zimmern) (paragraphs 4 and 5); 3) the very general theory of dynamic programming (paragraph 6) of R. Bellman.

3. Rules of linear decision.

The following analysis seeks decision rules which will minimize the mathematical expectation of production and inventory costs. It implicitly presupposes, therefore, a given volume of receipts.

a) Presentation of the model.

The system which is submitted for discussion is presented in Fig. 12. The difference between production and sales during the period (i-1), positive or negative, determines the variation in stocks during the period and, consequently, the level of stocks at the beginning of month i. A knowledge of the sales effected during previous periods and external sources of information, on the other hand, make it possible to establish forecasts for future periods, i.e., to estimate the probability distribution of future sales. The decision rule serves to define the production of month i in relation to forecasts and to the existing (or, more usually, past) level of stocks.

Figure 12 is seen to contain one of the essential elements of a servomechanism. The variable which results from the system, the output (in this case production), is subjected to feedback for comparison with the input (in this case the sales during the period).

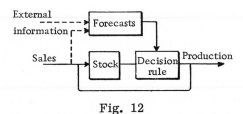

Fig. 12

More generally, one can consider the diagram in Fig. 13, in which appear two outputs, the production during a period i and the employment during the same period (the number of employees in the firm), one input (sales of the period) and two return circuits:

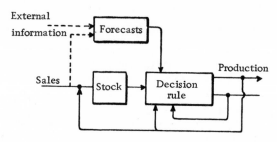

Fig. 13

1) that of production P_i which, on the one hand, is compared to sales V_i to obtain the inventory level at the beginning of period $i + 1$, and, on the other hand, is directly introduced as a decision element (in effect, costs can be dependent upon variation $P_{i+1} - P_i$ of the production from one period to another, and P_i must therefore be taken into account when choosing P_{i+1}); and 2) that of employment E_i, which also serves as a decision element if costs are dependent upon a variation $E_{i+1} - E_i$ in employment.

Consequently, in this representation of the firm as a servomechanism, the firm's production and employment appear as responses to the impulse constituted by sales and forecasts. The form of the response depends essentially upon the decision rule adopted and, according to the case, can be oscillatory or aperiodic.

Modigliani, Holt, and Simon have studied a specific case in which cost functions are quadratic; decision rules are then linear [27, 28].

These authors made the following hypotheses:

1) At the beginning of each period, an enterprise must fix its production P_t and employment E_t for the period. In effect, the same production can be obtained starting from different levels of employment by varying the number of hours of overtime work.

2) It is possible to deliver orders with some delay. Consequently, over a long period cumulative production is equal to cumulative orders, and it is sufficient to take the costs into account which are a function of the allocation of production over a period of time. Receipts and other costs do not need to be taken into account. Costs to be considered include: a) normal wage costs in the absence of overtime work, which may be assumed to be proportional to employment: $D_1 = C_1 E_t$; b) costs linked to a variation in manpower (training costs, severance pay, etc.) which appear, relative to $E_t - E_{t-1}$, as indicated by the two heavy straight

lines in Fig. 14, and which can be shifted closer to the origin by the parabolic function:

$$D_2 = C_2 (E_t - E_{t-1})^2.$$

c) the costs for overtime work occur when production exceeds the KE_t level normally attainable with available manpower. These costs are zero for P_t - KE_t, and then increase linearly with P_t - KE_t. They can be represented approximately by a second degree function (dotted line in Fig. 15).

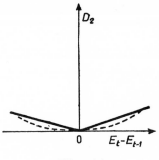

Fig. 14

$$D_3 = C_3 (P_t - C_4 E_t)^2 + C_5 P_t - C_6 E_t$$

and d) inventory costs and delivery delay costs.

Let us designate S_t as the (positive or negative) difference between available stock and unfilled orders. Such costs are certainly high both for small S_t and large S_t. They are inventory costs if S_t is large, and "dissatisfied customers" costs if S_t is negative. A minimum cost is reached for a certain value of S_t. This optimal level of stock is notably dependent upon: a) the reliability of supply to be guaranteed to customers, and b) the optimum length of various production runs which condition the resupplying of stock.

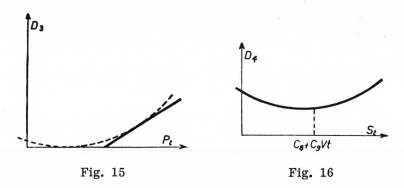

Fig. 15   Fig. 16

We have seen that, under the influence of these two factors, the optimum volume of stocks is substantially proportionate to the square root of the expected volume of sales V_t. As a first approximation, the optimum volume of stock can be expressed by a linear function in the form of: $C_8 + C_9 V_t$, which makes it possible to put inventory costs in the form (Fig. 16):

$$D_4 = C_7 \, (S_t - C_8 - C_9 \, V_t)^2.$$

Finally, the costs for the period t are taken as equal to:*

$$C_t = C_1 E_t + C_2 (E_t - E_{t-1})^2 + C_3 (P_t - C_4 E_t)^2 + C_5 P_t - C_6 E_t$$
$$+ C_7 (S_t - C_8 - C_9 V_t)^2.$$

and the problem lies in minimizing the total cost over N periods:

$$C = \overset{N}{\underset{1}{\Sigma}} C_t \tag{III.1}$$

it being understood, of course, that one should not omit the interest rate unless the period is sufficiently short and the anticipated horizon of decision is sufficiently near. This verification must be made a posteriori.

It will be noted that we are interested merely in a determination of P_1 and of E_1 because we can always assume that we are at the beginning of the first period.

On the other hand, Simon has demonstrated that if the anticipated V_t's were equal to the mathematical expectations of future sales, a minimization of the mathematical expectation of costs would be obtained by determining the minimization of costs in a model where the future is known and future sales equal V_t. From now on, we will consider that the future is known and reason accordingly [51].

b) Determination of the decision rule** [26].

In order to avoid proliferation of algebraic symbols, the principal stages of the calculation are recorded in a particularly simple numerical example with the following coefficient values:

$$
\begin{array}{lll}
C_1 = 10 & C_5 = 0.5 & C_9 = 0.5 \\
C_2 = 2 & C_6 = 0.5 & \\
C_3 = 1 & C_7 = 1 & \\
C_4 = 1 & C_8 = 5 &
\end{array}
$$

The purpose is then to minimize:

$$C = \overset{N}{\underset{1}{\Sigma}} (10 E_t + 2 (E_t - E_{t-1})^2 + (P_t - E_t)^2 + 0.5 P_t - 0.5 E_t$$
$$+ (S_t - 5 - 0.5 V_t)^2).$$

---

*Much could be said as to the value of approximation by parabolas of functions, derivatives of which present discontinuities.

**This paragraph is only for those wishing to use linear decision rules.

Account is taken of the relation:

$$S_{t-1} + P_t = S_t + V_t \tag{III.2}$$

which verifies the variables for each period.

For each period there are two independent variables, one of which is necessarily E_t while the other can be either P_t or S_t. We will adopt S_t as the second variable. For values of variables which minimize $C, \dfrac{\partial C}{\partial E_t} = 0$ and $\dfrac{\partial C}{\partial S_t} = 0$ i.e.,:

$$\frac{\partial C}{\partial E_t} = 9.5 + 4(E_t - E_{t-1}) - 2(P_t - E_t) - 4(E_{t+1} - E_t) = 0. \tag{III.3}$$

$$(t = 0, 1, 2, \cdots N - 1)$$

By solving in relation to P_t and by introducing symbols

$$\Delta x_t = x_{t+1} - x_t$$
$$\Delta^2 x_t = \Delta(\Delta x_t).$$

one obtains:

$$P_t = 4.25 - 2\Delta^2 E_{t-1} + E_t. \tag{III.4}$$

Similarly:

$$\frac{\partial C}{\partial S_t} = 2(P_t - E_t) + 0.5 + 2(S_t - 5 - 0.5 V_t)$$
$$- 2(P_{t+1} - E_{t+1}) - 0.5 = 0. \tag{III.5}$$

whence:

$$S_t = \Delta P_t - \Delta E_t + 0.5 V_t + 5. \tag{III.6}$$

By then carrying the value obtained for S_t into relation (III.2), one arrives at relations:

$$P_1 - V_1 = \Delta P_1 - \Delta E_1 + 5 + 0.5 V_1 - S_0. \tag{III.7}$$

$$P_t - V_t = \Delta^2 P_{t-1} - \Delta^2 E_{t-1} + 0.5 V_{t-1} \quad (t = 2, 3, \cdots, N) \tag{III.8}$$

Now, relation (III.4) enables us to calculate P_t, ΔP_t, $\Delta^2 P_t$. It is therefore possible to eliminate the variable P_t within relations (III.4), III.7, and III.8) and to obtain a sequence of linear equations containing solely the variables E_t. The principle of the method now becoming apparent and the calculations presenting no difficulty, we will write directly in vectorial form the system of linear equations resulting therefrom:

$$
\begin{bmatrix}
11 & -8 & 2 & 0 & & 0 \\
-10 & 17 & -10 & 2 & 0 & \\
2 & -10 & 17 & -10 & 2 & 0 \\
0 & 2 & -10 & 17 & -10 & 2 & 0 \\
\cdot & & & & & \\
\cdot & & & & & \\
\cdot & & & & & \\
0 & \cdots \cdots \cdots
\end{bmatrix}
\times
\begin{bmatrix}
E_1 \\
E_2 \\
E_3 \\
E_4 \\
\cdot \\
\cdot \\
\cdot
\end{bmatrix}
=
$$

$$
=
\begin{bmatrix}
1.5\,V_1 - 4\,E_0 & + 0.75 - S_0 \\
-0.5\,V_1 + 1.5\,V_2 - 2\,E_0 & -4.25 \\
-0.5\,V_2 + 1.5\,V_3 & -4.25 \\
-0.5\,V_3 + 1.5\,V_4 & -4.25 \\
\cdot & \cdot \\
\cdot & \cdot \\
\cdot & \cdot \\
\cdot & \cdot
\end{bmatrix}
$$

The equation of t rank (t different from 1 and from 2) is thus:

$$
2E_{t-2} - 10E_{t-1} + 17E_t - 10E_{t+1} + 2E_{t+2} = -0.5\,V_{t-1} + \\
+ 1.5\,V_t - 4.25.
$$

In order to solve this system of equations, it should be noted that we are solely interested in E_1 and that the number N of periods (.n be increased indefinitely because what occurs in remote periods has a negligible influence upon the value of E_1.

Let us now multiply the first equation by 1, the second by u, the tth by u^{t-1} and so on, and then let us add the new equations term by term. This gives us:

$$
(2u^{-2} - 10u^{-1} + 17 - 10u + 2u^2) \sum_{t=1}^{\infty} u^{t-1}E_t + (11 - 10u + 2u^2)\,E_1
$$

$$
+ (-8 + 17u - 10u^2 + 2u^3)\,E_2 = \sum_{t=1}^{\infty} u^{t-1}(1 + 0.5(1 - u))\,V_t
$$

$$
+ [2 + 2(1 - u)]\,E_0 - S_0 + 5 - \frac{4.25}{1 - u}. \tag{III.9}
$$

Choosing u in such a manner that the first term of the first member of the equation disappears:

$$
2u^{-2} - 10u^{-1} + 17 - 10u + 2u^2 = 0. \tag{III.10}
$$

If u is a root, $1/u$ is also a root. This equation therefore has two roots u_i ($i = 1,2$) of a modulus less than unity, and when one replaces u by these values equation (III.9) has a meaning. It is written:

$$(11 - 10u_i + 2u_i^2) E_1 + (-8 + 17u_i - 10u_i^2 + 2u_i^3) E_2 =$$

$$\sum_{1=t}^{\infty} u_i^{t-1} (1 + 0.5(1 - u_i)) V_t + (2 + 2(1 - u_i)) E_0 - S_0 + 5 - \frac{4.25}{1 - u_i}.$$
$$\text{(III.11)}$$

The two equations (III.11) are linear in E_1 and E_2. Once the u_i have been calculated, they permit a determination of E_1 and E_2. P_1 can then be deduced from relation (III.4).

The solution of equation (III.10) poses no problem because it can be successively written:

$$2\left(u^2 + \frac{1}{u^2}\right) - 10\left(u + \frac{1}{u}\right) + 17 = 0$$

$$2\left(u + \frac{1}{u}\right)^2 - 10\left(u + \frac{1}{u}\right) + 13 = 0$$

and, in this latter form, it appears as a second degree equation in $u + \frac{1}{u}$.

c) Significance of the decision rule.

The solution of equations (III.11) makes it possible to place P_1 and E_1 in the form:

$$P_1 = \sum_{t=1}^{\infty} a_t V_t + b + c E_0 - d S_0 \qquad \text{(III.12)}$$

$$E_1 = \sum_{=1}^{\infty} \alpha_t V_t + \beta + \gamma E_0 - \delta S_0. \qquad \text{(III.13)}$$

Coefficients a_t, α_t, b, β, c, γ, d, δ, are constants which are dependent only upon the coefficients of the cost function.

Functions (III.12 and 13) constitute decision rules, because they determine the decisions to be made after considering sales forecasts and the situation of the firm at the beginning of a period. The essential characteristic of these decision rules is that they are linear and lead, therefore, to very simple calculations once the coefficients of the parameters of the situation are known. Any accountant can perform the calculation of P_1 and E_1 at the beginning of each period. This simplicity is the premium offered in exchange for the crudeness of the hypotheses on cost functions. Abandoning strategic variables and a quadratic presentation of costs has permitted consideration of the future as though it were predetermined and the development of linear decision rules.

In actual application, it is up to the analyst to compare the advantages and the drawbacks of such a model.

4. Control of the future and marginal expectation.

We will continue to assume that time is divided into basic periods of finite duration, and we will consider for each period the values assumed by a natural random variable x having the dimensions of a flow. Probability distributions of this variable are known for each period. On the other hand, the firm has a storage capacity at its disposal which permits it, during each period, either to increase the initial stock X or to increase the transmitted flow q by destocking.

Here are two examples of such problems:

1. x designates the monthly flow of water to a hydroelectric reservoir. The storage capacity is the maximum quantity of water that the reservoir can contain. X indicates the quantity of water in storage at the beginning of the month. During the month, there are two alternatives: either a) store all or part of the flow x, or b) increase the flow of water q through the turbines by destocking water.

2. x designates the random demand for coal in the course of a year. The storage capacity is the maximum quantity of coal that can be stored by the coalfields. X indicates the stock of coal at the beginning of the year. The national production per year cannot exceed P, and if demand is too high it will be necessary to import foreign coal. If demand is too low it may be necessary to reduce the national production by closing mines. At the beginning of the year a choice must be made, taking into account the available stock X, the level of national production, and the level of imports needed to satisfy the demand under optimum conditions. This results either in stockpiling or in increasing the quantity of national coal available for consumption by destocking.

These two problems are analogous, although in one of them the random variable is linked to production, and in the other, to consumption.

A very general presentation could be adopted applying to all problems of this type, but at this level of abstraction the significance of the successive stages might not be too clear. For this reason we refer constantly to the example of hydroelectric reservoirs, for which P. Massé was the first to develop a stochastic economic analysis.

The management rule in this problem consists of selecting at the beginning of a period t the transmitted flow q in relation to available stock X at the beginning of the period and the natural flow x during the period. The latter flow is assumed to be known at the beginning of the period. In other words, the problem's unknown is a function q (X, x, t). Once q has been determined, all of the remaining magnitudes are easily obtained including Y, the stock at the end of the period.

By hypothesis, the firm's objective is to maximize the mathematical expectation of its future profits.

At the beginning of period t, when seeking to determine the optimal value of q, one must take account of the values of X and of x. Let us assume that we know the optimum behavior for periods t, t +1, t +2, etc., if at the end of the period t a stock Y is available. The present value calculated at time t of the mathematical expectation of future income of periods subsequent to t is then a well-determined function of Y and of t: S (Y, t).

On the other hand, the income of period t is a known function of q or (which amounts to the same thing) of Y. Let R (Y, t) be this function.

The mathematical expectation of profit at the beginning of period t is therefore the sum:

$$R\ (Y,\ t)\ +\ S\ (Y,\ t).$$

The first term represents immediate and certain income; the second, random future income. The first term is a diminishing function of Y because, if the transmitted flow q is increased, immediate income is increased. On the other hand, the second term increases with Y, because the presence of reserves at the end of the period will permit a subsequent increase in the transmitted flow. It is therefore necessary to seek a compromise between immediate and assured income and random future income.

If we omit the variation limits imposed upon Y, the mathematical expectation of profit at the beginning of period t is at a maximum if:

$$\frac{\partial R}{\partial Y}(Y,\ t) + \frac{\partial S}{\partial Y}(Y,\ t) = 0.$$

Let us pose:

$$\frac{\partial S}{\partial Y}(Y,\ t) = s\ (Y,\ t)$$

We shall designate s(Y, t) as the marginal expectation of stock Y. s (Y, t) is none other than the probable supplemental value of future profits when stock at the end of a period is increased by one unit.

The foregoing equation states that the necessary and sufficient condition for the mathematical expectation of profit to be at a maximum is that there be during each period equality between the marginal profit associated with transmitted flow and the marginal expectation associated with residual stock.

This statement omits the variation limits imposed upon Y and q by the values of strategic variables. In actual practice, inventories cannot be less than zero and can be limited to a maximum value A which is the storage capacity. Similarly, the transmitted flow (in this case, the quantity of water flowing through the turbine) necessarily falls between zero and the productive capacity Q. When one of the variables q or Y reaches one of its limits, the system becomes blocked and equality of marginal profit and of marginal expectation no longer necessarily occurs:

a) When stock is zero or the transmitted flow is equal to Q, the marginal profit must be greater than or equal to the marginal expectation. It would be to the operator's advantage to increase the transmitted flow or to reduce the final stock, but he finds himself unable to do so.

b) When the transmitted flow is zero or the final stock is equal to A, the marginal profit must be less than or equal to the marginal expectation. The operator, in this case, would find it to his advantage to reduce the transmitted flow or to increase the final stock, but he is unable to do so.

The above conditions completely determine the management rule for a t period if the marginal expectation of residual stock, s (Y, t), or its total expectation S (Y, t) is known. A method to obtain one or the other of these two functions is required. Iterative analysis will provide the solution either on the basis of total expectation or of marginal expectation.

Total expectation.

Let us assume that the total expectation S (Y, t + 1) at the end of period t + 1 is known in relation to the residual stock at the end of this period. If we behave in optimal fashion during the period t + 1, the mathematical expectation at the beginning of the period t + 1.

$$R\,(Y, t + 1) + S\,(Y, t + 1)$$

is a well-determined function of stock X at the beginning of the period and of the value x_{t+1} of the natural flow during the period t + 1, i.e., P(X, x_{t+1}, t + 1). x_{t+1} has a known probability distribution $f(x_{t+1})$ which can, moreover, depend upon values assumed by x during the preceding periods.

Total expectation S (X, t) at the end of period t is equal to the mathematical expectation of future profits, or, designating i as the rate of interest:

$$S\,(X, t) = \frac{1}{1 + i} \int_{0}^{+\infty} P\,(X, x_{t+1}, t + 1)\,f\,(x_{t+1})\,dx_{t+1}.$$

In other words, if the total expectation at the end of period t + 1 is known, the total expectation at the end of period t can be calculated.

Marginal expectation.

The recurrence relation of marginal expectations can be developed either by derivation from that of total expectations, or by direct reasoning. The latter method is employed here.

In the situation of two optimal activities starting at the end of period t, one with stock X and the other with stock X + dX, the use of additional stock dX will be contingent upon the value x_{t+1} assumed by x during the period t + 1. As the case may be, the system will either be in equilibrium or will be a blocked system.

If the system is in equilibrium, the marginal profit derived from dX is equal to the marginal expectation of the stock at the end of period t + 1. Consequently, little importance need be attached to the use of dX.

When the transmitted flow is zero or equal to Q, the dX quantity, of necessity, is stocked, and the value of dX during the period t + 1 is equal to the marginal expectation of the stock at the end of that period.

When the final stock is zero or equal to A, the dX quantity is used to increase the transmitted flow, and its value during period t + 1 is equal to the marginal flow realized during the period.

If we designate j (X, x_{t+1}, t + 1) as a quantity equal to the marginal expectation at the end of period t + 1 in the case of limit sales, equal to marginal profit during the period t + 1 in the case of limit stocking or limit-destocking, and equal to one or the other of these quantities in the case of equilibrium, we can write:

$$s(X, t) = \frac{1}{1 + i} \int_0^{+\infty} j(X, x_{t+1}, t + 1) f(x_{t+1}) \, dx_{t+1}.$$

a relation which expresses that s is equal to the present value of the mathematical expectation of j.

If the marginal expectation and the marginal profit for the period t + 1 are known, the marginal expectation for the period t can be calculated.

The problem is, therefore, completely solved from the moment we are able to determine the expectation, whether marginal or total, of the final period. However, we should distinguish between a finite and an infinite number of periods.

If the number of periods is finite, the operator is certainly able to attach a value to the stock available at the end of the final period. This value can be zero if the stock is unusable, and equal to the market value if the stock can be sold.

If the number of periods is infinite, the problem changes. Nevertheless, a solution can be found in a great number of cases. Reversing the numbering order of the periods and designating as 1 the final period infinitely distant in time, the serial number of present period is then infinitely great. Let S (Y, 1) be the total expectation. S (Y, n) will designate total expectation at the end of period n when the available stock at the end of that period is Y. S (Y, n) is functionally lined to S (Y, 1) through the recurrence relations established above. However, it can be demonstrated that, under somewhat general conditions, S(Y, n) tends toward an S(Y) function which is independent of the arbitrary function S (Y, 1) when n increases indefinitely. This property enables us to calculate by successive approximations the total expectation at the end of the present period, i.e., of the period for which the tactical variables are to be chosen.

On the basis of an arbitrary inventory expectation for a period infinitely removed in time, it is therefore possible to determine successively: a) the expectation of stock at the end of the present period, b) the tactical choices to be made during the present period, and c) the mathematical expectation of all future income at the beginning of the present period.

This mathematical expectation is a function of strategic variables. Once the question of tactical choices has been solved it is a simple matter, at least theoretically, to determine the optimum values of the strategic variables.

Since the above theory may appear to be extremely abstract, the simplest case to which it may apply will be analyzed [40]. Several additional hypotheses may be made: 1) Elemental periods are of equal length. The probability density $f(x)$ of x is identical for all periods and is independent of the values assumed by x during preceding periods. 2) The operator receives for each period a remuneration cq_0. When q is greater than q_0, he receives a unit bonus a for a quantity $q - q_0$. When q is less than q_0, he pays a penalty b on a quantity $q_0 - q$. Furthermore, the cost of a stockout is greater than the advantage of the surplus $(b > a)$. 3) The transmitted flow q can assume any positive value, whereas stock is necessarily included between zero and A. 4) For the sake of simplicity, the interest rate is assumed to be zero.

Under these conditions, it is relatively easy to demonstrate that the marginal expectation of stock X at the end of the first period (the present period) is necessarily between a and b. As a matter of fact, if the horizon is infinite, any quantity of stock at the end of the first period will be used either as surplus (yielding a), or to avoid a stockout (yielding b). We do not know the probabilities of these two events, but we do know that their sum is equal to 1 and that neither of them is equal to 0 or 1. Consequently, whatever stock Y may be at the end of the present period, the marginal expectation $s(Y)$ is such that:

$$a < s(Y) < b.$$

Quantities a and b are none other than marginal profit when the transmitted flow is greater or less than q_0. By comparing the

preceding dual inequality with the theorem which defines the management rule, it will be observed that there is an advantage in stockpiling rather than in producing to excess, and in destocking rather
than in defaulting on delivery.

If account is taken of blocked systems, three cases can be
examined:

1. $X + x < q_0$. A stockout must occur. The operator uses his
total reserve: $Y = 0$.

2. $q_0 < X + x < q_0 + A$. The operator can supply exactly q_0 and
increase his reserve since final stock $Y = X + x - q_0$ is less than
the storage capacity A.

3. $q_0 + A < X + x$. The operator finds himself obliged to supply
surplus since the final stock Y cannot exceed A. Such surpluses
are equal to $X + x - q_0 - A$.

These various situations can be
represented graphically. P. Massé's
method of presentation will be
adopted.

In a system of rectangular axes,
the stock Y in the final period is taken
as the ordinate and its marginal
expectation s (Y) as the abscissa.
It can be shown that the marginal
expectation is a diminishing function
of Y. That is, when stock increases,
additional quantities stocked are of
less and less use. Furthermore, in
the particular case under study:

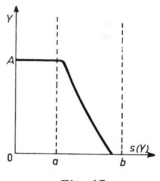

Fig. 17

$$s\,(A) > a \qquad s\,(\text{o}) < b.$$

In another system of rectangular axes, the transmitted flow q
is taken as the ordinate and marginal profit as the abscissa. In
the general case, the latter is naturally a diminishing function of
q. In this particular instance, marginal profit is equal to b if
$q < q_0$, to a if $q > q_0$; and it moves from a to b for $q = q_0$.

However, as a result of the equation of conservation of flows,
the equality:

$$X + x = Y + q$$

always holds. X + x being a known quantity at the beginning of a
period, the above relation will enable us to superimpose the two
diagrams by subjecting the diagram in Fig. 18 to the transformation
resulting from the substitution in ordinates from Y to q : Y =
(X + x) - q.

In Fig. 19, the marginal profit and the marginal expectation
then appear simultaneously. The intersection of these two curves

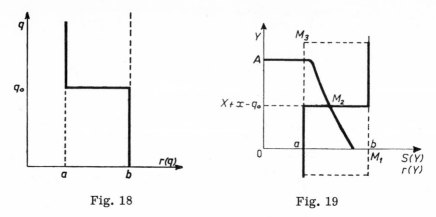

Fig. 18   Fig. 19

defines the stock available at the end of the period, the transmitted flow, and the common value of marginal profit and marginal expectation.

The figure is valid both for equilibrium and for blocked systems:

1) If $X + x < q_0$, the horizontal segment of the marginal profit curve has an ordinate which corresponds to a negative value of Y, and the point of equilibrium is M_1. A stockout occurs.

2) If $q_0 < X + x < q_0 + A$, the horizontal segment of the marginal profit curve intersects the marginal expectation curve. The equilibrium point is M_2.

3) If $q_0 + A < X + x$, the horizontal segment of the marginal profit curve is above the marginal expectation curve. It is the vertical segment of abscissa a which intersects this curve. The equilibrium point is M_3. Final stock is equal to A.

This geometrical presentation is very general in character, but when the marginal profit curve does not have the simple form appearing in Fig. 18, the management rule is dependent upon a precise tracing of the marginal expectation curve.

Let us now go beyond the simple considerations shown above and describe the laws of probability which govern the evolution of the system. The laws of probability permit a determination of all functions related to the rule of management already defined. Knowing the probable costs and the risks of stockout, for example, is necessary in an analysis of strategic choices. Moreover, such probability considerations serve to introduce the primary concepts of models which are frequently used and have Markov processes as a basis.

1. The rule of management being known, it is possible to calculate the probability of change of an initial stock X to a final stock Y, i.e., f(x) and F(x) are taken as the functions of the probability distribution and the total probability of x; g(X, Y), the probability density of change from a stock X to a stock Y neither zero nor

maximum; G(X, 0), the probability of change from a stock X to zero stock; and G(X,A), the probability of change from a stock X to maximum stock.

The calculation of the latter three quantities is simple:

1) The final stock is Y if x = Y + q_0 - X. Consequently:

$$g(X, Y) = f(Y + q_0 - X).$$

2) The final stock is zero if x < q_0 - X. Consequently:

$$G(X, o) = \int_0^{q_0 - X} f(x) \, dx.$$

3) The final stock is at a maximum if x > A + q_0 - X. Consequently:

$$G(X, A) = \int_{A + q_0 - X}^{+\infty} f(x) \, dx.$$

These three functions are connected by the relation:

$$G(X, o) + \int_0^A g(X, Y) \, dY + G(X, A) = \mathrm{I}$$

which states that the sum of the probabilities of possible events is equal to 1.

2. The above calculation will provide a recurrence equation of marginal expectation. Designating such expectation at the beginning of the first period as s(X), it can be demonstrated, as already pointed out, that this expectation is not dependent upon the value of the stock for an infinitely remote period. The marginal expectation at the end of the first period is therefore represented by the same function s(Y).

If, at the beginning of the first period, the operator has available stock X + dX instead of stock X, three eventualities are possible for the additional dX quantity:

1) If the stock is empty, the probability of stockout is reduced. Such an event has a probability G (X, o) and yields bdX.

2) It is stored and the final stock is Y. This event has a probability density g (X, Y) and yields s (Y) dX.

3) It is sold as surplus if the final stock is A. This event has a probability G (X, A) and yields adX.

Therefore, by applying the theorem of addition of mathematical expectations of exclusive events:

$$s(X) = bG(X, o) + \int_0^A g(X, Y) s(Y) \, dY + aG(X, A).$$

Marginal expectation is the solution of a nonhomogeneous Fredholm equation, the core of which is g(X, Y). This equation can be solved by successive approximations starting from an arbitrary initial function $s_0(Y)$. In the specific problem under discussion, $s_0(Y)$ is none other than the marginal expectation of stock for a period infinitely removed in time.

3. It is intuitive, but it can actually be demonstrated, that the laws of probability governing the state of the system during a period are less and less dependent upon the initial stock as one goes farther and farther into time. Making such an assumption, we will consider a period such that the influence of initial conditions will be negligible. The probability of having stock Y at the end of the period is then independent of the serial number of the period. Let

1) p(Y) be the probability density of having a stock Y;
2) P(o) be the probability of having no stock; and
3) P (A) be the probability of having a full stock.

In order to have a full stock, one must have at the beginning of the period:

1) a stock X and change to a stock A;
2) a zero stock and change to a stock A;
3) a full stock and change to a stock A.

Under the theorems of composition and of addition of probabilities, the relation:

$$P(A) = \int_0^A p(X)\,G(X, A)\,\mathrm{d}X + P(o)\,G(o, A) + P(A)\,G(A, A). \quad (1)$$

is among the various functions introduced. Similarly, the following relations would be demonstrated:

$$P(o) = \int_0^A p(X)\,G(X, o)\,\mathrm{d}X + P(o)\,G(o, o) + P(A)\,G(A, o) \quad (2)$$

$$p(Y) = \int_0^A p(X)\,g(X, Y)\,\mathrm{d}X + P(o)\,g(o, Y) + P(A)\,g(A, Y). \quad (3)$$

By eliminating (1), (2), (3), P(o), and P(A) from the system of equations (it can be shown that this is always possible), a homogeneous Fredholm equation is obtained in p (X), which actually has a non-zero solution determined by a nearly constant factor. This constant factor derives from writing that the sum of the probabilities of the various states of stock is equal to 1:

$$P(o) + \int_0^A p(Y)\,\mathrm{d}Y + P(A) = 1.$$

4. Once p(Y), P(0), and P(A) have been obtained through the use of classical methods of solution (which are of no concern to us here), it is possible to calculate probable surpluses and stockouts.

The probability density of q for $q > q_0$ is given by the relation:

$$m(q) = \int_0^A p(X) f(q - X) \, dX + P(0) f(q) + P(A) f(q - A)$$

since such a state is obtained by assigning to the initial state:
X of probability p(X) an adjunct q - X of probability f(q - X);
0 of probability p(0) an adjunct q of probability f (q);
A of probability p(A) an adjunct q - A of probability f(q - A).
Similarly, the probability density of q for $q < q_0$ is:

$$n(q) = \int_0^A p(X) f(A + q - X) \, dX + P(0) f(q + A) + P(A) f(q).$$

The difference:

$$\mathrm{I} - \int_{q_0}^{+\infty} m(q) \, dq \; - \int_0^{q_0} n(q) \, dq$$

represents the (finite) probability that q will be equal to q_0.
Probable surpluses are then:

$$E = \int_{q_0}^{+\infty} (q - q_0) \, m(q) \, dq$$

and probable stockouts (terms negative):

$$D = \int_0^{q_0} (q - q_0) \, n(q) \, dq.$$

We thus arrive at the following result. For a period sufficiently remote, the mathematical expectation of income is equal to:

$$c q_0 + aE + bD.$$

independent of the period. It is unnecessary to emphasize that E and D are functions of q_0 and of A.

5. The above calculations complete the analysis on the tactical plane. We now come to the strategic analysis. Strategic variables here are two in number: the quantity determined by the contract q_0 and the storage capacity A. The mathematical expectation of future real income is therefore a function $R(q_0, A)$. Knowledge of this function permits an analysis of two new problems:

1) a contract problem whose purpose is to determine the optimum value of q_0 for a given A;

2) an equipment problem whose purpose, once the contract problem has been solved, is to calculate the optimum value of storage capacity A.

Naturally, except in rare instances, it is useless to hope to obtain an analytic expression of the function $R(q_0, A)$. The best plan, therefore, is to use the Monte Carlo method. For different values of q_0 and of A, a large number of future possibilities are studied with the help of a computer and the arithmetic mean of income for each test is calculated.

In concluding this brief analysis of the splendid work by P. Massé, it seems proper to emphasize two of the most interesting aspects of this study:

1) The laws of probability governing a system situated in a remote period are practically independent of initial conditions. This property, which is common to problems of this kind, has been designated as "ergodic" and is closely linked to the Markov chain theory. Considering its importance, we will give a second example thereof, borrowed from an analysis of production lines.

2) Expectations, whether total or marginal, are determined by iteration. If the horizon is finite, their values as of the end of the last period are taken as given. If the horizon is infinite, one generally can arbitrarily choose the value for a period infinitely distant in time because final conditions do not influence initial expectation. This method of calculation also forms the basis of R. Bellman's dynamic programs which are discussed at the end of this chapter.

5. Markov phenomena and analysis of production lines [18].

A few elements concerning the Markov chains can place studies of the management of production and of inventories in a more general context.

1. The state of a system which evolves in time may be considered in a certain number of consecutive periods of finite duration. Let us designate by $j = 1, 2, \ldots p$ the various possible states of the system in each period (p can be either finite or infinite).

Designate q_j as the probability that the system is in a state j at period 0.

We will assume that the probability p_{jk} that the system will be in a state j during a certain period if it has been in a state k in the preceding period is independent of the period considered. Under these conditions, the probability that in the initial periods $n + 1$ the system assumes states $j_0, j_1, \ldots, j_n$ is equal to:

$$q_j \, p_{j_0 j_1} \, p_{j_1 j_2} \, \cdots \cdots \, p_{j_{n-1} \, j_n}$$

By definition, and following Feller [18], a series of random states obeying the above conditions will be given the name of "Markov chain."

Probabilities of transition p_{jk} form a matrix P of which all the elements are positive or zero, and for which the sum of the elements in each row is equal to 1.

$$P = \begin{bmatrix} p_{11} & p_{12} & p_{13} \cdots \cdots \\ p_{21} & p_{22} & p_{23} \cdots \cdots \\ \cdot & & \\ \cdot & & \\ \cdot & & \end{bmatrix}$$

In the case of the hydroelectric reservoirs, the inflow of water consequently constitutes a Markov chain if the probability distribution of the inflow during the period t is dependent only upon the inflow during the period t - 1.

2. The probability p_{jk}^{n} that the system will change in exactly n periods from a state j to a state k is easily calculated. In order that the system may be in a state k at the end of n periods, it has had to change in n - 1 periods from a state m to a state k, if at the end of the first period it was in an m state. Therefore:

$$p_{jk}^{n} = \sum_{m} p_{jm} p_{mk}^{n-1}.$$

In particular:

$$p_{jk}^{2} = \sum_{m} p_{jm} p_{mk}.$$

This latter relation indicates that probabilities p_{jk}^{2} are elements of the P^{2} matrix.* More generally, it may be observed that probabilities p_{jk}^{n} are elements of the matrix P^{n}.

The absolute probability q_{k}^{n} of finding the system is a state k at the nth period is immediately obtained once p_{jk}^{n} has been calculated:

$$q_{k}^{n} = \sum_{j} q_{j} p_{jk}^{n}.$$

One of the most interesting analyses of a Markov chain is the study of the behavior of q_{k}^{n} when n increases indefinitely. A few additional definitions will provide an outline of the essential result.

3. A Markov chain is said to be irreducible if it is impossible to classify all the states of the system into two groups I and II in such manner that, whatever j may be in I and k in II, the probability of transition p_{jk} will be zero. The use of the term "irreducible" is self-explanatory. If it were possible to find two groups such as I and II, the system would never leave the states in group I if it were located there initially. In such case, an analysis of the

---

*See the appendix to Chapter 12.

system could be limited to the simpler study of a Markov chain which would include only states in group I.

A state j is said to be periodic at period t (t in its entirety is greater than 1) if p_{jj}^n is zero at all times when n is not divisible by t. In other words, a state is periodic if it can only reappear at certain equal intervals of time.

A Markov chain is said to be aperiodic if none of its states is periodic.

The following theorem is then demonstrated:

In any irreducible and aperiodic Markov chain, the probability q_k^n of finding the system in a state k at a period n tends toward an independent limit of the initial distribution q_j. This property is considered ergodic.

4. Subject to a few additional conditions, the u_k limit of q_k is easily calculated if the states of the chain are neither zero nor transitory.

A state is transitory if, the system being at j at period 0, the probability of a return to j is less than 1. In other words, if a state is transitory it is by no means certain that the system will return to that state.

A state is zero if it is recurrent (that is, if the probability of a return to this state equals 1) but if the mathematical expectation of the time when its return takes place is infinite.

If the states in an irreducible chain are neither periodic, nor transitory, nor zero, the u_k's are all positive and form a probability distribution. Furthermore, they represent a solution of the system of equations:

$$u_k = \sum_m u_m \, p_{mk}.$$

As will be immediately observed, these equations state that the probability that the system will be in a state k is sufficiently large for n, independent of the period and of initial conditions.

If u designates the vector whose components are the u_k, the above equations can be written:

$$u = P. \, u$$

Under these specific conditions, the Markov chains are characterized by a certain tendency toward a state of equilibrium (as a probability).

Finally, it is demonstrated:

a) that all of the states in an irreducible Markov chain belong to one class. They are either transitory, or zero, or recurrently non-zero;

b) that if a state k is transitory or zero, p_{jk}^n tends towards o whatever j may be;

c) that a finite irreducible chain contains neither zero nor transitory states.

In the light of the foregoing, let us examine the specific instance of the management of hydroelectric reservoirs considered previously. The states of the system are the various possible volumes of stock Y at the end of the period. These states form a non-enumerable group, but there is nothing to prevent a generalization of the results which have been obtained above in connection with enumerable groups.

The system does, in fact, obey a Markov chain since the probabilities of stock X's changing to a stock Y, g (X, Y), G(X, 0), G(X, A), are independent of the period. In order to write the relations (1), (2), and (3) for the calculation of P(A), P(0), p(Y), we have implicitly assumed that the chain was irreducible, aperiodic, and had only non-zero recurrent states. Equations (1), (2), and (3) are therefore merely a particular formulation of equations u = Pu. Like the latter, they show that the system tends towards a probability distribution which is independent of initial conditions.

An example of application to the analysis of production lines will provide a clearer understanding of the foregoing. It has been borrowed from an interesting analysis by B. Zimmern [61].

Let us consider two consecutive stations in a production line. Their stoppages are assumed to be totally random and independent of each other. Generally, the causes of stoppage are sufficiently complex that the probability of stoppage of one production station between time t and time t + dt assumes the form pdt, where 1/p is the average time between stoppages.

The restarting of a stopped station is also random, and very often the probability that a stopped station will restart between time t and t + dt is also in the form qdt, where 1/q represents the average duration of a stoppage.

In order to simplify the calculations which follow, it will be assumed that the two stations are characterized by the same values p and q. In addition, it will be taken for granted that the tempo of production k of these two stations in working order is the same.

When the downstream station fails, but the upstream station is working, it is not necessary to stop the latter if there is sufficient storage capacity available between the two stations. If the cost of creating such storage capacity is high, it would be useful to derive the optimum storage capacity between the two stations.

At each moment, the system can be characterized by a state s (0 ≤ s ≤ S) of the stock between the two stations. It can be demonstrated that the development of s is represented by a Markov chain possessing the necessary properties for the application of the fundamental theorem. We will therefore designate by:

1. $s \neq 0$ $f_1(s)\,ds$ a probability that the stock is included between s and s + ds,   station 1 in working order and station 2 having failed,
   $s \neq S$

       $f_2(s)\,ds$ stations 1 and 2 in working order,

       $f_3(s)\,ds$ station 1 having failed, and station 2 in working order,

       $f_4(s)\,ds$ stations 1 and 2 having both failed.

2. $s = 0$ $G_1(0)$ a probability that stock s is zero,   station 1 having failed, and station 2 in working order, but obviously stopped,

       $G_2(0)$ the two stations being in working order.

3. $s = S$ $K_1(S)$ a probability of full stock   station 2 having failed, and station 1 in working order, but obviously stopped,

       $K_2(S)$ The two stations being in working order.

Equations analogous to relations u = Pu must now be written.

If at moment t + dt a stock s + kdt (station 1 in working order, station 2 stopped) is available, this indicates that at time t:

a) the stock was s (station 1 working, 2 stopped) and that nothing has changed during time dt; or

b) the two stations were stopped and station 1 was restarted during time dt; or

c) the two stations were working and station 2 stopped during time dt.

Consequently,

$$f_1(s + k\mathrm{d}t) = f_1(s)(1 - p\mathrm{d}t - q\mathrm{d}t) + qf_4(s)\,\mathrm{d}t + pf_2(s)\,\mathrm{d}t.$$

This equation can be written:

$$k \frac{df_1}{ds} = - (p + q) f_1 + q f_4 + p f_2.$$

By following similar reasoning for the other states, the following eight-equation system is arrived at, whose verification is left to the reader:

$$k \frac{df_1}{ds} = - (p + q) f_1 + q f_4 + p f_2$$

$$0 = 2p f_2 + q f_1 + q f_3$$

$$- k \frac{df_3}{ds} = - (p + q) f_3 + p f_2 + q f_4$$

$$0 = - 2q f_4 + p f_1 + p f_3$$

$$G_1 (0) = K_1 (S) = \frac{k}{q} f_1$$

$$G_2 (0) = K_2 (S) = \frac{k}{2p} f_3.$$

By adding the first four equations, it can be verified that they have a first integral:

$$f_1 - f_3 = \text{Const.}$$

Inasmuch as the probability of having a full stock is indefinitely zero, the probability of attaining a full stock must be equal to the probability of having had a full stock. It can be deduced from the foregoing that $f_1 (S) = f_3 (S)$. The preceding constant is therefore zero and $f_1 = f_3$. In establishing the difference between the first and the third equations, it will be observed that these two functions are equal to a constant c. A calculation of f_2 and f_4 can then be made without difficulty.

The various functions introduced are expressed:

$$f_1 = f_3 = c \qquad f_2 = c \frac{p}{q} \qquad f_4 = c \frac{p}{q}$$

$$G_1 (0) = K_1 (S) = c \frac{k}{q} \qquad G_2 (0) = K_2 (S) = c \frac{k}{2p}$$

c is determined by assuming that the probability of possible states as a whole at moment t is the unity:

$$\int_0^S (f_1 + f_2 + f_3 + f_4) \, ds + G_1 (0) + K_1 (S) + G_2 (0) + K_2 (S) = 1$$

i.e.,

$$Sc \left(2 + \frac{q}{p} + \frac{p}{q} \right) + c \left(\frac{2k}{q} + \frac{k}{p} \right) = 1.$$

This relation completes the description of the development of the system as a probability. It is now necessary to consider the economic aspects of optimum storage capacity.

The mathematical expectation of the production Q of the line, per unit of time, is the product of k and the probability that the second station will be in working order:

$$Q = k \left[\int_0^S (f_2 + f_3) \, ds + G_2 (o) + K_2 (S) \right]$$

$$Q = kc \left(\left(1 + \frac{q}{p} \right) S + \frac{k}{p} \right).$$

With respect to the expression of c, Q is an increasing homographic function of S. If r is the marginal income received when Q is increased by dQ and d is the marginal cost of increasing the storage capacity, the optimum value of S is the solution of the equation:

$$r \, dQ - d \, dS = o$$

in which Q is the function of S which has just been obtained.

In this problem where there is only a strategic choice, the application of fundamental results utilizing Markov chains has been extremely helpful for economic analysis.

6. Dynamic programming.

Like P. Massé, R. Bellman has tackled management problems covering a succession of consecutive periods. He started with a fundamental statement (like P. Massé): "An optimum policy has the following property: Whatever the situation and the initial decisions may be, subsequent decisions must constitute an optimum policy within the framework of the environment created by the first decisions" [5].

For the sake of simplicity, we will outline dynamic programming first in the case of certain future, and then in the instance of the future considered as a probability.

a) Future considered as certainty.

Let us consider the development of an economic system over N successive periods. At the beginning of the period i, the state of the system is characterized by a parameter x_i or, more generally, by a group of parameters. x_i, for example, could be the inventory level, production, or employment during the previous period, the level of demand during the period, etc. Consequently, x_1 will represent the system in its initial state.

Within a space of N dimensions, the point whose coordinates are $x_1, ..., x_N$ will completely describe the development of the system in time. The point x_i is usually bounded below and above and has its area of variation limited by the choice of previous values, especially by x_{i-1}.

Possible decisions at the beginning of each period can be represented symbolically by a parameter u (u can assume finite values or nonenumerable ones, or can vary in a continuous manner). A decision u, taken at the beginning of period i, causes the system to change from x_i at the beginning of the period to x_{i+1} at the end of the period. The effect of a decision can therefore be described with the help of a function d (x_i, u) such that:

$$x_{i+1} = d(x_i, u).$$

We shall assume that function d (x_i, u) is such that the representative point of the system will be in the region of the N dimensional space. A series of decisions is characterized by a series $u_1, ..., u_{N-1}$ such that:

$$x_2 = d(x_1, u_1)$$
$$\dots\dots\dots\dots\dots$$
$$x_N = d(x_{N-1}, u_{N-1}).$$

The criterion adopted is that of maximizing real income over the N periods. Let $f_N(x_1)$ be the maximum revenue which can be obtained, starting from an initial state x_1, by practicing an optimum policy (as defined).

If at the beginning of the first period we have chosen u_1, thereby obtaining a new state d(x_1, u_1), the maximum revenue that can be obtained during the following N - 1 periods is, by definition: $f_{N-1}(d(x_1, u_1))$. Consequently, if the revenue during the first period is designated by r(x_1, u_1), f_N and f_{N-1} are linked by the relation:

$$f_N(x_1) = \underset{u}{\text{Max}}\left(r(x_1, u_1) + \frac{1}{1+i}.f_{N-1}(d(x_1, u_1))\right).$$

In this form, the problem is to determine a series of functions f meeting the above condition. Calculation by successive approximations may be expected to make it possible to solve functional equations which appear to be so difficult.

When the N number of periods increases indefinitely, $f_N(x)$ and $f_{N-1}(x)$ tend, under rather general conditions, toward a limit function f(x) which is a solution of the functional equation:

$$f(x) = \underset{u_1}{\text{Max}}\left(r(x, u_1) + \frac{1}{1+i}f(d(x, u_1))\right).$$

Example: This example is entirely theoretical, but it will help clarify the foregoing. A farmer who initially disposes of a quantity of wheat y_1 attempts to determine the quantity z he should sell and the quantity y_1 - z he should sow. He knows that y_1 - z will insure the availability of a quantity $Q(y_1$ - z) of wheat at the beginning of the following year. Designating as r(z) the income produced by an immediate sale of the wheat, and retaining the same notations for the remainder, function $f(y_1)$ is a solution of the functional equation:

$$f(y_1) = \underset{0 \leqslant z \leqslant y_1}{\text{Max}} \left(r(z) + \frac{1}{1+i} f(Q(y_1 - z)) \right)$$

b) Future considered as a probability.

When the future is known only as a probability, the decision u no longer positively defines the new state of the system. x_{i+1} is a random variable whose probability distribution $p(x_{i+1}, x_i, u_i)$ is dependent upon x_i and u_i.

Let $f_N(x_1)$ be the maximum mathematical expectation of revenue over N periods starting from an initial state x_1. If decision u_1 is made at the beginning of the first period, the mathematical expectation of revenue over the following N - 1 periods will be:

$$\int f_{N-1}(x_2)\, p(x_2, x_1, u_1)\, dx_2$$

$r(x_1, u_1)$ designates the income of the first period. The two functions f_N and f_{N-1} are linked by the functional equation:

$$f_N(x_1) = \underset{u_1}{\text{Max}} \left(r(x_1, u_1) + \int f_{N-1}(x_2)\, p(x_2, x_1, u_1)\, dx_2 \right)$$

Example. Bellman gives the following example on the management of stocks [12].

At the beginning of each period, but prior to receiving any deliveries, the firm has x stock available. The decision rule defines the quantity y which the firm should have in stock at the beginning of a period after it has received initial deliveries (the delay in delivery is assumed to be negligible).

The cost of an order is a function of the quantity ordered y - x or c(y - x). Let g (d)dd represent the probability that the demand will be between d and d +dd during a certain period. p(d-y) indicates the total cost of a stockout when demand d is greater than stock y. Finally, $f(x_1)$ is the present value of costs over an infinite series of periods when the initial stock is x_1 and the policy followed is optimal.

We may assume that when deliveries to the firm have been made, the stock at the beginning of the first period is y. During this period, expenditures will amount to:

c(y - x) of ordering costs,

$\int_y^\infty$ p(d - y) g(d) dd of mathematical expectation of stockout cost. Future costs will be:

a) f(o) if a stockout occurs, an event with probability $\int_y^\infty$ g(d) dd, and, b) f(y - d) if there has been no stockout and if the final stock is y - d, an event whose probability is g(d) dd.

A line of reasoning similar to that already used therefore demonstrates that f(x) obeys the functional equation:

$$f(x) = \min_{y \geqslant x} \left(c(y - x) + \int_y^{+\infty} p(d - y) g(d)\, \mathrm{d}d + \right.$$

$$\left. \frac{1}{1 + i}\, (f(o) \int_y^\infty g(d)\, \mathrm{d}d + \int_0^y f(y - d) g(d)\, \mathrm{d}d. \right.$$

If the reader will refer to Massé's equations, he will notice without difficulty the close similarity between the two approaches. The term introducing $f_{N-1}(x)$ into the equations of dynamic programs is the same as P. Massé's total expectation.

This identity is again found in the calculation methodology. Functional equations of dynamic programs, except in very special cases, are not amenable to analytical solution but they can be solved by methods of successive approximation. Bellman suggests two distinct methods of calculation:

a) In the first, the horizon N can be either finite or infinite. If N is finite, f_1, i.e., the last period's revenue, is determined directly. This is always possible; the calculation is made through the use of the functional relation f_2, ..., f_N. When N is infinite, f_1 corresponds to the revenue for a period indefinitely distant in time. It can then be demonstrated, under rather general conditions, that function f calculated by successive approximations is independent of the f_1 value adopted for the revenue of a remote period. As in the recurrence calculation of P. Massé's marginal and total expectations, f_1 can therefore be chosen arbitrarily, and the function f can be determined by a series of approximations such as:

$$f_{n+1}(x) = \operatorname*{Max}_u G(f_n(d(x, u))).$$

b) The second method applicable to an infinite N consists of selecting a particular function f_1 so as to obtain a monotonic convergence, i.e., a series of functions $f_1(x), f_2(x), ..., f(x)$ such that:

$$f_1(x) \leqslant f_2(x) \dots \leqslant f_n(x) \leqslant \dots \leqslant f(x)$$

In order to illustrate this method, let us reexamine the wheat example. In order to determine $f_1(x)$, let us choose an arbitrary policy and assume that it is optimal. Thus, we can presuppose that the best policy is to sow all the wheat: $x = 0$. Function $f_1(y_1)$ is then the solution of the functional equation:

$$f_1(y_1) = \frac{1}{1+i} f(Q(y_1))$$

since $r(0) = 0$.

It is clear that the function $f_2(y_1)$ determined by the equation:

$$f_2(y_1) = \underset{0 \leqslant z \leqslant y_1}{\text{Max}} \left(r(z) + \frac{1}{1+i} f_1(Q(y_1 - z)) \right)$$

is always greater than or equal to $f_1(y_1)$. With the help of reasoning by recurrence, this property immediately extends to $f_n(y_1)$ and $f_{n+1}(y_1)$.

This second method requires the prior solution of a functional equation, but it has the immense advantage of leading to a monotonic convergence, which makes it possible at all times to have a limit which will be less than real income.

By applying dynamic programming to inventory problems, R. Bellman, I. Glicksberg, and O. Gross have independently arrived at certain results obtained by P. Massé.

Dynamic programming constitutes at present one of the most promising avenues for economic analysis, but its use requires a certain mathematical dexterity frequently associated with a thorough knowledge of the theory of Markov chains.

Conclusion

Some of the most difficult problems of economic analysis have been discussed in this chapter. However, the difficulties are essentially mathematical in character and derive from the consideration of a series of consecutive periods, from the occurrence of inequalities in problems of maximization (e.g., stocks cannot become negative), and from the fact that functions which most closely represent costs do not easily lend themselves, at times, to analytic treatment.

These difficulties, together with the novelty of this area of study, explain the coexistence of numerous avenues of research. We have attempted to present the problems systematically, but a real synthesis has proven impossible. The various authors use different cost functions and, as a result, the mathematical nature of the problem is often turned upside down. We are faced with a multitude of partial results obtained under varying conditions. It is probable that within a few years, when the various approaches have been subjected to the test of experience, this essential chapter of economic analysis will assume a more synthesized and definitive form.

In the meantime, however, the difficulties should not be over-estimated. An economist is interested in the result and is little concerned with whether it is impossible to express the solution analytically. Similar calculation problems have been encountered many times by engineers, and they have always been solved by successive approximations when the need arose. Calculations on the basis of Markov chains are already common in physics. In this respect, economic analysis has fallen behind other disciplines insofar as the use of modern mathematical tools is concerned.

This gap will soon be closed. There will then remain the essential problem of ascertaining, in each particular instance, what order of magnitude of figures is involved, how accurate are the quantitative data, and whether the potential gains justify a long and costly analysis; then choosing, when the answer is affirmative, the optimum degree of complexity.

BIBLIOGRAPHY

1. R. L. ACKOFF:
   Production scheduling, a case study. Case Institute of Technology.

2. R. L. ACKOFF:
   "Production and inventory control in a chemical process." Journal of the Operations Research Society of America, August 1955, 3.

3. ARROW, HARRIS, and MARSCHAK:
   "Optimal inventory policy." Econometrica, July 1951.

4. R. BELLMAN:
   "Bottleneck problems, functional equations, and dynamic programming." Econometrica, 23, 1955.

5. R. BELLMAN:
   "On the theory of dynamic programming." Proceedings of the National Academy of Sciences, 38, 1952.

6. R. BELLMAN:
   An introduction to the theory of dynamic programming. Report of the Rand Corporation, No. 245, 1953.

7. R. BELLMAN:
"Some functional equations in the theory of dynamic programming." Proceedings of the National Academy of Sciences, 39, 1953.

8. R. BELLMAN:
"Bottleneck problems and dynamic programming." Proceedings of the National Academy of Sciences, 39, 1953.

9. R. BELLMAN:
"Some applications of the theory of dynamic programming." Journal of the Operations Research Society of America, August 1954, 3.

10. R. BELLMAN:
"On some applications of the theory of dynamic programming to logistics." Naval Research Logistics Quarterly, vol. 1, No. 2, 1954.

11. R. BELLMAN, I. GLICKSBERG, and O. GROSS:
"On some variational problems occurring in the theory of dynamic programming." Proceedings of the National Academy of Sciences, 39, 1953.

12. R. BELLMAN, I. GLICKSBERG, and O. GROSS:
"On the optimal inventory equation." Management Science, vol. II, No. 1, October 1955.

13. M. BOITEUX:
Coûts marginaux de l'énergie produite par un dypôle hydraulique thermique (Marginal costs of energy produced by a thermal hydraulic dipole). Document of Electricité de France, April 1950.

14. M. BOITEUX:
Coûts marginaux de l'énergie thermique (Marginal costs of thermal energy). Document de l'Electricite de France, February 1950.

15. G. DANNERSTEDT:
"Production scheduling for an arbitrary number of periods given the sales forecast in the form of a probability distribution." Journal of the Operations Research Society of America, August 1955, 3.

16. A. DVORETSKY, J. KIEFER, and J. WOLFOWITZ:
"On the optimal character of the (s, S) policy in inventory policy." Econometrica, October 1953.

17. A. DVORETSKY, J. KIEFER, and J. WOLFOWITZ:
    "The inventory problem." Econometrica, April and June
    1952.

18. W. FELLER:
    Probability theory and its applications. Wiley, New York 1950.

19. P. GARDENT, J. LESOURNE:
    Le coût du stockage et de l'irrégularité de l'extraction du
    charbon lié au caractère aléatoire de la production hy-
    draulique (The cost of stockpiling and of the irregularity
    in coal mining linked to the stochastic character of hydraulic
    production). Document Interne de Charbonnages de France,
    1955.

20. P. GARDENT:
    Etude sur le stockage (A study of stockpiling). Document
    interne de Charbonnages de France, 1956.

21. GIBRAT and BOURLA:
    Méthodes d'exploitation des réservoirs saisonniers annexés
    aux grandes centrales hydroélectriques (Methods of opera-
    tion of seasonal reservoirs attached to large hydroelectric
    power stations). Report presented at the Congrès du Syn-
    dicat Professionnel des Producteurs et Distributeurs
    d'énergie électrique, June 1938.

22. R. GIGUET:
    "Exploitation optimum d'un barrage en régime connu"
    (Optimal operation of a dam of known flow). Annales des
    Ponts et Chaussées, March-April 1956.

23. M. J. GORDON and W. J. TAYLOR:
    The condition for lot size production. School of Industrial
    Management, Massachusetts Institute of Technology.

24. VAN HARE Jr. and C. HUGLI:
    Applications of Operations Research to Production. Sched-
    uling and inventory control. Case Institute of Technology,
    1957.

25. R. HENON:
    "La gestion des stocks" (Management of stock). Université
    de Paris, Revue de statistique appliquée, 1955, vol. III,
    No. 2.

26. C. C. HOLT, F. MODIGLIANI, and J. F. MUTH:
    "Derivation of a linear decision rule for production and

employment scheduling." Management Science, vol. II, No. 2.

27. C. C. HOLT and H. A. SIMON:
"Optimal decision rules for production and inventory control". Proceedings of the conference on production and inventory control. Case Institute of Technology, Cleveland, 1954.

28. C. C. HOLT, F. MODIGLIANI, and H. A. SIMON:
"Linear decision rules for production and employment scheduling." Management Science, vol. II, No. 1, October 1955.

29. KLEINMANN, MIASKEVICZ, ZIMMERN:
"Méthode de détermination des séries économiques de fabrication" (Method for the determination of economic manufacturing series). Revue Française de Recherche Opérationnelle, vol. I, No. 1.

30. W. KNECHT, Jr.:
Applications of Operations Research to production, scheduling and inventory control, I. Case Institute of Technology, 1955.

31. G. KREWERAS:
"Mise en équations du problème des stocks" (Equations of the inventory problem). University of Paris, Revue de statistique appliquée, 1955, vol. III, No. 1.

32. J. LESOURNE:
"La régulation simultanée de la production et des stocks" (Simultaneous control of production and of inventory). Revue de Recherche Opérationnelle, vol. I, No. 2, 1957.

33. J. D. LITTLE:
"The use of storage water in a hydroelectric system." Journal of the Operations Research Society of America, May 1955, 2.

34. P. MASSÉ:
"La notion d'espérance marginale, la théorie générale de J. M. Keynes et le problème de l'intérêt" (The notion of marginal expectation, J. M. Keynes' general theory, and the interest problem). Revue d'Économie Politique, January-February 1948.

35. P. MASSÉ:
"Quelques problèmes d'optimum économique" dans:

Stratégie et Décisions économiques. Etudes théoriques et applications aux entreprises ("Some problems of economic optimum" in: Economic Strategy and Decisions. Theoretical studies and applications to enterprises). Centre d'Econométrie, Cours et conférences de recherches, 1951-1953, CNRS, 1954.

36. P. MASSÉ:
Application des probabilités en chaîne à l'hydrologie statistique et au jeu des réservoirs (Application of chain probabilities to statistical hydrology and to connected reservoirs). Communication to the Société de Statistique de Paris, 1944.

37. P. MASSÉ:
"Les problèmes économiques de l'équipement hydroélectrique" (Economic problems of hydroelectric equipment). La houille blanche, No. 5, 1949.

38. P. MASSÉ:
"Les choix économiques dans un monde aléatoire et la notion d'espérance marginale" (Economic choices in a stochastic world and the concept of marginal expectation). Econometrica, vol. XVII, supplement, July 1949.

39. P. MASSÉ:
"Le mecanisme des prix et de l'intérêt dans une économie concurrentielle aléatoire" (Price and interest mechanism in a stochastic competitive economy). Revue d'Économie Politique, January-February 1951.

40. P. MASSÉ:
Les reserves et la régulation de l'avenir (Reserves and control of the future). Hermann, Paris, 1946.

41. P. MASSÉ:
Les choix des investissements (The selection of investments). Dunod, 1959.

42. F. MODIGLIANI and F. E. HOHN:
"Production planning over time and the nature of the expectation and planning horizon." Econometrica, January 1955.

43. F. MODIGLIANI and J. F. MUTH:
Optimum lot size under uncertainty and joint costs, part II. Carnegie Institute of Technology, 1954.

44. F. MORIN:
"Note on an inventory problem." Econometrica, October 1955.

45. G. MORLAT:
"Sur la consigne d'exploitation optimum des réservoirs saisonniers" (On the optimal operational requirement of seasonal reservoirs). La houille blanche, July-August 1951.

46. E. NADDOR:
Some models of inventory and an application. Case Institute of Technology, 1956.

47. H. C. PLESSING:
"Problems of telephone economy seen from a statistical point of view." Nord Tidskr. Tek. Okon, 1948, 12, 201-13.

48. J. RICARD:
La détermination du programme optimum d'usines hydrauliques et thermiques interconnectées (The determination of optimal programming for interconnected hydraulic and steam generating power plants). Revue Générale d'Electricité, September 1940.

49. H. A. SIMON:
"On the application of servo-mechanism theory in the study of production control." Econometrica, April 1952.

50. H. A. SIMON and C. C. HOLT:
"The control of inventories and production rates: a survey." Journal of the Operations Research Society of America, August 1954, 3.

51. H. A. SIMON:
"Dynamic programming under uncertainty with quadratic criterion function." Econometrica, XXVI, January 1956.

52. M. J. SOLOMON:
"Optimum operation of a complex activity under conditions of uncertainty." Journal of the Operations Research Society of America, November 1954.

53. P. THIONET:
"Essai de détermination du stock optimum" (Attempt at determining an optimal inventory). Journal de la Société de Statistique, Paris, 1945, 86, 99-122.

54. VARLET:
"Etude graphique des conditions d'exploitation d'un réservoir de régularisation (Graphic analysis of operating conditions of a regulating reservoir). Annales des Ponts et Chaussées, 1923, No. IV, July-August.

55. H. J. VASSIAN:
"Application of discrete variable servotheory to inventory control." Journal of the Operations Research Society of America, August 1955, 3.

56. T. M. WHITIN:
"Inventory control and price theory." Management science, vol. II, No. 1, October 1955.

57. T. M. WHITIN:
"Erich Schneider's inventory control analysis." Journal of the Operations Research Society of America, August 1954, 3.

58. T. M. WHITIN:
The theory of inventory management. Princeton University Press, New Jersey, 1953.

59. T. M. WHITIN:
"Inventory control research: a survey." Management Science, I, 1, 1954.

60. T. M. WHITIN, J. G. BRYAN, G. P. WADSWORTH:
"A multi-stage inventory model." Naval Research Logistics Quarterly, vol. II, 1-2, 1955.

61. B. ZIMMERN:
"Etude de la propagation des arrêts aléatoires dans les chaînes de production" (Analysis of the propagation of stochastic stoppages in production sequences). University of Paris, Revue de statistique appliquée, 1956, vol. IV, No. 1.

Chapter 12

The determination
of optimum programs

In the foregoing chapters, as well as in the two chapters which follow, methods are described which relate to specific problems of an enterprise. In this chapter, however, we outline some methods that apply to an area which is extremely broad and whose actual content is not specified a priori. These methods can be used to solve problems in a variety of areas including transportation, production, and investment, as well as problems which do not come within the scope of economic analysis. Developed and elaborated since the end of the Second World War, these methods have proved to be among the most efficient tools for management analysis. They are still in process of development, and improvements in both methodology and application are being made regularly.

These methods are based on principles of simulation and model constructs whose design permits the rational consideration of the various elements leading to a decision. A rational decision consists of selecting from among a group of possible solutions a solution which has the greatest "value," i.e., the one which maximizes a certain function.

Let us consider such a situation mathematically. The decision will consist of selecting a program, i.e., the values of a certain number of parameters x_1, x_2, . . . , x_n. As a premise, it may be assumed that x_1, x_2, . . . , x_n are monthly manufacturing rates of various products. A program is selected to maximize the value function

$$g(x_1, x_2, ..., x_n) \tag{1}$$

which is, for example, the payment received by an enterprise when it produces x_1, x_2, . . . , x_n. However, the x_i parameters cannot assume all of the possible values. In general, they are subject to two types of conditions:

1. They must be positive, an obvious restriction since the x_i's usually are dimensions of a quantity.

$$x_i \geqslant 0 \qquad (i = 1, 2, ..., n) \tag{2}$$

2. They must verify a certain m number of inequalities, or equalities such as:

$$f_j (x_1, x_2, ..., x_n) \geqslant 0 \qquad (j = 1, 2, ..., m) \tag{3}$$

The conditions (3) may have an entirely different significance from one problem to another:

a) In a problem relating to the blending of gasoline these conditions would indicate that the various blends have prescribed characteristics insofar as the octane rating, viscosity, etc. are concerned.

b) In a problem involving the production and distribution of different types of coal, they would indicate that the various types are produced simultaneously in specified proportions, etc. Further examples will be given later.

The general problem of maximization of the value function (1) under the conditions (2) and (3) is extremely difficult to solve when the number of parameters becomes large. For this reason, we begin by analyzing the case in which a function g is a linear form, and in which the conditions (3) are either equalities or linear inequalities. This simpler problem is called "linear programming." We devote the first two sections of this chapter to this type of problem.

In the first section we shall outline the essential points of the theory, and in the second section we shall give some applications and extensions. In the third section we shall state a few results in the area of nonlinear programming.

I

LINEAR PROGRAMMING [25], [105]

1. Definition and examples.

In accordance with the above, the solution of a linear program consists of determining the parameters x_1, x_2, . . . , x_n which are subject to the following conditions:

1) $$x_i \geqslant 0 \qquad (i = 1, 2, \cdots, n) \tag{I.1}$$

2) $$\sum_i a_{ki} x_i - b_k \geqslant 0 \ (k = 1, 2, \cdots, m; \ i = 1, 2, \cdots, n) \tag{I.2}$$

and maximize the linear form:

$$\sum_i c_i x_i \tag{I.3}$$

where the a_{ki}'s, the b_k's, and the c_i's are known coefficients, and some of the inequalities (I.2) may be equalities.

Before proceeding any farther, two examples of such a model are given in order that the reader may see, at the outset, the actual significance of the foregoing.

The first example is a transportation problem [106]. Merchandise stored in cities $1, 2, \ldots, i, \ldots, p$ in quantities $a_1, a_2, \ldots, a_i, \ldots, a_p$ must be shipped to consumption centers $1, 2, \ldots, j, \ldots, q$ where demand is $b_1, b_2, \ldots, b_j, \ldots, b_q$. Shipment is to be effected at minimum cost.

Let us designate as x_{ij} the quantity shipped from depot i to center j, and as c_{ij} the cost of shipping one unit from i to j. The problem consists of determining x_{ij} such that

1) $x_{ij} \geqslant 0 \quad (i = 1, 2, ..., p; j = 1, 2, ..., q)$

2) $\sum_j x_{ij} = b_j$ (j = 1, 2, . . . , q). These equalities indicate that a

quantity exactly equal to the demand is shipped to each center.
$\sum_{ij} x_{ij} \leq a_i$ (i = 1, 2, . . . , p). These inequalities indicate that the

quantities removed from the depot do not exceed the stock.

Naturally, in order that the problem may be meaningful, it is necessary that the available stock be such as to meet the demand function:

$$\sum_i a_i \geqslant \sum_j b_j$$

3) $\sum_{ij} c_{ij} x_{ij}$ should be a minimum.

This particularly simple example of linear programming can be dealt with by the use of special techniques; in later paragraphs we will consider them.

The second example, borrowed from works by P. Massé and R. Gibrat [23], [124], pertains to investment plans in the field of electric power. It is necessary to build new power stations in order to meet a given increase in demand for electricity. The problem is to develop the investment plan which is the least costly alternative among those able to meet the objective represented by a future given demand.

Studies by electrical engineers have demonstrated that the annual demand curve for electricity—a curve which represents the power required in relation to time—can be adequately characterized, as a first approximation, in terms of three magnitudes:

a) annual power supplied,
b) peak power,
c) guaranteed power.

In other words, the objective can be represented by three numbers A, B, C which represent, respectively, the increases in annual power, peak power, and guaranteed power which it must meet. Any investment plan which is able to furnish A, B, and C will satisfy the entire curve of future demand. Four types of power stations, which can be considered as continuous and homogeneous, can be constructed; these are:

1) steam generating plants;
2) river current power plants;
3) canal lock water power plants;
4) lake or reservoir power plants.

Let x_1, x_2, x_3, x_4 represent the number of plants of each type provided for in a plan—such quantities are measured with respect to size by an arbitrary scale, such as nominal power. A steam generating plant of nominal standard power will be able to supply a quantitiy a_1 of annual power, will have a peak power b_1, and a guaranteed power c_1. By defining similar coefficients for each type of plant, and by observing that peak power, guaranteed power, and annual power are additive, it will be seen that to be feasible a program must satisfy the following conditions:

$$x_1, x_2, x_3, x_4 \geqslant 0$$
$$a_1x_1 + a_2x_2 + a_3x_3 + a_4x_4 \geqslant A$$
$$b_1x_1 + b_2x_2 + b_3x_3 + b_4x_4 \geqslant B$$
$$c_1x_1 + c_2x_2 + c_3x_3 + c_4x_4 \geqslant C$$

A program is optimal if it minimizes cost D, this being the form assumed here by a maximization of profit since future demand is supposedly given. D can be described by:

$$d_1x_1 + d_2x_2 + d_3x_4 + d_3x_4$$

in which d_1, d_2, d_3, d_4 are constant coefficients and represent the actual costs for the construction and operation of a standard size plant of each type.

This second example has an advantage in that it highlights the assumptions which had to be made in arriving at linear equalities. It has been assumed that all plants in the same series have the same coefficients a_i, b_i, c_i, and that it is possible to arrive at a continuous scale of x_i by constructing such plants. The first hypothesis is only roughly verified by hydroelectric power stations, and the second neglects the fact that only plants of a certain size can be built economically. This assumption can, however, be retained in the first approximation if the x_i's are large in relation to the size of individual plants.

We now approach the general subject of linear programming, and, at the outset, we shall give a definition of the terminology used. The terminology suggested by the following particular model can conveniently be adopted.

Consider the case of a plant which utilizes a certain number n of production techniques or activities. An activity consists of a number of production factors combined in a certain way to obtain a certain set of products. The word "goods" will relate to manufactured products (output) and to the input factors. It is clear that some goods can be considered as output from one activity and as an input factor for another activity. The number of goods will be designated by m.

Consider, now, the following two hypotheses:

1. Technically, the activites are such that they can combine the various goods only within certain given proportions. In other words, no substitution is possible within an activity between factors or between products. Thus, for example, it will be possible to define an activity level in terms of the quantity of given goods brought into play by such activity. All quantities of goods consumed or produced by this activity will be proportionate to this level.

2. Within a well-determined interval, the activity level can assume any positive value. In other words, there are no indivisibilities.

In the case of the production of pig iron with iron ore and coke, the two hypotheses above have the following significance: the required quantities of iron ore and of coke are proportionate to the quantity of pig iron produced, and, technically, it is possible to produce any quantity of pig iron between a minimum and a maximum.

If the plant engages in the first activity at level x_1, it will then consume (or produce) quantities:

$$a_{11}x_1, \ a_{21}x_1, \ ..., \ a_{k1}x_1, \ ..., \ a_{m1}x_1$$

of m goods. Constant coefficients $a_{11}, a_{21}, \ldots, a_{k1}, \ldots, a_{m1}$ are the quantities of goods brought into play for a unit level of activity.

More generally, a_{ki} will designate the quantity of good k brought into play by activity i at the unit level. By agreement, a_{ki} will be considered as positive if good k is produced by the ith activity, and negative if good k is consumed by the ith activity.

When the various activities are used at levels $x_1, x_2, \ldots, x_i, \ldots, x_n$, the quantity of good k produced or consumed by the plan as a whole is:

$$a_{k1}x_1 + \cdots + a_{kn}x_n = \sum_i a_{ki}x_i.$$

If this quantity is positive, it is a production. If it is negative, it is a factor consumption.

Among all programs, only the following are possible:

a) those which produce in sufficient quantity to meet demand;

b) those which do not consume more factors of production than are available.

These conditions can be represented by inequalities such as:

$$\sum_i a_{ki}x_i \geqslant b_k \qquad (k = 1, 2, \cdots, m)$$

b_k being positive for plant output, negative for a production factor, and zero for intermediate goods which are neither purchased nor sold by the enterprise.

If an enterprise seeks to maximize its profit, it will attempt to maximize an expression of the form of:

$$c_1 x_1 + \ldots + c_n x_n$$

in which c_i represents the profit realized by the plant when it utilizes activity i at a standard unit level. Such an expression presupposes that the profit realized from an activity is substantially proportional to its level and independent of other activity levels.

We have thus interpreted, on the basis of a simple model, all parameters which occur in the more general problem of linear programming. Although some subtlety may at times be required to conceive realistically the activities and goods associated with each linear program, it will be found convenient to make use of the terminology summarized as follows:

1. Each vector of m dimensions represents an activity which combines m goods in given proportions:

$$a_i = \begin{bmatrix} a_{1i} \\ a_{2i} \\ \cdot \\ \cdot \\ a_{mi} \end{bmatrix}$$

2. The set of characteristic vectors of the n activities forms a matrix A, called a production matrix:

$$A = \begin{bmatrix} a_{11} \cdots\cdots\cdots a_{1n} \\ a_{21} \cdots\cdots\cdots a_{2n} \\ \cdot \qquad\qquad \cdot \\ \cdot \qquad\qquad \cdot \\ a_{m1} \qquad\qquad a_{mn} \end{bmatrix}$$

This matrix has m rows and n columns.*

3. The parameters x_i represent the levels at which the n activities are used. A group of values for each of the n x_i is the program associated with a given decision. The group x_i in a program constitutes a vector x of n dimensions.

4. The b_k's represent availabilities (if they are negative) or demands to be met (if they are positive) for m goods used. They are the components of a vector b of m dimensions.

---

*See the appendix at the end of this chapter devoted to the theory of matrices.

5. Unit profits on various activities form a vector c of n dimensions.

In vector notation, a problem of linear programming is, therefore, formulated as follows. Among possible x programs:

$$\left\{ \begin{array}{l} x \geqslant o \\ Ax \geqslant b \end{array} \right.$$

determine that program which maximizes:

$$c'x$$

c′ being the vector $[c_1, c_2 \ldots c_n]$.*

This terminology pinpoints the fundamental hypotheses of linear programming.

1. No substitutions are possible within an activity, and activities can be used at levels which vary continuously. The hypothesis then refers to a fixed production. If 100,000 tons of coke are required to produce 100,000 tons of pig iron, it will be taken for granted that 1 million tons of coke will be required to produce 1 million tons of cast iron. Furthermore, the fact is ignored that activities frequently cannot be utilized economically except at discontinuous levels. For example, at present the only steam generating plants built are those which produce 100,000 kw; the total power is then some multiple of such value.

Studies are being conducted in connection with cases in which the x_i's are made to assume integer values only; these studies, however, result in methods which are much more complex than the original programs.

2. The production and consumption of activities are additive. This hypothesis amounts to ignoring savings and losses which can result from the simultaneous utilization of several activities.

The two hypotheses outlined above are the two traditional hypotheses of linear analysis, i.e., multiplication by a scalar, and additivity.

3. The hypotheses of multiplication by a scalar and additivity are also verified by the function which expresses profit, i.e., that:

a) unit profit is independent of the level of the activity;

b) profit derived from one activity is independent of other activities.

It will be observed that there is a close relationship between linear programming and models of interindustry relationships (cf. Chapter 4); the marked differences which separate these two

---

*Hereafter, symbols without prime indicate column vectors, and symbols with prime horizontal transpositions of such vectors.

groups of analyses from the classic theory of production functions presented in Chapter 10 can also be observed.

2. Properties of a maximum.

A few of the most important mathematical results relating to a maximum in linear programming are summarized at this point.

It will be found to be more convenient to modify the initial problem by transforming into equalities the inequalities which appear in (I.2). In order to simplify the presentation, let us assume that the m conditions (I.2) are actually inequalities. These will be changed into equalities by introducing m additional activities of x_{n+1} x_{n+2}, ..., x_{n+m} levels, and by writing:

$$\left\{ \begin{array}{l} \sum_{i=1}^{n} a_{ki} x_i - x_{n+k} = b_k \qquad (k = 1, 2, \cdots, m) \\ x_{n+k} \geqslant 0. \end{array} \right.$$

The level of the additional activities must also be either positive or zero. The components of the vector representing one of these activities are all zero, except one which is equal to -1. Furthermore, such activities do not produce any unit profit. For this reason, we will refer to them as neutral activities. By designating the matrix as M:

$$M = \begin{bmatrix} a_{11} \cdots a_{1n} & -1 & 0 & \cdots & 0 \\ a_{21} \cdots a_{2n} & 0 & -1 & \cdots & 0 \\ \cdot & \cdot & \cdot & & \\ \cdot & \cdot & \cdot & & \\ a_{m1} \cdots a_{mn} & 0 & 0 & \cdots & -1 \end{bmatrix}$$

which has m rows and p = n + m columns, the problem now consists of determining the vector x of components $x_1, x_2, \ldots, x_n, x_{n+1}$, ..., x_{n+m} so that:

$$\left\{ \begin{array}{l} x \geqslant 0 \\ M x = b \\ c' x \text{ maximum} \end{array} \right.$$

The vector c' now being a vector of m + n dimensions: $[c_1, c_2, \ldots, c_n, 0, \ldots, 0]$. We will designate as m_i (i = 1, 2, ..., p) the column vectors of matrix M (i = 1, 2, ..., p). The relationship Mx = b can be written:

$$\sum m_i x_i = b.$$

When some of the (I.2) conditions are already equalities, no corresponding neutral activity is introduced and the number of columns of M is reduced by a corresponding amount.

It will be noted that in the geometrical presentation of a linear program, two spaces occur:

a) a space of p dimensions which is the space of the activities. Any program can be represented by a point in this space. This space will be designated by the letter (A).

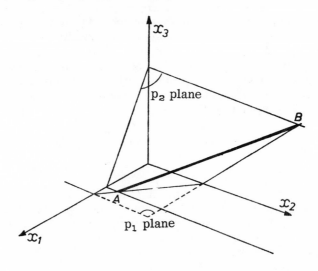

Fig. 1.

b) a space of m dimensions which is the space of goods. Vectors m_i, Mx, and b which are vectors of m dimensions are easily representable in this space designated by the letter (B).

Example: Maximize $x_1 + x_2 + x_3$ subject to restrictions:

$$x_1, \quad x_2, \quad x_3 \geqslant 0$$
$$x_1 + x_2 - 2x_3 = 1$$
$$3x_1 \quad + \quad x_3 = 2$$

The space of activities is a three-dimensional space (Fig. 1) in which the possible programs are represented by the segment of straight line AB; AB is the portion of the straight line common to the planes and included in the first angle.

$$x_1 + x_2 - 2x_3 = 1 \quad (P_1)$$
$$3x_1 \quad + \quad x_3 = 2 \quad (P_2)$$

It will be seen that $x_1 + x_2 + x_3$ is maximal at point B whose coordinates are:

$$x_1 = 0$$
$$x_2 = 5$$
$$x_3 = 2$$

It will be observed that, at a maximum, the number of activities started at nonzero levels exactly equals the number of linear restrictions, a property which is common to linear programming.

The commodity space is two-dimensional. The four vectors in Fig. 2 are represented:

$$m_1 = \begin{bmatrix} 1 \\ 3 \end{bmatrix} \quad m_2 = \begin{bmatrix} 1 \\ 0 \end{bmatrix} \quad m_3 = \begin{bmatrix} -2 \\ 1 \end{bmatrix} \quad b = \begin{bmatrix} 1 \\ 2 \end{bmatrix}.$$

The abscissa corresponds to commodity 1 and the ordinate to commodity 2. A program is represented by vectors: $x_1 m_1$, $x_2 m_2$, $x_3 m_3$, which are respectively colinear to m_1, m_2, m_3 and whose sum is vector b. In Fig. 2, the vectors corresponding to a maximum program are indicated.

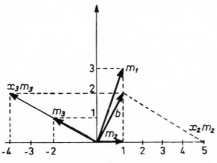

Fig. 2.

It should be remembered that the rank of a matrix is the order of the nonzero determinant of the highest order which can be extracted from such matrix. In order to analyze the general properties of a maximum, the following hypotheses will be made:

a) The rank of the matrix M is m, and the same applies to all submatrices of m rows and m columns extracted from M. This condition indicates that if any m activities are undertaken, they are linearly independent. It is a generalization of hypothesis 4 in the previous section.

b) A matrix of m rows and p + 1 columns obtained by adding vector b to matrix M:

$$\begin{bmatrix} a_{11} & \cdots & 0 & b_1 \\ \cdot & & & \cdot \\ \cdot & & & \cdot \\ a_{m1} & \cdots & 1 & b_m \end{bmatrix}$$

has all its submatrices of m rows and m columns of rank m. This condition means that vector b is linearly independent of any group of vectors m_i which includes fewer than m vectors. It excludes the degeneracy of the problem (we shall return later to the precise significance of this term).

c) A matrix of (m + 1) rows and p columns obtained by adding to M the vector c':

$$\begin{bmatrix} a_{11} \cdots \cdots & \text{o} \\ \cdots \cdots \cdots \cdots \cdots \\ a_{m1} \cdots \cdots & -\text{I} \\ c_1 \cdots \cdots & \text{o} \end{bmatrix}$$

has all its submatrices of m + 1 rows and m + 1 columns of m + 1 rank. This condition means that the coefficients which are used to express an activity with respect to other m's do not at the same time express the unit profit of such activity with respect to the unit profits of other m's. In other words, there are no numbers λ_1, λ_2, λ_j, . . . , λ_m such that one can have both a vectorial relation:

$$m_i = \Sigma \, \lambda_j m_j$$

and an algebraic relation:

$$c_i = \Sigma \, \lambda_j c_j,$$

the summation being effected upon any subentity of m numbers from series 1, 2, . . . , p and i being a number in such series which is not included in the subentity. Condition c) facilitates demonstration, but it is of less importance than condition b).

Within the framework of these hypotheses, one may demonstrate fundamental theorems regarding linear programming. The first two theorems are the result of algebraic considerations; the others derive from a geometrical presentation.

Algebraic demonstrations.

Theorem I: A possible program includes at least m activities at a nonzero level. As a matter of fact, if a program x contains less than m activities, for example m - 1, the vectorial relation:

$$\Sigma_i \, m_i x_i = b$$

would indicate that a linear relation exists between m vectors of a submatrix of m rows and m columns of the matrix obtained by adding vector b to matrix M. This submatrix would therefore not be of rank m, which is contrary to hypothesis b).

Theorem II: An optimum program, if such exists, contains at most m activities at a nonzero level. R. Dorfman provides the following demonstration of this theorem [62].

He demonstrates that, if an optimal program were to contain more than m activities, one of the a), b), or c) hypotheses would not be verified. Let us assume that such a program exists. The matrix M can be separated into three matrices M_1, M_2, M_3 such that:

a) matrix M_3 will be formed by vectors associated to activities which have a zero level in the optimum program;

b) matrix M_1 will be a square matrix of m rows and m columns formed by any m vectors associated with activities incorporated in the optimum program;

c) matrix M_2 will be formed by vectors excluded from M_1 and M_3. If the optimum program contains q activities, M_2 has m rows and q - m columns.

Choose a vector x of nonzero components q which represents the level of activities in the optimum program. By hypothesis, such a program is possible. Therefore:

$$[M_1 \ M_2] \, x = b$$

which can be written:

$$M_1 x_1 + M_2 x_2 = b \tag{I.4}$$

if x_1 and x_2 are vectors which have m and q - m components respectively, whose levels of activities enter into matrices M_1 and M_2. By multiplying the two members of (I.4) by the inverse of matrix M_1, the following relation is obtained:

$$x_1 = M^{-1}_1 b - M^{-1}_1 M_2 x_2. \tag{I.5}$$

The program being optimum, $c'x$ is maximum. Such an expression can be written:

$$c'x = c'_1 x_1 + c'_2 x_2 \tag{I.6}$$

by introducing vectors c'_1 and c'_2 which have components m and q - m respectively, representing unit profits of the activities entering into matrices M_1 and M_2. Once x_1 has been replaced by its expression derived from (I.5), relation (I.6) becomes:

$$c'x = (c'_2 - c'_1 M^{-1}_1 M_2) x_2 + c'_1 M^{-1}_1 b. \tag{I.7}$$

It must not be possible to increase $c'x$ by modifying x_2 in a manner which would be compatible with their relationships. But (I.7) already takes the Mx = b condition into account through the intermediary of (I.5). The only relationships to which any attention should be accorded are, therefore, inequalities

$$x_1 \geqslant 0 \qquad x_2 \geqslant 0. \tag{I.8}$$

Since, initially, none of the components of x_1 or of x_2 is zero, it is certainly possible to cause a slight variation in the components of x_2 on one side or the other of their initial values while continuing a verification of (I.8). The program cannot be optimum, therefore, unless $c'x$ is independent of x_2, i.e.:

$$c'_2 = c'_1 M^{-1}_1 M_2. \tag{I.9}$$

On the other hand, however, we have the identity:

$$M_2 = M_1 \, M_1^{-1} \, M_2. \tag{I.10}$$

In matrix notation, the (I.9) and (I.10) groups of equalities can be replaced by the equality:

$$\begin{bmatrix} M_2 \\ c_2' \end{bmatrix} = \begin{bmatrix} M_1 \\ c_1' \end{bmatrix} \begin{bmatrix} M_1^{-1} \, M_2 \end{bmatrix}. \tag{I.11}$$

The existence of a linear relation between each vector of matrix $\begin{bmatrix} M_2 \\ c_2' \end{bmatrix}$ and the m vector-columns of $\begin{bmatrix} M_1 \\ c_1' \end{bmatrix}$ results directly from a definition of the product of two matrices. Consequently, sub-matrices of m + 1 rows and m + 1 columns of matrix $\begin{bmatrix} M \\ c' \end{bmatrix}$ are not of rank m + 1. This contradiction results in the fact that the number of activities incorporated in an optimum program cannot exceed m, which demonstrates the theorem. Theorem I then informs us that this number is exactly m. This fundamental result, which makes it possible to determine the number of activities which will occur in the solution, completely dominates the entire theory of linear programming.

Geometrical demonstrations.

These demonstrations, being geometrical, require some prior definitions.

Convex set. Within a space of any number of dimensions, the name of "convex set" is given to any set of points such that any point in the segment joining any two points of the set belongs to the set.

Extreme point of a convex set. This is a point which is not found over any segment joining two points of the set.

For example, the plane surface of a circle or of a triangle constitutes a convex set. The extreme points are apexes of the triangle and all points in the circumference of the circle.

Convex polyhedron. "Convex polyhedron" is the name given to a convex set which consists of a finite number of extreme points.

For instance, the plane surface of a triangle constitutes a convex polyhedron, but that of a circle does not.

The definitions of a convex set and an extreme point relate to the fact that a convex set is perfectly determined when its extreme points are known. These definitions will be used to demonstrate the following three theorems:

Theorem III. The set of points representing possible programs in space (A) forms a convex polyhedron K. An isolated point is a convex polyhedron. Therefore, the theorem is valid if only one program is possible. Let us assume that there are two points representing possible programs, x and y being the corresponding vectors. By hypothesis:

$$Mx = My = b \quad x \geqslant 0 \quad y \geqslant 0$$

Therefore, if u is an actual number such that $0 \leq u \leq 1$,

$$M(ux + (1 - u)y) = (u + 1 - u)b = b \text{ et } ux + (1 - u)y \geqslant 0.$$

Program ux + (1 - u) y is therefore possible when u is included between 0 and 1. However, points associated with this program are all those of the segment joining the two initial points. Consequently, in accordance with the first definition, the set of possible points is convex. It can also be demonstrated (via theorem V) that this series has a finite number of extreme points. It is therefore a convex polyhedron.

Theorem IV. Function $c'x$ attains its maximum at one or more of the extreme points of K, and at all points of the set created by these points. A demonstration of this theorem, subject to a few variants, was given by A. Charnes [25].

Let x_0 represent a point of (K) for which the function $g(x) = c'x$ is maximal, and designate as K_j the vectors which are representative of the extreme points of (K). In accordance with a property of convex polyhedrons (of which a demonstration will not be given), vector x can be easily expressed in relation to vectors K:

$$x = \sum_j n_j(x) K_j,$$

the n_j's being positive or zero x-function numbers whose sum is equal to 1 and whose summation is extended to all extreme points of (K).

Consequently:

$$g(x_0) = \sum_j n_j(x_0) g(K_j)$$

Let $g(K_k)$ be the largest of the $g(K_j)$'s. Since the n_j's are positive or zero numbers and their sum is equal to 1, and since, on the other hand, $g(x_0)$ is a maximum, one necessarily obtains $g(x_0) = g(K_k)$.

a) If $g(K_k) > g(K_j)$ for $j \neq k$, there is only one optimum program represented by K_k.

b) If $g(K_k) = g(K_r)$, the maximum is reached at extreme points K_k and K_r, and at all points of the segment they create.

If one returns to the example given at the beginning of this section, this result appears intuitively. In space (A), the planes

$c'x$ = constant are parallel and the constant is proportionate to their distance from the origin. A determination must be made to find which of these planes contains at least one point of the convex polyhedron (K) (segment AB) farthest removed from the origin. It may be seen that this plane passes through at least one extreme point of the polyhedron; if it passes through two, it contains the segment which joins them. Hypothesis (c) has not been used in the demonstration of theorem IV. In fact, it excludes the possibility of two extreme points giving the same value to function $c'x$.

Theorem V. The necessary and sufficient condition for the vector x to correspond to an extreme point of (K) is that it should have exactly m non-zero components. This theorem, together with theorem IV, makes it possible to get back to the substance of theorem II.

The sufficient condition. If a possible point represented by vector x has exactly m non-zero coordinates, it is an extreme point of (K). Let us assume that x is not an extreme point; then there are two points of (K) represented by vectors y and z such that point x is located on the segment joining them. In other words, there is an actual number u between 0 and 1 such that:

$$\begin{cases} x = uy + (1-u)z & 0 < u < 1 \\ Mx = b. \end{cases}$$

Since all the components of x, y, and z are positive or zero, and u and 1 - u are positive, the components of y and z which correspond to the zero components of x must also be zero. One can therefore consider vectors x, y, and z as vectors having m dimensions only, and write:

$$M_1 x = M_1 y = M_1 z \tag{I.12}$$

matrix M_1 being the square sub-matrix of m rows and m columns formed by the columns of matrix M which correspond to the non-zero m components of x. (I.12) can therefore be written in the form:

$$M_1 (x-y) = M_1 (y-z) = 0 \tag{I.13}$$

However, in accordance with hypothesis (a), (I.13) constitutes a system of homogeneous linear equations of m unknowns whose determinant differs from 0. Matrix M_1 is of rank m. Consequently, vectors x-y and y-z must be identically zero, which implies x = y = z and demonstrates that x is an extreme point.

The necessary condition. If a point represented by a vector x is an extreme point of (K), it has exactly m non-zero coordinates.

On the basis of h as the number of non-zero components of x, and considering x as a vector of h dimensions, the following can be written:

$$M_h x = b \tag{I.14}$$

M_n designates the sub-matrix of m rows and h columns of M formed by columns corresponding to non-zero components of x. Theorem I insures that h is greater than or equal to m.

If h > m, the h vector columns entering into M_h are not linearly independent since, within an area of m dimensions, there cannot be more than m independent vectors. There exists, therefore, a vector y of h dimensions such that:

$$M_h y = o \tag{I.15}$$

By combining (I.14) and (I.15), it will be seen that for a sufficiently small positive constant k, two points can be defined:

$$\begin{aligned} u &= x - ky \\ v &= x + ky \end{aligned} \tag{I.16}$$

all their coordinates being positive and belonging to the series (K) since:

$$M_h u = M_h v = b \tag{I.17}$$

Point $x = \dfrac{u + v}{2}$ is in the middle of the segment joining u and v. It cannot therefore be an extreme point, which contradicts the hypothesis h > m and prescribes that h = m.

These theorems, as a whole, indicate that in order to obtain a maximum, it is necessary merely to consider the extreme points of (K), i.e., points which have exactly m non-zero components.

The foregoing theorems have been demonstrated by using hypotheses (a) and (b), and eventually hypothesis (c). Since hypothesis (a) can always be verified, hypotheses (b) and (c) remain to be discussed.

Hypothesis (b): When hypothesis (b) is not verified, theorem I is no longer valid. A possible program — and especially an optimum program — can include only a number of activities less than m. Theorems II, III, and IV are valid without change. However, theorem V's new description reads: the necessary and sufficient condition for a point represented by vector x to correspond to an extreme point of (K) is that x have at most m non-zero components.

The geometrical consequences of hypothesis (b) with respect to the example supplied in this section can be easily observed. If this hypothesis were not verified, vector (b) would be collinear with one of the M_1, M_2, M_3 vectors. There would therefore be one possible program which would represent one activity only. For example, if the second equality is transformed and replaced by:

$$2x_1 + x_3 = 2$$

vector b becomes collinear with vector M_1. Point A, which is one of the extreme points of segment AB to which polyhedron (K) is reduced, here becomes the point of coordinates (1,0,0). It has a number of non-zero coordinates less than 2.

Hypothesis (c): This hypothesis has been used solely in the demonstration of theorem II. Theorems I, III, IV, and V therefore remain unchanged if hypothesis (c) is not verified. When not satisfied, it becomes necessary to modify the description and the demonstration of theorem II. The new description is as follows: Among optimal programs, if such exist, there will be at least one which includes a maximum of m activities at a non-zero level. Hypothesis (c), in actual fact, excludes the possibility of several optimum programs; geometrically, it means that in space (A) none of the sides of the convex polyhedron (K) is parallel to the $c'x = $ Const family of planes.

The simplex method for a systematic determination of a maximum is a direct result of the above theorems. In outlining the method, hypothesis (b) will be retained, but hypothesis (c) will no longer be taken into account.

3. The simplex method and its significance.

Developed principally as a result of research performed by G. Dantzig [45], the simplex method determines a maximum by exploring, in sequence, the extreme points of (K).

As long as hypothesis (b) can be verified, there is a biunivocal relationship between the extreme points of (K) and the series of m vectors m_i linked to the possible programs derived from matrix M.

In accordance with hypothesis (a), any m vectors m_i are independent. Consequently, any vector in space (B) can be expressed in the form of a linear combination of m vectors m_i. For this reason, the name "basis" will be applied to any series of m vectors m_i associated with any possible program.

Let us therefore assume that we have found an extreme point. Corresponding thereto is a series of m independent vectors m_i associated with a possible program. If, among these vectors, we replace vector m_r by vector m_k, making sure that the new program is possible, we obtain a new series of m independent vectors, and we replace the initial extreme point by an adjacent extreme point.

If the $m_r m_k$ substitution is selected in such manner that the profit function does not decrease during the interval, we will not be far from attaining an optimum, and, in fact, we may have come closer thereto. Since there is a finite number of extreme points and the convexity of the polyhedron excludes local maxima, this method will make it possible for us to attain a maximum in a finite number of approximations. It will be much more economical than a method which would consist of exploring the extreme points, one after the other, without any preconceived plan.

Such a procedure would be practically impossible once the goods and the activities exceed a few units. Let us therefore consider an extreme point to which are associated vectors $m_1, ..., m_i, ..., m_m$. Since these vectors are independent, the p vector-columns m of matrix M can be put in the form:

$$m_j = \sum_{i=1}^{m} u_{ij} m_i. \tag{I.18}$$

For this extreme point, the profit function g has a value g_0, and the corresponding program x $(x_1, ..., x_i, ..., x_m)$ is defined by the system of m equations of m unknowns:

$$\sum_{i=1}^{m} m_i x_i = b. \tag{I.19}$$

In accordance with the hypotheses, the solution to this system is unique and is such that:

$$x_i \geqslant 0. \tag{I.20}$$

If we wish to replace a certain vector m_r by a new vector m_k, we can write (since relation (I.18) must still be valid):

$$\sum_{i=1}^{m} m_i x_i - tm_k + tm_k = b$$

t being any actual number. Therefore, taking (I.18) into account (for j = k):

$$\sum_{i=1}^{m} m_i (x_i - tu_{ik}) + tm_k = b. \tag{I.21}$$

A new extreme point will have been defined if t is positive and if all coefficients $(x_i - tu_{ik})$ are positive, with the exception of the coefficient of r which is zero. The new basis will include the m-1 vectors m_i ($i \neq r$) and vector m_k. Let us calculate the new value assumed by function g, $g'o$:

$$g'_0 = \sum_{i=1}^{m} c_i \left(x_i - tu_{ik}\right) + tc_k = g_0 + t\left(c_k - g_k\right) \qquad (I.22)$$

by posing:

$$g_k = \sum_{i=1}^{m} u_{ik} c_i.$$

The above calculations provide the means of selecting vectors k and r.

1. Vector m_k must be selected among vectors for which:

$$c_k - g_k \geqslant 0$$

in order that its introduction in the basis may not cause a decrease in profit. In actual practice, the vector can be retained for which c_k-g_k has the largest positive value.

2. Vector m_k must replace vector m_r which disappears from the basis when the greatest possible positive value is assigned to t. This greatest value, if one considers relation (I.21), is obviously a minimum when i varies by:

$$\frac{x_i}{u_{ik}} \text{ for positive } u_{ik}.$$

Indeed, if t were to exceed this value, some of the coefficients of the m_i's in (I.21) would become negative, which amounts to saying that the program would no longer be possible. Since we now have a new basis in which vector m_k replaces vector m_r, the p vectors m_j must be expressed in relation to the m independent vectors of the new basis. It will be noted that:

$$m_k = u_{rk} m_r + \sum_{i \neq r} u_{ik} m_i ,$$

i.e., by withdrawing m_r from this relation and by carrying into (I. 18):

$$m_j = \sum_{i \neq r} \left(u_{ij} - u_{ik} \frac{u_{rj}}{u_{rk}}\right) m_i + \frac{u_{rj}}{u_{rk}} m_k. \qquad (I.23)$$

The new program is directly deduced from the (I. 21) relationship. The activity levels are:

t for the kth activity;

$x_i - tu_{ik}$ for the other activities of the new basis.

At each stage in the calculation, when determining vectors m_k and m_r, three distinct cases are possible.

1. For a minimum j, $c_j - g_j$; 0, and for any i, $u_{ij} \le 0$. t can be taken to be as large as desired and one still has a feasible program. The maximum of g is therefore infinite.

2. $c_j - g_j \le 0$ for any j. Under these conditions, we have determined an extreme point at which function g attains its maximum.

3. For a minimum j, $c_j - g_j > 0$, and for a minimum i, $u_{ik} > 0$. A modification of the basis does not diminish the g function. Since there is a finite number of extreme points, this instance cannot occur indefinitely.

The simplex method therefore constitutes an iteration process for obtaining a maximum in a finite number of stages when one extreme point is known.

A last problem remains to be solved: how can an extreme point be systematically determined? Given below is the method to be used in two particular instances. The method to be followed in the other cases can be deduced immediately therefrom:

a) The m conditions initially set — before the introduction of neutral activities — are inequalities, and all the b_k's are negative. m neutral activities are therefore available. The vectors associated with these m activities are the opposite of the m unit vectors of the axes of coordinates in space (B). A possible program corresponds thereto:

$$x_1 = x_2 = \ldots\ldots x_n = 0 \qquad x_{n+1} = -b_1 \ldots\ldots x_{n+m} = -b_m$$

since the b_k's are negative. These vectors, consequently, constitute a basis and define an extreme point which can be utilized in order to apply the simplex method. The program associated with such a basis consists of doing absolutely nothing and naturally leads to zero profit.

b) The m conditions as set were initially equalities. It will therefore be assumed arbitrarily that they were inequalities and the following will be written:

$$\sum a_{ki} x_i \pm x_{n+k} = b_k \, ,$$

the symbol before x_{n+k} being the same as that of b_k. The x_{n+k}'s are associated with m additional artificial activities which form a basis, since this possible program is associated therewith:

$$x_1 = \ldots = x_n = 0 \qquad x_{n+1} = |b_1| \ldots\ldots x_{n+m} = |b_m|.$$

In order to be certain that such additional activities will disappear from the optimum program, a negative unit profit -M will be associated as large as desired in absolute value. Under these conditions, the maximum of g cannot be attained as long as all additional activities are not returned to zero levels, i.e., as long as all equalities have not been verified.

In actual practice, an attempt should be made to select the best possible starting basis, and to resort to the preceding basis only when it is found to be impossible to determine directly one that is more satisfactory. In effect, these bases are far removed from the maximum and require a large number of approximations. Very often, a knowledge of the economic significance of a problem can facilitate the determination of a possible program, including exactly m activities, which is not too far from the optimum.

The simplex method has been outlined above by presenting it solely in its mathematical aspect. It has, however, a very important economic significance. Relations (I. 18) and (I. 21) indicate that if activity k is introduced into the program at the unit level, the levels of other activities in the program must be reduced by u_{ik}. In other words, u_{ik} is the marginal rate — compatible with the relationships — of substitution of activity k for activity i. The expression:

$$g_k = \sum c_i u_{ik}$$

represents the loss in profit due to the reduction in the levels of activities i. In order to ascertain whether activity k can be profitably introduced, one must therefore compare g_k with the unit profit c_k created by activity k. c_k-g_k appears, therefore, as the marginal income corresponding to the introduction of activity k in the basis. That activity k is selected which has the highest marginal income and whose level t is the highest value compatible with the relationships, i.e., the minimum of x_i/u_{ik} for positive u_{ik}. If the maximum is not infinite, iterations cease when:

$$c_k - g_k \leqslant 0 \text{ for any k,}$$

i.e., when the marginal income which corresponds to the introduction of any activity outside the basis is negative or zero. In the case of basis activities c_i-g_i is zero since, as will be readily observed, g_i reduces itself to c_i.

On the theoretical plane, two last problems remain to be examined:

1. The method described above permits determination of an optimum program. However, the problem is actually solved only when all optimum programs are known. If one of them is known, how can all optimum programs be obtained?

2. What are the difficulties which can be encountered in an application of the method when hypothesis (b) is not verified, i.e., when there is degeneracy?

1. The total number of optimum programs is determined when all extreme points leading to a maximum are known. In order to ascertain whether there are several such points, time need not be wasted in checking whether hypothesis (c) has been verified or not. It is merely necessary to examine the table of calculations which led to the first optimum program. The introduction of a new vector k into the basis will not change function g if:

$$t\,(c_k - g_k) = 0.$$

This can occur either because c_k-g_k is zero or because t is zero. A simple examination will make it possible to determine the vectors for which c_k-g_k is zero. These vectors can be introduced into the basis by using the traditional simplex method.

Parameter t associated with a vector k is zero if the minimum of $\dfrac{x_i}{u_{ik}}$ is zero for positive u_{ik}. A determination is then made of those i vectors in the basis for which x_i is zero, and the k vectors for which u_{ik} is positive are introduced into the basis.

Such mechanisms of substitution must be continued until all possibilities have been exhausted.

2. In a case of degeneracy, it is possible that vector b, in certain bases, can find expression only as a function of a number of vectors in the basis inferior to m. Since the components of vector b are the activity levels of the program associated with the basis, the latter includes, therefore, only a number less than m activities at a non-zero level.

In applying the simplex method, degeneracy is observed as follows:

When changing from a certain basis for which b is expressed in relation to the m vectors of the basis to a new basis for which b is expressed as a function of fewer than m vectors (m-1, to fix this in mind), a new activity is introduced into the basis; however, two activities in the former basis have a self-cancelling level. One of these must be preserved in the basis since the optimum may very well include m activities at a non-zero level. The activity to be preserved remains to be selected.

In order to resolve this difficulty, we imagine that it is not the initial problem which is being dealt with but a closely related problem obtained by slightly modifying vector b and selected in such a way as to avoid degeneracy. When vector b approaches its initial value, the solution to the modified problem tends toward that of the initial problem. In fact, it is not even necessary actually to consider the modified problem, since the theory provides the means of deducing a simple rule which indicates the activity to be retained in the basis in case of degeneracy. Let us assume that m_q and m_r are the two vectors in the basis and the problem is to select one for retention. The following relations are calculated for increasing values of j:

$$\frac{u_{qj}}{u_{qk}} \ \text{et} \ \frac{u_{rj}}{u_{rk}} .$$

Whenever, for a certain j, the quantities calculated for q and r are different, one selects the vector whose quantity is the smallest in algebraic value as the vector to be excluded from the basis. Since this rule introduces the order in which vectors are classified, this order must not be modified during the entire length of the calculations [25].

4. A practical presentation of the calculations.

To render this method practical, a "simplex table" condensing all usable information is determined at each stage. The columns of such a table indicate the components in the basis of the following vectors, from left to right:
(a) vector b;
(b) the n vectors associated with the activities.
The rows correspond in the following order:
(a) to the vectors of the basis;
(b) to unit profits c_i;
(c) to quantities g_j;
(d) to quantities c_j-g_j.
In order to demonstrate how this table can be utilized, we will deal with an extremely simple example in which, initially, there are only four activities and three goods associated with the inequalities. Matrix A is:

$$\begin{bmatrix} 1 & -2 & 2 & -2 \\ -4 & 1 & 0 & -1 \\ -3 & -1 & -1 & +2 \end{bmatrix}$$

which means that the first activity consumes four units of good 2 and three units of good 3 to produce one unit of good 1. Vector b is vector:

$$\begin{bmatrix} -100 \\ -500 \\ -200 \end{bmatrix}$$

which indicates that there are available 100 units of good 1, 500 of good 2, and 200 of good 3. Finally, vector c' is: [2 1 3 1] and all restraints are inequalities.

These will be converted into equalities by introducing three neutral activities. Matrix M has, therefore, 3 rows and 7 columns. Its vector-columns are numbered from m_1 to m_7:

$$M = \begin{bmatrix} & m_1 & m_2 & m_3 & m_4 & m_5 & m_6 & m_7 \\ & 1 & -2 & 2 & -2 & -1 & 0 & 0 \\ & -4 & +1 & 0 & -1 & 0 & -1 & 0 \\ & -3 & -1 & -1 & +2 & 0 & 0 & -1 \end{bmatrix}$$

The components of vector b all being negative, the neutral activities form a basis to which is associated program:

$$x_1 = x_2 = x_3 = x_4 = 0 \qquad x_5 = 100 \qquad x_6 = 500 \qquad x_7 = 200.$$

Vectors m_1, m_2, m_3, and m_4 must then be expressed as a function of vectors m_5, m_6, and m_7. We will do this only for m_1. Three numbers u_{51}, u_{61}, and u_{71} have to be calculated, such that:

$$\begin{bmatrix} 1 \\ -4 \\ -3 \end{bmatrix} = u_{51} \begin{bmatrix} -1 \\ 0 \\ 0 \end{bmatrix} + u_{61} \begin{bmatrix} 0 \\ -1 \\ 0 \end{bmatrix} + u_{71} \begin{bmatrix} 0 \\ 0 \\ -1 \end{bmatrix}$$

The solution is immediately obtained: $u_{51} = -1$ $u_{61} = 4$ $u_{71} = 3$. It will be noted that, when the basis constituted by neutral activities is used, the components of the other vectors are obtained by changing the symbol of their initial components. This calculation permits the establishment of the first table.

Unit profits of vectors of the basis	Basis vectors	b	m_1	m_2	m_3	m_4	m_5	m_6	m_7
0	m_5	100	−1	+2	−2	+2	1	0	0
0	m_6	500	+4	−1	0	+1	0	1	0
0	m_7	200	+3	+1	+1	−2	0	0	1
	c_i		2	1	3	1	0	0	0
	g_i		0	0	0	0	0	0	0
	$c_i - g_i$		2	1	3	1	0	0	0

The values of c_i-g_i are such that it is interesting to introduce into the basis any one of the activities 1, 2, 3, 4. Activity 3 will be introduced in which c_i-g_i has the highest value. The minimum of

x_i/u_{i3} for u_{i3} positive is attained for $i = 7$. Vector m_7 will therefore be eliminated from the basis.

In the new program, activity 3 will be started at level:

$$t = x_7/u_{73} = 200$$

and activities 5 and 6 at levels:

$$x_5 - t\,u_{53} = 100 - 200\,(-\,2) = 500$$
$$x_6 - t\,u_{63} = 500 - 200\,(\quad 0) = 500.$$

Vectors 1, 2, 4, and 7 must now be expressed in relation to m_3, m_6, m_5. It would be just as quick here to solve system (I. 18) directly, but, by way of illustration, we will apply relations (I. 23) which lead to much shorter calculations when m is raised slightly.

In accordance with (I. 23), the components which follow m_3 are obtained by dividing the components of m_7 by $u_{73} = 1$. The third line in the simplex table therefore remains unchanged.

Let us now calculate another component, for example that of m_1 following m_5. In the new basis, it is equal to:

$$u_{51} - u_{53}\,\frac{u_{71}}{u_{73}} = -\,1 - (-\,2)\,\frac{+\,3}{1} = +\,5.$$

The other components are calculated similarly and a second table is finally developed:

Unit profits of vectors of the basis	Basis vectors	b	m_1	m_2	m_3	m_4	m_5	m_6	m_7
0	m_5	500	4	4	0	−2	1	0	2
0	m_6	500	5	−1	0	1	0	1	0
+ 3	m_3	200	3	1	1	−2	0	0	1
	c_i		2	1	3	1	0	0	0
	g_i		9	3	3	−6	0	0	3
	$c_i - g_i$		−7	−2	0	+ 5	0	0	−3

An examination of the table indicates that m_4 must be introduced instead of m_6 at level:

$$t = x_6/m_{64} = 500.$$

The levels of activities 5 and 3 become:

$$x_5 - tu_{54} = 500 - 500(-2) = 1,500$$
$$x_3 - tu_{34} = 200 - 500(-2) = 1,200.$$

By calculating the new components of the various vectors, a third table is obtained:

Unit profits of vectors of the basis	Basis vectors	b	m_1	m_2	m_3	m_4	m_5	m_6	m_7
0	m_5	1,500	13	2	0	0	1	2	2
1	m_4	500	4	−1	0	1	0	1	0
3	m_3	1,200	11	−1	1	0	0	2	1
	c_i		2	1	3	1	0	0	0
	g_i		37	−4	3	1	0	+7	+3
	$c_i - g_i$		−35	+5	0	0	0	−7	−3

This table demonstrates that m_2 must be introduced instead of m_5. The calculations — which will not be given here — then lead to a new table, the last, since all quantities $c_i - g_i$ are negative or zero.

Unit profits of vectors of the basis	Basis vectors	b	m_1	m_2	m_3	m_4	m_5	m_6	m_7
1	m_2	750	13/2	1	0	0	1/2	1	1
1	m_4	1,250	21/2	0	0	1	1/2	2	1
3	m_3	1,950	19/2	0	1	0	1/2	3	2
·	c_i		2	1	3	1	0	0	0
	g_i		91/2	1	3	1	5/2	12	8
	$c_i - g_i$		−87/2	0	0	0	−5/2	−12	−8

Finally, the optimum program consists of utilizing activity 2 at level 750, activity 3 at level 1,950, and activity 4 at level 1,250. The profit is 7,850. The basis does not include any neutral activity, which means that the plant is using all its available resources.

This method, which may seem slightly cumbersome in connection with so simple an example, is very convenient when m and n are fairly large. Thanks to this method, it has been possible to solve — with the help of electronic computers — problems which included a hundred or so activities and several scores of goods. Naturally, whenever possible, it may be advantageous to derive some benefit from the form peculiar to matrix M. An example of this will be given later in connection with the transportation problem. It is toward this elegant utilization of specialized structures that research is currently oriented in the field of linear programming.

5. The duality problem and its economic interpretation [92].

A theorem of major importance for the significance and the utilization of linear programming refers, in connection with the foregoing problem, to another problem known as a duality problem. This association is doubly interesting because it presents:

a) a practical interest for, at times, it is easier to solve a duality problem than the original problem;

b) a theoretical interest because the economic significance of the two problems are closely related. If the first problem attempts to determine activity levels — i.e., quantities — the second problem seeks to arrive at a scale price system leading to an optimum organization of production.

In order to clarify the exposition, which is rather intricate, we will proceed by stages:

a) On the basis of M_1, a square matrix of m rows and m columns formed by the vectors of a certain basis, the components u_{ij} (i = 1, 2, ..., m; j = 1, 2, ..., p) constitute a matrix U of m rows and p columns which is precisely represented on the right side of the simplex table. In matrix notation, relation (I.18):

$$m_j = \sum_i u_{ij} m_i$$

is written:

$$M = M_1 U$$

or:

$$U = M_1^{-1} \cdot M.$$

The vector having as components:

$$g_k = \sum_i u_{ik} c_i$$

it is therefore expressed:

$$c_1' U = c_1' M_1^{-1} M$$

if c_1 indicates the vector of m dimensions made up of unit profits of basis activities.

The row-vector whose components are (c_k-g_k) is then written:

$$c' - c_1' M_1^{-1} M.$$

b) Let us now consider vector π of m dimensions:

$$\begin{bmatrix} \pi_1 \\ \pi_2 \\ . \\ . \\ \pi_m \end{bmatrix} \tag{I.24}$$

obtained by solving equation:

$$- \pi' M_1 = c_1'.$$

This vector equation represents the system of linear equations:

$$- \sum \pi_i m_{ij} = c_j. \tag{I.25}$$

in which m_{ij} is the jth component of vector m_i. Now, m_{ij} represents the quantity of goods i which is put into production by activity j at the unit level (with a negative symbol if a factor of production is involved, or a positive symbol if this is related to a product). The π_i's can therefore be interpreted as follows: They are the prices which should be assigned to goods i in order that the cost of goods obtained through the various activities of the basis

$$- \sum \pi_i m_{ij}$$

may be exactly equal to their profit c_j.* For this reason, the name "price vector" will be assigned to the vector π. Such a vector is associated with each basis. In accordance with (I. 24), it is expressed:

$$\pi = - c_1' M_1^{-1}. \tag{I.26}$$

---

*The minus sign is used to represent the factors of production.

By using vector π, vector $c' - c_1' M_1^{-1} M$ can be written:

$$c' + \pi' M. \qquad (I.27)$$

Vector $-\pi' M$ — a row vector of p dimensions — can be interpreted as the vector representing the cost of goods produced by the various activities of the problem. This particular point deserves special attention because this is where, for the first time, the dual nature of the problem appears.

At this stage, in order to introduce — in a manner compatible with the relationships — the other activities in the program, we express, in two different forms, the vector whose components g_k represent reductions in profit due to a lowering of the activity levels in the base:

1. In the form

$$g_k = \sum_i u_{ik} c_i$$

which corresponds to the vector expression $c_1' M_1^{-1} M$, g_k appears as the sum of substitution marginal rates balanced by unit profits.

2. In the form

$$g_k = \sum \pi_i m_{ik}$$

which corresponds to the vector expression $\pi' M$, g_k appears as the sum of the cost of the goods consumed by activity k.

When the simplex method is applied, a comparison of c_k with g_k can be interpreted in terms of either one or the other of the above standpoints.

c) Profit $c_1' x$ derived from a program can also be expressed by using relationship (I. 26) through the use of vector π':

$$c_1' x = c_1' \cdot M_1^{-1} b = -\pi' b.$$

It can therefore be considered as the total cost of available goods.

d) At this point it is now possible for us to outline, and then to demonstrate the theorem of duality, using the following two problems:

Problem I. $g = c'x$ being a linear form in which c' is a row-vector of p dimensions and x a column-vector also of p dimensions, determine the maximum of g under restraints:

$$\begin{cases} Mx = b \\ x_i \geqslant 0 \end{cases}$$

in which M is a matrix of m rows and p columns and b a column-vector of m dimensions.

Problem II. $f = -\pi'b$ being a linear form in which π' is a row-vector of m dimensions and b the same vector as above, determine the minimum of f under restraints:

$$- \pi' M \geqslant c',$$

M and c' having the same significance as in problem I.

With the significance assigned to π' in a), b), and c), the solution of this problem would determine a scale order price which minimizes the value of resources, as each activity is either in balance or shows a loss.

It will be noted that no condition has been set as to the symbol for the components of vector π.

The duality theorem is as follows:

> If either of problems I or II includes possible programs and if the linear form g or f associated therewith is limited in the direction to be determined (above for problem I, below for problem II), there are also possible programs for the other problem and the associated linear form is limited. Furthermore, the maximum of g is equal to the minimum of f.

> If one of the problems includes possible programs without its linear form being limited, the other problem will not include any possible program.

A demonstration of this theorem developed by G. Dantzig and A. Orden [92] is given:

Returning to the notations in paragraphs a), b), and c), but assuming now that the basis considered is optimum, this basis can be associated with a π vector such that, because of inequalities $c_k - g_k \leq 0$:

$$- \pi' M \geqslant c'.$$

This vector π constitutes a possible program in problem II. Furthermore:

$$- \pi'b = c_1'x = \text{Max } g. \tag{I.28}$$

However, in the case of all vectors x and π which respectively constitute possible programs for problems I and II, there are relations:

$$- \pi' Mx = - \pi'b = f(\pi)$$
$$- \pi' Mx \geqslant c'x = g(x)$$

i.e.,

$$f(\pi) \geqslant g(x) \text{ and Min } f(\pi) \geqslant \text{Max } g(x) \tag{I.29}$$

But, in accordance with (I. 28) which states that a π exists such that f (π) = Max g (x), (I. 29) can be replaced by the equality:

$$\text{Min } f(\pi) = \text{Max } g(x)$$

which completes the demonstration of the theorem.

With the solution of either problem I or II, one can either:

1) determine the levels of activities for which profit is at a maximum within the limits allowed by specific resources; or

2) determine the price system for which available resources have a minimum value, and where the marginal income of the various activities are either negative or zero.

Later we will give a second proof of the duality theorem, in accordance with the theorem by Kuhn and Tucker.

e) A certain dissymmetry exists between problems I and II. The equal symbol in Mx = b is replaced by symbol $\geq$ and the conditions $x_i \geq 0$ of problem I have no equivalent in problem II. This dissymmetry vanishes when problem I is considered in its original form — before the introduction of neutral activities — and when all restraints therein are inequalities. In effect, the following theorem is indeed demonstrated:

If the two problems are considered:

I. To maximize $g = c'x$

$$Ax \geqslant b$$
$$x_i \geqslant 0 \qquad i = 1, 2, ..., n.$$

II. To minimize $f = -\pi'b$

$$-\pi'A \geqslant c'$$
$$\pi \geqslant 0 \qquad j = 1, 2, ..., n$$

and if both include: a) possible programs, and b) a maximum and a minimum, respectively finite, then:

The maximum of the first is equal to the minimum of the second.

Note: There is an interesting connection between convex sets representing the possible programs of a problem and its duality. Let us transform the two problems by introducing neutral activities.

Following the introduction of m neutral activities (I designating unit-matrices), the first problem becomes:

A maximization of c'x

$$[A-I] \quad x = b$$
$$x \geqslant 0.$$

Following the introduction of n neutral activities, the second is expressed as:

A minimization of $-\pi'b$

$$- \pi' [A - I] = c'$$
$$\pi' \geqslant 0.$$

Vectors x and π now both have two p components.

Let (K) and (H) be the convex polyhedrons representing the entire group of possible x programs of these two problems within spaces of p dimensions. In accordance with the method described in paragraph b), it is possible to have a point π in the space in which (H) is found which can be made to correspond to an extreme point of (K). However, if the extreme point is not optimal, its image is not in (H) since there is at least one activity which produces a positive income. Conversely, a point x of the space in which (K) is found can be made to correspond to an extreme point π of (H); but if the extreme point is not optimal, its image is not in (K) since at least one of the goods is being utilized over and above available resources. The only points of (K) and (H) between which there is a biunivocal correspondence are the extreme point solutions of the two problems.

f) To clarify the foregoing, the prices at each stage in the example discussed in paragraph 4 will be calculated. In the case of a basis consisting of neutral activities, vector $\pi(\pi_1, \pi_2, \pi_3)$ is determined by the equations:

$$\pi_1 + 0. \pi_2 + 0. \pi_3 = c_5 = 0$$
$$0. \pi_1 + \pi_2 + 0. \pi_3 = c_6 = 0$$
$$0. \pi_1 + 0. \pi_2 + \pi_3 = c_7 = 0$$

In other words, all the components of vector π are zero. This is a natural result. Goods 1, 2, 3 have a zero value since we are not using all of the resources available to us.

At the second stage, the first two equations remain unchanged but the third becomes

$$- 2 \pi_1 - 0. \pi_2 + \pi_3 = c_3 = 3$$

i.e.,

$$\pi_1 = \pi_2 = 0 \qquad \pi_3 = 3.$$

At the third stage, the first equation remains unchanged, but the other two equations become:

$$2 \pi_1 + \pi_2 - 2 \pi_3 = c_4 = 1$$
$$- 2 \pi_1 + \pi_3 = c_3 = 3,$$

i.e.,

$$\pi_1 = 0 \quad \pi_2 = 7 \quad \pi_3 = 3.$$

Finally, at the last stage, prices are determined by the system of equations:

$$\begin{aligned}
2\,\pi_1 - \pi_2 + \pi_3 &= c_2 = 1 \\
2\,\pi_1 + \pi_2 - 2\,\pi_3 &= c_4 = 1 \\
-2\,\pi_1 \quad + \pi_3 &= c_3 = 3
\end{aligned}$$

i.e.,

$$\pi_1 = 5/2 \quad \pi_2 = 12 \quad \pi_3 = 8.$$

Therefore (since the price of good 2 is 12), it would be to the best advantage of the plant to relax constraint (2).

Profit amounts to:

$$\frac{5}{2} \times 100 + 12 \times 500 + 8 \times 200 = 7{,}850$$

From an economic standpoint a duality problem is of major importance, but it should be remembered that it also furnishes a means of indirectly solving the initial problem. In order to familiarize the reader with the simplex method, we will derive the solution of the example given in paragraph 4 by using the duality problem in the general form of part e):

A minimization of

$$100\,\pi_1 + 500\,\pi_2 + 200\,\pi_3$$

under conditions:

$$\begin{aligned}
-\ \pi_1 + 4\,\pi_2 + 3\,\pi_3 &\geqslant 2 \qquad \pi_1,\ \pi_2,\ \pi_2 \geqslant 0 \\
2\,\pi_1 - \pi_2 + \pi_3 &\geqslant 1 \\
-\ 2\,\pi_1 \quad + \pi_3 &\geqslant 3 \\
+\ 2\,\pi_1 + \pi_2 - 2\,\pi_3 &\geqslant 1
\end{aligned}$$

Matrix M associated with this problem is the following 4-row 7-column matrix:

$$\begin{bmatrix}
-1 & +4 & +3 & -1 & 0 & 0 & 0 \\
2 & -1 & +1 & 0 & -1 & 0 & 0 \\
-2 & 0 & +1 & 0 & 0 & -1 & 0 \\
2 & +1 & -2 & 0 & 0 & 0 & -1
\end{bmatrix}$$

In order to shorten the calculations, we will attempt to start from a basis including vectors π_1, π_2, π_3, π_4. It will be very easily verified that the basis consisting of vectors $\pi_1, \pi_2, \pi_3, \pi_4$ leads to a possible program: $\pi_1 = 5/2 \ \pi_2 = 12 \ \pi_3 = 8 \ \pi_4 = 135/2$ and makes it possible to establish the following simplex table.

Unit profits of vectors of the basis	Basis vectors	c	π_1	π_2	π_3	π_4	π_5	π_6	π_7
+ 100	π_1	5/2	1	0	0	0	−1/2	−1/2	−1/2
+ 500	π_2	12	0	1	0	0	−1	−1	−2
+ 200	π_3	8	0	0	1	0	−1	0	−1
0	π_4	135/2	0	0	0	1	13/2	−9/2	−21/2
	b_i		100	500	200	0	0	0	0
	f_i		100	500	200	0	−750	−550	−1,050
	$b_i - f_i$		0	0	0	0	+750	+550	+1,050

An examination of the above simplex table reveals that, since we are seeking a minimum and all the $b_i - f_i$ are positive or zero, the program obtained is optimal.

We were already aware of this by application of the simplex method to the original problem.

The duality problem brings to a close the exposition of the fundamental elements of the linear programming theory. Before completing this outline by the presentation of a few additional special points, a certain number of complications selected to provide a real idea of the practical possibilities of linear programming will be examined.

II

APPLICATIONS AND COMPLEMENTS

1. Linear programming applications.

These are numerous and varied, but the earliest one, the one which played an essential part in the formulation of the theory, is known as the Hitchcock-Koopmans transportation problem.

a) The transportation problem [35], [106].

It is unnecessary to repeat its formulation, already outlined at the beginning of this chapter (p. 400). It will be analyzed here in its simplest form with:

$$\sum_j x_{ij} = a_i \text{ et } \sum_i a_i = \sum_j b_j.$$

Each x_{ij} represents the level of an activity which consists of transporting a unit from a point of origin i to a destination j. The goods are available quantities at i and quantities delivered to j. Matrix M is, therefore, the matrix below in which X_{ij} represents the vector associated with x_{ij}.

With the exception of two columns which contain 1 (one of these corresponding to an origin and the other to an extremity), each of its columns contains only zeros. This peculiarity makes it possible to simplify the simplex method and to solve transportation problems very quickly.

Activities	x_{11} . . . . x_{ij} . . . .
Goods: Origins 1	1 . . . . 0 . . . .
. i	. 0 . . . . 1 . . . .
. p Destinations	. 0 . . . . 0 . . . .
1	1 . . . . 0 . . . .
. j	. 0 . . . . 1 . . . .
. q	. 0 . . . . 0 . . . .

It will be noted at the very outset that, as a result of equality

$$\sum a_i = \sum_j b_j$$

there are p + q - 1 activities in the optimum program and it will be necessary to explore programs which include this number of activities. The use of a simplex table here would not be very convenient since it would not take into account this problem's special form. It is preferable to resort to the two following tables: the first covers activities and the second covers costs:

TABLE I   TABLE II

Destinations	1 2... j... q		Destinations	1 2... j... q	
Origins 1 2	x_{11} x_{12}..v_{1j}..x_{1q}	a_1 .	Origins 1 2	c_{11} c_{12}..c_{1j}..c_{1q}	
i	x_{i1} x_{i2}..x_{ij}..x_{iq}	a_i	i	c_{i1} c_{i2}..c_{ij}..c_{iq}	
p	x_{p1} x_{p2}..x_{pj}..x_{pq}	a_p	p	c_{p1} c_{p2}..c_{pj}..c_{pq}	
	b_1 b_2...b_j....b	$\Sigma a_i = \Sigma b_j$			

G. Dantzig [35] has adopted the simplex method to transportation problems. He has demonstrated that it is always possible to determine a basis in the following manner. Starting from the top left corner of Table I and assigning to x_{11} the smallest value among numbers a_1 and b_1, if a_1 is greater than b_1, destination 1 is saturated and column 1 can be eliminated. The same operation takes place on the reduced table in which a_1 is replaced by a_1-b_1.

If b_1 is greater than a_1, origin 1 is exhausted and the first row can be eliminated. The same operation takes place on the reduced table in which b_1 is replaced by b_1-a_1.

By continuing such operations, one eliminates at each stage either one of the rows or one of the columns in Table I and a possible program is progressively built. In such a program, an x_{ij} activity is always followed by an $x_{i,j+1}$, or $x_{i+1,j}$ activity. The program obtained is associated with a basis since the total number of activities introduced is exactly equal to p + q - 1. In point of fact, it is definitely so when there are two origins and one destination, or two destinations and one origin. Since, in the final stage, one of these situations is always arrived at, the total number of activities introduced is:

$$N + (2 + 1) - 1$$

(2 + 1) representing the sum of the number of rows and columns in the final situation and N the number of activities previously introduced. However, N is equal to the sum of the number of rows and columns which have been eliminated since, for each row or column eliminated, there is one activity, and only one, introduced. Consequently,

$$N = p + q - 3$$

for in the final stage there are, in all, 3 rows or columns. The total number of activities introduced is therefore:

$$p + q - 3 + (2 + 1) - 1 = p + q - 1.$$

The next stage in the general theory consists of expressing representative vectors of all activities in relation to the vectors of the basis. It will be seen that this is unnecessary here but it will be noted in passing, without stressing the point, that the u_{ik}'s are all equal to -1, or +1. If, for example, X_{13}, X_{33}, and X_{32} are included in the basis, X_{12} is equal to:

$$X_{12} = X_{13} - X_{33} + X_{32}.$$

The above relation is written by limiting oneself to rows associated with the first three origins and the first three destinations (all other rows contain zeros only):

$$\begin{bmatrix} 1 \\ 0 \\ 0 \\ 0 \\ 1 \\ 0 \end{bmatrix} = \begin{bmatrix} 1 \\ 0 \\ 0 \\ 0 \\ 0 \\ 1 \end{bmatrix} + \begin{bmatrix} 0 \\ 0 \\ -1 \\ 0 \\ 0 \\ -1 \end{bmatrix} + \begin{bmatrix} 0 \\ 0 \\ 1 \\ 0 \\ 1 \\ 0 \end{bmatrix}$$

In order to determine whether it is advantageous to introduce activity X_{ij} in the basis, the c_{ij} transportation cost must be compared with the gain resulting from a reduction in the levels of the other activities. To calculate the latter, the theory of duality will be used. For a given basis, it is possible to associate a price with each of the independent goods. However, these independent goods correspond either to an origin or to a destination. Economically, the price associated with the origin, u_i, therefore will be the price of the item to be transported when it is warehoused at this point of origin, and the price associated with destination j, v_j, will be the price of the item to be transported when it is delivered to such destination. Since there are only $p + q - 1$ independent goods, one of the u_i's or the v_j's can be selected arbitrarily; this indicates that the solution depends merely upon the differences in price between origin and destination, and that the scale of prices is defined only within a constant or so. This is obviously economical. The program of optimum transportation is the same whether we transport gold or iron ore. For example, the price at departure from the first origin will be selected as equal to 0. In the case of basis activities, the relations will be:

$$c_{ij} = v_j - u_i$$

(these equalities correspond to equalities: $c_i - g_i = 0$ of the general theory), which constitute a system of $p + q - 1$ equations of $p + q - 1$ unknowns. Once this system has been solved, the following table of quantities will be established:

$$c_{ij} - (v_j - u_i)$$

for activities which are not included in the basis. If one of these quantities is negative, the difference in price $(v_j - u_i)$ between the destination and the origin is greater than the cost of transportation c_{ij}; consequently, it would be more advantageous to introduce the corresponding activity into the basis.

In applying the general theory, one therefore incorporates into the basis the activity in which $c_{ij} - (v_j - u_i)$ is negative and maximum in absolute value. Since all u_{ik}'s are equal to -1, 0, or +1, the new activity will be incorporated at a level t equal to the level of the activity eliminated from the basis. In order to determine the latter, it will be noted that the new X_{rk} activity cannot replace an activity which, once incorporated into Table I, is the only one in its row or its column. By eliminating rows and columns which contain only one activity, one arrives, in general, at a table of low dimension, which — taking relationships into account — permits a very speedy determination of the maximum of t and the activity which disappears from the basis.

An example will facilitate comprehension of this method. This example, borrowed (as a tribute) from Koopmans, relates to the traffic of the worldwide merchant fleet in 1913 [106]. In selecting representative ports for various regional zones, this commerce can be represented by transportation between the following ports:

a) Rotterdam, Odessa, Bombay, Singapore, Sydney, New York, La Plata.

b) Lisbon, Athens, Lagos, Durban, Yokohama, San Francisco, St. Thomas (in the Antilles).

With regard to the ports in the first row, the incoming tonnage is lower than the outgoing tonnage. The converse occurs in the case of the ports listed in the second row. From this it is possible to determine the navigational diagram of empty ships from ports in the second row to the ports in the first row. Such transportation is intended to allow these ports to export more than they import. The a_i's and the b_i's are expressed in millions of metric tons and represent the absolute value of monthly averages of net incoming tonnages for the various ports. The c_{ij}'s are expressed in 1,000 nautical miles; they are omitted when they correspond to transportation which will certainly not take place in the optimum transportation.

Applying the method described above to determine a basis, Lisbon will supply 0.46 to Rotterdam, 0.29 to Bombay, 0.02 to Singapore, 0.24 to Sydney and the remainder, i.e., 0.23 to New York. (The method described has been slightly modified in order to

TABLE I

Destination	Rotter-dam	Odessa	Bom-bay	Singa-pore	Sydney	New York	La Plata	a_i
Origin:								
Lisbon	1.1		5.2	7.2	10.6	3.0	5.3	1.34
Athens		0.7	3.7	5.7	9.0	4.8	7.1	1.55
Lagos			8.1	9.0	12.7	4.9	4.3	0.12
Durban			4.1	4.9	6.2		4.6	0.10
Yokohama			5.4	2.9	4.3	9.7	13.2	0.17
San Francisco			9.8	7.3	6.4	5.2	8.7	0.02
St. Thomas			8.3	10.2	8.8	1.4	4.6	0.35
b_j	0.46	0.69	0.29	0.02	0.24	1.28	0.30	3.55

exclude the Lisbon-Odessa transportation). Similarly, Athens will supply 0.96 to Odessa, 0.59 to New York, and so forth. This results in the following table which actually includes the desired number of activities, i.e., 13:

TABLE II

Destination	Rotter-dam	Odessa	Bom-bay	Singa-pore	Sydney	New York	La Plata	a_i
Origin:								
Lisbon	0.46		0.29	0.02	0.24	0.23		1.24
Athens		0.96				0.59		1.55
Lagos						0.12		0.12
Durban							0.10	0.10
Yokohama					x	0.17		0.17
San Francisco						0.02		0.02
St. Thomas						0.15	0.20	0.35
b_j	0.46	0.96	0.29	0.02	0.24	1.28	0.35	3.55

Let us assume that the price at departure from Lisbon is zero. The delivered price in Rotterdam is therefore 1.1, in Bombay 5.2, ..., in New York 3.0. Consequently, the price at departure must be $3.0 - 4.8 = -1.8$ at Athens, $3.0 - 4.9 = -1.9$ at Lagos, and so forth. The table below indicates departure prices and delivered prices, as well as the difference: delivered price-departure price.

TABLE III

	Rotter-dam	Odessa	Bom-bay	Singa-pore	Sydney	New York	La Plata	De-par-ture price
Lisbon	1.1		5.2	7.2	10.6	3.0	6.2	0
Athens		0.7	7.0	9.0	12.4	4.8	8.0	−1.8
Lagos			7.1	9.1	12.5	4.9	8.1	−1.9
Durban			3.6	5.6	9.0		4.6	+1.6
Yokohama			11.9	13.9	17.3	9.7	12.9	−6.7
San Francisco			7.4	9.4	12.8	5.2	8.4	−2.2
St. Thomas			3.6	5.6	9.0	1.4	4.6	+1.6
Delivered price	1.1	−1.1	5.2	7.2	10.6	3.0	6.2	

Table IV compares these differences in transportation costs and groups the quantities $c_{ij} - (v_j - u_i)$. (In actual practice, one limits oneself to establishing Table IV without going through the intermediary of Table III).

TABLE IV

	Rotter-dam	Odessa	Bom-bay	Singa-pore	Sydney	New York	La Plata
Lisbon	0		0	0	0	0	−0.9
Athens		0	−3.3	− 3.3	− 3.4	0	−0.9
Lagos			1.0	− 0.1	0.2	0	−3.8
Durban			1.5	− 0.7	− 2.8		0
Yokohama			−6.5	−11.0	−13.0	0	0.3
San Francisco			2.8	− 2.1	− 6.4	0	0.3
St. Thomas			4.7	− 4.6	− 0.2	0	0

It is of interest to introduce all activities for which the calculated values are negative. The Yokohama-Sydney transportation, which is associated with the largest negative figure in absolute value, will be considered here. This activity is indicated by a cross in Table II. Columns 1, 2, 3, 4, and 6, and rows 2, 3, 4, 6, and 7 which contain only one activity can be eliminated. In order to determine the level t of the new activity, one returns to the reduced problem below:

	Sydney	New York
Lisbon	$0.24 - t$	$0.23 + t$
Yokohama.	$+ t$	$0.17 - t$

The t maximum is obviously 0.17. The Yokohama-New York activity disappears from the new basis presented in Table V.

TABLE V

	Rotter-dam	Odessa	Bom-bay	Singa-pore	Sydney	New York	La Plata
Lisbon	0.46		0.29	0.02	0.07	0.40	
Athens		0.96				0.59	
Lagos						0.12	
Durban							0.10
Yokohama					0.17		
San Francisco						0.02	
St. Thomas						0.15	0.20

It is therefore necessary, with this new basis, to recompute the calculations which have just been outlined. It should be noted that this systematic method has the drawback of starting from a basis which is far from being optimal. (Many coefficients in Table IV are negative.) Therefore, it is sometimes preferable to use a less systematic method, but one which will give greater weight to the value of the c_{ij}'s. This method, credited to H. S. Houthakker [99], always results in a basis and, consequently, in a single system of v_j and u_i, and makes it possible to solve problems of average size rapidly.

One begins by examining Table I for the following activities: Lisbon-Rotterdam, Athens-Odessa, Durban-Bombay, Yokohama-Singapore, St. Thomas-New York, Lagos-La Plata. Beginning at the top of the table, their "second-best destination" is given to nonsaturated shipping ports; for instance, Lisbon will ship to New York, Athens to Bombay, New York, La Plata, Sydney, and so forth, thus obtaining Table VI:

TABLE VI

	Rotter-dam	Odessa	Bom-bay	Singa-pore	Sydney	New York	La Plata
Lisbon	$\boxed{0.46}$					0.78	1.24
Athens		$\boxed{0.96}$	0.19		0.07	0.15	0.18 1.55
Lagos							$\boxed{0.12}$ 0.12
Durban			$\boxed{0.10}$				0.10
Yokohama				$\boxed{0.02}$	0.15		0.17
San Francisco					0.02		0.02
St. Thomas						$\boxed{0.35}$	0.35
	0.46	0.96	0.29	0.02	0.24	1.28	0.30

In a second phase, a check is made as to whether binary exchanges between two ports can bring about a reduction in the total cost. For example, Athens ships to Bombay and Sydney with transportation costs of 3.7 and 9.0 respectively, and Durban ships to Bombay at a cost of 4.1. The cost of the Durban-Sydney trip is 6.2. It is obvious that a certain advantage would be gained if Durban, rather than Athens, were to ship to Sydney. It can still be seen that Athens ships to Bombay and La Plata (Athens-La Plata: 7.1); however, it would be preferable for Durban to replace Athens partially as a shipping point to La Plata (Durban-La Plata: 4.6) because:

$$7.1 - 4.6 > 4.1 - 3.7.$$

Those are the only binary exchanges which would be profitable. From this we can go very rapidly to the program in Table VII. We leave it to the reader to verify whether this program is optimal.

The second method, therefore, makes it possible to optimize very quickly; but this would no longer be so if, to obtain the latter, changes had to be made among three ports. Once all binary exchanges had been made, it would be necessary to return to the general method.

TABLE VII

	Rotter-dam	Odessa	Bom-bay	Singa-pore	Sydney	New York	La Plata	
Lisbon	0.46					0.78		1.24
Athens		0.96	0.29			0.15	0.15	1.55
Lagos							0.12	0.12
Durban					0.07		0.03	0.10
Yokohama			0.02		0.15			0.17
San Francisco					0.02			0.02
St. Thomas						0.35		0.35
	0.46	0.96	0.29	0.02	0.24	1.28	0.30	

Before leaving the problem of transportation, the matter of degeneracy remains to be examined. If, in the course of an iteration, more than one activity is eliminated from the basis, only one of them should be treated as eliminated. Which one? G. Dantzig has demonstrated that degeneracy occurs when a partial sum of the a_i's is equal to a partial sum of the b_j's.

In effect, assuming $p \geq q$ (demonstration by permutation of the role of rows and columns would be similar for $p < q$), at least one row contains exactly one activity of the basis, for were this not so, the number of basis activities would be at least $2p$, which requires that $2p \leq p + q - 1$ or $p \leq q - 1$, which is contrary to the hypothesis. Therefore, for a row, $x_{ij} = a_i$. By eliminating the ith row and replacing b_j by b_j-a_i, one returns to a similar problem, and the same operation can again take place. At each stage, the new row or column totals will differ from the previous ones by a term a_i-b_j or b_j-a_i. There will therefore be differences of partial sums of the a_i's and b_j's. Thus, in order that an x_{ij} of the basis may be zero, one of the new row or column totals must be self-canceling, i.e., a partial sum of the a_i's must be equal to a partial sum of the b_j's. This circumstance occurs rather frequently. In order to prevent its occurrence, the related problem obtained is dealt with by replacing:

1) a_i by $a_i + \epsilon$ $(i = 1, 2, \ldots, p)$ and
2) b_j by b_j for $j = 1, 2, \ldots, q-1$ and by $b + p\,\epsilon$ for $j = q$.

ϵ can be as small a quantity as desired. Once a solution to the modified problem has been obtained, it is merely sufficient to have $\epsilon = 0$ to have the solution of the initial problem.

The method used in the solution of transportation problems has been developed at some length because it reveals recent trends in research in the field of linear programming: the exploitation of the structures which are peculiar to matrix M with a view to simplifying the simplex method and arriving at a solution more rapidly. The above method is moreover applicable to problems which, economically, are not transportation problems but whose algebraic formulation is similar. The example given on page 7 of Chapter 1, regarding the optimum distribution of the production and distribution of coal in the United States, falls within this category. Another example, relating to the allocation of tasks among workmen, follows.

Assume that, in a shop, there are p workmen and q machines and each machine is operated by a single workman. When workman i operates the machine j during one hour, the value of the production (for example, measured by the number of pieces) is v_{ij}. If the workman is not qualified to operate the machine, $v_{ij} = 0$. Each workman works eight hours a day, and each machine is available h_j hours. Designating as x_{ij} the number of hours during which workman i works at machine j, the problem consists of maximizing the total value of production, i.e.,:

$$\sum v_{ij} x_{ij}$$

under restraints:

$$x_{ij} \geqslant 0 \qquad \sum_j x_{ij} \leqslant 8 \qquad \sum_i x_{ij} \leqslant h_j.$$

This problem can be solved in the same way as a transportation problem, but it leads very naturally to a consideration of problems of allocation which do not occur in transportation problems.

b) Allocation problems.

Two examples will be given. The first example relates to the allocation of tasks among machine tools [24][120]. In the same way that a small number of tools (i.e., a saw, a plane, etc.) is sufficient in carpentry to produce a great number of different objects, a small number of machine tools in the mechanical industry is sufficient to develop a great variety of products. Generally, the machines used by a factory are not identical although they may belong to a few homogeneous classes. The time required to accomplish a given task is contingent upon the class. The problem is to determine how a task should be allocated among the various classes of machine tools to produce the maximum profit.

To clarify the above somewhat, we will consider the hypothetical case of a factory which produces four types of items P_1, P_2, P_3, and P_4, and must meet the respective minimum demands b_1, b_2, b_3 and b_4. To be manufactured, each item must be worked on by two types of machines, a lathe and a drill press. The plant owns three homogeneous classes of lathes and two homogeneous classes of drill presses. The maximum number of hours available for these classes is given, i.e., h_1, h_2, h_3, h_4, h_5. We will assume that the maximization of profit is equal to a maximization of receipts. In other words, the unit profit of an activity can be assumed to be equal to the selling price v_i of item P_i produced by this activity. Matrix A of possibilities, for example, is the following matrix in which the crosses indicate the different coefficients of 1 or of 0. These coefficients represent the time required to fashion a given item on a given type of machine.

Activities \\ Goods	1	2	3	4	5	6	7	8	9	10	11	12	Availability or Demand
1. Item P_1	1	1	1	1	0	0	0	0	0	0	0	0	b_1
2. Item P_2	0	0	0	0	1	1	0	0	0	0	0	0	b_2
3. Item P_3	0	0	0	0	0	0	1	1	1	0	0	0	b_3
4. Item P_4	0	0	0	0	0	0	0	0	0	1	1	1	b_4
5. Lathes 1	x	x			x		x			x			h_1
6. Lathes 2						x		x			x		h_2
7. Lathes 3			x	x					x			x	h_3
8. Drilling machines 4	x		x		x	x				x	x	x	h_4
9. Drilling machines 5		x		x			x	x	x				h_5
Unit profits	v_1	v_1	v_1	v_1	v_2	v_2	v_3	v_3	v_3	v_4	v_4	v_4	

Mathematically, the problem is formulated as follows: designating as a_{ij} the coefficient of the ith row of machines and the jth column ($i = 1, ..., 5$; $j = 1, ..., 12$):

To be maximized:

$$v_1(x_1 + x_2 + x_3 + x_4) + v_2(x_5 + x_6) + v_3(x_7 + x_8 + x_9) + v_4(x_{10} + x_{11} + x_{12})$$

under restraints:

$$x_1 + x_2 + x_3 + x_4 \geqslant b_1 \qquad\qquad x_5 + x_6 \geqslant b_2$$
$$x_7 + x_8 + x_9 \geqslant b_3 \qquad\qquad x_{10} + x_{11} + x_{12} \geqslant b_4$$
$$\Sigma a_{ij} x_j \leqslant h_i \qquad (i = 1, 2, ..., 5) \qquad\qquad x_j \geqslant 0$$

The second example, borrowed from R. A. King and R. J. Freund [104], relates to an interesting application of linear programming to agriculture. In the case of an important agricultural operation, possible activities include the raising of cattle or the cultivation of potatoes, corn, soya, fall cabbage, and fall lettuce. The goods, which are reduced here to factors of production, represent capital as well as soil and manpower during various periods of the year. The matrix of possibilities is reproduced below. The figures in rows 1 and 2 are in acres, those of rows 3 to 8 in hours, and those of rows 9 and 10 are in dollars.

Production of:

Activities Goods	Potatoes	Corn	Soya	Cattle raising	Fall cabbage	Fall lettuce	Resources
1. Spring soil	1	1	1	2	0	0	60
2. Fall soil	0	0	1	2	1	1	60
3. Labor (Jan. - Feb.)	2.400	1.540	0	0	0	0	351
4. Labor (Mar. - Apr.)	2.000	1.960	0	0	0	0	448
5. Labor (May- June)	1.800	3.300	5.330	0	0	0	479
6. Labor (Jul. - Aug.)	0	0	2.070	0	8.700	0	388
7. Labor (Sept. - Oct.)	0	0	0.436	0	19.100	12.363	424
8. Labor (Nov. - Dec.)	0	3.000	0.364	0	0.100	26.737	359
9. Capital	99.400	37.750	19.750	54.400	74.750	52.000	2.000
Unit profit	83.40	72.35	27.30	72.05	207.250	455.000	

The problem consists of maximizing profit within the framework of resources and available techniques.

c) Inventory problems.

These problems, dealt with especially by A. Charnes and W. Cooper [22], provide an excellent illustration of the use of the theorem of duality. They can be formulated as follows: "Given a store which has at its disposal a fixed storage capacity and a given initial stock of a certain product, what would be the best policy of purchase, stockage, and sales, for known seasonal variations in selling price and purchase price?"

In order to formulate this problem mathematically, let us designate as:

B the fixed storage capacity;
A the initial stock;
c_i the purchase price during period i (i = 1, 2, ..., n);
p_i the selling price during period i;
x_i the quantity purchased during period i;
y_i the quantity sold during period i.

The problem consists of maximizing the profit:

$$\sum_{j=1}^{n} - c_j x_j + \sum_{j=1}^{n} p_j y_j \tag{I.30}$$

under the following restraints:

1) Purchase restraints: the stock at the end of the ith period must not exceed the available capacity:

$$A + \sum_{=1} (x_j - y_j) \leqslant B$$

or:

$$\sum_{j=1}^{n} x_j - \sum_{1=j}^{n} y_j \leqslant B - A \quad i = 1, 2, \ldots n. \tag{I.31}$$

2) Sales restraints: the quantity sold during the ith period must not exceed the quantity available at the end of the period (i - 1). (Deliveries are assumed to take place at end of period):

$$y_j \leqslant A + \sum_{j=1}^{i-\gamma} (x_j - y_j)$$

or:

$$-\sum_{i=1}^{i-1} x_j + \sum_{j=1}^{i} y_j \leqslant A. \tag{I.32}$$

3) The quantities sold and bought during each period must not be negative:

$$x_j, y_j \geqslant 0.$$

In order to determine the expression of the duality problem, we will indicate as $t_1, ..., t_n$ the n variables associated with purchase restraints, and as $u_1, ..., u_n$ the n variables associated with sales restraints. The function to be minimized will be:

$$(B - A) \sum_{i=1}^{n} t_i + A \sum_{i=1}^{n} u_i$$

and the restraints will be expressed:

$$(1) \quad \sum_{i=k}^{n} t_i - \sum_{i=k+1}^{n} u_i \geqslant -c_k \quad k = 1, 2, ..., (n-1)$$

$$t_n \qquad \geqslant -c_n.$$

These n restraints relate to purchase activities.

$$(2) \quad -\sum_{i=r}^{n} t_i + \sum_{i=r}^{n} u_i \geqslant p_r \quad r = 1, 2, ..., n.$$

These n restraints relate to sales activities.

$$(3) \quad t_i, u_i \geqslant 0.$$

The expression for the duality problem demonstrates that it is of interest to introduce the sums of variables t_i and u_i. Let us therefore pose:

$$T_k = \sum_{i=k}^{n} t_i \qquad U_k = \sum_{i=k}^{n} u_i.$$

The duality problem assumes a new form:
To minimize: $(B - A) T_1 + A U_1$
under restraints:

a) $\quad T_k \geqslant U_{k+1} - c_k \quad k = 1, 2, ..., n-1$
b) $\quad T_n \geqslant -c_n$
c) $\quad U_r \geqslant T_r + p_r \quad r = 1, 2, ..., n$
d) $\quad T_{r-1} \geqslant T_r \quad r = 1, 2, ..., n$
e) $\quad U_{r-1} \geqslant U_r \quad r = 1, 2, ..., n$
f) $\quad T_r, U_r \geqslant 0.$

Restraints d) e) f) as a whole replace the former conditions:

$$t_i, u_i \geqslant 0.$$

The solution to the duality problem in this form is extremely simple. To obtain a minimum, T_1 and U_1 must also be as small as possible. The T's and U's will then be determined alternately by ascribing to them the smallest value compatible with the relationships. For instance, T_n has as its smallest value the larger of the quantities $-c_n$ and 0. T_n being known, U_n has as its smallest value the larger of the two values $T_n + P_n$ and 0. T_n and U_n being known, T_{n-1} has as its smallest value the largest of values $U_n - c_{n-1}$, T_n and 0, and so forth.

Once the series of U_n and T_n is known, the t_j's and the u_j's can very easily be calculated, then the basis activities, and, finally, the optimum program.

d) Mixing problems.

Mixing problems can be dealt with by linear programming when — as is frequently the case — the properties of the mix are linearly linked to the properties of the component products. There follow three relevant examples, the first relating to a mixture of wheat, the second to a blend of gasolines, and the third to the composition of animal food.

1. Wheat mixture.*

A grain dealer receives from farms three qualities of wheat, I, II, III in given quantities A_0, B_0, C_0, and sells on the grain market three mixtures, Nos. 1, 2, and 3, whose specifications must fall within the limits prescribed as to percentages of mold and impurities. The characteristics of wheats A, B, and C, and the limits set for mixtures 1, 2, and 3, are indicated in the following table:

	Mold	Impurities	Availability	Sales Price
I	3%	—	A_0	
II	—	2%	B_0	
III	12%	4%	C_0	
n° 1	< 2%	<1%		p_1
n° 2	< 4%	<2%		p_2
n° 3	<10%	<5%		p_3

*This example is credited to Professor Houthakker.

The problem consists of maximizing the receipts of the grain dealer within the framework of the above specifications.

On the basis of q_i as the quantity of mixture i and b_i, m_i, e_i as the weights of wheat, mold, and impurities in mixture i,

$$q_i = b_i + m_i + e_i.$$

For the three mixtures, specifications resolve into inequalities:

$$m_1 \leqslant 0.02 \, q_1 \qquad e_1 \leqslant 0.01 \, q_1$$
$$m_2 \leqslant 0.04 \, q_2 \qquad e_2 \leqslant 0.02 \, q_2$$
$$m_3 \leqslant 0.10 \, q_3 \qquad e_3 \leqslant 0.05 \, q_3$$

Nine x_{ij} (i = 1, 2, 3; j = 1, 2, 3) activities will be introduced, x_{ij} designating the quantity of lot j incorporated in mixture i. The six previous inequalities therefore have as a new expression:

$$0.03 \, x_{11} + 0.12 \, x_{13} \leqslant 0.02 \, (x_{11} + x_{12} + x_{13}) \quad \text{specifications mold mixture 1}$$
$$0.02 \, x_{12} + 0.04 \, x_{13} \leqslant 0.01 \, (x_{11} + x_{12} + x_{13}) \quad \text{impurities}$$
$$0.03 \, x_{21} + 0.12 \, x_{23} \leqslant 0.04 \, (x_{21} + x_{22} + x_{23}) \quad \text{mold mixture 2}$$
$$0.02 \, x_{22} + 0.02 \, x_{23} \leqslant 0.04 \, (x_{21} + x_{22} + x_{32}) \quad \text{impurities}$$
$$0.03 \, x_{31} + 0.12 \, x_{33} \leqslant 0.10 \, (x_{31} + x_{32} + x_{33}) \quad \text{mold mixture 3}$$
$$0.02 \, x_{32} + 0.12 \, x_{33} \leqslant 0.05 \, (x_{31} + x_{32} + x_{33}) \quad \text{impurities}$$

The availabilities for lots I, II, and III impose inequalities:

$$x_{11} + x_{21} + x_{31} \leqslant A_0$$
$$x_{12} + x_{22} + x_{32} \leqslant B_0$$
$$x_{13} + x_{23} + x_{33} \leqslant C_0$$

Finally, the profit to be maximized is:

$$p_1 (x_{11} + x_{12} + x_{13}) + p_2 (x_{21} + x_{22} + x_{23}) + p_3 (x_{31} + x_{32} + x_{33})$$

It is of interest to determine the amount of goods associated with the first six inequalities. The coefficient of x_{11} in the first of such inequalities is $0.03 - 0.02 = 0.01$. This represents the percentage of excess mold in lot I over and above the specifications of mixture No. 1. In this particular case, the product contains excess mold and impurities.

2. Gasoline blends in the oil industry.

In the final stage of production in an oil refinery, a great number of distilled products are blended with a view to obtaining finished products meeting certain specifications. According to the measure in which this stage can be considered as independent of previous stages, one can attempt to determine the blend which, for given quantities of distilled products, will maximize profit. The problem can be dealt with by linear programming if the unit profit for a finished product is independent of quantities delivered by the refinery and if a blend's characteristics are considered the average characteristics of the components. The first condition possibly may not be fulfilled in the case of a very large refinery.

As to the second condition, it can at times only be approached, as in the case of octane ratings.

The most interesting analyses in this area have been made by A. Charnes, W. W. Cooper, and B. Mellon [27], A. S. Manne [118], and Symonds [143]. The first group of authors considered the case of a refinery which has available given quantities of various products (alkylate I, gasoline derived from catalytic cracking, gasoline derived from preliminary distillation, isopentane) and which must be blended to obtain either three types of aviation gasoline M, N, and Q, or high-octane gasoline Z. With a view to improving the octane number, tetraethyl lead, of maximum possible concentration, is added to each of these four finished products. The function to be maximized is therefore:

$$g = mM + nN + qQ + zZ - aM - bN - cQ - dZ$$

in which m, n, q, z represent selling prices, and a, b, c, d the cost of tetraethyl lead for standard quantities of the different blends. Since the components are in given quantities, the sum $M + N + Q + Z$ is fixed and g is merely a function of M, N, Q. The three aviation gasolines must meet the following specifications:

a) the pressure of Reid vaporization must not exceed a certain maximum;

b) the octane number must be sufficient. In regard to the latter, two tests are made with respect to mixtures of air and fuel:

1) lean in fuel for normal operation in flight;

2) rich in fuel for take-off.

Minimum octane numbers (varying according to the type of gasoline) must be obtained in each of these two tests.

By introducing activities x_{ij}, representing the quantity of component j in blend i, the above restraints can be expressed as inequalities and result in a formulation analogous in all respects to that for the mixture of wheat.

3. Composition of animal feed.

Studies on the composition of animal feed have been undertaken notably by certain American enterprises engaged in the breeding and raising of chickens. They desired to sell these chickens at a certain age and at a certain weight. However, in order that most of the chickens may fulfill this requirement, their feed must contain prescribed minimum quantities of certain nutritive elements (protides, glucides, lipides, various vitamins, etc.). Since the various possible feeds contain these elements in given proportions, the problem consists of mixing the various feeds in order to minimize the cost of chicken breeding while at the same time meeting the conditions prescribed for adequate nutrition. Studies on animals other than chickens, it seems, have been limited to date by the lack of valid data as to a minimum nutritive diet.

e) Investment problems.

The first example in this chapter related to investments in the electrical industry. It is therefore unnecessary to provide an additional example at this time. It will be simply noted that in this area, linear programming — despite the drawbacks of basic hypotheses — offers the advantage of making it possible to determine quickly the broad lines of an acceptable plan. A more specific consideration of realized income in various studies then provides the possibility of improving the plan in detail.

f) Integrated problems.

By integrated problems, we refer to problems whose components are "blends" by virtue of basic process or source and cannot be disassembled. Two examples follow:

1. Production and distribution of coal in France.

In France, coal is produced by a certain number of coalfields i ($i = 1, 2, ..., n$), but each field produces different quantities and different qualitative types of coal. Qualitative types represent coals of different nature for different uses and are usually produced independently. The quantitative types are related qualitative products differing as to size (dust, grains, graded, calibrated, etc.). Let us limit ourselves to a given qualitative type, but at the same time consider the quantitative types j within the qualitative type ($j = 1, 2, ..., p$). Then let us divide the national territory into regions k ($k = 1, 2, ..., q$), i.e., A_{jk} being the demand for type j in region k. Next let us designate as x_{ijk} the quantity of type j forwarded by field i in region k. The plan of production and distribution must be such that:

$$\sum_i x_{ijk} \geqslant A_{jk}.$$

For social and economic reasons, each field's production — during the next few years — must be situated between a minimum and a maximum which may be determined in advance:

$$p_{mi} \leqslant \sum_{jk} x_{ijk} \leqslant p_{Mi}$$

naturally, one must have:

$$\sum_i p_{mi} \leqslant \sum_{jk} A_{jk} \leqslant \sum_i p_{Mi}.$$

Finally, the various types are produced simultaneously in fixed proportions by the various fields, which can be written by introducing constant coefficients m_{ij}:

$$\sum_k x_{ijk} = m_{ij} \sum_{jk} x_{ijk}.$$

The main object is to minimize the cost of delivered coal which is:

$$\sum_{ijk} (K_i + c_{ik}) x_{ijk}$$

if K_i is the marginal cost of production in field i, and c_{ik} is the cost of transportation from field i to region k.

This problem combines a transportation problem and a problem of production of related products. In order to solve it, the following method can be applied. The production of the fields is ascertained; then an optimum distribution of the coal is determined. The corresponding prices are calculated and then compared with marginal costs, which results in a modification of the production of the fields, then of the redistribution of coal, and so forth.

2. Production and blends in a refinery [117].

Alan S. Manne analyzes a simplified refinery as diagrammed in the figure below:

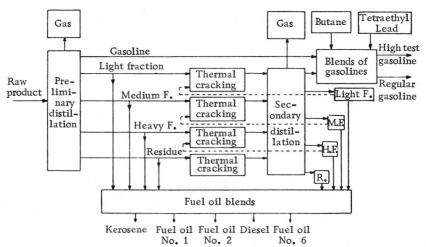

Raw petroleum arrives in a primary distillation shaft from which we obtain gases, gasolines, light, medium, and heavy fractional distillates, and a residue. The quality of the raw petroleum is given and it is assumed that the preliminary distillation mechanism has been set once and for all. The outflow quantities of the various fractions are therefore fixed. Upon outflow from the primary distillation shaft, a first choice is possible: that of determining the percentage of each of the four light fractions (light, medium, heavy, and residue) which will be transmitted to the corresponding thermal cracking units. The fractions resulting from thermal cracking units enter at appropriate levels in a secondary distillation shaft from which we obtain gasoline, light, medium, and heavy fractions, and a residue. A second choice then relates to the quantities of light, medium, and heavy fractions which are recycled in the thermal cracking process. The gasolines are blended to provide high-test gasoline and regular gasoline. The light, medium, and heavy fractions and the residue are blended to provide, in American terminology:

a) kerosene,
b) fuel oil No. 1,
c) fuel oil No. 2,
d) diesel oil,
e) fuel oil No. 6.

If to this list are added propane and propyl gas, butane and butyl gas, and dry combustible gases, it will be seen that the refinery is able to provide 10 different finished products.

Without going into the detail of the equations, it is interesting to enumerate the activities and products in a problem of this magnitude. Excluding neutral activities, the activities are distributed as follows:

a) four activity levels relating to the quantities derived from preliminary distillation and transmitted to thermal cracking units;

b) three activity levels relating to the quantities of products recycled in thermal cracking units;

c) twenty-eight activities corresponding to blending operations enumerated as follows:

1) one activity level relating to the volume of high-test gasoline produced; this can be obtained only by starting from cracked gasoline.

2) Two activity levels relating to the volume of kerosene produced obtainable only following preliminary light fractional distillation.

3) Four activity levels relating to quantities of preliminary or secondary light or medium distillation which constitute fuel oil No. 1.

4) Six activity levels relating to quantities of preliminary or secondary light or medium distillation which constitute fuel oil No. 2.

5) Six similar activities associated with diesel oil.

6) Finally, eight activity levels relating to quantities of light, medium, and heavy fractions and of residue, derived from preliminary or secondary distillation, constituting fuel oil No. 6.

The restraints (or goods) are 26 in number.

Four restraints are to the effect that the capacities of the first three cracking units (light, medium, and heavy fractions), and of the secondary distillation shaft, cannot be exceeded.

Five restraints are to the effect that — in the course of processing — utilization will not be made of quantities over and above the availability of gasoline, light, heavy and medium fractions, and residue issuing from the primary distillation shaft.

Five others are to the effect that more gasoline of cracked light, medium, and heavy fractions and of residue will not be introduced into the blends than is produced in cracking operations.

Finally, there are 12 other restraints corresponding to specifications prescribed for finished products and relating to:

a) the octane number for regular gasoline;

b) viscosity for fuel oil No. 1;

c) viscosity, the ketane number, the "flash point," and the "final point" of distillation for fuel oil No. 2;

d) viscosity, ketane number, specific weight, 90% point and final distillation point for diesel oil;

e) viscosity for fuel oil No. 6.

The main object remains to be determined. Since the refinery exists, it is merely necessary to consider:

a) the selling price of the various products;

b) the variable costs which, here, are mainly energy, steam, and water-cooling costs.

In the case of the first seven activities, the unit profit will be equal to the (positive) difference between the selling price of cracking gases and the variable costs. In the case of the 28 blending activities, the unit income will be equal to the selling price of the product.

Now, instead of assuming that the refinery exists and that the problem is to utilize it to best advantage, we could examine a problem involving the construction of a new refinery. Capacities would then become variables, and investment costs would have to be introduced.

g) Looking toward new uses for linear programming.

It would seem that, aside from these now standard applications, linear programming should facilitate the solution of problems of an entirely different order. In this connection, Charnes and Cooper have used it in determining a salary scale [19].

They assume that, in order to occupy a position — and, consequently, to receive a corresponding salary — there must be a given "quantity" of a certain number of qualities i (initiative, experience, education, intelligence, etc.). To each unit quantity of a quality is associated a value s_i. The problem is to determine the s_i's in order that:

a) the salaries for the various functions — which are an average of the s_i's weighted according to the required quantities of the various qualities — follow a predetermined hierarchical order,

b) the salary of the lowest echelon is greater than or equal to a prescribed minimum, and the salary of the highest echelon is smaller than or equal to a prescribed maximum,

c) the sum of absolute values of differences or gaps between the salaries for certain functions with numbers fixed in advance (for instance, salaries paid by competitors) is minimal.

It is thus possible to determine a scale of salaries which will follow a hierarchy, take qualifications into account, and be consistent with market conditions.

2. Complements.

To make it possible for the reader to obtain a clearer idea of the possibilities of application, we have postponed until the end of this first part a few complements with respect to the theory of linear programming. These complements relate to:

a) parametric linear programming,
b) dynamic linear programming,
c) linear programming in integers,
d) problems of flows.

a) Parametric linear programming.

Let us return to the example provided for investments in the electrical industry. It is possible to determine an optimum plan for a future demand and given current unit costs. But neither future demand nor current unit costs are known with certainty. It would therefore be of interest to determine what becomes of an optimum solution when either current unit costs or future demand is changed.

The first case corresponds to the introduction of a parameter into the objective, the second, to the introduction of a parameter into the availability of restraints.

1. The objective is contingent upon a parameter.

With the notations in paragraph 1: $c_j(\alpha) = c_j + \alpha d_j$ or, in vector notations: $c(\alpha) = c + \alpha d$. α is a parameter, c and d are vectors of p dimensions, and $c(\alpha)$ is the unit profit vector.

Possible programs are defined by conditions $Mx = b$, $x \geq o$. The entire group of possible programs is therefore not contingent upon α.

The same applies to the convex polyhedron (K) in space (B). On the other hand, when α varies, the orientation of planes $\Sigma_j c_j(\alpha) x_j =$ Const varies. It is geometrically apparent that, within certain limits, a variation in α will not affect an extreme-point solution. If α goes beyond this limit, the solution point shifts from the initial extreme point to an adjacent extreme point.

A basis will be optimal for a certain α_0 value of α if:

$$c_k(\alpha_0) - \sum_i u_{ik} c_i(\alpha_0) \leqslant 0 \tag{I.33}$$

the equality being verified for base vectors. The u_{ik}'s are not contingent upon α since they are merely a function of matrix M. It will be noted that for basis vectors, relation (I.33) reduces to:

$$c_k(\alpha) - c_k(\alpha) = 0$$

and is verified whatever α may be. The program will cease to be optimal immediately upon contradiction of one of the (I.33) inequalities. In other words, the upper limit of the area of variation of α is reached when — in the case of one of the vectors not included in the basis — the quantity:

$$c_k(\alpha) - \sum_i u_{ik} c_i(\alpha)$$

initially negative, cancels out. The upper limit of α is therefore the minimum of the α values which cancel the above quantities.

In determining such minima, a determination is also made thereby of the vector to be introduced into the new basis. The simplex method is used to discover the vector to be eliminated. Once a new basis has been obtained, a return is made to the initial problem.

As long as a basis is optimal, profit is a given linear function of α; however, the linear relation coefficients change when changing from one basis to another. In relation to α, profit is formed as indicated in Figure 3 (if the d_j's are positive). The curve in Figure 3 is none other than the curve of variation of profit with unit profit in standard economic theory.

Let us now place ourselves within the space of activities and let us study the configuration of solution-points for the various values of α. In order to make a simple geometrical presentation, we will limit ourselves to one plane in this space and to two activities, x_1 and x_2. The levels of these activities for an optimum program are indicated in abscissas and in ordinates (Figure 4). For example, in the case of $\alpha_0 < \alpha < \alpha_1$, x_1 alone figures in the optimum program (point A). In the case of $\alpha_1 < \alpha < \alpha_2$, the representative point is B.

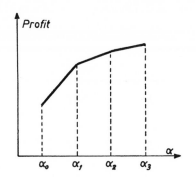

Fig. 3.

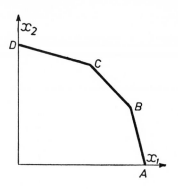

Fig. 4.

In the case of $\alpha_2 < \alpha < \alpha_3$ the representative point is C, and for $\alpha > \alpha_3$, it is D. When α is equal to α_1, any program in the AB segment is optimum since programs A and B result in the same profit. The broken line ABCD represents, therefore, optimum programs as a whole when α varies. Furthermore, the curve in Figure 4 is, in terms of linear programming, analogous to a standard curve of economic theory; that is, the curve of possible substitutions of two products, or of two factors, when quantities brought into play by other products and other factors are fixed (cf. Chapter 10).

When consideration of a single parameter α is not sufficient, two α and β parameters can be introduced. A determination is then made of the areas of the plane $(\alpha\beta)$ in which a basis remains optimal. The limits of the various areas are made up of sets of straight line segments.

2. Availabilities dependent upon parameters.

Quantities b_k are those which are now linearly dependent upon a parameter α.

$$b_k\,(\alpha) = b_k + \alpha f_k$$

The entire set of possible programs is therefore dependent upon α. On the other hand, since the c_k's and u_{ik}'s are independent of α (the latter are a function only of matrix M), quantities:

$$c_k - \sum_i u_{ik} c_i$$

are independent of α. Consequently, a program remains optimal as long as this is possible. Starting as of a certain α_0 value of α, it is possible to increase the parameter as long as none of the components of the program vector of m dimensions x — defined by relation Mx = b — becomes negative. The upper limit of the area of variation of α is therefore the minimum of the values of α which cancel the x_j's. A knowledge of the x_j which is the first to cancel out simultaneously determines the vector m_r which must be eliminated from the basis. We still have to select the vector m_k that must be introduced into the basis in order that the program may be possible and optimal.

a) Let us note at the outset that vector k must be selected from among vectors j in which u_{rj} is positive. In effect, vector b is expressed relative to the former basis by the relation:

$$b = \sum x_i m_i \tag{I.34}$$

However:

$$m_k = u_{rk} m_r + \sum_{i \neq r} u_{ik} m_i. \tag{I.35}$$

Therefore:

$$b = \sum_{i \neq r} \left(x_i - x_r \frac{u_{ik}}{u_{rk}} \right) m_i + \frac{x_r}{u_{rk}} m_k. \tag{I.36}$$

For the coefficient of vector m_k in (I.35) — the coefficient which is equal to the value of x_k in the new basis — to be positive or zero, it is necessary that u_{rk} be positive since x_r is not negative.

b) Let us now consider all j vectors for which u_{rj} is positive. When vector r is replaced by a vector k, the components of these vectors in the new basis become u'_{ik}. A necessary condition in order that the new base may be optimal is that:

$$c_j - \sum_i u'_{ij} c_i \leqslant 0 \tag{I.37}$$

i.e., by replacing the u'_{ij}'s by their expression relative to the u_{ij}'s (cf. I.23),

$$c_j - \sum_{i \neq r} \left(u_{ij} - u_{ik} \frac{u_{rj}}{u_{rk}} \right) c_i - \frac{u_{rj}}{u_{rk}} c_k \leqslant 0$$

which is written:

$$\left(c_j - \sum_{i \neq r} u_{ij} c_i \right) - \frac{u_{rj}}{u_{rk}} \left(c_k - \sum_{i \neq r} u_{ik} c_i \right) \leqslant 0. \tag{I.38}$$

Since, according to hypothesis, u_{rj} is positive and u_{rk} must be positive, the foregoing inequality can be written:

$$\sum_{i \neq r} \frac{u_{ik}c_i - c_k}{u_{rk}} \leqslant \sum_{i \neq r} \frac{u_{ij}c_i - c_j}{u_{rj}}. \tag{I.39}$$

It will be noted that c_r can be added to the two members, which results in the inequality:

$$\frac{g_k - c_k}{u_{rk}} \leqslant \frac{g_j - c_j}{u_{rj}}. \tag{I.40}$$

The result of (I. 40) is that it is necessary to take for vector k the vector for which $\dfrac{g_k - c_k}{u_{rk}}$ is minimum among vectors j of which the u_{rj} component is positive.

c) This necessary condition is also sufficient. In point of fact, if u_{rj} is negative, the (I.38) condition is automatically verified since the left member of the inequality is the sum of two negative terms.

Once m_k has been introduced, a return is made to the initial situation. It is also possible, in this second instance, to trace curves representing the optimum program and profit in relation to α.

b) Dynamic linear programming.

The word dynamic is not employed here quite correctly. It would be better to speak of linear programming covering several periods, but we have accepted the widespread practice.

Let us designate the various periods as t (t = 1, 2, ..., T). An activity will now be characterized not only by its technical coefficients but also by the period during which it is brought into play. The same will apply to products. Furthermore, a product manufactured during a period cannot, by hypothesis, be used in another production operation until the following period.

Let us examine the case of an enterprise which may utilize four production methods. The first two methods — numbered 3 and 4 for reasons which will be presented later — employ labor and produce intermediate goods. The other two methods, numbered 1 and 2, combine the intermediate goods with labor to provide a finished product which is sold. Labor will be indicated as index 1, the intermediate good by index 2, and the finished product by index 3. The matrix of a period's technical possibilities presents itself as follows:

	Activity 1	Activity 2	Activity 3	Activity 4
Labor 1	a_{11}	a_{12}	a_{13}	a_{14}
Intermediate good 2	a_{21}	a_{22}	a_{23}	a_{24}
Finished product 3 .	a_{31}	a_{32}	0	0

At the beginning, the enterprise has a certain stock of intermediate goods available. Over the period T, the matrix of production as a whole appears as indicated in Table I. The first period is at the upper left and the rank of the periods increases as one shifts toward the lower right side. Only coefficients differing from 0 are indicated. It is not contradictory or irrational to assume that, at a period T, a certain quantity of intermediate goods is manufactured since one may wish to have a stock of goods available for later periods which are not part of the model.

The matrix of production can be written more simply by introducing two matrices A and B. Matrix A is reduced to:

$$\begin{bmatrix} 0 & 0 & 0 & 0 \\ a_{21} & a_{22} & 0 & 0 \\ 0 & 0 & 0 & 0 \end{bmatrix}$$

This is the matrix of coefficients of production relative to goods produced during the period i - 1 and utilized in production during the period i. Matrix B represents coefficients of production as a whole for a same period i. This is reduced to:

$$B = \begin{bmatrix} a_{11} & a_{12} & a_{13} & a_{14} \\ 0 & 0 & a_{23} & a_{24} \\ a_{31} & a_{32} & 0 & 0 \end{bmatrix}$$

With matrices A and B, the matrix of possibilities of production in Table I assumes the simple form shown in Table II.

There is nothing to prevent introducing, in each period, any number of goods and activities. Table II will remain valid.

We have assumed until now that, during a period, only factors of production for such period or for the preceding period were utilized. However, in actual fact, one can be induced to use intermediate goods produced several periods previously. The matrix of possibilities then assumes the more general form found in Table III in which A_i represents the matrix of coefficients of production associated with factors used i periods later. In accordance with this

TABLE I

Period	Good Activity	1				2				3		.....	T			
		1	2	3	4	1	2	3	4	1	2	.....	1	2	3	4
0	2	a_{21}	a_{22}									.....				
1	1	a_{11}	a_{12}	a_{13}	a_{14}							.....				
	2			a_{23}	a_{24}	a_{21}	a_{22}					.....				
	3	a_{31}	a_{32}									.....				
2	1					a_{11}	a_{12}	a_{13}	a_{14}			.....				
	2							a_{23}	a_{24}	a_{21}	a_{22}	.....				
	3					a_{31}	a_{32}					.....				
. . .																
T−1	1											.....	a_{21}	a_{22}		
	2											.....				
	3											.....				
T	1											.....	a_{11}	a_{12}	a_{13}	a_{14}
	2											.....			a_{23}	a_{24}
	3											.....	a_{31}	a_{32}		

Table II

Periods	1	2	3	.....	T−1	T
0	A					
1	B	A				
2		B	A			
3			B			
.						
T−1				A		
				B	A	
T					B	

Table III

Periods	1	2	3	....	T−1	T
0	A_1	A_2	A_3	....	A_{T-1}	A_T
1	A_0	A_1	A_2	....	A_{T-2}	A_{T-}
2		A_0	A_1	....		
3			A_0	....		
.			.			
.						
.				.		
T−1					A_0	A_1
T						A_0

understanding, B has been replaced by A_0. One of the main characteristics of matrix III is its triangular form. There is no matrix A_i whatever below the main diagonal. This results in an important simplification of calculations.

In this type of problem the restraints are generally:

a) the initial stock of intermediate goods;

b) the maximum volume of available factors of production during each period (excluding here, naturally, the factors of production for intermediate goods);

c) sales (minimum or maximum for each period);

d) the desired stock of intermediate goods at the end of period T.

Finally, with each activity producing a unit profit, the objective is to maximize the total profit. It is by no means necessary that the unit profit be the same for two technically similar activities brought into play during two different periods. If the period were sufficiently long, the interest rate could very easily be taken into account.

Theoretically, the utilization of linear programming for problems covering several periods poses no difficulty. In actual practice, however, there is a major drawback. The number of activities and goods increases in relation to the number of periods. A problem of modest size in one period may assume formidable proportions when extended over a small number of periods. For this reason, every effort must be made to benefit from all possibilities offered by the very special form of the matrices of production.

Let us now consider a problem in the form found in table II once neutral activities have been introduced. Each of the A and B matrices has m rows and n columns. Consider x_1, x_2, ..., x_T as program-vectors for the periods 1, 2, ..., T; c_1, c_2, ..., c_T and b_1, b_2, ..., b_{T-1} the unit profit vectors and corresponding availabilities, respectively. (It is assumed that there are no restraints for the last period.) The problem is as follows:

To minimize:

$$c_1 x_1 + c_2 x_2 + \ldots + c_t x_t + \ldots + c_T x_T \qquad\qquad x_t \geqslant 0$$

under restraints:

$$(1) \qquad\qquad Ax_1 \qquad\qquad = b_0$$
$$(2) \qquad\qquad Bx_1 + Ax_2 \quad = b_1$$
$$\cdots\cdots\cdots\cdots\cdots\cdots$$
$$(T-1) \qquad Bx_{T-1} + Ax_T = b_{T-1}$$

An excellent basis for the application of the simplex method can be obtained by determining successively: the program which minimizes $c_1 x_1$, account being taken of relation (1); then, x_1 having been determined, the program which minimizes $c_2 x_2$, account being taken of relation (2), and so forth, until utilization of relation (T - 1) permits a calculation of x_{T-1}. G. Dantzig has exploited all the calculation possibilities offered by triangular matrices [53] but, despite such improvements, linear programming appears less promising in the instance of dynamic models than the methods outlined in Chapter II which are better adapted to the structure of such problems.

c) Linear programming in integers.

On numerous occasions we have drawn attention to the drawbacks presented in certain practical applications by the hypothesis that activity levels can assume any positive values. As a matter of fact, certain production, investment, or transfer operations are, by their very nature, discontinuous. A number of researchers (Gomory in particular [93] have attempted to develop methods for the solution of linear programs in which all or part of such activities can assume only integer values. Such research is all the more interesting because problems can thus be solved in which the relationship with integer linear programming is not apparent.

First example: Maximize $c'x$ under alternate conditions:

$$A_1 x \geqslant b_1 \text{ or } A_2 x \geqslant b_2 \dots \text{ or } A_p x \geqslant b_p$$

the defined area is usually not convex. It can, in fact, be formed by several separate parts (Figure 5 A and B).

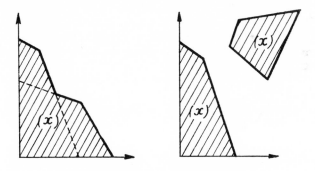

Fig. 5 A and B.

Let us introduce p positive subsidiary unknowns y_1, y_2, ..., y_p capable of taking only 0 or 1 integer values and an N positive number sufficiently large, and write that:

$$A_1 x \geqslant b_1 + N(y_1 - 1)$$
$$\dots\dots\dots\dots\dots\dots\dots$$
$$A_p x \geqslant b_p + N(y_p - 1)$$
$$y_1 + y_2 + \dots + y_p = 1$$

The x, y program thus obtained is equivalent to the initial program because only one of the y's can be equal to 1, and only the corresponding subtotal of restraints enters into play in such programming.

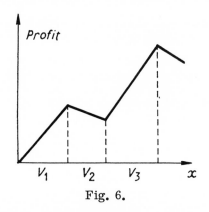

Fig. 6.

Second example: Assuming that the profit derived from an activity x is in direct ratio to x_i represented by a non-convex broken line (Figure 6), such profit can be indicated as the sum:

$$\sum a_i \, x_i$$

the a_i's representing the successive slopes of the various segments of the broken line, and the x_i's subsidiary variables such that:

$$x_i \leqslant v_i$$

(the v_i's representing the length of the various segments).
But it is necessary that:

$$x_i > 0 \quad \text{should include } x_{i-1} = v_{i-1}$$
and that $x_i < v_i$ should include $x_{i+1} = 0$.

Subsidiary variables y_i are then introduced, hypothetically equal to 0 or 1, and the following additional conditions are incorporated:

$$y_{i+1} \leqslant \frac{x_i}{v_i} \leqslant y_i$$

Therefore:

$$\frac{x_{i+1}}{y_{i+1}} \leqslant y_{i+1} \leqslant \frac{x_i}{v_i} \leqslant y_i \leqslant \frac{x_{i-1}}{v_{i-1}} \leqslant y_{i-1}$$

It will be observed that

$$\frac{x_i}{v_i} > 0 \text{ entails } y_i = 1 \text{ and } x_{i-1} = v_{i-1}$$

$$\frac{x_i}{v_i} < 1 \text{ entails } y_{i+1} = 0 \text{ and } x_{i+1} = 0;$$

the initial program can therefore be replaced by an x_i or y_i programming where an attempt must be made to maximize

$$m \sum a_i x_i$$

and to add to the initial restraints the following:

$$\begin{cases} y_{i+1} \leqslant \dfrac{x_i}{v_i} \leqslant y_i \\ 0 \leqslant y_i \leqslant 1 \\ y_i \text{ an integer.} \end{cases}$$

A brief exposition will now be made of the principle in Gomory's method. Assume the following:

$$\begin{cases} c'x \text{ maximum} \\ Mx = b \\ x \geqslant 0 \text{ , an integer.} \end{cases}$$

Let us indicate by $x_i (i = 1, 2, \ldots, m)$ the m non-zero coordinates of the program's supposedly unique maximum P. When we take into account that the x_i's can assume integer values only, two cases are possible: all of the P coordinates are integers and the problem is solved, or at least one of the P coordinates, x_1 for instance, is not an integer ($x_1 > 0$).

From $Mx = b$ relations we can deduce the x_i ($i = 1, 2, \ldots, m$) associated with this base in the function of the other p-m activities:

$$x_i = x_i - \sum_j \alpha_{ij} x_j \qquad (j = m + 1, \ldots, p). \tag{I.41}$$

Given any number a, its decimal portion will be designated as a_d and its integer part as a_e. (I. 41) can then be written, for x_1:

$$x_1 = (\bar{x}_{1e} - \sum_j \alpha_{1je} x_j) + (\bar{x}_{1d} - \sum_j \alpha_{1jd} x_j). \tag{I.42}$$

Should all α_{ijd} result in zero, (I.42) cannot be solved by integers; there is no integer point and no integer maximum for $c'x$ and the search is stopped.

If at least one of the α_{ijd} is positive, let us consider the function:

$$f(x) = \bar{x}_{1d} - \sum_j \alpha_{1jd}\, x_j$$

The f (x) = 0 equation is that of a plane which divides the p dimension of the space of activities into two areas: area 1 in which f (x) > 0, and area 2 in which f (x) ≤ 0. P is located in area 1 since the x_j's are zero. Should an Ω integer point be possible, it would lie in area 2. In effect, the x_j coordinates of such a point are positive or zero whereas those of P are zero. Since the α_{ijd}'s are ≥0, f(Ω)≤f(P). Should x move along the PΩ segment of P toward Ω, f(x) will be non-increasing as a positive value x_{1d}, and less than 1. All of the Ω coordinates being integers, in accordance with (I. 42) fΩ is integer, therefore negative or zero, which shows that Ω is in area 2.

Consequently, by removing the area 1 polyhedron, we are certain to reduce the number of possible programs without eliminating any point with integer coordinates.

We will add, therefore, the following conditions to the initial conditions:

$$\begin{cases} f(x) = -x_{p+1} \\ x_{p+1} \geqslant 0 \end{cases}$$

Thus, when the initial program has been solved by means of any of the x's, we will be in a position to consider another program containing p + 1 variables which, in turn, will be solved, and so forth until either a complete solution is arrived at or until it can be demonstrated that there is no solution.

Naturally, the process described above can be used only when it converges after a few iterations, because the size of the intermediate programs to be solved increases by one unit after each iteration. The present limit used for this method is about 30 variables.

d) The flow problems.

Ford and Fulkerson [75] [76] [77] have worked jointly in a study of linear programming with special emphasis on maximum flow problems. In this connection, the problem consists of transporting, from one end of a communications network to the other, the maximum quantity of material consistent with the capacity of the network's various branches.

More particularly, a network is defined as a finite number of points (communication nodes) and a specified number of oriented arcs (routes) linking the various points of the set X in such manner that:

1. There will be one and only one point that no arc will border. This point, x_0, is the network's point of entry.

2. There will be one and only one point from which no arc will leave. This point z is the network's point of exit.

Any arc u is associated with: a capacity c (u) which, for our purposes, will be considered to be an integer; at any peak x, a subtotal Ex of arcs converging on x, and a subtotal S_x of arcs leaving x.

A flow for this transportation network represents a function f (u) such that:

a) for any $u : \mathrm{o} \leqslant f(u) \leqslant c(u)$;

b) for any $x \neq x_o$ and $x \neq z$ $\displaystyle\sum_{u \varepsilon E_s} f(u) = \sum_{u \varepsilon S_s} f(u).$

(The latter relations demonstrate the impossibility of aggregating at points other than the entry and exit.)

The total value of the flow is:

$$f = \sum_{u \varepsilon S_{x_0}} f(u) = \sum_{u \varepsilon E_s} f(u)$$

The problem lies in maximizing f.

It is needless to stress the obvious interest presented by the solution of such a problem. On the other hand, it is clearly evident that we have a linear programming structure and that the traditional algorithms could be called upon; but it is preferable, of course, to make use of the structure's own characteristics.

C. Berge's presentation will be adopted here [11]; i.e., A represents a number of peaks such that:

$$x_o \notin A \qquad z \varepsilon A$$

The total number E of arcs arising from points not included among A and reaching peaks of A is a cross-section of the network whose capacity, by definition, is:

$$c(E_A) = \sum_{u \varepsilon E_A} c(u)$$

Any unit of material going from y to z makes use, at least once, of an E_A arc. Therefore, whatever may be the flow φ and the cross-section E_A:

$$\varphi \leqslant c(E_A)$$

Hence, if a cross-section and a possible flow, equal to the capacity of such cross-section, are found, it can be maintained that:

a) the flow is the maximum flow;

b) the cross-section is of minimum capacity.

The algorithm which we are about to describe demonstrates that, within a transportation network, the maximum flow value is indeed equal to a cross-section's minimum capacity. Furthermore, this property is merely one of the various forms of the duality theorem.

The Ford and Fulkerson algorithm is as follows:

a) An arc u is said to be saturated if f (u) = c (u). A flow is said to be complete if any path going from y to z contains a saturated arc. Consider a departure flow f (which can be zero). If this flow is not complete, an r path can be determined wherein all arcs are non-saturated. Let us then consider the flow:

$$f'(u) = f(u) + 1 \quad \text{if } u \, \varepsilon \, r$$
$$f'(u) = f(u) \quad \text{if } u \notin r$$

This flow is possible and has a value $f_0 + 1$. This procedure can be continued until such flow is complete.

b) Consider f_1 to be a complete flow. We will attempt to indicate successively all network points to which a supplemental flow unit can be brought. x_0 will be indicated by the coefficient 0. If x_1 is an indicated point, this indicates that:

1) any point x_j will be marked by a coefficient +i in such manner that there will be an $x_i x_j$ arc and the flow along such arc will be less than its capacity;

2) any point x_j not already marked will be marked by a coefficient -i so that there will be an $x_i x_j$ arc and the flow along such arc will be positive.

If one can reach a vertex z, there will be, between x_0 and z, a path r in which all vertices are marked with a sign of the coefficient of the preceding point. Let us put:

$$f'(u) = f_1(u) \quad \text{if } u \notin r$$
$$f'(u) = f_1(u) + 1 \quad \text{if } u \, \epsilon \, r \text{ and } u \text{ is oriented toward } x_0 z$$
$$f'(u) = f_1(u) - 1 \quad \text{if } u \, \epsilon \, r \text{ and } u \text{ is oriented toward } z x_0$$

It will be seen that f'(u) remains a flow of value $f_1 + 1$.

c) If, in the case of a flow f, the value can no longer be increased by the foregoing procedure, f is the maximum flow; A being the total number of unmarked vertices:

$$x_0 \notin A \qquad z \varepsilon A$$

A defines an E_A cross-section and:

$$f = \sum_{u \varepsilon E_a} f(u) = \sum_{u \varepsilon E_a} c(u) = c(E_A)$$

Therefore f is the maximum flow.

The details given here are limited, of course, to the simplest type of flow problem. However, this problem represents an example of the vast possibilities offered to operational research by the theory of graphs [11].

This paragraph completes the introduction to linear programming. We have attempted to demonstrate the value of this method and of the great number of its potential applications. An outline of the first results obtained in the field of non-linear programming will then place it within its proper perspective.

III

A FEW REMARKS ON NON-LINEAR PROGRAMS.

To the extent that it has been defined, linear programming is a case in point illustrating the more general problem of maximization of a function whose argument is subject to a certain number of restraints. Problems encountered in actual practice do not always lead to restraints and to a criterion of value which can be expressed linearly in relation to parameters of decision. This occurs in a mix, when the properties of this mix are not the weighted average of the properties of the components. This is also the case in the instance of an enterprise which seeks to maximize its income and whose marginal income and/or marginal cost are not independent of production. Finally, it is reasonable to believe that the number of non-linear problems will increase as economic calculations develop and as more precise numerical data become available.

For all these reasons, it would be most desirable to lay out a general theory of programs which does not start with the hypothesis of linearity, and in which the theory of linear programming would appear only as a special case. This theory has not yet been established, but H. W. Kuhn and A. W. Tucker have obtained a very important result in connection therewith. We will consider below the Kuhn and Tucker method, non-linear programming approximation by linear programming and the solution of quadratic programs, following which we will outline some new methods of computation.

1. The Kuhn and Tucker theorem [111].

Kuhn and Tucker consider the more general problem of the search for a program, i.e., the determination of n positive or zero x_i (i = 1, 2, ..., n) parameters which verify m restraints:

$$f_j (x_1, x_2, ..., x_n) \geqslant 0 \qquad (II.1)$$

and which maximize a function:

$$g (x_1, x_2, ..., x_n) \qquad (II.2)$$

The n parameters x_i are activity levels. They form a vector which will be represented by x.

In order to solve the foregoing problem, the traditional method consists of introducing m Lagrange multipliers u_j, forming a vector u, and considering the function:

$$F (x, u) = g (x_1, ..., x_n) + \sum_{j=1}^{m} u_j f_j (x_1, ..., x_n). \qquad (II.3)$$

The Kuhn and Tucker theorem establishes — subject to certain hypotheses — an equivalence between the initial introductory functions f and g and a new problem relating to the associated F (x,u) function.

Two restrictive hypotheses are made as to functions f_j and g:

1. Functions $f_j (x_1, ..., x_n)$ and $g (x_1, ..., x_n)$ are defined and differentiable functions for $x_i \geq 0$ whatever i may be.

2. Functions $f_j (x_1, ..., x_n)$ and $g (x_1, ..., x_n)$ are concave functions for $x_i \geq 0$.

By definition, an f (x) function is said to be concave in a space if, for any u, $0 \leq u \leq 1$ and for all pairs of points $x' = (x'_1, ..., x'_n)$ and $x'' = (x_1, ..., x''_n)$ in this space:

$$(1 - u) f (x') + u f (x'') \leqslant f ((1 - u) x' + u x'') \qquad (II.4)$$

In a case where f (x) is a function of a single variable x, concavity signifies that the representative point of f (x) between A (x', f (x')) and B (x'', f (x'')) is below the AB line, whatever may be points A and B on the curve representative of f (x).

Note: Concavity, as defined above, imposes upon the f (x) function conditions which are much more restrictive than simple concavity in relation to each of the $x_1, x_2, ..., x_n$ parameters. In other words, f (x) is not necessarily concave in the sense of hypothesis 2 if the following inequality is verified for any i:

$$(1 - u) f (x'_1, .., x'_i, .., x'_n) + u f (x'_1, ..., x''_i, ..., x'_n) \leqslant$$
$$f (x'_1, ..., (1 - u) x'_i + u x''_i, ..., x'_n). \qquad (II.5)$$

This having been posed, the theorem is stated as follows:

If hypotheses 1 and 2 are verified, a series of parameters $x_0 (x_{10}, ..., x_{n0})$ is a solution to the problem of maximization if, and only if, one can associate with x_0 a series of m non-negative parameters u_0 (u_{10}, ..., u_{m0}) such that:

$$F(x, u_0) \leqslant F(x_0, u_0) \leqslant F(x_0, u)$$

for any $x \geq 0$ and any $u \geq 0$.

In the case of function F (x,u), point (x_0, u_0) is called a "saddle point". The Kuhn and Tucker theorem therefore establishes a biunivocal correspondence, subject to the hypotheses indicated, between the determination of a saddle point of F (x,u) and the determination of a maximum of g (x) under restraints f_j. Within the framework of hypotheses made concerning functions f_j (x) and g (x), the necessary and sufficient conditions in order that vectors x_0 and u_0 may define an F (x,u) saddle point are expressed as follows:

(1) either $x_{i0} = 0$ and $\left(\dfrac{\partial F}{\partial x_i}\right)_0 \leqslant 0$

or $x_{i0} > 0$ and $\left(\dfrac{\partial F}{\partial x_i}\right)_0 = 0$

(2) either $u_{j0} = 0$ and $\left(\dfrac{\partial F}{\partial u_j}\right)_0 \geqslant 0$

or $u_{j0} > 0$ and $\left(\dfrac{\partial F}{\partial u_j}\right)_0 = 0$.

These conditions take on important economic significance when the form of function F (x,u) is taken into account, a form given in (II. 3). They are expressed as follows:

(1) either x_{i0} is zero and $\dfrac{\partial g}{\partial x_i} + \sum_j u_{j0} \dfrac{\partial f_j}{\partial x_i} \leqslant 0$ (II.6)

or $x_{i0} = 0$ and $\dfrac{\partial g}{\partial x_i} + \sum_j u_{j0} \dfrac{\partial f_j}{\partial x_i} = 0$ (II.7)

(2) either $u_{j0} = 0$ and $f_j(x) \geqslant 0$ (II.8)

or $u_{j0} > 0$ and $f_j(x) = 0$.   (II.9)

However, in terms of activities and products, x is the vector of activity levels, g(x) the profit, and $f_j(x)$ the unused quantity of products j. Under these conditions:

a) $\partial g/\partial x_i$ is the marginal profit associated with activity i;

b) $\partial f_j/\partial x_i$ is the marginal quantity of goods j required to raise the level of activity i;

c) u_j is the price of goods j. u_j therefore has the same meaning as π_j in the duality theorem of linear programming.

Conditions (II. 6 to II. 9) therefore have a direct economic interpretation.

The first two indicate either: a) that activity i is within the optimum program and the marginal profit and cost associated therewith are equal, so that there is no particular advantage in modifying its level; or b) that activity is not in the optimum program, and the marginal profit associated therewith is smaller than the corresponding marginal cost, so that it would be disadvantageous to introduce it in the program.

The last two conditions signify either: a) that product j is not totally used and its price is zero; or b) that product j is totally used and a positive or zero price is assigned to it.

As could be foreseen, the Kuhn and Tucker theorem permits a direct demonstration of the duality theorem in the case of a linear program. Using the notations of the first section, function F (x,u) is written:

$$F(x, u) = \sum_i c_i x_i + \sum_k \sum_i (a_{ik} x_i - b_k) u_k$$

$$F(x, u) = \sum_i c_i x_i - \sum_{ik} b_k u_k + \sum_k a_{ik} u_k x_k$$

The minimum and maximum roles associated with u and x can be transposed by replacing F (x,u) by -F (x,u). Thus the determination of an F (x,u) saddle point is equivalent to the following problem: Minimize:

$$- \sum_k b_k u_k$$

under restraints:

$$\sum_k a_{ik} u_k + c_i \geqslant 0 \quad u_k \geqslant 0.$$

Here one again encounters the duality theorem with the aid of proof which is not lacking in elegance.

2. Linear programming as an approximation of non-linear programming.

The simplex method and a certain number of closely related methods which have not been developed here are all methods of iteration which consist of shifting from one extreme point to an adjacent extreme point on the boundary of the convex sets of possible programs. An immediate question is whether these methods remain applicable when, without changing the restraints, the profit function is no longer linear.

It is geometrically intuitive that a maximum can be found at an extreme point for a large category of profit functions (Figure 7 A).

But a maximum can also be found on one of the faces of the polyhedron (Figure 7 B).

Finally, several local maximums may exist (Figure 7 C).

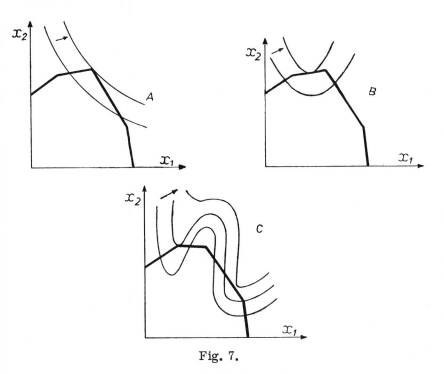

Fig. 7.

Charnes and Lemke have demonstrated that the simplex method could be extended to cover the problem of minimizing a sum of separable convex functions (or, consequently, to maximize a sum of separable concave functions) [31]. More recently, A. Hoffman has extended the results obtained by Charnes and Lemke to a case of minimization, under linear restraint, of any convex function. We will limit ourselves here to a brief description of the work performed by Charnes and Lemke.

With notations contained in paragraphs 1 to 3, the problem consists of minimizing:

$$g(x) = \sum_{1}^{p} g_i(x_i)$$

under restraints:

$$x \geqslant 0$$
$$Mx = b.$$

The p functions $g_i (x_i)$ are convex functions; i.e., whatever the following may be:

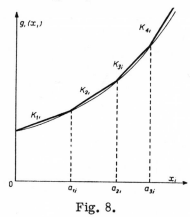

Fig. 8.

x_i^1, x_i^2 and u $(0 \leqslant u \leqslant 1)$;
$g_i (ux_i^1 + (1 - u) x_i^2) \geqslant ug_i (x_i^1) +$
                           $(1 - u) g_i (x_i^2)$.

Charnes and Lemke, substituting for the foregoing problem a somewhat similar problem, replace each g_i function by a linear approximation (see Figure 8):

$k_{1i} \, x_i$ $x_i \leqslant a_{1i}$
$k_{1i} \, x_i + (k_{2i} - k_{1i})$
$(x_i - a_{1i})$ $a_{1i} \leqslant x_i \leqslant a_{2i}$

               . . . .

$$\sum_{j=1}^{q_i} (k_{ji} - k_{j-1,i}) (x_i - a_{j-1,i}) (k_{0i} = 0) \; a_{q_i i} \leqslant x_i \leqslant a_{q_i + 1, i}$$

One can then introduce in place of x_i, $2q_i$ new variables x_{ij}^+ and x_{ij}^- defined by relations:

$$x_{ij}^+ - x_{ij}^- = x_i - a_{j-1} \tag{II.10}$$

and subject to restraints:

$$x_{ij}^+, x_{ij}^- \geqslant 0 \tag{II.11}$$
$$x_i^+ . x_{ij}^- = 0. \tag{II.12}$$

In point of fact, due to the latter restraint, x_{ij}^+ or at least x_{ij}^- is zero.

If it is x_{ij}^+, x_i is smaller than $a_{j-1,i}$. If it is x_{ij}^-, x_i is greater than $a_{j-1,i}$. With the help of these new variables, function $g_i (x_i)$ can therefore be approximated by the expression:

$$\sum_{=1}^{q_i} (k_{ji} - k_{j-1,i}) \, x_{ij}^+ .$$

The compensation or offset for this linearization of the profit function is the introduction of additional restraints (II. 10, 11, and 12).

The new problem is not linear, because of II.12. However, let us consider the linear problem obtained by not taking (II.12) into account. The coordinates of the extreme points of this problem are the coefficients of a set of independent vectors. However, relations (II.10) indicate that vectors associated with activities $x_{i\bar{j}}^{+}$ and $x_{i\bar{j}}$ are linearly dependent. Consequently, at extreme points one still finds either: $x_{i\bar{j}}^{+} = 0$, or $x_{i\bar{j}}^{-} = 0$. Restraint (II.12) is therefore automatically met when a determination is made of the extreme points of the similar linear problem.

In other words, the extreme points of the linear problem correspond to possible programs of the non-linear problem which contains (II.12). If an optimum is found among these possible programs, it is sufficient merely to solve the linear problem in order to obtain an approximation of the solution to the initial problem.

Charnes and Lemke [31] have demonstrated that this was actually so when functions $g_i (x_i)$ were convex, and they have elaborated a method making it possible to consider only the space of m dimensions of the initial restraints.

3. Quadratic problems [57].

In accordance with usual practice, we have designated as quadratic programming programs in which the x vector of activities must meet a certain number of linear inequalities while maximizing a second degree function in x. The replacement of a linear function $c'x$ by a second degree function makes it possible to take into account, to a certain extent, the interdependency of profits derived from the various activities and of the variation in unit profit as the level of an activity increases or decreases. A quadratic program can be outlined as follows:

$$
\begin{cases}
\sum_i c_i x_i - \dfrac{1}{2} \sum_{ij} x_i d_{ij} x_j \text{ maximum} & i, j = 1, 2, \ldots, p \\
x_i \geqslant 0 & k = 1, 2, \ldots, m \\
\sum_k m_{ik} x_i = b_k
\end{cases}
$$

or, in terms of matrix notation:

$$
\begin{cases}
c'x - \dfrac{1}{2} x'Dx \text{ maximum} \\
x \geqslant 0 \\
Mx = b
\end{cases}
$$

D represents a matrix of p rows and p columns which may be considered symmetrical without affecting its general character.

To insure that any local maximum will also be a maximum in the larger sense, we must further assume that the second degree function is concave, i.e., that the D matrix is semi-definite positive. $x'Dx$ is therefore positive or zero for any x.

Applying the Kuhn and Tucker theorem to this problem, function F (x,u) assumes the shape of:

$$F(x, u) = c'x - \frac{1}{2} x'Dx + (Mx - b)'u$$

the vector u being a vector of m dimensions whose components are of any sign. (This difference from the theorem outlined in Part 1 stems from the fact that, in this particular case, the restraints are equalities).

The $\dfrac{\partial F}{\partial x_i}$ vector is expressed:

$$c' - Dx + M'u$$

This vector's $\dfrac{\partial F}{\partial x_i}$ component must be negative or zero if x_i is zero, and zero if x_i is positive. By introducing a v vector with p dimensions, such that

$$v \geqslant 0$$

conditions can be expressed which will meet the requirements of the $\dfrac{\partial F}{\partial x_i}$ vector in the form of:

$$\begin{cases} c' - Dx + M'u + v = 0 \\ v'x = 0 \\ v \geqslant 0 \end{cases}$$

In other words, a vector $x \geq 0$ becomes a solution of a quadratic program if a vector $v \geq 0$ and a vector u can be found such that:

$$\begin{cases} Mx = b \\ c' - Dx + M'u + v = 0 \\ v'x = 0 \end{cases}$$

The first two series of relations linked with conditions $x \geq 0$ and $v \geq 0$ define a convex polyhedron (K) within a space of $2p + m$ dimensions. The third relation confirms that p variables x, u, v, amount to zero in the solution of the initial problem. Therefore, at most, there are $p + m$ non-zero variables x, u, v; that is, there are as many variables as there are defining relationships, in this case, the (K) polyhedron.

The solution of the initial problem corresponds therefore to one of the extreme points of (K). A determination of the extreme point solution can be made as follows: starting from a particular $x = x_0$, $v = 0$, $u = 0$ series of vectors, x_0 is selected in order that $Mx_0 = b$. Under such conditions:

$$c' - Dx_o = - Ez$$

z being a p dimension vector whose components are positive or zero, and E being a diagonal matrix whose coefficients are +1 or -1. The linear programming is considered as x, u, v, z:

$$\begin{cases} \sum_i z_i \text{ minimum} \\ \text{with } z \geqslant 0 \quad x \geqslant 0 \quad v \geqslant 0 \\ Mx = b \\ c' - Dx + M'u + v + Ez = 0 \end{cases}$$

which can be solved according to traditional methods, avoiding those bases in which there simultaneously appear the same components of vectors v and x. Wolfe [157] has demonstrated that the

$$\sum_i z_i$$

minimum is actually zero, and that a solution of the quadratic program is thus attained.

4. New methods of computation [65] [1].

To our knowledge, R. Frisch is the first to have suggested a method of computation, applicable to linear programming, entirely different from that of the simplex method. This method is presented at this time because of its likely applications in the area of non-linear programming.

The simplex method consisted of shifting, over the surface of a convex polyhedron, possible programs from extreme point to extreme point.

The R. Frisch method, on the contrary, suggests (during successive approximations) a path always located within the polyhedron. In order to do this, R. Frisch introduces a logarithmic potential which, by using the notations of the Kuhn and Tucker theorem, is none other than:

$$V(x) = \text{Log} \prod_{j=1}^{m} f_j(x_1, \ldots, x_n).$$

When, starting from a point located within volume K of possible programs, one nears the boundary, V(x) increases indefinitely.

In the case of linear programming, and, in fact, in more general cases, the maximum of g (x) is attained at one point of the surface of (K). From a point M located inside (K), it is therefore necessary to shift:

a) in the direction of the growth of g (x);
b) in the direction of the surface of (K).

In order to do this, at point M we will consider, on the one hand, the vector of components $\dfrac{\partial g}{\partial x_i}$ which is normal at surfaces of equiprofit and which is directed toward the growth of g (x), and, on the other hand, the gradient of the potential of components $\dfrac{\partial V}{\partial x_i}$ which indicates substantially the direction of the surface.

From point M, an attempt will be made at shifting in the direction of the vector of components:

$$m_i = \frac{\partial g}{\partial x_i} + e\, \frac{\partial V}{\partial x_i} \text{ of a quantity u.}$$

u and e are selected in order to avoid any contact with the surface (see Fig. 9 below).

The success of this method, which is more flexible than the sim-

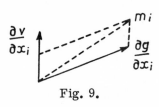

Fig. 9.

plex method, is contingent upon the skill with which numbers e and u are selected at each approximation. According to R. Frisch, it is very easy after a little practice to arrive at a solution quickly.

M. Ablow and G. Brigham have proposed, independently, a fairly analogous method.

Conditions $x_i \geq 0$ are introduced in restraints f_j. The method consists of starting from a given program which does not necessarily meet the restraints, and integrating with the help of a computer, systems of differential equations of the form:

$$\frac{dx_i}{dt} = \sum_{j=1}^{m} S_j\, \frac{\partial f_j}{\partial x_i} + e\, \frac{\partial g}{\partial x_i} \qquad (i = 1, 2, \ldots n). \tag{II.13}$$

e is a non-negative number which can be rendered as small as desired. S_j is defined, according to the variant used, by the conditions below in which p_j is an arbitrary positive number:

$$\text{Variant A} \quad S_j = p_j \text{ if } f_j < 0$$
$$0 \text{ if } f_j \geq 0$$

$$\text{Variant B} \quad S_j = -p_j f_j \text{ if } f_j < 0$$
$$0 \text{ if } f_j \geq 0$$

In other words, it is imagined that the program point is a particle whose velocity comprises two groups of terms:

a) a velocity which draws it in the direction of increased profit;

b) a velocity which is the result of m velocities associated with each of the restraints. The velocity associated with a restraint is zero if the latter is verified but tends to lead the point in the direction indicated by the restraint in the opposite case. The main difference from the R. Frisch method is that in this case the extension beyond any boundary is authorized in the course of iterations. If an analog computer is available, the selected equations are simulated on the computer. Starting from a group of initial values, e being fixed, the computer is started. The computer integrates the (II. 10) system of equations. A key makes it possible to control the value of e manually. When a solution has been obtained for a given value of e, e is reduced. When e tends toward 0, the program obtained tends to maximize g (x). Since, in the case of non-linear problems, there may be several local maximums, it is advisable to effect numerous iterations starting from a considerable number of different initial conditions.

These new methods of computation would seem to indicate that important developments are to be anticipated in the field of mathematical programming, thus completing the elaboration of one of the most remarkable theories evolved by economic analysis since the end of the Second World War.

APPENDIX

ELEMENTS OF THE THEORY OF MATRICES

1. Definition. A nxm matrix is a series of numbers a_i grouped into a rectangular table including n rows and m columns:

$$\begin{bmatrix} a_{11} & a_{12} \cdots \cdots a_{1m} \\ a_{21} & a_{22} \cdots \cdots a_{2m} \\ \cdot & \\ \cdot & \\ \cdot & \\ \cdot & \\ a_{n1} & a_{n2} \cdots \cdots a_{nm} \end{bmatrix}$$

which can be symbolically noted as $A = [a_{ij}]$.

Numbers a_{ij} represent the elements of the matrix, index i indicating the row (i = 1, 2, ..., n), index j the column (j = 1, 2, ..., m).

When n = m the matrix is said to be square. The number of rows or columns is then, by definition, the "order" of the matrix.

2. Operations based on the matrices.

2.1. Two matrices nxm $A = [a_{ij}]$ $B = [b_{ij}]$ are equal if all their elements are equal. $A = B$ therefore implies:

$$a_{ij} = b_{ij}$$

whatever i and j may be.

2.2. The sum of matrices nxm A and B is matrix C, whose elements are the numbers

$$c_{ij} = a_{ij} + b_{ij}.$$

This is written symbolically $C = A + B$.

2.3. The product of an A matrix by a u scalar is the matrix D whose elements are numbers $d_{ij} = ua_{ij}$.
This is symbolically written: $D = uA$.

2.4. The product of matrix nxm A by matrix mxp B is matrix nxp E whose elements are numbers:

$$e_{ij} = \sum_{k=1}^{m} a_{ik} b_{kj}.$$

The ith element of the jth column of E is the sum of the products of the ith line of A by the jth column of B.
This is noted symbolically:

$$E = AB.$$

When the matrices are square and of the same order, one can define both products AB and BA, but, generally:

$$AB \neq BA.$$

The product of two square matrices is not commutative.

2.5. The square of a square matrix A is a matrix AA which is noted as A^2. Defined in the same way are the diverse powers of a square matrix.

2.6. Known as a unit matrix and designated by I are square matrices whose elements are all zero, except elements a_{ii} which are equal to 1.

2.7. The inverse of a square matrix A is the matrix F, such that:

$$F.A. = I.$$

It is noted symbolically: $F = A^{-1}$.
It is shown that: $A^{-1} A = AA^{-1}$.

2.8. The transposition of a matrix A is matrix G whose elements are numbers:

$$G_{ij} = a_{ji}$$

G is obtained by transposing the columns and rows of A. This is often written $G = A'$.

3. Matrices and linear equations.

3.1. The result of the definition of matrices is that a vector of n components can be considered as a matrix of n rows and 1 column or 1 row and n columns. These two matrices are transposed. In order to distinguish them, reference is frequently made to a column-vector (1 column n rows) or to a row-vector (1 row n columns).

3.2. This results in the fact that the following system of linear equations:

$$\begin{cases} a_{11}\,x_1 + \cdots\cdots\cdots + a_{1m}\,x_m = b_1 \\ a_{21}\,x_1 + \cdots\cdots\cdots + a_{2m}\,x_m = b_2 \\ \cdot \\ \cdot \\ \cdot \\ a_{n1}\,x_1 + \cdots\cdots\cdots + a_{nm}\,x_m = b_n \end{cases}$$

can be written either:

$$\begin{bmatrix} a_{11} \cdots\cdots a_{1m} \\ \cdot \\ \cdot \\ a_{n1} \cdots\cdots a_{nm} \end{bmatrix} \begin{bmatrix} x_1 \\ \cdot \\ \cdot \\ x_m \end{bmatrix} = \begin{bmatrix} b_1 \\ \cdot \\ \cdot \\ b_n \end{bmatrix}$$

or: $Ax = b$
by posing:

$$A = [a_{ij}] \qquad x = \begin{bmatrix} x_1 \\ \cdot \\ \cdot \\ x_m \end{bmatrix} \qquad b = \begin{bmatrix} b_1 \\ \cdot \\ \cdot \\ b_n \end{bmatrix}$$

x and b are vectors.

Let us assume now that m = n.

Multiplying the two members of the preceding relation by matrix A^{-1} produces:

$$A^{-1} A \ x = A^{-1} b$$

i.e., $Ix = A^{-1} b$

and since $Ix = x$

$$x = A^{-1} b.$$

This relation symbolically solves the system of linear equations.

3.3. The rank of matrix a is the order of the largest non-zero determinant that can be extracted from this matrix. A determinant is extracted from a matrix by selecting rows and columns and by retaining elements common to such rows and columns.

Example: The matrix:

$$\begin{bmatrix} 1 & 4 \\ 2 & -1 \end{bmatrix}$$

is of rank 2 since the determinant

$$\begin{vmatrix} 1 & 4 \\ 2 & -1 \end{vmatrix}$$

has a value of -1 -8 = -9.

On the other hand, the matrix

$$\begin{bmatrix} 1 & 4 & 5 \\ 0 & 0 & 2 \\ 0 & 0 & -1 \end{bmatrix}$$

is of rank 2 because the determinant

$$\begin{vmatrix} 1 & 4 & 5 \\ 0 & 0 & 2 \\ 0 & 0 & -1 \end{vmatrix}$$

is zero, whereas the determinant

$$\begin{vmatrix} 4 & 5 \\ 0 & 2 \end{vmatrix}$$

is not.

3.4. The theory of the systems of linear equations is indicative of the role played by the order of the determinant of the system of equations. This theory will not be reproduced here since it appears in all manuals on higher mathematics.

BIBLIOGRAPHY

1. C. ABLOW and G. BRIGHAM:
   "An analog solution of programming problems." Operations Research 3, 388-394, 1955.

2. S. AGMON:
"The relaxation method for linear inequalities." Canadian Journal of Mathematics, 6, 382-393, 1954.

3. AITKEN:
Determinants and matrices. Oliver and Boyd, London, 1948.

4. H. A. ANTOSIEWICZ (ed.):
Proceedings of the second symposium in linear programming. June 27-29, 1955, 1 and 2 N B S and Hq. USAF.

5. E. L. ARNOFF:
"An application of linear programming." Proceedings of the conference on operations research in production, and inventory control, January 20-22, 1954. Case Institute of Technology, 1954.

6. K. J. ARROW, L. HURWICS, H. UZAMA:
Studies in linear and non-linear programming. Stanford University Press, 1958.

7. E. M. L. BEALE:
"Cycling in the dual simplex algorithm." Naval Research Logistics Quarterly, 2, 269-275, 1954.

8. E. M. L. BEALE:
"An alternative method for linear programming." Proceedings of the Cambridge Philosophical Society, 50, 4, 1954.

9. M. BECKMANN, C. B. MacGUIRE, C. B. WINSTEN:
Studies in the economics of transportation. Yale University Press, New Haven, 1956.

10. R. BELLMAN:
"On the computational solution of linear programming problems involving almost block diagonal matrices." Management Science, 3, 4, 1957.

11. C. BERGE:
Théorie des graphes et applications (Graph theory and applications). Dunod, 1959.

12. F. BESSIERE:
"Applications de la dualité à un modèle de programmation à long terme" (Duality applications to a model of long-term programming), Revue Française de Recherche Operationnelle, No. 12.

13. Edward H. BOWMAN:
"Production scheduling by the transportation method of linear programming." Operations Research, 4, 100-102, 1956.

14. D. BRATTON:
The duality theorem in linear programming. Cowles Commission Discussion. Papers, Math., No. 415, 16 July 1952, Math. No. 416, 17 October 1952, Econ. No. 2109.

15. J. CARTERON:
"Du bon usage des programmes linéaires" (Proper use of linear programming). Revue de Recherche Opérationnelle, 2, 6, first quarter 1958.

16. A. CHARNES:
Mathematical background for linear programming. Carnegie Institute of Technology, Department of the Air Force research program in intra-firm behavior.

17. A. CHARNES:
"Minimization of non-linear separable convex functionals." Naval Research Logistics Quarterly, 1, 301-312, 1954.

18. A. CHARNES:
"Optimality and degeneracy in linear programming." Econometrica, 20, 1952.

19. A. CHARNES and W. W. COOPER:
"Optimal estimation of executive compensation by linear programming." Management Science, 1, 138-151, 1955.

20. A. CHARNES and W. W. COOPER:
"Such solutions are very little solved." Operations Research, 3, 345-346, 1955.

21. A. CHARNES and W. W. COOPER:
"The stepping stone method of explaining linear programming calculations in transportation problems." Management Science, 1, 49-69.

22. A. CHARNES and W. W. COOPER:
Generalizations of the warehousing model. O.N.R. research memorandum No. 34. Carnegie Institute of Technology.

23. A. CHARNES and W. W. COOPER:
"Management models and industrial applications of linear programming." Management Science, 4, 1, 1957.

24. A. CHARNES, W. W. COOPER, D. FARR et al:
"Linear programming and profit scheduling for a manufacturing firm." Operations Research, 1, 114-129, 1953.

25. A. CHARNES, W. W. COOPER and A. HENDERSON:
An introduction to linear programming, Wiley, New York, 1953.

26. A. CHARNES, W. W. COOPER and B. MELLON:
A model for optimizing production by reference to cost surrogates (in reference 4, p. 117-150).

27. A. CHARNES, W. W. COOPER and B. MELLON:
"Blending aviation gasolines. A study in programming interdependent activities in an integrated oil company." Econometrica, 20, No. 2, 1952.

28. A. CHARNES, W. W. COOPER and G. H. SYMONDS:
Stochastic programming of heating oil by the horizon method. O.N.R. report No. 33, Carnegie Institute of Technology.

29. CHARNES and C. E. LEMKE:
A modified simplex method for control of round-off error in linear programming. Presented at the Pittsburg meeting, Association for Computing Machinery, 21 May 1952 (see reference 43).

30. CHARNES and C. E. LEMKE:
Computational theory of linear programming I. The bounded variables problems, O.N.R. research memorandum, No. 10, Graduate School of Industrial Administration. Carnegie Institute of Technology, January 1954.

31. A. CHARNES and C. E. LEMKE:
"Minimization of non-linear separable convex functionals. Naval Research Logistics Quarterly, 1, 301-312, 1954.

32. J. S. CHIPMAN:
"Linear programming." R. Econ. Statist., 35, May 1953.

33. J. S. CHIPMAN:
"Computational problems in linear programming," R. Econ. Statist., 34, November 1953.

34. G. B. DANTZIG:
"A note on a dynamic Leontief model with substitution." Econometrica, 21, 179 (Abstract) 1953.

35. G. B. DANTZIG:
Application of the simplex method to a transportation problem
(in [105]).

36. G. B. DANTZIG:
A proof of the equivalence of the programming problem and
the game problem (in [105]).

37. G. B. DANTZIG:
Computational algorithm of revised simplex method. Report
of the Rand Corporation, 1953.

38. G. B. DANTZIG:
Composite simplex. Dual simplex algorithm I, Report of the
Rand Corporation, 1954.

39. G. B. DANTZIG:
"Discrete variable extremum problems." Seventh National
Meeting of the Operation Research Society, Los Angeles,
15-17 August, 1955, Operations Research 3, 560, item C2
(Abstract) 1955.

40. G. B. DANTZIG:
The dual simplex algorithm. Report of the Rand Corporation.
1954.

41. G. B. DANTZIG:
"Linear programming under uncertainty." Management
Science, 1, 1955.

42. G. B. DANTZIG:
"Dynamic linear programming." Presented at the West
Coast Regional Meeting of the Econometric Society, Pasadena,
California, 18-19 June 1954, Econometrica 23, 100 (Abstract)
1955.

43. G. B. DANTZIG:
Note of Klein's direct use of extremal principles in solving
certain problems involving inequalities. Operations Research
4, 247-249, 1956.

44. G. B. DANTZIG:
Notes on linear programming, Part III: Computational algorithm for the simplex method. Report of the Rand Corporation, 1953.

45. G. B. DANTZIG:
Maximization of a linear function of variables subject to
linear inequalities (in [105]).

46. G. B. DANTZIG:
Notes on linear programming optimal solution of a dynamic Leontief model with substitution. Report of the Rand Corporation. 1954.

47. G. B. DANTZIG:
"Thoughts on linear programming and automation," Management Science 3, 2, 1957.

48. G. B. DANTZIG:
Note on solving linear programs in integers, Naval Research Logistics Quarterly, 6, 1, 1959.

49. G. B. DANTZIG:
"On the significance of solving linear programming problems with some integer variables," The Rand Corporation, P.-61486, 1958.

50. G. B. DANTZIG and D. R. FULKERSON:
On the Min Cut Max Flow Theorem of Networks. Report of the Rand Corporation. 1955. (in reference 158, pp. 215-221).

50a. G. B. DANTZIG, L. R. FORD and D. R. FULKERSON:
A primal dual algorithm. Report of the Rand Corporation. 1956 (in reference 158, p. 171-181).

51. G. B. DANTZIG:
"Recent advances in linear programming." Management Science, 2, 2 November 1956.

52. G. B. DANTZIG:
The programming of interdependent activities: mathematical model (in [105]).

53. G. B. DANTZIG:
"Upper bounds, secondary constraints, and block triangularity in linear programming." Econometrica, 23, 174-183 1955.

54. G. B. DANTZIG and D. R. FULKERSON:
"Computation of maximal flows in networks." Naval Research Logistics Quarterly, 2, 277-283, 1955.

55. G. B. DANTZIG and D. R. FULKERSON:
"Minimizing the number of tankers to meet a fixed schedule." Naval Research Logistics Quarterly, 1, 217-222, 1954.

56. G. B. DANTZIG and D. R. FULKERSON:
Notes on linear programming: minimizing the number of carriers to meet a fixed schedule. Report of the Rand Corporation. RM, 1328, 24, August 1954.

57. G. B. DANTZIG and S. JOHNSON:
"Solution of a large—scale traveling—salesman problem. Operations Research 2, 393-410, 1954.

58. G. B. DANTZIG and W. ORCHARDHAYS:
Alternate algorithm for revised simplex method. Report of the Rand Corporation. 1955.

59. G. B. DANTZIG and A. ORDEN:
A duality theorem based on the simplex method (in ⌈92⌉).

60. G. B. DANTZIG and A. ORDEN:
Notes on linear programming, Part. II: duality theorems. Report of the Rand Corporation. 1953.

61. G. B. DANTZIG and M. K. WOOD:
The programming of interdependent activities: general discussion (in [105]).

62. R. DORFMAN:
Application of linear programming to the theory of the firm. University of California Press, Berkeley, 1951.

63. R. DORFMAN:
"Mathematical, or linear programming: A nonmathematical exposition." Am. Econ. Rev. (December 1953).

64. R. DORFMAN, P. A. SAMUELSON and R. M. SOLOW:
Linear programming and its economic applications. Report of the Rand Corporation, 1955.

65. R. DORFMAN, P. A. SAMUELSON and R. M. SOLOW:
Linear Programming and Economic Analysis, McGraw-Hill, 1958.

66. DOSTOR:
Eléments de la théorie des déterminants (Elements of the theory of determinants). Gauthier-Villars.

67. L. C. EDIE:
"Linear programming." Proceedings of the Conference on Operations Research. 28-29 January 1954, Society for the advancement of Management, New York.

68. Kurt EISEMANN:
"Linear programming." American summer meeting of the Econometric Society, Montreal, Canada, 10-13, September 1954. Econometrica 23, 334 (Abstract) 1955.

69. Kurt EISEMANN:
"Linear Programming," Quart. Applied Math. 13, 209-232, 1955.

70. Tibor FABIAN:
"Application of linear programming to steel production planning," presented at the "Seventh National Meeting of the Operations Research Society in Los Angeles," August 15-17, 1955, Operations Research 3, 565 (Abstract) 1955.

71. Merrill M. FLOOD:
"Application of transportation theory to scheduling a military tanker fleet." Operations Research 2, 150-162, 1954.

72. Merrill M. FLOOD:
On the Hitchcock distribution problem (in [92]).

73. Merrill M. FLOOD:
"The traveling salesman problem." Operations Research 1, 61-75, 1956.

74. L. R. FORD, Jr. and D. R. FULKERSON:
A simple algorithm for finding maximal network flows and an application to the Hitchcock problem. Report of the Rand Corporation. 1955.

75. L. R. FORD:
"Network flow theory," The Rand Corporation, P.-923, 1956.

76. L. R. FORD, D. T. FULKERSON:
"Maximal flow through a network," The Rand Corporation, R.M.-1400, 1954.

77. L. R. FORD, D. R. FULKERSON:
"A Primal-dual algorithm for the Capacitated Hitchcock Problem," The Rand Corporation, R. M. 1798, 1956.

78. L. R. FORD, D. R. FULKERSON:
"Solving the Transportation Problem," Management Science, 3, 1, 1956.

79. R. FRISCH:
Principles of linear programming. Socialokonemiske Institutt, Oslo, 18 October 1954, 219 pages.

80. J. W. GADDUM, A. J. HOFFMAN and SOKOLOWSKY:
"On the solution of the caterer problem." Naval Research Logistics Quarterly 1, 223-229, 1954.

81. Leon GAINEN, D. P. HONIG and E. D. STANLEY:
"Linear programming in bid evaluations." Naval Research Logistics Quarterly, 1, 48-54, 1954.

82. David GALE:
Convex polyhedral cones and linear inequalities (in [105]).

83. GALE, H. W. KUHN and A. W. TUCKER:
Linear programming and the theory of games (in [105]).

84. S. GASS:
Linear Programming Methods and applications, McGraw-Hill, 1958.

85. S. I. GASS and Thomas SAATY:
"Parametric objective function," part I. Operations Research 2, 316-319, 1954.

86. S. I. GASS and Thomas SAATY:
"Parametric objective function," part II: Generalization. Operations Research 3-395-401, 1955.

87. S. I. GASS and Thomas SAATY:
"The computational algorithm for the parametric objective function," Naval Research Logistics Quarterly 2, 39-45, 1955.

88. M. GERSTENHABER:
Theory of convex polyhedral cones (in [105]).

89. R. GIBRAT:
Le problème général des plans et les usines maremotrices (The planning problem in general and tidewater plants). May 24, 1955.

90. R. GIBRAT:
La détermination des plans optimums dans le domaine des investissements électriques (The determination of optimal plans in the area of electrical investments). Multilithed memorandum 1955.

91. A. GOLDMAN and A. W. TUCKER:
Theory of linear programming (in reference 89), pp. 53-97.

92. L. GOLLSTEIN and A. ORDEN:
Project Scoop, symposium on linear inequalities and programming, Planning Research Division, Director of management and analysis service, comptroller, Hq. U.S.A.F. April 1952.
1. New techniques for linear inequalities and optimization T. S. Motzkin.
2. Application of the simplex method to a variety of matrix problems. A. Orden.
3. A duality theorem based on the simplex method: G. B. Dantzig and A. Orden.
4. A geometrical interpretation of the simplex method: J. P. Mayberry.
5. Hitchcock distribution problem: M. M. Flood.
6. Theorems of alternatives for pairs of matrices A. W. Tucker.
7. Convex programming E. W. Blackett.

93. R. GOMORY, EC.:
An algorithm for integer solutions to linear programs, Princeton I. B. M. Mathematics Research Projects, Technical Report No. 1, 1958.

94. Oliver GROSS:
A simple linear programming problem explicitly solvable in integers. Report of the Rand Corporation. 1955.

95. Paul GUNTHER:
Use of linear programming in capital budgeting. Operations Research 3, 219-224, 1955.

96. G. F. HADLEY and M. SIMONNARD:
A simplified two phase technique for the simplex method, Naval Research Logistics Quarterly, 6, 3, 1959.

97. HENDERSON:
Efficiency and pricing in the coal industry. Review of Economics and Statistics, January 1956.

98. A. HENDERSON and R. SCHLAIFER:
Mathematical programming: better information for better decision making. Harvard Business Review, 32, 73-100, 1954.

99. H. S. HOUTHAKKER:
On the numerical solution of the transportation problem. Operations Research 3, 210-214, 1955.

100. Z. HURWICS:
The Minkowski. Farkas Lemma for bounded linear transformations in Banach spaces. Cowles Commission discussion papers math., No. 415, July 16, 1952, math., No. 416, October 17, 1952 and Econ., No. 2109.

101. W. W. JACOBS:
The caterer problem. Naval Research Logistics Quarterly 1,
154-165, 1954.

102. J. E. KELLEY, Jr.:
A dynamic transportation model. Naval Research Logistics
Quarterly 2, 175-180, 1955.

103. S. E. KELLEY:
Parametric programming and the Primal-Dual Algorithm,
Operations Research, 7, 3, 1959.

104. R. A. KING and R. J. FREUND:
Some applications of activity analysis in agricultural economics. Journal of Farm Economics, December 1953.

105. T. J. KOOPMANS:
Activity analysis of production and allocation. John Wiley,
New York, 1951. A series of essays brought together by
T. J. Koopmans. Among these are the following essays which
relate especially to linear programming:
  1. The programming of interdependent activities: General
     discussion by M. K. Wood and G. B. Dantzig.
  2. The programming of interdependent activities: Mathe-
     matical model by G. B. Dantzig.
  These two essays are from the revisions of two articles
  published in Econometrica, vol. 17, July-October, p. 193-199
  and 200-211.
  3. Analysis of production as an efficient combination of
     activities by T. J. Koopmans.
  4. On the choice of a crop rotation plan by: G. Hildreth and
     S. Reiter.
  5. Development of dynamic models for program planning by
     M. K. Wood and M. A. Geisler.
  6. Representation in a linear model of non-linear growth
     curves in the aircraft industry: M. K. Wood.
  7. A model of transportation by T. C. Koopmans and
     S. Reiter.
  8. Convex polyhedral cones and linear inequalities by
     D. Gale.
  9. Theory of convex polyhedral cones by M. Gerstenhaber.
 10. Linear programming and the theory of games; by
     D. Gale, H. W. Kuhn and A. W. Tucker.
 11. A proof of the equivalence of the programming problem
     and the game problem: G. B. Dantzig.
 12. Maximization of a linear function of variables subject to
     linear inequalities by G. B. Dantzig.

13. Application of the simplex method to a game theory problem by R. Dorfman.

14. Application of the simplex method to a transportation problem by G. Dantzig.

106. T. C. KOOPMANS:
Optimum utilization of the transportation system. Econometrica 17, supplement, 136-146 July 1949.

107. H. W. KUHN:
The hungarian method for the assignment problem. Naval Research Logistics Quarterly 2, 83-97, 1955.

108. H. W. KUHN and A. W. TUCKER:
Linear inequalities and related systems. Princeton University Press, 1956.

109. H. W. KUHN and A. W. TUCKER:
Contributions to the theory of games. Ann. Math. Studies 24, Princeton, 1950.

110. H. W. KUHN and A. W. TUCKER:
Contributions to the theory of games II. Ann. Math. Studies 28, Princeton, 1953.

111. H. W. KUHN and A. W. TUCKER:
Non-linear programming. Proceedings of second Berkeley symposium on mathematical statistics and probability 481-492, 1951. Operations Research 3, 560, item C1. (Abstract) 1955.

112. C. E. LEMKE:
The dual method of solving the linear programming problem. Naval Research Logistics Quarterly 1, 36-47, 1954.

113. K. S. LOMAX:
Allocation and programming in modern economics. Manchester Sch. Econ. Soc. Stud. 21, September 1953.

114. A. MADANSKEY:
Inequalities for stochastic linear programming problems, Management Science, 6, 2, 1960.

115. P. MAILLET:
"Une nouvelle technique économique: les programmes linéaires" (A new economic technique: linear programming). R. Econ. Polit., Paris, 63, January-February 1953.

116. E. MALINVAUD:
"Introduction à l'étude des programmes linéaires" (Introduction to the study of linear programming). Revue de statistique appliquée, vol. III, No. 2, 1955.

117. ALAN S. MANNE:
Scheduling of petroleum refinery operations. Harvard University Press. Cambridge (Mass.) 1956.

118. Alan S. MANNE:
Notes on parametric linear programming. Report of the Rand Corporation, 1953.

119. H. MARKOWITZ:
Industry-wide, multi-industry and economy-wide process analysis. Memorandum of the Rand Corporation, 1954.

120. H. MARKOWITZ:
The nature and applications of process analysis. Memorandum of the Rand Corporation, 1954.

121. H. MARKOWITZ:
Portfolio selection. Cowles commission papers, No. 60, 1952.

122. H. M. MARKOWITZ:
The elimination form of the inverse and its application to linear programming, Management Science, 3, 3, 1957.

123. P. MASSÉ:
"Le problème des investissements à l'Electricité de France" (Electricité de France's investments problems). Nouvelle Revue de l'Economie Contemporaine, No. 62, February 1955.

124. P. MASSÉ and R. GIBRAT:
Applications of linear programming to investments in the electric power industry, Management Science, 3, 2, 1957.

125. P. MASSÉ:
Le choix des investissements (The selection of investments). Dunod, Paris, 1959.

126. W. ORCHARD-HAYS:
A composite simplex algorithm, II. Report of the Rand Corporation, 1954.

127. W. ORCHARD-HAYS:
Background, Development and extensions of the revised simplex method. Report of the Rand Corporation, 1954.

128. W. ORCHARD-HAYS:
Computational experience in solving linear programming problems. Proceedings of a symposium on operations research in business and industry, April 1954, Midwest Research Institute, Kansas City, Mo., 1954.

129. W. ORCHARD-HAYS:
Computing experience with linear programming and its variants. Presented at the annual meeting of the Association for Computing Machinery. Philadelphia, 14-16 September 1955, Computers and automation 4, No. 11, 22, item 47 (Abstract) 1955.

130. W. ORCHARD-HAYS:
Evolution of linear programming computing techniques, Management Science, 4, 2, 1958.

131. A. ORDEN and D. F. VOTAW:
Personnel assignment problem (in [76]).

132. A. ORDEN:
The transshipment problem, Management Science.

133. A. E. PAULL and John R. WALTER:
The trim problem: An application of linear programming to the manufacture of newsprint paper. Presented at the American summer meeting of the Econometric Society, Montreal, Canada, 10-13 September 1954, Econometrica 23, 336 (Abstract) 1955.

134. R. RADNER:
The linear team: An example of linear programming under uncertainty (in [4]).

135. S. RICOSSA:
"La programmazione lineare et il metodo del simplesso" (Linear programming and the simplex method). Industria 3, 1953.

136. T. SAATY:
Approximation of the value of the objective function in linear programming by the method of partitions, Operations Research 4, 352-353, 1956.

137. M. E. SALVESON:
A computational technique for the fabrication scheduling problem, Los Angeles, Management Sciences Research Project, University of California, 1953.

138. M. E. SALVESON:
The Assembly line balancing program. The Journal of industrial engineering, May-June 1955.

139. P. A. SAMUELSON:
Linear programming and economic theory (in [4]).

140. P. A. SAMUELSON:
Spatial price equilibrium and linear programming. Am. Econ. Rev. 42, 283-303, 1952.

141. P. A. SAMUELSON:
The Le Chatelier principle in linear programming, Report of the Rand Corporation, 1949.

142. M. SIMONNARD:
"Structure des bases dans les problèmes de transport" (Basic structure in transportation problems). Revue Française de Recherche opérationnelle, No. 12, 1959.

143. Gifford SYMONDS:
Linear programming: The solution of refinery problems, Esso Standard Oil Co., New York, 1955.

144. G. TINTNER:
Stochastic linear programming with applications to agricultural economics (in ref. 4, pp. 179-228). Published in French in the Revue d'Economie Politique, 1957, No. 1.

145. A. W. TUCKER:
Linear inequalities and convex polyhedral sets (in [4]).

146. A. W. TUCKER:
Linear programming and the theory of games. Econometrica, 18, 189-190, 1950.

147. S. VAJDA:
Théorie des jeux et programmation linéaire (Theory of games and linear programming). Dunod, 1959.

148. A. VAZSONYI:
Optimizing a function of additively separated variables subject to a simple restriction (in [4]).

149. A. VASZONYI:
Scientific Programming in Business Industry, J. Wiley, 1958.

150. E. VENTURA:
Un exemple de recherche opérationnelle: la détermination
d'un plan optimum de production d'énergie électrique par la
théorie des programmes linéaires (An operations research
example: the determination of an optimal plan for the production of electrical power according to linear programming
theory). SOFRO, 1956.

151. M. L. VIDALE:
A graphical solution of the transportation problem. Journal
of the American Society of Operations Research IV, No. 1,
1956.

152. D. F. VOTAW, Jr:
Methods of solving some personnel classification problems.
Psychometrika 17, 255-266, 1952.

153. D. F. VOTAW, Jr:
Programming under conditions of uncertainty (in [4]).

154. H. M. WAGNER:
A practical guide to the dual theorem, Operations Research,
6, 3, 1958.

155. H. M. WAGNER:
The dual simplex algorithm for bounded variables, Naval
Research Logistics Quarterly 5, 3, 1958.

156. F. V. WAUGH and G. L. BURROW:
A short-cut to linear programming, Econometrica, January
1955.

157. Ph. WOLFE:
The simplex method for quadratic programming, The Rand
Corporation., P.-1205, 1957.

158. B. ZIMMERN:
"La résolution des programmes linéaires de transport par
la méthode de séparation en étoile" (Solution of transportation linear programming by the stellate separation method).
Revue Française de Recherche Operationnelle, 1957, No. 3.

Chapter 13

Investment problems
and calculation of
effective income

As with many economic terms, the term "investment" has a variety of meanings, each with a unique application to a specific environment. Here, we define investment as the goods acquired by a firm in anticipation that these goods will provide services during subsequent periods. The purchase of a bus by a passenger transportation company, for example, constitutes an investment. This definition precludes the completely distinct phenomenon of a private individual's "investment" of savings in shares or bonds.

Investment can be separated into two main categories. It can relate to the purchase of capital equipment which will subsequently serve to produce, but will not be a part of, finished products; or it can consist of raw materials which are acquired, stored, and finally consumed in the production process. Since the stockage problem has been dealt with at great length in Chapter 10, the emphasis here will be on investments which fall within the first category.

On the other hand, there will be no need to distinguish between replacement (the acquisition of durable goods to replace similar goods which have outlived their usefulness) and expansion (the acquisition of durable goods to enlarge rather than to rehabilitate capacity). No major differences distinguish these two possibilities; when a machine is worn out and replacement is indicated, management must consider various alternatives. The operator may well decide to acquire entirely different equipment or none at all. The problem is more basic than one of mere replacement; it involves a decision respecting the purchase of durable goods.

Investment decisions bind the future, frequently for long periods of time; thus they play an essential part in the life of a firm or of a nation. It is therefore necessary to study the profit potential of investments.

The results of such studies, however, will constitute only one of the elements of choice, and it will also be necessary to take social and political aspects into consideration. A rational choice implies the balancing of advantages against disadvantages; consequently, an analysis of profit potential is an integral element of information. It may be considered advisable, for noneconomic reasons, to make investments which may not be very profitable, provided that the cost of such action is understood.

A decision to invest consists of choosing among alternative projects for which estimates of effective income are available.

The first part of this chapter will introduce basic terminology and will then consider the problem of the determination of investment programs. The latter is the thorniest part of our subject. The second part of the chapter will be devoted to the practical calculation of effective income. It may seem more appropriate to begin with the second part. In point of fact, however, the problem of calculating effective income can be clearly presented only after a discussion of the theoretical aspects. Finally, the chapter will close with examples of actual applications.

I

INVESTMENT THEORY

Following the introduction of the main concepts found in this theory, possible situations will be classified on the basis of a few appropriate distinctions, and such situations will then be analyzed.

1. Terminology and geometric presentation [2], [21].

Let us consider an investment involving the construction of a plant with a useful life of q years. Once the project has been decided upon, it is known that its construction and use will require $D_0, D_1, \ldots, D_q$ expenditures and will produce $R_0, R_1, \ldots, R_q$ annual income. The expenditures and total income are represented over time in Fig. 1 as continuous variables for purposes of simplification. The curve OABC represents anticipated income. This income is zero during the construction phase (OA); it then increases to a level BC corresponding to the normal operation of the installation. The curve MNP represents actual expenditures as they occur. The term "actual" is stressed to emphasize that these are not theoretically derived expenditures following amortization calculations but actual expenditures corresponding to payments made by the firm. Under these conditions, MNQR is the income curve; this is negative during the initial phase of investment, but then becomes positive and substantially reaches a level QR for normal operation.

An investment can be viewed as an exchange of future income for current (or anticipated) expenditures.

This is an economic interpretation of the fact that an investment is an indirect process of production in which the basic ingredients are first obtained in order to make subsequent production possible. To compare the future advantages of an investment with the present disadvantages, the most convenient procedure is to determine effective income. Over a period (O, q), this income is expressed:

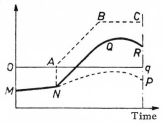

Fig. 1

$$R = \sum_{1}^{q} \frac{R_p - D_p}{(1 + i)^p}.$$ (I.1)

In Chapter 2 we have already considered the problem of selecting a period to determine effective income. The following definitions and observations are valid regardless of the period, but obviously they have economic significance only if the period of effective income is correct. In the following we will take an interval of time (O, q) as this period.

The following procedure is of interest only if the effective income is positive. R being a function of i, in actual practice it is very useful to consider the curve R(i), which relates the effective income to the rate of interest (Fig. 2).

Assuming that curve R_p - D_p is formed as indicated in Fig. 1:

a) For an infinitely large rate of interest, the effective income is very small and negative. For example, if m is the last year for which R_p - D_p is negative, the following can be written:

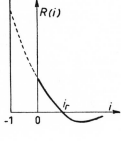

Fig. 2

$$R = \sum_{0}^{m} \frac{R_p - D_p}{(1 + i)^p} + \sum_{m+1}^{q} \frac{1}{(1 + i)^m} \frac{R_p - D_p}{(1 + i)^{p-m}}$$

i.e.,

$$R = \frac{1}{(1 + i)^m} \left((1 + i)^m \sum_{0}^{m} \frac{R_p - D_p}{(1 + i)^p} + \sum_{m+1}^{q} \frac{R_p - D_p}{(1 + i)^{p-m}} \right).$$

Accordingly, for a very large i the effective income is represented by the symbol of the first term, i.e., it is negative.

b) In the case of a rate of interest approaching -1, effective income is very large.

R, therefore, cancels out at least once for a value of i. To demonstrate that this value is unique, let us calculate $\frac{\partial R}{\partial i}$:

$$\frac{\partial R}{\partial i} = -\frac{1}{1+i} \sum_{0}^{q} p \, \frac{R_p - D_p}{(1+i)^p}.$$

In $\frac{\partial R}{\partial i}$, the positive values of $R_p - D_p$ which are the farthest removed are multiplied by p values larger than the negative values. Consequently, in the case of an i value which reduces R(i) to zero, $\frac{\partial R}{\partial i}$ is negative. The curve R_i can therefore intersect the i axis at only one point.

The corresponding rate of interest is i; it has been named the average rate of return of an investment. The average rate of return is the rate of interest at which an operation ceases to be advantageous. If a project has an average rate of return of 10%, its effective income is zero if the project finds it necessary to borrow at a 10% rate of interest.

Until now we have considered individual projects with well-defined technical characteristics: for example, a coal mine extracting 3,000 tons per day from a given field having shafts of a certain diameter; a local power plant of 200 MW containing groups of boilers of prescribed characteristics; a canal whose geographical tracing, section, flow, and number of locks have been selected. Let us now assume that this project is modified slightly. To simplify notations, it will be more convenient to designate as r_p the income for the year p.

The technical modification of the project will be translated into variations in income Δr_1, Δr_2, ..., Δr_q and the variation in effective income will be:

$$\Delta R\,(i) = \sum_{1}^{q} \frac{\Delta r_p}{(1+i)^p}. \tag{I.2}$$

The technical modification of the project can be regarded as a small investment or a small additional disinvestment, added algebraically to the initial project.

In the first case, the expenditures are increased slightly during the investment period; this amounts to an increase in subsequent receipts. The series Δr_p has the same property in relation to time as the r_p series.

In the second case, expenditures are reduced during the investment period; this results in a reduction of subsequent receipts. The $-\Delta r_p$ series has the same property in relation to time as the r_p series.

In both cases, therefore, the demonstration can be repeated proving the existence of i_r and pinpointing the existence of a single root i_m of the expression (I.2).

i_m has been named the marginal rate of return of the project for a technical modification corresponding to the series $(\Delta r_1, \ldots, \Delta r_p)$.

Considerable care should be exercised in distinguishing the average rate of return of an investment from its marginal rate of return. The two concepts are analogous to average and marginal costs.

To explain this phenomenon further, we can assume that the project is technically well defined once the volume D of investment expenditure has been fixed. This means that for each D value there is a corresponding project which is likely to maximize effective income; this is a function of D and i : $R(D, i)$.

The average rate of return is the root of the equation:

$$R(D, i) = 0 \tag{I.3}$$

This root $i(D)$ is dependent upon parameter D.

When D varies from ΔD, $R(D, i)$ varies from $\Delta R(D, i)$. The marginal rate of return is the root of equation:

$$\Delta R(D, i) = 0 \tag{I.4}$$

This root $i_m(D)$ is also dependent upon D.

The use of capital can be considered a factor of production within the general theory of production functions. As investment expenditures are increased, effective income increases rapidly but at an ever-decreasing rate until a point is reached where further investment causes income to decrease.

Curves $R(D)$ and $\dfrac{dR(D)}{dD}$ have in general, for a given i, the form indicated in Fig. 3. This results in:

a) for $D < D_m$, $\dfrac{\partial R}{\partial D}(D, i) > 0$, from which is deduced (limiting oneself to the zone in which $\dfrac{\partial R}{\partial D}$ is a diminishing function of D) $i < i_m$, and

b) for $D < D_m$, $\dfrac{\partial R}{\partial D}(D, i) < 0$, from which is deduced:

$$i > i_m.$$

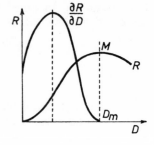

Fig. 3

In other words, the marginal rate of return is greater (or smaller) than the market rate if an increase in invested capital yields (or does not yield) an increase in effective income.

The curves supplying the average and marginal rates of return with respect to D are traced in Fig. 4. The marginal rate of return is, at first, greater than the average rate; this implies that the project would produce more income if its size were enlarged. Subsequently, the marginal rate of return decreases through saturation and becomes equal to and, finally, less than the average rate of return. It will be of interest to the reader to compare the figure below with Fig. 3 in Chapter 10.

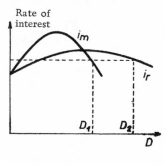

Fig. 4

In the case of a rate of interest i, effective income is at a maximum for $i_m = i$, $D = D_1$, and zero for $i_r = i$, $D = D_2$.

In actual practice, the difficulties encountered in constantly varying the hypothetical size of projects reduce the value of the concept of a marginal rate of return. It is essential, however, to keep in mind the distinction between average and marginal returns. It is often stated that a project must be undertaken because it is profitable, implying that its average rate of return is greater than the market rate. However, a correct decision must point toward the most profitable projects and, consequently, must consider marginal rates of return.

2. A few useful distinctions in the theory of investment.

In the following paragraphs we consider investment problems from an essentially theoretical standpoint. This presentation has been adopted because concrete studies on the return potential of investments in large enterprises constantly pose difficulties which fall within the field of economics and which must be solved in such terms. If these difficulties in abstract analysis are not sufficiently well mastered, one may be led into adopting fallacious methods.

In all of the following, it is assumed:

a) that the effective income is correctly calculated, i.e., only expenditures and future income are included and cover comparable periods (cf. Chapter 2);

b) that the forecast is perfect, meaning that all of the future consequences of our decisions are precisely known. This hypothesis, though unrealistic (because risk is one of the essential aspects of investment), is justified for two reasons:

1) The theoretical development to follow is readily extended to cover the future known as probability.

2) In the general case in which the future is not even known as a probability, the only solution is to calculate effective income as though the forecast were perfect, and to determine thereafter the orders of magnitude of the variations in income created by errors in forecast.

In order to master the investment theory fully, it is well to keep in mind the five following fundamental distinctions:

a) Permanent and nonpermanent systems. A permanent system is a system in which, during each future period, prices and the flow of goods produced and exchanged remain invariant. In other words, economic life repeats itself identically from period to period. There is no technical progress nor any variation in the national income.

In a permanent system, all equipment is replaced at the end of its life by identical equipment. To choose among several possible investments is therefore to choose between several permanent systems. A consideration of permanent systems has the great advantage of simplifying an evaluation of effective income, but the abstract character of this hypothesis strongly limits the conclusions.

b) Large and small investments. Small investments are those which, successful or not, have no effect on the price system at any future time. In accordance with this hypothesis, it becomes possible to examine small investments individually. Their simultaneous culmination will not affect their individual profit potential, and their effective incomes will be additive. For instance, the opening of a new coal mine and the construction of a new steel plant will not change the price of coal or the price of steel, inasmuch as such investments are small increments to large industries. On the other hand, this hypothesis no longer holds if the goods produced by the investment have their own demand curve, either as a result of the size of the investment (e.g., the program as a whole for the construction of power plants by Electricité de France) or as a result of its unique product or service (e.g., a bridge, a tunnel, a plant manufacturing a new product).

The analysis of large investments poses complex problems in economic theory.

c) The existence or nonexistence of a perfect money market. A perfect money market is, theoretically, a market in which, for any given entrepreneur, the availability of capital is entirely elastic (i.e., the entrepreneur will be able to secure, at a market interest rate i, the volume of capital he desires). The case of a perfect market which corresponds to the simplest theoretical conditions constitutes an indispensable frame of reference.

Quite frequently, however, the State or individuals lend money to an entrepreneur at one time or regularly each year at a given rate of interest. A new problem arises if these sums are smaller than those which the entrepreneur would have requested at this interest rate. In actual practice there are many situations other than these two schematic cases; an examination of these, however, is sufficient to highlight the essential points.

d) Spacing investment returns over time. Let us consider the two following situations:

1) An entrepreneur has a certain amount of available capital to invest and he has a choice among a number of alternative projects. In any event, he cannot invest in them all. Furthermore, he cannot postpone either beginning the projects or using the available capital. In this situation, he need not classify the projects. It is merely necessary for him to separate them into two groups, those which will and those which will not be started.

2) Each year an entrepreneur can borrow capital and postpone the start of a project to a later date. In this case, it becomes necessary not only to segregate the projects in accordance with whether or not they will be started, but also to identify the order in which they are to be started.

In the first case the problem has one less dimension, because it is unnecessary to determine the order in which the operations are to occur.

e) Technically compatible or incompatible investments. Earlier, we considered a continuous series of alternatives within the same project. It is quite obvious that these alternatives are incompatible because they cannot be effected simultaneously.

We will analyze this fundamental distinction here, discarding the hypothesis of a continuous series of alternatives since, in actual practice, consideration is always limited to a small number of alternatives.

Let us assume, for example, that a large mining company desires to exploit a coal mine and that there are alternative means for effecting this operation. These alternatives would constitute incompatible investments. On the other hand, the simultaneous enlargement of two different coal fields would constitute technically compatible investments. They are separate projects.

The selection of the best investments for a long-term program can be arranged in tabular form. In this table, each line represents a series of investments that are incompatible with respect to one another; each investment on every line, however, is compatible with each investment on all other lines, constituting scales of compatible investments:

$$A_1, B_1, C_1, \ldots \ldots$$
$$\ldots \ldots \ldots \ldots \ldots$$
$$A_i, B_i, C_i, D_i, \ldots$$
$$\ldots \ldots \ldots \ldots \ldots$$
$$A_n, B_n, \ldots \ldots \ldots$$

Two investments represented by similar index subscripts (A_i and C_i for example) would be impossible to make simultaneously. On the other hand, B_i and A_n can both be effected at the same time. If, for a given investment, it is possible to select the year in which it is realized, this investment must be represented in the table by as many "incompatible" alternatives as there are possible years of realization. The same investment maturing in two different years must be considered, economically, as constituting two separate investments. The various possibilities of a project correspond, therefore, either to the different dimensions which can be assigned to this project or to the different years in which the project can be undertaken.

The five distinctions outlined above will make it possible for us to specify in what follows the limitations of these methods. One object of these methods is to provide an answer to the following question: Which criteria should be used in choosing between compatible and incompatible investments with respect to the alternative interests of the firm and the community?

The difference between these two points of view, already touched upon in Chapter 2, stems essentially from:

a) Imperfect competition. For instance, in cases where the interest rate on loans is not equal to the interest rate which would prevail in a perfect market, "such an investment can be profitable for the Charbonnages de France because of its financing at advantageous rates of interest, without necessarily being so for the community as a whole" [28];

b) The size of the investments (especially in cases of decreasing costs). It can be demonstrated that in the case of very small investments the effect upon the community, neglected in the entrepreneur's calculations, is of secondary importance. This is not so in the case of large investments:*

"The construction of a plant in the metropolitan area of Paris may seem profitable to a private industrialist considering the economic advantages resulting from the industrial concentration near Paris (the proximity of skilled labor and concentrations of consumers). On the other hand, this investment can actually be nonprofitable for the nation when one takes into account the increased cost of public utilities and services stemming from the building of a large complex (roads, housing, traffic problems). Here lies the entire problem of industrial decentralization." Similarly, an investment "may or may not be profitable depending on whether account is taken of the cost of relocating manpower which has been released as a consequence of the investment" [28].

---

*Once again it appears that in a monopolistic situation, the interest of an entrepreneur does not coincide with the general interest.

This distinction between the interests of business and those of the community will invariably come up when considering either an imperfect money market or very large investments.

Since it is not feasible to examine all cases arising from various combinations of the foregoing possibilities, we limit the following discussion to its most interesting aspects:

a) Permanent system—small investments, existence of a money market;

b) Permanent system—small investments, absence of a money market;

c) Nonpermanent system—small investments, existence of a money market;

d) Permanent system—large investments.

Finally, attention will be devoted to the special aspects of the equipment replacement problem.

3. Permanent system—small investments, existence of a money market.

In such an instance, it is unnecessary to know whether or not there is a possibility of spacing investment returns over a period of time. In effect:

a) Any particular sum can be borrowed at the prevailing money market rate i. Those projects which are considered interesting can therefore be started immediately.

b) No project which has been considered unsuitable at the outset will subsequently become profitable. The system being permanent, nothing need be done as long as there is no occasion to renew one of the successful investments; at that time, a similar investment will again be made.

This procedure results in the selection of an equipment replacement program in which the period of time is equal to the smallest common multiple of the lifespans of possible equipment. For instance, if N is the number of years obtained, the effective income of each solution over N years can be calculated by introducing the cost of replacing the initial equipment by similar equipment.

A determination of maximum total effective income leads to these two rules:

a) Within each scale of incompatible investments, a determination must be made of the investment from which effective income is a maximum. When this scale is continuous, the marginal rate of return for this investment is equal to the market rate.

b) Those compatible optimum investments must be effected for which the average rate of return is greater than the market rate; i.e., effective income is positive.

What would be likely to occur if account were not taken of the renewal of short-term projects?

a) Within a range of incompatible investments, short-term projects would be disadvantageous relative to long-term projects. As a matter of fact, because the system is permanent, renewal of a short-term project results in positive effective income.

b) On the other hand, no additional error would be introduced in the calculation of the average rate of return because this is independent of renewal. Let us suppose an investment is to last 10 years and is to produce r_p during the year p; let us also assume that a study is to be made regarding technological development in the next 20 years. The effective income then to be taken into account is:

$$R = \sum_{1}^{10} \frac{r_p}{(1 + i)^p} + \frac{1}{(1 + i)^{10}} \sum_{1}^{10} \frac{r_p}{(1 + i)^p}.$$

The average rate of return is the value of i which cancels R. It also cancels

$$\sum_{1}^{10} \frac{r_p}{(1 + i)^p}$$

which indicates that it also constitutes the investment's rate of return independently of any renewal program.

By tracing curve R(i) of Fig. 2 for each alternative, the relative character of the various solutions is easily ascertained; this procedure facilitates a discussion of investment programming.

Three fundamental observations will make it easier to obtain a better understanding of the significance of the foregoing management rules:

a) Let us assume that, within each range of incompatible investments, all alternatives are listed. These would include the possibility of incurring no expenses, collecting no receipts, and realizing zero effective income. Both foregoing rules of management can then be replaced by the simpler rule: "Within each range of incompatible investments, the investment should be made for which effective income is maximum."

This revised form of the rule has the advantage of being more general than the previous one because it sometimes happens that there is no solution to zero income (for example, the determination of when to close a plant showing a deficit is complicated by severance payments).

b) From the very moment a search is made in each range for an investment possibility whose effective income is maximum, there is no longer any need to proceed beyond a calculation of the differences in effective income among the various alternatives. One of the calculations is taken as a reference solution.

The fundamental notion of relative return of an alternative in relation to a reference solution is thereby underscored. In contradistinction, a calculation of the effective income of each alternative permits a determination of its absolute profit potential.

It is frequently preferable to analyze relative profit potential because the difference in effective income between two alternatives is more easily determined than the effective incomes themselves. The use of a relative profit potential, however, requires some care. The reference solution being arbitrary, the differences in effective income have no value as such. They will all be higher the more the reference solution is unrealistic from the economic standpoint. To obviate the possibility of error it is therefore necessary:

1) to determine carefully which investment possibility provides the likelihood of maximum effective income;

2) to avoid using reference solutions in which the absolute profit potential is negative and, in any case, to determine quickly that the absolute profit potential of the project selected is, in fact, positive.

c) For an economist, the only criterion of choice among small incompatible investments is that of maximum effective income. Other criteria used in actual practice must therefore be rejected when they are not consistent with this one—in particular, the three criteria below:

1) Maximizing the average rate of return. A high rate of profit potential means that if the company's preference for a current investment were to increase to any great extent, the investment would continue to be profitable. But this does not imply that the investment is optimal; its preferential position in the company's investment schedule actually derives from its superiority to the market rate of interest.

Thus, in Fig. 5, the two incompatible investments A_1 and B_1 are classed differently if we consider average profit rates or effective income at the i_0 market rate.

The average rate of return, all other things being equal, will tend to be high if production is limited. The use of a criterion like the maximum average rate of return can lead to the setting aside of investments which are more attractive but are spaced over longer periods of time. This criterion should therefore be rejected in cases of substantially permanent systems and in the case of a well-determined future.

2) Maximizing the relative yield in capital. A relative yield in capital p is frequently defined as the ratio of effective income to effective expenditures. The latter may include either all costs

incurred over the life of the equipment or merely acquisition costs. As a result of the decrease in the marginal productivity of capital, this criterion leads to smaller investments than does that of the maximization of effective income. A graphic presentation proposed by M. Terra [32] and used earlier in Fig. 3 will provide an explanation of the above. For a given interest rate the various solutions within a range of incompatible investments are represented by the points in a system of axes in which the effective expenditure is carried along the abscissa and the effective income is along the ordinate (Fig. 6). As a result of the decreasing marginal productivity of capital, the polygonal line $OA_iB_iC_i$ is nearly always concave downward. Or, to put it another way, the relative yield in capital decreases when effective costs rise. In the case of Fig. 6, one would be induced to select investment A_i, a relatively small amount of capital, instead of investment C_i.

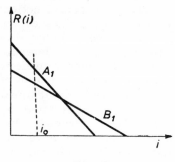

Fig. 5

3) Minimizing the amortization period. This criterion is not satisfactory because it means that the annual net income makes it possible to repay the cost of investment very rapidly. This repayment, of itself, is of no particular interest as long as the forecast is assumed to be perfect. However, this criterion is a useful adjunct in real life, as will be seen later.

Consider, for example, investments 1 and 2, for which the net income curves are shown in Fig. 7. Investment 1 has a negative

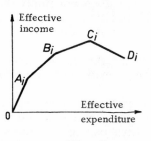

Fig. 6

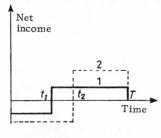

Fig. 7

net income equal to $-d_1$ from o to t_1 and a positive net income equal to r_1 from t_1 to T. t_2, d_2, and r_2 are similarly related in the case of investment 2.

In the notation of continuous functions, if the rate of interest is i the effective incomes from investments are:

$$R_1 = - d_1 \int_0^{t1} e^{-it} \, dt + r_1 \int_{t1}^{T} e^{-it} \, dt$$

$$= \frac{1}{i} r_1 \left(e^{-it_1} - e^{-iT} \right) - \frac{1}{i} d_1 \left(1 - e^{-it_1} \right)$$

with an analogous expression for R_2. R_1 is greater than R_2 if:

$$r_1 \left(e^{-it_1} - e^{-iT} \right) - d_1 \left(1 - e^{-it_1} \right) > r_2 \left(e^{-it_2} - e^{-iT} \right) - d_2 \left(1 - e^{-it_2} \right).$$

$$(I.5)$$

The amortization period for the first investment corresponds to the time u_1 at the end of which the effective income is zero; it is equal to the root of the equation:

$$r_1 \left(e^{-it_1} - e^{-iu_1} \right) = d_1 \left(1 - e^{-it_1} \right). \tag{I.6}$$

By replacing, in relation (I.5), the second member of equality (I.6) by the first, the following inequality is obtained:

$$r_1 \left(e^{-iu_1} - e^{-iT} \right) > r_2 \left(e^{-iu_2} - e^{-iT} \right). \tag{I.7}$$

u_1 and u_2, respectively, are only dependent (for fixed t_1 and t_2) upon $\dfrac{r_1}{d_1}$ and $\dfrac{r_2}{d_2}$. These two quantities can be such that: $u_2 < u_1$.

However, there is nothing to prevent choosing $\dfrac{r_1}{r_2}$ so that, relation (I.7) having been verified, R_1 will be greater than R_2. In this case, the investment with the longest period of amortization is the one which has the highest effective income.

The major drawback of the criterion of minimizing the period of amortization is that it disregards income from investments once they have been amortized. This drawback appears clearly in relations (I.6) and (I.7):

a) (I.6) expresses that costs and effective income are equal at the end of time u_1;

b) (I.7) compares the effective income from the two investments over periods (u_1, T) and (u_2, T), i.e., once the investments have been amortized.

Notes: If the various investment possibilities correspond to an identical increase in production, the criterion of maximizing effective income is equivalent to that of determining maximum gain per unit of production. For instance, let us designate as q the annual increase in production. If the investment remains effective T years and E is the decrease in cost per unit, the effective income

$$\sum_1^T \frac{qE}{(1 + i)^p},$$

reaches its maximum for a given q and T at the same time that E reaches its maximum.

For engineers, effective income presents only one disadvantage: it does not provide data on receipts and expenditures per unit of production. Chapters 9 and 10, however, have demonstrated that the introduction of amortization and long-term marginal cost concepts can provide the answer once the determination of effective income has made it possible to select investments.

4. Permanent system—small investments, absence of a money market.

This new set of hypotheses is more compatible with the present situation of certain businesses. In the case of nationalized enterprises, for instance, the financial market plays only a limited role; a large proportion of investments for these enterprises is financed by means of loans from the Fonds de Modernisation et d' Equipement (Modernization and Equipment Fund). Under these conditions, the supply of capital is frequently insufficient to permit these firms to carry out every profitable investment at the market interest rate.

This situation is illustrated by the diagram in Fig. 8. The abscissas represent the market interest rate; the ordinates indicate capital supply and demand for the entire production sector. The supply of capital, assumed to be completely inelastic, is represented by the straight line (O). Curve (D) represents the production sector demand, i.e., the quantity of capital required to effect, for each interest rate, the total number of profitable investments according to the method outlined in the previous paragraph.

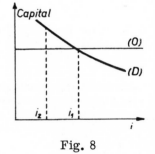

Fig. 8

The point of equilibrium of the interest rate would be the abscissa of the intersection of curves (D) and (O), i.e., i_1. Under various conditions, however, the State can fix the interest rate at an i_2 value smaller than i_1. This limits the supply of capital, and it is no longer possible for the production sector to achieve its entire program.

Let us now introduce a fourth hypothesis, i.e., the impossibility of spacing investments over a period of time. In other words, the entire supply of capital is available at only one time, and it is impossible to convert it into funds that can be made available as needed. What procedures should then be followed to favor either the general interest or that of the firm?

If a general interest viewpoint is adopted, then, in accordance with theorems on economic optimum (summarized in Chapter 2), the firms behave as though the interest rate tends to balance the supply of and demand for capital. A priori, however, i_1 is unknown.* To determine i_1 approximately, it is conceivable that the Commissariat au Plan would ask business firms to report the volume of capital they would like to acquire at various rates of interest. This information would make it possible for the Commissariat to reconstruct the demand curve, deriving i_1 therefrom; then it would invite the firms to make their calculations on the basis of this new rate of interest. Economic techniques used in private industry are not yet sufficiently developed for this method to be used with facility except where it applies to a very limited sector of the economy.

If the point of view of the firm's interest is adopted, it will be necessary to determine from the table of projects, taking into account the exclusions noted, a mix of projects which will maximize the effective income to be anticipated from the program as a whole at an interest rate i_2.

We will assume that the entrepreneur does not know a priori whether he will receive the amount of capital required in order to replace equipment. Where the entrepreneur is assured of the necessary capital to buy new equipment, he will systematically prefer short-term investments; these will enable him to obtain additional amounts of capital at the time of their replacement. These amounts are of some significance because at market interest rates the firm's demand for capital is greater than the amount initially allocated. When it is assumed, on the other hand, that an actual allocation is final, the comparison covers corresponding investment costs and effective income without renewal.

Actually, an entrepreneur is never placed in situations as cut and dried as those outlined above. It is important, however, to examine the interplay of various hypotheses. It then becomes possible to integrate certain elements into the model which play a role in investment decisions.

To solve the problem posed above, we will define the relative growth in capital p from an investment as the ratio of effective income to investment cost, i.e., the proportion of allocated capital devoted to investment. This is the situation outlined in Fig. 6. For an identical scale, relative growth in capital decreases as investment cost increases.

If we had a continuous scale i of possible investments, we would define for the M_i possible investment on this scale:

a) the average rate of relative growth in capital (OM_i slope);

---

*It should be noted that a classification by the average rate of return of various compatible projects would, at this stage, be of some interest for the firm; this rate helps identify those investments which would have the best chances of being achieved.

b) the marginal rate of relative growth in capital [slope of the tangent on M_i to $R_i(D_i)$].

If there were n possible scales it would be necessary to maximize, using invested capital D_0:

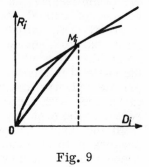

$$\sum_i R_i(D_i)$$

account to be taken of the relation:

$$\sum_i D_1 = D_0.$$

Fig. 9

It would then be deduced that when total income is at a maximum:

$$R_1'(D_1) = \ldots\ldots = R_n'(D_n).$$

These conditions express the fact that marginal relative yields are equal for all ranges of investment.

We now examine the same problem assuming, however, that the scale is not continuous. The method is sufficiently intuitive to permit immediate description. For a single investment scale (cf. Fig. 6), A_i would be executed if only a small amount of capital were available. Relative increases would be represented by the p_{Ai} slope of OA_i. Should a little more capital be available, $B_i - A_i$ could be added to A_i which, for its part, has a relative increase $p_{Ai \, Bi}$ equal to the A_iB_i slope, and so forth.

When there are several scales, all p_{Ai}, p_{AiBi}, p_{BiCi} are classified relative to all scales in decreasing order. A chart is established with p as the abscissa and the additional capital required to effect all investments which have a relative yield greater than or equal to p as the ordinate.

This step chart is then intersected by the ordinate straight line D_0, and all investments are effected which have a relative yield greater than or equal to p_0.

For example, if:

$$p_{Ai} > p_{AiBi} > p_0 > p_{BiCi}$$
$$p_{Aj} > p_0 \quad > p_{AjBj}.$$

On the one hand:

$$A_i + (B_i - A_i), \text{ i.e., } B_i$$

is effected, and on the other, A_j.

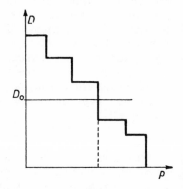

Fig. 10

It will be noted that the method provides an acceptable solution only if, in the step curve, A_i always precedes B_i and B_i precedes C_i. Otherwise, the method could produce a solution such as $B_i - A_i$, which would have no meaning.

Because of the decreasing marginal productivity of capital, it is to a firm's advantage to make a greater number of compatible investments, allocating to each a smaller expenditure of capital. It can be asked if this property serves to explain the proliferation of small units of production formerly employed by producers of electricity. In order to derive the maximum revenue from the limited capital at their disposal these producers apparently did not hesitate to reduce the size of hydroelectric equipment, even at the cost of creating a greater number of items of such equipment.

Note: The above method, hard and fast when the curve $D(p)$ is continuous, is so no longer if the curve is a step chart (unless the invested capital is exactly equal to the value of one of the steps in the curve). Assume that by applying such a method a certain number of projects are selected (in the order of their decreasing relative yield of capital) without exhausting the available capital; some advantage may be derived from adding still another project, even one of very low relative yield, if sufficient capital remains available. There can even be some advantage to substituting a project of lower relative yield which allows the utilization of a greater percentage of the capital. Such is the case in Fig. 11.

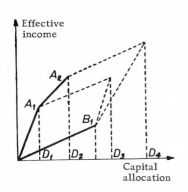

Fig. 11

$A_1 A_2$ is a scale of incompatible investments, B_1 another project. The diminishing order of relative yields is: $A_1 B_2 A_1$. With allocated capital located between D_3 and D_4, investments A_1 and B_1 are made even though B_1's relative yield is smaller than that of A_2.

In concluding this section, let us briefly consider what occurs when the fourth hypothesis is set aside and we assume that the enterprise receives $D_1, D_2, \ldots$ allocations during years $1, 2, \ldots$, on the understanding that it can carry over into the pth year a portion of the credits of previous years but that it cannot advance the allotments.

A firm can still exercise a choice among alternative solutions, but it has one additional degree of freedom, i.e., the fixing of the year of completion for each project, if it is technically possible to do so.

Inasmuch as the system is permanent and investments are independent, the effective income for each solution, calculated for the first year of its completion, is the same regardless of the year. If R represents such income, the income taken into account by the firm is $\dfrac{R}{(I + i)p}$, p being the year of completion.

In actual practice, an approximate determination will be made of the consistency and the scaling of a program leading to maximum effective income. Without attempting to elaborate an exact management rule, it is of interest to analyze a few of the consequences resulting from the new situation in which the entrepreneur finds himself. This differs from earlier considerations in that one cannot now consider fictitious solutions such as $B_i - A_i$ because completion can be scaled, and if one begins by A_i, B_i will never be reached except possibly at the time of renewal. An optimal program is therefore a compromise between:

a) completion within a short time of certain solutions producing high capital yields; however, such behavior causes the loss of effective income which would have been obtained in selecting, for each scale, a solution requiring greater capital investment;

b) the choice among higher capital investment solutions and, consequently, the completion each year of a smaller number of projects. Such behavior postpones until later dates the effective income from the other projects.

The number of possibilities offered is, in general, sufficiently small so that an optimum can be determined without too much difficulty.

Note: Investments in plants showing a loss. Up to the present, investments per se have been studied, i.e., without taking into account the situation of the plants in which they are made. When, prior to any investment, the existing operation itself is profitable, it is quite clear that an investment study can be considered apart from the general problem of the profit potential of the operation. What must be done, however, when this is not the case?

Aside from any political or social considerations, a company would not hesitate to close a plant when its operation was likely to lead to a negative effective income. The additional income derived by an investment in such a plant is therefore not equal to the "income from a plant with investment minus income from the plant without investment", but simply to the income of the plant with investment.

If such income is positive, the investment is likely to save the plant. The final decision will therefore not be contingent upon the profit potential of the investment alone, but upon that of the operation of the plant as a whole.

If, on the other hand, the plant's effective income remains negative despite the investment, then it becomes necessary to close the plant. Imperative extraeconomic reasons, however, can postpone the closing of the plant until the year p or even preclude it entirely. If the plant is not closed, the investment can be studied as though the plant were profitable. If the plant is closed during year p, the investment can be studied per se only by assuming that its life ends in year p. If, so curtailed, an investment nevertheless still appears to be highly profitable, it may be desirable to make the investment; consequently, priority may be given to making a profitable investment in a plant which is not flourishing over a very nominally profitable investment in a flourishing plant. This behavior is not without danger; it risks postponing an economically desirable closing because there is always some reluctance to abandon new installations.

5. Nonpermanent system—small investments, existence of a money market.

The absence of a permanent system considerably complicates investment problems.

At this point it is convenient to distinguish production investments from productivity investments. Moreover, an actual investment is almost always a blend of both these types of investment. Thus:

a) a productivity investment does not modify annual production of the plant in which it is made, but it reduces operational costs per unit of production;

b) a production investment can help to increase annual production, but without a decrease in the operational costs per unit of production.

The purchase of a new machine with the attendant layoff of a certain number of workmen (whose production is constant) constitutes a simple example of a productivity investment. As an example of production investment, the case can be cited of the construction of a new steel plant completely similar to existing plants and having the same cost structure. On the other hand, the construction of a new steam generating plant is both a production investment and a productivity investment; it thus becomes possible to increase the production of electrical energy while at the same time reducing the number of hours of utilization of older, less efficient power plants.

Nonpermanent systems pose three principal problems: a) that of the evolution of prices; b) that of choice among variants; c) that of taking replacement into account.

a) In a nonpermanent system, account must be taken of the development of prices from three standpoints:

1) future changes in interest rates;

2) future changes in the price of factors of production and, more especially, in wages;

3) future changes in the selling price of a product (but only in the case of investment for production).

In an expanding economy, with a national income growing at an annual rate K, it is logical to assume that such growth must normally occur at constant prices and that the quantity of money adjusts itself to production. The hypothesis of a constant quantity of money and of a reduction in nominal prices is contradicted by recent economic history.

When an increase occurs at constant prices, the monetary rate of interest i, despite the fact that it may vary from year to year, remains equal to the actual interest rate i_r.

On the contrary, in cases where nominal prices P decrease at rate $K = \dfrac{I}{P}\dfrac{dP}{dt}$ there would be between i_r and i the relation:

$$i_r = i - \frac{\mathrm{I}}{P}\frac{\mathrm{d}P}{\mathrm{d}t} = i + K$$

and it would be necessary to increase the nominal rate of interest by the rate of growth of the economy.

It is assumed in what follows that nominal prices remain constant.

1) If the prices of goods and services offered to consumers remain constant on the average, wages tend to increase. Real and nominal wages increase, in fact, as the real national income grows, with a very strong correlation between one branch of industry and another. If the distribution of income were to remain constant, the best hypothesis would be that wages have the same rate of growth K as the national per capita income. Because this is not the case, it is necessary to take into account a probable modification in the distribution of manpower in the economy.

2) As to the prices of the other factors of production, if, on the average, these are constant for the economy as a whole, they may very likely increase or decrease for a specific industry. The best course is to study the development of the prices of the major factors while holding all other prices constant.

In order to estimate future costs, account must also be taken of technical improvements possibly available in the future to plants constituting the investment.

3) The sale price of a product deserves very special study. It can show an upward or a downward trend according to the development of the market, even in an economy of stable prices.

b) In a nonpermanent system, investment possibilities are not the same each year and the effective income of a variant is contingent upon its date of completion.

What, then, are the solutions from which one must choose if one is limited to small investments whose effective income is independent? The first year, for example, two scales of investment are possible. The second year new variants appear in each of these scales. Some of these may be technically identical with the variants of the first year, but economically different because their effective income is different as a result of price developments. Other variants are new projects which were technically impossible during the first year. New scales of investment can also appear in the second year.

Thus, theoretically, one could construct complex scales of incompatible investments whose variants would differ either by technical characteristics or by the year of completion. After having calculated the effective income of each variant on the basis of the initial year:

1) a choice would be made, within each scale, of the variant which produces the maximum effective income;

2) all optimal variants which produce positive effective income would be realized.

There is a major difference in the case of a permanent system. As long as there is a money market, no advantage can be gained by making, each year, all possible investments during that year that produce positive effective income. Indeed, by waiting, benefits can be derived either from technical progress or from price development, thereby realizing more profitable returns from the same capital invested at staggered periods.

c) How are differences in lifespan taken into account in the various investments? The answer to this question affects the choice between incompatible investments.

Assuming a perfect forecast, we will consider whether replacement of an investment will or will not procure positive effective income.

In the first case, it is obvious that account must be taken of a certain amount of replacement of equipment which has reached the end of its usefulness. Otherwise, in the same scale of investments, this would place short-term investments at a disadvantage. Assuming, however, that, at the end of its lifetime, equipment is replaced by the best currently available equipment, short-term investments are still systematically penalized. For instance, a steam generating plant built in 1956 may be replaced at the end of 30 years by an atomic installation of entirely different construction instead of by an improved steam generating plant. A short-lived plant presents a certain superiority over a long-lived one because it permits an earlier utilization of technological improvements. Short-term investments have the advantage of making it possible to correct forecasting errors more quickly.

It may be, on the other hand, that the replacement of equipment is not profitable. In this connection, a distinction must be made between the interest of the entrepreneur and the general interest.

When equipment ceases to produce, new possibilities of investment appear in the economy. For example, if we consider a coal mine as a capital investment, its closing may make a new oil refinery a profitable venture. For this reason, calculations of profit potential which conform to the general interest must take replacement into consideration.

An individual firm, however, may be limited by legal or technical constraints. For example, the Charbonnages might wish to replace an unproductive coal mine with a new oil refinery. However, they are legally prohibited from so doing and so cannot benefit from investment possibilities outside the coal-mining sector.

Replacement decisions that benefit the firm are usually beneficial to the general interest through increased production or productivity and lower prices. However, if the owners cannot finance a required replacement, the firm loses its advantages, its market, and its income.*

In short, in all cases in which we have considered replacement, assuming the availability of accurate forecasting, the conclusions are quite clear: a) from the standpoint of the general interest, calculations must always postulate replacement regardless of the branch of economy in which this replacement is to be effected; b) the entrepreneur's viewpoint is more subtle because there are either loans which he cannot obtain (paragraph 4) or activities from which he may be excluded (paragraph 5).

6. Permanent system—large investments.

The hypothesis of small investments is often satisfactory in the case of materiel, but it is too restrictive in the case of complete installations. For instance, the completion of an important plant for the production of aluminum will increase the supply of aluminum and will tend, all other things being equal, to reduce the price. This results in two important consequences. First, the effective income from a group of investments is not necessarily equal to

---

*In actual practice, where forecasting is imperfect, the replacement problem is a very delicate one. There can be no doubt that consideration must be given to what will occur at the end of the lifetime of equipment, but what is not known is the level of effective income which can be produced by replacement investment.

An enterprise which, for example, assumes that replacement of equipment will provide positive effective income must assume that it will be able to preserve a profit despite efforts of competitors and developments in the entire economy. This hypothesis is as difficult to justify as the opposite hypothesis.

the sum of the effective incomes from each such investment. It can be lower or higher depending on whether the investments are substitutes or complementary.

Second, a firm bases its calculation of income on marginal receipts rather than on sales price. This results in a further, rather significant distinction between entrepreneurial and general interests.

a) Complementary and substitute investments. Two investments are complementary when the exploitation of one increases the income from the other. They are substitute investments when the exploitation of one reduces the effective income from the other. Substitutability and complementarity are functions of the goods produced or of the factors of production employed.

A coal-mining operation and the adjoining washing plant, or a factory for the production of automobiles and a tire manufacturing plant, are examples of complementary investments relative to the goods produced. A new coal-mining operation and an oil refinery are substitutes.

The cement plant using the residue of steel production in its production process is an example of investments that are complementary by virtue of production factors. An example of substitute investments is a steam generating plant and a compressor plant both using coal in their production processes. On the scale of the economy as a whole, manpower is the most important production factor. It is essential to identify those investments whose exploitation will consume considerable manpower (coal mining, for instance) and those which require very little manpower (hydroelectric plants). In this sense, investments of different types are complementary, and those of the same type are substitutes.

Figures 12, 13, and 14 illustrate possible relationships between two "large investments." The quantity of capital D_1 allocated to the first investment is indicated as an ordinate and the quantity of capital D_2 allocated to the second as an abscissa. In the plane D_1D_2, curves are drawn on which the effective income R_1 from the first investment is constant. There is always a limiting curve on which income is at a maximum.

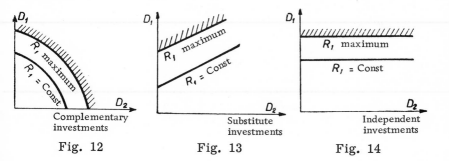

| Complementary investments | Substitute investments | Independent investments |
| Fig. 12 | Fig. 13 | Fig. 14 |

b) The selection of large investments from the standpoint of an enterprise and from that of the general interest. The simplest procedure is, first, to consider the problem as it relates to a firm. A firm naturally seeks to maximize its effective income. Let us assume that it is offered a choice among various investments leading to different Q levels of production of certain goods and that, for a level Q, the price is q(Q) and effective costs D(Q). It has already been demonstrated that a firm will set as its marginal cost, not the price p(Q), but the marginal income $p(Q) + D \dfrac{dp}{dQ}$, which is smaller.

It must be noted that the curve p(Q) is not an ordinary demand curve. This curve represents the price at which Q can be sold, taking into account all the effects the investment has on other prices, income, etc. Similarly, the D(Q) function represents effective costs for the various levels of production, account being taken of the effect of the investment on the prices of the production factors. In actual practice, D(Q) can be merged with the ordinary cost function in which the prices of production factors are constant.

From the standpoint of the general interest, however, the rule of choice is much more subtle [22]. We will set it forth without further proof. Consideration must be given—for the various levels of production—to the demand curve p(Q) and the marginal cost $D'(Q)$ obtained: a) by taking into account the effect the investment has on all other prices and on incomes; and b) by assuming that as Q increases income is modified, so that the "effective income" of the consumers will vary in the same direction.

The expression $\int_0^Q [p(Q) - D'(Q)] \, dQ$ represents economic surplus. Surplus is represented by the shaded area in Fig. 15.

Furthermore, from the standpoint of the general interest, the economic surplus (which, subject to certain precautions, can also be realized) must be substituted for effective income.

From a table of all possible investments, one can select, within each range of incompatible investments, the one which leads to maximum surplus, and one should carry out all optimal investments which provide a positive surplus.

Notes:

1. When marginal cost $D'(Q)$ decreases, the surplus can be positive and the effective income negative (see Fig. 16). In other words, firms may not wish to make profitable investments on a community scale.

2. Surplus is maximum when the price p(Q) and marginal cost $D'(Q)$ are equal. The optimal size of projects is therefore not the same for both the firm and the community.

3. The differing context for investment between the public and private sectors was not pertinent in the case of small investments

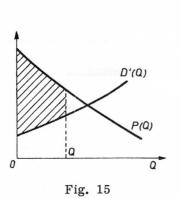

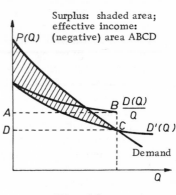

Fig. 15   Fig. 16

because sales price was essentially not contingent upon Q, and the surplus and effective income were then equal to the same expression: $pQ - D(Q)$.

4. The introduction of surpluses in actual econometric calculations is quite recent. One of the first applications was made in France in connection with studies on the availability of consumer gas from the Lacq area. These concepts are of interest only in the case of broad phenomena having a profound effect either upon the national economy or upon the economy of a region. An examination of the profit potential of large investments, from the standpoint of the general interest, could be the subject of important theoretical and practical developments during the next few years, adding new chapters to economic analysis.

c) Method of calculation. Let us now examine the methods of selecting an investment program when the various scales are not independent. To simplify, we will assume a money market and will adopt the viewpoint of the firm.

In a permanent system, an investment which was of no initial interest will not become attractive later, and each investment made will be replaced on expiration by a similar investment.

The forecast is accurate, the future demand curves are known, and with each program there is a corresponding increase in production and receipts.

The selection of a program can be made by successive approximations. If the firm establishes a priori a price at which the investment would appear attractive, then it can also calculate the effective income for all of the investments in the table of solutions. The firm can also determine an optimal program by means of the method in paragraph 3 above. It can then anticipate the increase in production which will result from such a program and, therefore, the level of future prices. If these prices differ little from those postulated a priori, the program is correct. Otherwise, it must be adjusted to a new schedule of future prices to replace those which had just been determined. And so on, until compatibility is reached between program and prices.

Instead of starting with a schedule of future prices, we may start with a production schedule. This is generally an easier approach because forecasting studies are frequently made on the basis of production.

Consequently, a combination is sought in the table of solutions by means of which it will be possible to increase production by a desired quantity in order to obtain a basic program. In a second phase, this program is compared with all combinations of solutions which result in identical increases in production. Within all of these combinations a choice must be made of the program whose effective income has a maximum positive difference from the basic program. The sales price does not enter into this comparison because the receipts cancel themselves by difference. Once an optimal program has been determined, a calculation must be made of selling price in such a way that the effective income from all operations under the program will be positive except that of the last one, which must be zero. In a final phase, a check is made as to whether the selling price so determined is compatible with the hypothesis initially made concerning production. If such is not the case, this hypothesis is modified. This manner of proceeding is entirely justified because it is easier to predict an increase in production than future prices. The calculation of the selling price on the basis of the program and its comparison with the hypothetical production is merely an a posteriori means of control.

7. Policy on replacement of material.

In the foregoing it has been mentioned on several occasions that, in a permanent system, equipment is replaced at the end of its life by identical equipment. The apparent simplicity of this statement belies the complexity of its implications; the lifetime of equipment is by no means easily determined. The replacement cycle is economically determined by comparing projected levels of maintenance and operating costs with replacement costs.

The problem of an optimal policy for the replacement of material, moreover, is presented in two ways: a) that of replacing a single piece of equipment which, as time goes on, becomes obsolete as a result of technical progress; b) that of replacing equipment whose failure is random. Such is the case with radar tubes [1]. In this case, any equipment which fails is immediately replaced. If random failure is costly, there may be some advantage in periodically replacing all equipment or in replacing any equipment that reaches a certain age. The problem of replacement, in the case of material subject to failure, can be dealt with by means of models utilizing Markov chains. Since these models have already been discussed, this paragraph will limit itself to cases of equipment subject to wear and obsolescence.

Assuming that the system is permanent, the best technical equipment is always the newest equipment of the type under consideration. Assume c to be its purchase price. When a factory purchases new equipment in the year 0, during that year it has at its disposal the best equipment technically possible. During the year 1 the equipment is one year old, and the gross operational receipts are lower by d_1 than they would have been with new equipment. Therefore, to each of the years 1, 2, ..., n can be associated a figure d_n which is the difference between gross operational receipts with new equipment and with equipment of age n.

If an enterprise during a certain year has at its disposal equipment of m age, it will find it necessary to solve the following problem: should equipment of m age be replaced this year by new equipment? To answer this question, it will merely be necessary to compare the effective income of two solutions:

a) immediate purchase of new equipment;

b) preservation of the older equipment for another year.

Equipment should be replaced when the annual operating costs for the older machine are higher than the total annual cost associated with a new machine [2].

The operating cost of the older machine during an additional year is d_{m+1}, because this machine is compared with a new machine.

The total cost involved in the purchase of a new machine used n years is, similarly:

$$D(n) = c + \sum_1^n \frac{d_p}{(1 + i)^p}.$$

The total annual cost resulting from the purchase of a new machine is therefore:

$$q(n) = \frac{D(n)}{\sum_0^n \frac{1}{(1 + i)^p}}.$$

Naturally, one must take for n a value n_0 which minimizes q(n).

The older machine should be retained if $q(n_0) > d_{m+1}$ and replaced if $q(n_0) < d_{m+1}$.

It will be observed that this model remains valid even in a non-permanent system, provided: a) the purchase price of a new machine is essentially constant, and b) the d_p series of operational losses is independent of time and is contingent only upon the age of the machine.

A comparison of d_{m+1} with $q(n_0)$ presents no problem. Nevertheless, G. Terborgh has attempted to give it a very simple form, subject to a few additional hypotheses [31]. The interest of this method is in the judicious choice of these hypotheses, notably in connection with the development of d_p.

If one takes for granted that technical progress proceeds at a slow but essentially constant rhythm, it is plausible to adopt for d_p an expression of the form pd, where d represents the additional operational losses incurred when a machine becomes a year older. In the case of a small i, q(n) can then be considered as formed by the three following terms:

a) a constant $\dfrac{c}{n}$ amortization of the purchase price c;

b) financing costs $\dfrac{ic}{2}$ calculated on the basis of half the purchase price;

c) the mean value of terms $d_p = pd$, i.e., $\dfrac{d\,(n-1)}{2}$; n_0 is therefore the value of n which minimizes:

$$\frac{c}{n} + \frac{ic}{2} + \frac{d\,(n-1)}{2}.$$

From which:

$$n_0 = \sqrt{\frac{2c}{d}}$$

and:

$$q\,(n_0) = \sqrt{2\,cd} + \frac{ic - d}{2}$$

To determine quickly the decision to be made, an engineer calculates the expression:

$$q\,(n_0) - d_{m+1} = \sqrt{2\,cd} + \frac{ic - d}{2} - (m + 1)\,d.$$

in which the sign is contingent only upon the relation c/d, i.e., the relation of the value of the new installation to the annual operating loss.

The first part of this chapter has followed somewhat theoretical lines, and the various examples presented may have caused a certain confusion in the mind of the reader. The complexity of the problem, however, is very real; the apparent facility which would prevail in the absence of the distinctions which have been introduced would prove to be very dangerous in actual application. Although it is preferable to use a simple a model as possible, no significant element should be overlooked.

It is within the framework of a simple model that we shall now proceed to a calculation of effective income from various investments.

II

CALCULATION OF EFFECTIVE INCOME

We consider here the general case in which an investment is made by the creation of a new installation or the extension of an existing one. We examine the various steps for calculating the effective income from each of the possibilities in a scale of incompatible investments.

These steps are as follows:

1. First, it is necessary to isolate all possible variants and to define their main characteristics (productive capacity, approximate number of machines, manpower, etc.).

2. Next, an evaluation is made of investment costs.

3. Then the operational costs are calculated, item by item, at current prices.

4. Some forecasts are now in order:
   a) as to the future price of goods sold;
   b) as to the future price of factors utilized;
   c) as to the development of productivity.

5. The relationship between effective income and each operation can be calculated. At this stage, an engineer-economist must ascertain whether each variant cannot be improved by a slight modification in its technical characteristics or whether there may not be an external solution.

6. All these calculations call for a certain interest rate. How is the latter to be selected?

7. The future is uncertain; forecasts cannot be perfect. A risk is attached to any investment. How can this risk be taken into account?

8. Each choice has a financial and a sociological impact which should be considered before completion of the economic analysis.

Frequently, it is necessary to repeat the first five stages of this analysis several times because one cannot define at the outset all the variants in competition. The eight paragraphs in this section deal with the foregoing points in the order noted.

1. Outline of possible choices.

To start with, an investment is a creative effort. Economic analysis cannot substitute for creative insight. It can only define alternatives and indicate optimum choice. The methods which have been described make it possible to choose among various possibilities—provided, of course, that there are possibilities, i.e., that innovations are proposed by members of the company. Failing a flow of innovations, economic analysis is a machine without inputs.

Based on their experience and intuition, members of the firm will suggest possible investment. Each will develop the basic details of his suggestion (daily production, equipment requirements, etc.). When group discussions begin, the several points of view will manifest themselves and the discussion will crystallize around a few of the proposals. Thus, generally, are choices born.

In this preliminary phase, an engineer-economist can play an important role:

a) If, through daily conferences and contacts, he succeeds in awakening his colleagues to the economic aspects of choices, those who are considering the projects will tend to regard them as a viable economic whole and not just as a marvel of technical achievement.

b) When a study is begun, one should not concentrate on too small a number of choices. The economist must make sure that the range of choices under study actually covers the whole pertinent field of acceptable investment possibilities. Only in this way can some notion be gained of the range of effective income in relation to investment costs (Fig. 6). Because the cost of analysis can be fairly high, it might not be economic to examine each of the different choices with equal intensity; however, in making brief preliminary studies of all alternatives one insures oneself, at relatively small cost, against an initial error in judgment. The situation of an executive is similar to that of a general seeking to make contact with an enemy whose location is not known to him. The general will concentrate his strength in the direction of the most probable point of contact while at the same time spreading his reconnaissance groups over a large front in order to cover as much territory as possible.

c) An economist must insure that an alternative project is considered in such a way that no a priori assumptions can be made regarding the variation in effective income for each modification in the project. Let us explain the latter on the basis of an example taken from the coal industry. A coal mine can increase its extraction from 2,000 to 5,000 tons daily through increased investment. This coal mine, however, is firedamped and the emanation of the fumes is somewhat proportionate to the tonnage extracted; above 3,000 tons daily, the existing shafts no longer permit the passage of sufficient air to meet safety requirements. If it is desired to exceed 3,000 tons daily, it will be necessary to drill a ventilation shaft. Finally, to increase extraction beyond 5,000 tons daily, an additional shaft will be required. It is clear that, under such conditions, considerable advantage is to be gained by studying choices that make fuller use of the mines, trading off the incremental costs against the increased output.

The above observation is valid whenever there is reason to believe that the curve of effective income in relation to production has the shape of that in Fig. 17. Abscissas a, b, c correspond to threshold changes in the inventory of equipment. It will also be profitable to devote special study to choices A, B, C rather than to a variant such as B'.

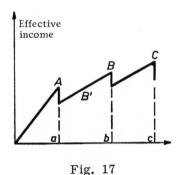

Fig. 17

2. Evaluation of investment costs.

Once the main choices have been established, an evaluation must be made of each of their respective effective incomes, but such a task can only be undertaken in stages.

The first of these stages is, invariably, the determination of investment costs, which stems from an understanding of the technical aspects of the project. Account having been taken of the general characteristics which have been decided upon, the technicians must attempt to reduce investment costs to a minimum without increasing maintenance and operating costs.

They will establish a schedule of projects to be started each year and will enumerate the significant costs (e.g., research and analysis costs, cost of material purchased abroad, payments to building contractors, supply and wage expenditures).

Having determined the investment requirement for each project to provide for the anticipated costs, the level of investment can be increased somewhat for contingencies. A standard investment whose risk is relatively small would require a small safety factor. A larger cushion would be required for a novel project or one whose completion is contingent upon imperfectly known conditions (the boring of a tunnel, for instance).

3. Calculation of operational costs.

An evaluation of operational costs is more difficult than that of investment costs since it covers the entire lifetime of an installation. This period, however, more often than not can be divided into two phases:

a) A phase of adjustment beginning with the end of the period of investment. During this phase, the repercussions from the investment are progressively felt throughout the operation. In the case of large investments this phase can last a few months or a few years.

b) A phase of normal operation during which the characteristics of equipment utilization are fairly constant.

Because the second phase is longer and is characterized by uniform operation, studies should be concentrated upon the latter. However, at the same time a limit should be obtained which operational costs are likely to approach during the adjustment period. The years of adjustment, moreover, are important because they border on the second phase and consequently carry considerable weight in the calculation of effective lifetime income.

To evaluate operational costs it will be found useful to set up an input-output table in accordance with the model described in Chapter 8, and to begin as of the first year of normal operation. The thorny problem of changing productivity during an installation's lifetime is thereby avoided. This problem, however, will be touched upon below.

The use of an input-output table is particularly appropriate in the case of expansion of an existing operation; once established, an input-output table describing a continuing operation can easily form the basis for an input-output table for the expanded installation, subject to a small number of technical hypotheses (for instance, the number of grams of coal consumed by a power station per kw.-hr. produced; the yield per man and per station in a coal mine; the number of calories consumed per ton of clinker in a cement-making plant; etc.). Since an evaluation of future costs is highly contingent upon the values retained for such parameters, they must be selected with care and an idea must be obtained of their limits of variation.

Included as operational costs are current expenditures, excluding amortization of equipment during the investment phase. Failing such a precaution, the same expenditure would be counted twice. The replacement problem must be dealt with separately.

In the case of large installations (a new factory, for example), the term "lifetime" is ambiguous since, of all equipment installed during the investment period, only a few units would have a lifetime equal to that of the plant itself. Moreover, the lifetime of the equipment determines that of the factory. The greater proportion of the remaining equipment has a lifetime of shorter duration and will have to be replaced during the lifetime of the installation. The corresponding costs must be taken into account in the calculation of effective income. A separate consideration of each of these pieces of equipment, however, can require considerable work, and the added precision obtained is hardly worth the cost. It is therefore preferable to separate equipment into two groups.

1) The first group will include equipment which requires a considerable outlay of funds. This equipment will be treated individually, and the year during which it will probably need to be replaced will be indicated in a table, together with corresponding costs.

2) The second group will include all other investments to be replaced during the lifetime of the installation. These replacements will result in a flow of annual expenditures. A constant flow of annual costs, approximately equivalent thereto, will be determined; eventually this cost flow will take the form of the annual amortization schedule for the total equipment of this type for equivalent installations. For instance, in their studies on the profit potential of investments the Charbonnages de France have assumed that new work each year would amount to about 200 to 300 francs per ton.

4. A discussion of forecasting.

The soundness of investments will directly reflect forecasting accuracy. An attempt should therefore be made to obtain the best forecasts, taking all available information into account. Avoiding forecasts in the name of future uncertainty is futile, since any action—and an absence of decision is a particular form of the latter—implicitly presupposes forecasts. It is therefore in its investment studies that an enterprise will utilize the results of detailed market analyses as described in the beginning of this book.

Aside from the interest rate (to which a special section is being devoted), forecasts relate to the future demand for goods produced by a firm, the future price of the factors utilized, and the development of productivity within the enterprise.

Future demand. The period covered by the forecasts and the estimated lifespan of investments should be identical. A public transportation company, when purchasing buses, does not need to consider as long a period as does an electric company in constructing a dam.

Future prices of factors. It is convenient to separate the operational costs into two or three categories (salaries, raw materials, supplies) and to analyze separately the probable development of the price index for these categories within the framework of a constant total price level.

Development of productivity. During its lifetime, an investment will benefit from certain technical improvements. Care should be exercised, however, in utilizing calculations of overall productivity increases to discriminate between the effect of technical changes in existing installations and the consequences of replacing older installations with highly modernized plants.

5. Study of the scale as a whole.

Once the effective income has been calculated for each choice, a study of the scale as a whole must include a reexamination of the questions discussed at the beginning, with emphasis on the following:

a) Do we have, for each choice, a solution indicating the maximum effective income?

b) How does effective income vary among the choices under study?

c) Has adequate consideration been given to the choice which is likely to produce the maximum effective income?

6. The rate of interest.

All studies concerning profit and potential presuppose a rate of interest. It is up to the managers of the firm to select an interest rate and to insure its use in any study regarding the profit potential of all suggested investments. This interest rate must be corrected periodically to reflect the "opportunity costs" affecting the firm in the context of the current market.

Funds invested by a firm in its own equipment can be derived from three different sources; 1) the issuance of bonds, 2) the issuance of shares, and 3) the use of the firm's own funds (self-financing).

The interest rate adopted must be the same for all investments and cannot be contingent upon the particular manner in which an investment is financed.

Interest should constitute a function of the composition of the firm's capital structure. However, we will consider financing via sales of bonds or shares as well as self-financing as a means of reviewing several investment decision alternatives.

a) When funds are derived from a loan, the cost of this loan is accurately defined. However, these loan costs should not necessarily be adopted as an interest rate. As we have observed in the chapter on amortization, the reimbursement rate of a loan can be very different from that of a loss in investment value. To offset the latter, the financial department is constantly compelled to engage in borrowing; these loan operations do not completely cancel each other. One is therefore justified in setting an interest rate which will be slightly higher than the cost of the loan. Contracting a loan always presents a certain risk for a firm. Consequently, an additional cost is implicitly attached to any loan.

b) The case of issuing additional shares is more subtle. The interest rate on new shares represents the company's future annual income which will have to be paid to stockholders. Let us consider the case of a company with 100,000 shares at 10,000 francs each, i.e., a capital of one billion francs. The market rate of interest is 5%, and at present the firm pays a 10% dividend per year, i.e., 1,000 francs per share. If potential buyers believe that such a dividend will be maintained in the future, the current price of the shares on the stock market anticipates the fact that these shares produce much more than the 5% rate. The price per share rises to 20,000 francs, a price at which the shares produce exactly 5%. Let us now assume that the firm wishes to build a second plant exactly like the first—thereby doubling its capital—and that potential buyers foresee that this new investment will be as "profitable" as the previous one. The market will discount the anticipated future income and will price the shares at a level so that the dividend yield equals the market interest rate.

Designating as n the number of new shares to be issued and p as the price which will be established on the market, p will be such that the firm's shares as a whole produce 5% per year. Now, the annual income of the firm will be $2 \times 10^3 \times 10^5$. Therefore:

$$\frac{2 \cdot 10^3 \cdot 10^5}{p \, (10^5 + n)} = 0.05.$$

On the other hand, the value of the new shares must cover the cost of constructing the new plant (one billion francs): i.e.,

$$pn = 10^9$$

The solution of the foregoing equations leads to the following values of p and n:

$$p = 30,000 \text{ francs} \qquad n = 33,333$$

Considering the essential difference in the case of bonds, however, this market mechanism takes into account the special risks which are inherent in the purchase of shares. A substantial difference may therefore remain between the implicit interest rate relative to the price of shares and the interest rate paid on bonds.

This question of risk has already been reviewed in Chapter 2, where it was demonstrated that under certain conditions it is reasonable to retain: a) an interest rate corresponding to the income from shares where the capital of an enterprise is entirely composed of shares; and b) an average interest rate with respect to the net asset value of the firm when its capital is composed of both shares and bonds.

c) In the case of self-financing it might appear as though interest is not applicable because the firm's own funds are involved. This is an erroneous viewpoint because, with the funds it invests, a company can engage in operations which would have produced a certain rate of interest: payment of old debts, loans on the money market, and other investments likely to produce income. The interest rate to be established must be calculated by the company after taking into consideration all alternative uses of its money. In actual practice, such a rate is difficult to determine. Terborgh [31] emphasizes that the rate established should never be below the rate which could be obtained by lending the amount indicated (i_1) or below the rate to borrow funds from outside (i_2). In a perfect market, moreover, these two rates would be equal.

It is reasonable to use the first estimation as a basis when a company disposes of sufficient funds of its own to effect all the profitable investments at rate i_1. If, on the other hand, the company must borrow in order to finance part of its investments, i_2 is a satisfactory evaluation.

Whatever may be the method of financing, the choice of the interest rate finally established is contingent upon the risks incurred and the uncertainty attached to the outcome of investment.

7. Uncertainty.

Two complementary approaches are possible. The first locates and discusses the main forecasting errors. The second attempts to evaluate the time lag of receipts.

First approach. If one refers to the mathematical expression of the present value, it will be observed that uncertainty can assume the three following forms:

a) inaccuracy of forecasts regarding the interest rate;
b) inaccuracy of forecasts of demand and future prices;
c) inaccuracy of forecasts of future costs.

a) Inaccuracy of forecasts regarding the interest rate.

If too low an interest rate has been selected, one is given a range of choice which could include investments which, subsequently, may not be profitable. On the other hand, if too high an interest rate has been selected, one inhibits one's choice, which may preclude consideration of some profitable investments. Preferring a loss of opportunity to an actual loss, many firms select, in profit calculations, a rate of interest which represents the sum of a rate determined without taking uncertainty into account (according to the methods outlined in the preceding paragraph), and a risk premium of a certain percent.

But generalized use of such a practice is subject to criticism. In fact, three entirely different situations are possible in this connection:

1) Let us consider a case involving alternative plans for handling one investment possibility. For example, consider the determination of the optimal size of a dam to supply a spillway. If the interest rate is too high, the size decided upon may save investment costs but will permit too small a dam to be constructed. Unfortunately, once made, the error is binding. In choosing the best alternative within a specific project it is preferable not to increase the interest rate.

2) On the other hand, if the interest rate is too high and the investment possibilities are limited, the future risks are also limited. For example, the date for equipping the spillway may be postponed. In this case, it is not necessary that a company should attempt to exploit all available opportunities. It can agree to earn less while incurring less risk.

3) The situation is quite different in the case of replacement. In fact, because an enterprise will wish to continue its level of activity, it will make replacements sooner or later, and the interest rate merely serves to establish the approximate date of such replacement. The choice of a high rate of interest favors existing equipment and postpones its replacement. However, errors in forecasts can lead to estimates of economic life which are too long or too short. To guard against these errors by systematically postponing replacements can only cause loss of money.

The following is an analogy which may illustrate the difference between the two last cases. A man on a railroad station platform is about to board a train in motion. The train begins to slow down; its speed reaches a minimum and then accelerates again without ever stopping. In the case of a replacement, the traveler knows that he must board the train come what may, and he will attempt to select the most favorable moment, that is, the moment when, according to his predictions, the train will be passing him at minimum speed. In the case of an expansion, a traveler is not obliged to board the train, and he can tell himself that he will not attempt to board if the train's speed does not go below a value which he has established in advance (which is contingent upon the risk he is willing to assume). This difference between expansion and replacement should not, however, be pushed too far. If the investment appears to be too risky, one can decide to drop any replacement.

b) Inaccuracy of forecasts of demand and future prices.

With regard to future demand, an attempt can be made to define an average hypothesis, a weak hypothesis, and a strong hypothesis. Very frequently, such hypotheses have a definite economic significance. For instance, in 1955 a French industrialist could make his calculations, taking for granted either maintenance or elimination of export markets.

The influence of a variation in future price can be shown very simply [28]. Let P_p represent production during the year p. The quantity:

$$P = \sum_p \frac{P_p}{(1 + i)^p}$$

has been named effective production. Let D represent total effective costs and v the future sales price, assumed to be constant. When D and P are calculated at a profit rate i:

$$vP = D$$

If v varies from dv, one can write:

$$P \, dv + v \frac{dP}{di} \, di = \frac{dD}{di} \, di$$

i.e.,

$$di = \frac{P \, dv}{\frac{dD}{di} - v \frac{dP}{di}}.$$

A variation in profit is therefore all the stronger as effective production is higher and as the expression: $\frac{dD}{di} - v \frac{dP}{di}$ is lower, i.e., as the costs are delayed and receipts are almost immediate.

c) Inaccuracy of forecasts of future costs.

This is often contingent upon the uncertainty of technical parameters, which vary considerably from one industry to another. Low in the case of certain industries like the highly mechanized ones, it can attain a very large value in cases of exploitation of natural resources such as the opening of a new coal mine. In this case it may be advisable to include some alternatives in the estimates.

All such studies make one aware of the variations which may occur in anticipated effective income. The decision then rests with the executive.

Second approach. We here seek to evaluate the time lag of receipts. This postulates that, as time passes, forecasts diverge more and more from reality. From such a standpoint one can consider:

a) the period of amortization previously determined, which is the time it takes for effective receipts to equal expenditures—the shorter this period the less risk is involved;

b) the average delay in the collection of net income. This quantity has been introduced by J. Ullmo.

Let $k = \dfrac{I}{I + i}$ and let us trace the transform R(k) of curve R (i) of Fig. 2. This curve is shown in Fig. 18. At an i_r profit rate there is a corresponding k_r value of k and

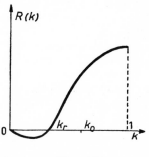

Fig. 18

at an i_0 market interest rate a value k_0. Let us calculate the elasticity of curve R(k). R_p designates the net income for the year p.

$$R\,(k) = \Sigma\, k^p R_p$$
$$e = \frac{k}{R} \cdot \frac{dR}{dk} = \frac{\Sigma\, pk^{p-1} R_p \cdot k dk}{\Sigma k^p R_p\, dk} = \frac{\Sigma\, pk^p R_p}{\Sigma\, k^p R_p}.$$

e represents the dimensions of time. This is the average delay in the collection of net income. Over the period of amortization, e presents the advantage of taking into account the probable income during the entire life of the investment.

8. Financial and sociological studies.

The main object of a financial study is to determine the various possible methods of financing and to choose the one which presents the greatest advantage for the firm. The choice is made on the scale of the whole program and not at the project level, since once the funds have been obtained it is of little import to a financial department whether these are used for one project or for another.

A sociological study, on the other hand, must be made with respect to each project. Its objective is to analyze a project's repercussions outside the firm. In this sense, one can go from a very simple case in which an investment will modify conditions of employment within an area to a complex case in which an entire region is economically and socially affected. Examples of the latter are the harnessing of the River Durance in France and the development of the Tennessee Valley in the United States, not to mention Soviet examples concerning which we have fewer details.

When an investment improves the economic situation of a region, there may be some disagreement between company objectives and the general interest (cf. the paragraph on large investments). Theoretically, a firm does not take into consideration external advantages resulting from an investment except where it can receive payment from beneficiaries. In actual fact, however, private firms are not insensitive to the external consequences of their investments; the object of a sociological study is precisely that of describing these consequences.

When all of the foregoing studies have been completed, they are gathered up and presented to the executives of the firm, with whom, in the final analysis, the decision rests.

III

SPECIFIC EXAMPLES

Although they all relate solely to the energy sector, the three examples selected each have unique attributes. The first highlights the use of effective income to estimate the incidence of delay in the execution of an investment. The second analyzes the profit potential of a mine-power plant group. The third, on the other hand, broaches the problem of a complex equipment plan on the specific basis of the case of the development of the production of electricity in Algeria.

1. Incidence of delay in the completion of a large mining combine.

Recently, a coal mining operation decided, because of a scarcity of coal, to transfer miners who had been engaged in constructing a large combine to the extraction of coal. As a result, the completion of the large combine was delayed by six months, but the displaced miners extracted additional coal. To ascertain whether the decision was justified, the following should be compared: 1) the loss resulting from the reduction in the present value of future receipts from the large combine and 2) the gain resulting from the sale of the additional coal extracted by the transferred miners.

a) Evaluation of loss. Let us consider the spread of receipts and expenditures for a given investment and for a variant differing from such investment only by a stoppage of duration t at the moment T followed by a return to identical operation (Fig. 19).

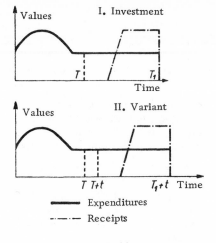

Fig. 19

The lifetime of the large combine is T_1.

D designates the expenditures during the period $(0, T)$ effective at instant 0, V the income from this investment effective at instant T and subsequent to T, and i the rate of continuous interest.

The present values at instant 0 for the investment and the alternative are, respectively:

$$Ve^{-iT} - D \qquad Ve^{-i(T-t)} - D.$$

These present values are equivalent at instant T to the sums obtained by multiplying them by e^{iT}, i.e.:

$$V - De^{iT} \qquad Ve^{-it} - De^{iT}.$$

By subtraction, we obtain the loss p in present value at instant T because of the stoppage:

$$p = V(1 - e^{-it})$$

V not being directly known, the effective income R of the large combine at instant T was substituted (R, unlike V, takes into account expenditures and receipts between 0 and T):

$$V = R + De^{iT}$$

p is then expressed:

$$p = (R + De^{iT})(1 - e^{-it})$$

i.e., since i and t are low: $(R + De^{iT})it$. R being of the order of 0.75 De^{iT}, De^{iT} being close to 6 billion, and i equal to 4.5%, the loss is then valued at:

$$0.045 \cdot \frac{6}{12} \cdot (0.75 + 1)\, 6{,}000 = 236 \text{ millions of francs.}$$

b) Evaluation of gain. For the duration of the delay, the 60 displaced miners—assuming that all of these miners were used for extraction—produced a yield of 4 tons per miner per day for 25 days of work per month for 6 months, a tonnage of coal equal to:

$$60 \times 4 \times 25 \times 6 = 36{,}000 \text{ net tons.}$$

If the short-term marginal cost of production per ton, as a result of an increase in manpower, rises to about 3,000 francs, and if this ton can be sold for about 4,500 francs, the transfer of the miners is translated into a gain of:

$$(4{,}500 - 3{,}000)\, 36{,}000 = 54 \text{ millions of francs.}$$

In total, the delay in the development of the large combine represents a loss of approximately 180 million francs.

2. Profitability of a central power station on the River Allier, supplied with coal from the Aumance Valley [35].

In the Aumance valley, near Moulins, is located a coal field containing ashy coal, difficult to wash, which cannot be used for much else than a steam generating plant. The French economy being short of power, the exploitation of this field was considered along with the construction of a nearby steam generating plant to absorb its entire production. In order to ascertain whether this project was worth developing, a study of profit potential was made to compare this solution with other possibilities of producing electrical energy. Under conditions prevailing at that time, the other alternative was easy to define: it consisted of installing in the Paris area equivalent steam generating power and supplying it with imported American coal. It was therefore necessary to study the relative profit potential of the "Aumance" solution with respect to this other project.

Electrical equipment is rated strictly in accordance with peak demand, and since, at peak periods, the electricity produced at Aumance had to be transmitted to Paris, it was necessary to compare two projects capable of supplying the same peak power to the Paris area. The distance from Aumance to Paris being about 300 kilometers, the loss of power in transit was approximately 6%. Therefore, a standard central power station constructed in

Paris to provide equivalent service would have to be replaced by a standard station on the Allier River and by a complementary station of 0.06 power in Paris.

On the other hand, how would the energy supplied by the Aumance station be used during the 30 years of the station's life from 1960 to 1990? Because Aumance coal has a very low cost of extraction (considerably below the price of American coal), it could reasonably be taken for granted that the Aumance station would work at capacity i.e., approximately 5,500 hours per year, during the major part of its life. There remained the question as to which types of power stations would supply the same energy if the Aumance project were abandoned. This was answered by examining groups of successive five-year periods.

1960-1965 period. The energy supplied by the Aumance station contributes 3,500 hours of supply to the Paris area and 2,000 hours of supply to the southern part of France. The study demonstrates that, in both cases, this energy is substituted for energy which would be produced by nearby stations with specific consumption amounting to 2,500 kcal./kw.-hr.

Using the Aumance station will require, in addition, the operation of the supplemental plant during 3,500 hours in winter but, on the other hand, its use will remove the necessity for putting this power into service during the 2,000 hours during which its energy is transmitted south.

To sum up, if p_1 is the proportional cost per therm of the Aumance coal, and p_1' the price per therm of American coal delivered to Paris, the annual cost for fuel will be, per unit of power:

5,500 × 2,540 p_1 + 3,500 × 2,500 p_1 0.06 if the specific consumption of the Aumance station is specified at 2,540 kcal./kw.-hr., and

5,500 × 2,500 p_1 + 2,000 × 2,500 p_1 0.06 in the opposite case.

Following periods. With regard to other periods, we will limit ourselves to indicating the distribution of energy in the form of a summary table. Aumance energy is substituted in Paris for that of more modern central power stations with lower specific consumption.

Having analyzed the distribution of energy, the problem of evaluating the various costs can be discussed:

a) Investment costs. These relate to the mine and to the electrical equipment. They are effective as of the date the station was put into operation.

Mine. Investment costs are expressed as a value per net kw.-hr. at varying rates of interest:

$$i = \text{o} \quad 6{,}3\text{oo francs}$$
$$i = 5\% \quad 6{,}85\text{o} \quad —$$
$$i = 10\% \quad 7{,}38\text{o} \quad —$$
$$i = 15\% \quad 7{,}95\text{o} \quad —$$

Aumance solution				Parisian station solution			
Station	Power	Number of hours	Price per kwh	Station*	Power	Number of hours	Price per kwh
1960-1965							
Aumance	1	5,500	$2,540p_1$	Paris	1	5,500	$2,500p_1$
Contribution	0.06	3,500	$2,500p'_1$	Contribution	0.06	2,000	$2,500p'_1$
1965-1970							
Aumance	1	5,500	$2,540p_2$	Paris	1	3,500	$2,500p'_2$
Contribution	0.06	3,500	$2,500p'_2$	"	1	2,000	$2,460p'_2$
				Contribution	0.06	2,000	$2,460p'_2$
1970-1975							
Aumance	1	5,500	$2,540p_3$	Paris	1	2,500	$2,300p'_3$
Contribution	0.06	3,000	$2,500p'_3$	"	1	1,000	$2,460p'_3$
				"	1	2,400	$2,300p'_3$
				Contribution	0.06	2,000	$2,300p'_3$
1975-1980							
Aumance	1	5,500	$2,540p_4$	Paris	1	1,500	$2,500p'_4$
Contribution	0.06	2,500	$2,500p'_4$	"	1	1,000	$2,460p'_4$
				"	1	1,000	$2,300p'_4$
				"	1	2,000	$2,240p'_4$
				Contribution	0.06	2,000	$2,240p'_4$
1980-1985							
Aumance	1	5,500	$2,540p_5$	Paris	1	1,000	$2,500p'_5$
Contribution	0.06	2,000	$2,500p'_5$	"	1	500	$2,460p'_5$
				"	1	1,000	$2,300p'_5$
				"	1	1,000	$2,240p'_5$
				"	1	2,000	$2,240p'_5$
				Contribution	0.06	2,000	$2,240p'_5$
1985-1990							
Aumance	1	5,500	$2,540p_6$	Paris	1	500	$2,500p'_6$
Contribution	0.06	2,000	$2,500p'_6$	"	1	500	$2,460p'_6$
				"	1	500	$2,300p'_6$
				"	1	4,000	$2,240p'_6$
				Contribution	0.06	2,000	$2,240p'_6$

*In this column the term "contribution" designates additional energy for which the construction of an additional power station is not required since the operation takes place during slack hours.

Electrical equipment. Central power stations. The Aumance station is more costly per installed kw.-hr. than the Paris station because it consumes much more ashy products and constitutes a two-group (200 MW) station. On the other hand, the replacement power in the Paris area would be obtained from four-group stations. Taking into account the investment represented by the contributing station, the additional costs created by the Aumance solution are, per installed kw.-hr.,

$$i = 0 \qquad 9,100 \text{ francs}$$
$$i = 5\% \quad 9,900 \quad —$$
$$i = 10\% \quad 10,800 \quad —$$
$$i = 15\% \quad 11,400 \quad —$$

Power line. Its purpose is to transmit energy to Paris from the Aumance station. It would cost approximately 8 million francs per kilometer. Account must also be taken of two protective cells (i.e., 90 million francs), or the following investments per net kw.:

$$i = 0 \qquad 9,600 \text{ francs}$$
$$i = 5\% \quad 10,200 \quad —$$
$$i = 10\% \quad 10,800 \quad —$$
$$i = 15\% \quad 11,300 \quad —$$

b) Fuel costs. These are deduced directly from a knowledge of the energy flow and of the assumptions with respect to the price of fuels. In the case of Aumance coal, a study indicates that the operational cost amounts to about 650 francs per million calories PCS.

With regard to American coal delivered to Paris, the study used the estimates made by the Commission de l'Energie du Commissariat Général au Plan, i.e., 870 francs per million calories until 1975, followed by a reduction of 1% per year as a result of the expected availability of nuclear energy.

c) Other costs. These relate to fixed maintenance costs for the power stations and the power line. They are higher in the case of the Aumance alternative because of the extended power line and because the power is obtained in a plant of two groups only.

These computations as a whole are used in tracing the curves in the following figure which represent, in relation to the rate of interest, the net margin (or effective income) in 1,000 francs per installed kw.-hr. Curve 1 corresponds to a 350-franc dollar, curve 2 to 350 + 15% francs per dollar, i.e., to a higher price for American coal in Paris. Under present conditions the latter rate of exchange was a more reasonable one; because of the deficit in the balance of payments France was attempting to obtain dollars, very frequently at a much higher rate than 350 francs per dollar. The shaded areas around curves 1 and 2 indicate what becomes of the net margin when the price per million calories of the Aumance coal varies by ±50 francs. In fact, this price is the least certain numerical estimate. Though the cost of constructing and operating power stations and power lines is fairly well known, on the other hand, much less is known regarding the operational cost of a mine in a still unmined coal field. An estimation error of the magnitude of 10% is not inconceivable.

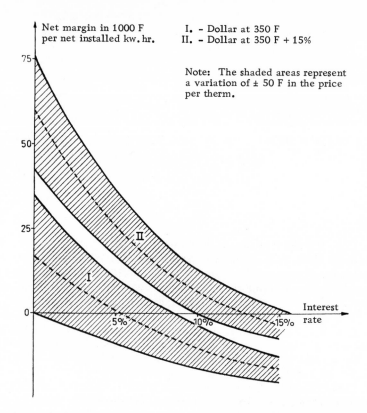

Net margin in 1000 F
per net installed kw. hr.

I. - Dollar at 350 F
II. - Dollar at 350 F + 15%

Note: The shaded areas represent
a variation of ± 50 F in the price
per therm.

Since the interest rate to be considered is between 5% and 8%, it will be observed that the study indicates that the Aumance solution is preferable, at least on the basis of a dollar rate equal to 350 francs + 15%.

On the other hand, this does not demonstrate that the construction of a power station near the mine would be the best possible solution. The construction in the Paris area of a power station using coal from Aumance could be considered. This new project would require special study.

This example indicates clearly what can be expected of a study on relative profit potential; it permits a comparison of solutions, but nothing more.

3. Development of the production of electricity in Algeria.

We quote here, practically verbatim, a summary of a 1955 analysis devoted to the above problem:

"... In order to meet increased consumption of electricity in Algeria, it will soon be necessary to begin the construction of new electrical equipment. A choice will therefore have to be made very shortly among the major competing projects.

"The studies which have been devoted to this problem have considered various possibilities, notably a steam generating plant at Kenadza, a hydroelectric plant at the Djen-Djen, and a fuel oil steam generating plant in Algiers. In order to compare the Kenadza plant with the Djen-Djen plant, two essential features must be taken into account:

"a) It is impossible to compare these two plants directly since the services rendered are different.* The only method whereby it becomes possible to choose among the various investments consists of setting up two or more programs for new projects for the purpose of meeting the future load curve. These programs are comparable since they provide equivalent services. The entire electrical development of Algeria must be considered in connection with Kenadza and the Djen-Djen.

"b) For policy reasons there can be no thought of closing the coal fields in the South Oran area which would supply coal to the Kenadza plant. Under these conditions, the actual economic cost of the million calories from Kenadza is the price at which the construction of the plant reduces the coal field's deficit."

The study includes two parts, corresponding respectively to points a and b.

a) Consistency of the programs compared.

1. Let us first attempt to construct two programs that are substantially equivalent with respect to services rendered. We will postulate an increasing demand for electricity of 10% each year and will assume that the load curve becomes parallel to the power axis at a specific point (see Figs. 20 and 21).

In addition to old steam generating plants, there are available the new plants at Oran (50 MW) and Bône (50 MW), the hydroelectric plant of the Agrioun, and 15 MW of power from plants using river current.

Let us examine how the consumption needs in 1959-1962-1965 can be met.

A) 1959. If the Djen-Djen plant is constructed (Fig. 20), it will be observed that demand can be met by using the Oran-Bône plants and the older steam generating plants at full capacity. From the top to the bottom of the load curve are respectively located: Agrioun, Djen-Djen, the older steam generating plants, Oran-Bône, and the river plants.

---

*The Djen-Djen plant is a reservoir whose use cannot exceed 4,000 hours per year.

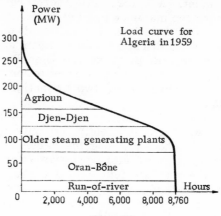

Fig. 20

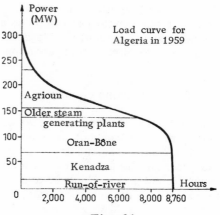

Fig. 21

If the Kenadza plant is built (Fig. 21), sufficient equipment becomes available. From top to bottom of the load curve are, respectively: Agrioun, the older steam generating plants, Oran-Bône and Kenadza.

B) 1962. The older plants are now 30 years old, and they can be considered as having been placed in reserve. If the Djen-Djen plant has been built (Fig. 22), 150,000 kw of additional thermal power will have to have been installed; this can, for example, be at:

Bône II or Oran II: 50,000 kw.
Algiers (fuel oil): 100,000 kw.

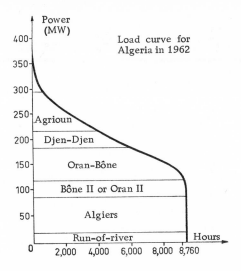

Fig. 22

If the Kenadza plant has been built (Fig. 24), it will merely be necessary to install 100,000 kw. of additional thermal power, for example at Algiers.

C) 1965. If the Djen-Djen plant has been installed, a new steam generating plant must be available; Kenadza would be sufficient. Since it seems there is agreement with respect to the

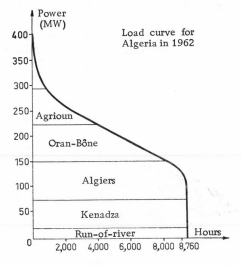

Fig. 23

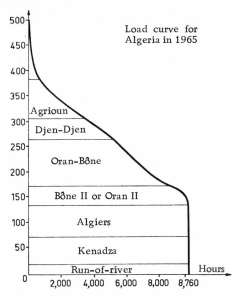

Fig. 24

necessity for building at Kenadza one day, it can be assumed that this is actually the plant which is to be built in this first program.

If, on the other hand, Kenadza has been built for 1959, the new power required to be installed can very well be supplied by the Djen-Djen and by Bône II or Oran II.

These represent the two programs which lead to the same electrical power plant by 1965. These programs are substantially equivalent as to services rendered. We say "substantially," because we have not had the time in this brief study to examine the problem of reserves and the question of peak power.

It is obvious that it will subsequently be necessary to introduce these elements into the calculations.

2. We will now compare the effective costs for the two programs. They are of three types: a) investment costs, b) fixed operational costs, c) fuel costs.

a) Investment costs.

In order to avoid the calculation of varying (time) interest, we will assume that the investment costs relating to a single project are concentrated within a single year.

b) Operating costs.

As of 1965, operating costs are the same for the two programs for a period of 24 years. As of 1989, there are slight differences

Program 1

Year	Project	Costs in billions	Present value in 1956 at 6%	Present value in 1956 at 8%
1956	Djen-Djen	12	12	12
1959	Algiers	7	5.88	5.56
1960	Bône II or Oran II	2.9	2.30	2.13
1963	Kenadza	14	9.31	8.16
			29.40	27.85

Program 2

1956	Kenadza	14	13.20	12.96
1960	Algiers	7	5.44	5.14
1962	Djen-Djen	12	8.46	7.56
1963	Bône II or Oran II	2.9	1.93	1.69
			29.03	27.35

Note: In the case of Bône II or Oran II, investment costs take into account the fact that the expansion of existing plants is planned.

since the various steam generating plants are theoretically down-graded in the same order. At interest rates of 6% or 8%, these differences are extremely small and can be omitted from calculations.

We will therefore merely evaluate the differences in operating costs between 1959 and 1965 resulting from the completion of the two programs.

Comparing the two programs, the first program is characterized:

1) by the saving, from 1959 to 1965, of 0.43 billions for the operation of Kenadza;

2) by the additional cost during five years of 0.095 billions for the Djen-Djen operation;

3) by the additional cost during one year (1961) of 0.32 billions for the Algiers operation;

4) by the additional cost during three years (1962-1965) of 0.16 billions for the Bône II or Oran II operation.

The following table summarizes the results.

Costs	Present value at 6% interest	Present value at 8% interest
1)	−1.46	−1.33
2)		
3)	+ 0.24	+ 0.22
4)	+ 0.32	+ 0.28
	−0.90	−0.83

c) Fuel costs.

Here again we will limit ourselves to calculating the fuel costs entailed by the two programs from 1959 to 1965.

The differences in costs as of 1965 are negligible for the following reason: the price of the Kenadza therm being very low (see below), it will be conducive to have Kenadza operate at capacity for many years. Therefore, large differences in fuel costs after 1965—according to whether Kenadza has been put in service in 1959 or 1965—should be anticipated.

We have adopted the following specific consumptions and prices per therm:

	Specific consumption in calories	Price per million kilocalories
Oran-Bône.	3,400	800 F
Kenadza	3,200	1,000 x
Algiers	3,000	800 F
Bône II or Oran II.	3,000	800 F

In the case of Kenadza, we have allowed the price of a million calories to remain undetermined in order to determine the value at which the two programs considered are economically equivalent.

The number of kw.-hr. supplied by the various power plants has been directly measured (graphically) for the years 1959, 1962, and 1965. Fuel consumption for the other years has been obtained by interpolation. The fuel costs for the older steam generating plants have been omitted since their use would be roughly equivalent under either program.

Fuel costs in millions of francs

	First program	Second program
1959.	1,768	1,670 x + 927
1960.	2,400	1,670 x + 1,480
1961.	3,000	1,670 x + 2,040
1962.	3,416	1,670 x + 2,592
1963.	3,800	1,670 x + 2,900
1964.	4,000	1,670 x + 3,160

The foregoing figures indicate differences in fuel costs between the first and the second program:

$$3,856 - 7,312 \, x \, \text{at} \, 6\%$$
$$3,495 - 6,616 \, x \, \text{at} \, 8\%$$

3. The total balance sheet for the two programs is as follows (difference between the present values of the two programs):

	i = 6%	i = 8%
Investments	+ 460	+ 500
Operation	— 900	— 830
Total.	— 440	— 330
	3,856	3,495
Fuel	— 7,312 x	— 6,616 x

The second program (Kenadza put into operation as early as 1959) is preferable to the first if:

$$x \leqslant 0.467 \; F \; (\text{at} \, 6\%)$$
$$x \leqslant 0.478 \; F \; (\text{at} \, 8\%)$$

It will be seen that x is much lower.

b) Determination of the Kenadza price per therm.

1. In order to determine the value of x at which the construction of the plant would be economically advantageous, assuming that the mine is not closed, a comparison will be made of annual receipts and expenditures of the coal fields in the South Oran area with and without the new plant.

2. If a plant is constructed, the South Oran coal fields will extract 600,000 gross tons from the field at Ksiksou in 1959. The new

plant will consume 415,000 tons and the remainder will be forwarded to the Oran plant and to a cement-making plant near Oran.

A yield of 1,300 kilograms has been reached in this field which has been in operation only a short while. It would seem entirely probable that a yield of 1,600 kilograms will be reached in 1959.

Taking into account savings in washing, energy, transportation, and overhead allowed by the construction of the plant, one can assume that the costs will amount to 2,560 francs per ton for the first 500,000 tons. The additional 100,000 tons can be produced at very little cost since only the necessary manpower and a few supplies will be required. The South Oran coalfields estimate 1,400 francs per ton as the cost of this slice of production.

As of 1959, the following costs can be anticipated:

$$
\begin{array}{l}
2{,}560 \times 500{,}000 = 1{,}280 \text{ million francs} \\
1{,}400 \times 100{,}000 = \underline{140} \text{ million francs} \\
\phantom{1{,}400 \times 100{,}000 = } 1{,}420 \text{ million francs}
\end{array}
$$

As a counterpart, the receipts will amount to:

470 million francs for the sale of 185,000 tons to the cement-making plant and to the power plant in Oran.

54 y million francs for the products consumed in the plant and used to produce power for Algiers and Colomb-Béchar (y is the fuel price per kw.-hr.).

3. If no plant is built, the South Oran coalfields will extract 500,000 gross tons, part of which will be washed out leaving a net product of 310,000 tons for sale.

The amount of costs can be established in the following manner. To the 1,380 million francs (2,560 × 500,000) must be added: 79 - 30 = 49 million francs difference between the present washing cost and the savings which can be anticipated from the construction of a new washing plant, 31 million francs for additional transportation, 20 million francs for the shipping service, and 10 million francs for the electricity for coal extraction. The costs would therefore amount to a total of 1,390 million francs.

As a counterpart, the receipts would be collected on 310,000 net tons, i.e., 290,000 sale tons. They would amount to 845 million francs, i.e., approximately 2,900 francs per ton.

4. The balance sheet is established as follows:

	Costs	Receipts
With plant.	1,420	540 y + 470
Without plant	1,390	845

The y value at which the construction of the plant is desirable is:

$$y = \frac{1,420 - 470 - (1,390 - 845)}{540} = 0.75 \text{ F.}$$

This corresponds to a price of 234 francs per million calories (x = 0.234).

By replacing this value for x in the formula giving the difference in present values between the two programs, it is apparent that the second program has an advantage of a) 1,705 million francs at 6% or b) 1,617 million francs at 8% capitalized at present value.

The brief account given of the three foregoing studies obviously cannot attempt to illustrate all of the theoretical aspects which were outlined at the beginning of this chapter.

When one knows how to analyze the problem, however, the theory applies quite reasonably in a discussion of actual cases. Our primary purpose was to indicate, by means of examples, how a definition and comparison of the main possibilities should be approached.

BIBLIOGRAPHY

1. ACKOFF, ARNOFF, CHURCHMAN:
   Introduction to Operations Research. Wiley, New York, 1957.

2. M. ALLAIS:
   Economie et intérêt (Economics and interest). Two volumes, Paris, Imprimerie Nationale, 1947.

3. M. ALLAIS:
   La gestion des houillères nationalisées et la théorie économique (Management of nationalized coal mines and economic theory). Imprimerie Nationale, 1953.

4. J. AUDIBERT:
   La rentabilité du matériel du fond (Profitableness of basic equipment). Documents techniques des Charbonnages de France, 1953.

5. M. BOITEUX:
   "Le choix des équipements de production d'énergie électrique" (The selection of equipment for the production of electrical power). Revue française de Recherche opérationnelle, vol. 1, No. 1.

6. M. BOITEUX:
   "Le choix entre différentes possibilités d'investissements"
   (Choice among various investment possibilities). Hommes et
   techniques, Nos. 139-140, July-August 1956.

7. M. BOITEUX:
   La coordination des investissements du secteur énergetique
   (Coordination of investments in the area of power). Lecture
   in Professor Allais' seminar, May 11, 1955.

8. J. BROUET:
   "Les investissements dans le cas de la création d'une usine
   nouvelle" (Investments in a case involving the creation of
   a new factory). Hommes et techniques, Nos. 139-140, July-
   August 1956.

9. J. EINARSEN:
   "Replacement in the shipping industry." Review of Economic
   Statistics, 1946, 28, 225.

10. ELECTRICITE DE FRANCE:
    Direction de l'équipement: Essai de détermination d'un
    criterium de valeur des équipements (Equipment manage-
    ment: Attempt at determining a criterion of equipment
    value). Two volumes, 1953.

11. R. GASPARD and P. MASSE:
    "Le choix des investissements énergetiques et la production
    d'électricité en France" (The selection of investments in
    power and the production of electricity in France). Revue
    française de l'Energie, October 1952.

12. O. GELINIER:
    "La fonction de contrôle des programmes d'investissement"
    (The control function of investment programs). Hommes et
    techniques, Nos. 139-140, July-August 1956.

13. R. GIBRAT:
    Le problème général des plans dans le secteur de l'élec-
    tricité (The general problem of planning in the sector of
    electricity). Multilithed document, 1955.

14. R. GIGUET:
    "Les programmes d'équipement électrique considérés du
    point de vue de l'économie appliquée" (Electrical equip-
    ment programming considered from the standpoint of applied
    economics). Economie appliquée, 1951, No. 1.

15. E. HALPHEN:
    "Un exemple d'application des méthodes statistiques: le
    problème du plan de développement de la production d'énergie

électrique'' (An example of the application of statistical methods: the problem involved in planning the development of electrical power production). Annuaire hydrologique de la France, 1945.

16. E. HALPHEN:
"Un exemple d'application des méthodes statistiques. Le probleme du plan pour l'équipement électrique français" (An example of the application of statistical methods. The problem involved in planning French electrical equipment). Revue de Statistique appliquée, 1953, vol. I, No. 1.

17. J. R. HICKS:
"L'économie de bien-être et la théorie des surplus du consommateur" (Welfare economics and the theory of consumer surpluses). Economie appliquée, Archives of the ISEA, No. 4, October-December 1948.

18. J. R. HICKS:
"The rehabilitation of consumer's surplus," Review of Economic Studies, February 1941.

19. R. JANIN:
"Le choix des équipements" (The selection of equipment). Cahiers du Séminaire d'Econométrie, CNRS, 1956, No. 3.

20. R. McKEAN:
"Criteria for the selection of water resource projects." Operations Research, February 1956, 4, 1.

21. J. LESOURNE:
"Réflexions sur la théorie des investissements" (Observations on investment theory). Nouvelle Revue d'Economie contemporaine, December 1955.

22. J. LESOURNE:
"A la recherche d'un critère de rentabilité pour les grands investissements" (Determination of a profitableness criterion for large investments). Cahiers du Séminaire d'Econométrie (to be published in 1958).

23. P. MASSÉ:
"Aperçus économiques sur l'efficience, le risque, et l'investissement" (Economic insights into efficiency, risk, and investments). University of Paris, Revue de Statistique appliquée, 1953, vol. I, No. 2.

24. P. MASSÉ:
"Les investissements électriques" (Investments in the electrical field). Revue de Statistique appliquée, 1953, vol. I, Nos. 3-4.

25. P. MASSÉ:
Quelques problèmes d'optimum économique (A few problems in economic optimum). Centre National de la Recherche Scientifique. Centre d'Econométrie. Cours et Conférences de recherches, 1951-1953 (published in 1954).

26. P. MASSÉ:
Le choix des investissements (Choice of investments). Dunod, 1959.

27. M. MIGEON:
"La politique des investissements" (Investment policy). Hommes et techniques, Nos. 139-140, July-August 1956.

28. R. MONTJOIE:
La théorie des investissements (Investment theory). Cours de l'Ecole des Mines de Nancy. Multilithed document.

29. G. MORLAT:
"Sur les dimensions des diverses parties d'un ouvrage" (On the dimensions of the various parts of a work). University of Paris, Revue de Statistique appliquée, 1953, vol. I, Nos. 3-4.

30. P. M. PRADEL:
L'optimum d'investissement" (Optimal investment). Revue d'Economie politique, May-June 1953.

31. G. TERBORGH:
Dynamic Equipment Policy. McGraw-Hill, New York, 1949.

32. A. TERRA:
"Essai sur les critères de rentabilité dan les houillères" (Essay on coal-mining profitableness criteria). Revue de l'Industrie Minerale, No. 610, July 1954.

33. A. TERRA:
"La rentabilité des investissements à long terme" (The profitableness of long-term investments). Nouvelle Revue de l'Economie contemporaine. Nos. 68-69, October-November 1955.

34. A. TERRA:
   "Les investissements dans un bassin minier" (Coal field investments). Hommes et techniques, Nos. 139-140, July-August 1956.

35. M. THERME:
   Rentabilité d'une centrale sur l'Allier alimentée avec des charbons du bassin de l'Aumance (Profitableness of a power plant on the Allier River supplied with coal from the Aumance coal field). House document of the Charbonnages de France, 1957.

36. C. A. de VAUGELAS:
   "Les investissements dans une industrie ayant une activité internationale" (Investments in an industry operating on an international basis). Hommes et techniques, Nos. 139-140, July-August, 1956.

Chapter **14**

Price policies

This chapter reexamines, from an entirely different viewpoint, the relationships which exist between a firm and its customers. In the first part of the book this analysis was concerned with the elements of information that a firm can obtain about its market. This chapter, on the contrary, is devoted to the decisions which make it possible for the firm to influence demand and, more particularly, to those concerning price. Strictly speaking, the essential decisions do not concern price policies, but investments and production levels. Prices merely reflect costs, on the one hand, and sales potential on the other.

With regard to the establishment of prices, the latitude of individual firms varies considerably. The pharmacist who sells medicine at fixed prices has no price policy. A street vendor, however, can price his wares somewhat differently from the market price. At the other end of the scale are such large firms as the S.N.C.F. and Electricité and Gaz de France. These firms develop complex pricing systems; in this respect they possess wide latitude, subject, however, to political and social constraints. Even broader latitude is possessed by a chemical products firm owning a recently developed product that other firms will be technically incapable of imitating for several years. A primary characteristic of price policy is that it is closely dependent upon the economic and social framework of the firm.

Price policy can be analyzed by examining varying points of view. We will first consider the significance of the theory of the general interest. This theory, which is known under various names (corporate returns, welfare, economic optimum, Pareto's optimum), has already been touched on in Chapter 2. It is now appropriate to undertake a more thorough examination of the relationships between general interest and the maximization of profit. This subject will be treated in the first section.

The theory of the general interest postulates sales at marginal cost. In the second section, therefore, we will consider the various aspects of sales at marginal cost while attempting to solve the paradoxes which are apparently raised.

The third section will consider the price policy of private firms in terms of profit maximization. This will be done in three stages based successively on the following assumptions:

1) a firm sells a single product at a single price but under various market conditions (monopoly, oligopoly, etc.);
2) a firm sells a whole range of physically differentiated products;
3) a firm seeks to increase its profit by varying its prices for the same product in accordance with the various geographical or sociological conditions of the market.

I

THE CONCEPT OF ECONOMIC OPTIMUM

The concept of economic optimum can be introduced in the following terms. It is not the role of the economist to decide whether butter or guns should be produced. This is a problem of general policy which is beyond the purview of his discipline. However, once the requirement for the production of military hardware has been established by the government, the economist can help determine the conditions whereby production for the civilian sector can be maximized.

Figure 1 symbolizes the problem diagrammatically; along the abscissa appears the quantity of butter produced by the economy; along the ordinates, that of guns. The quantity of factors of production available to us enables us to produce any type of butter-guns combination, represented by a point M located at the left of a limiting curve PQ. The points on this curve have an important property. If the economy is found to be at one of them, the simultaneous production of more butter and more guns is impossible. To produce more butter, therefore, it will be necessary to give up some guns.

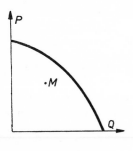

Fig. 1.

In other words, an economist cannot identify the best point along the PQ curve but, assuming that the points on curve PQ are economically optimal, he seeks how that situation can be attained.

This is the essence of an economic optimum. We will now give a more analytical definition to enable us to outline its effective conditions. Farther on we will discuss this theory's significance and value.

1. Definition and conditions for the realization of an economic optimum [1].

The economy under study is characterized by the production and consumption of goods (q_1), (q_2), (q_i), . . . , (q_n) and by the existence of m individuals, j consumers who possess "utilities" (cf. Chapter 4) which are a function of their q_1^j, . . . , q_i^j, . . . , q_n^j consumption. By hypothesis, factors of production such as labor and land are assumed in given quantities.*

The production apparatus includes two sectors which are distinguished by their technical characteristics:

a) the undifferentiated sector, which includes branches of industry in which the technical optimum limits productive capacity to a single plant (as in the case of the distribution of gas or electricity);

b) the differentiated sector, which includes branches of industry in which the juxtaposition of various substantially similar units of production is conceivable. Such units of production have either similar costs (case of metallurgy and textiles) or different costs resulting from natural characteristics of operation (mines, for instance).

In other words, within a liberal economy, competition is possible in the differentiated sector but not in the undifferentiated one.

The concept of economic optimum can now be more rigorously defined:

1) The organization of production is said to be economically optimal if, for given productions q_1, . . . , q_{n-1}, the production q_n is at a maximum. It can be verified very easily that the points on the curve PQ in Fig. 1 satisfy this definition.

2) A state of the economy as a whole is said to be economically optimal if, for given utilities U_1, . . . , U_{m-1}, of the first m - 1 consumers, utility U_m of the last is maximal. In other words, in an economically optimal situation, the situation of one individual cannot be improved without worsening that of at least one other.

In general, economists merely give definition 2), which has some theoretical advantages. However, it is not our purpose here to develop the theory of economic optimum in detail; moreover, some readers might prefer definition 1), which does not postulate the concept of utility.

To determine mathematically the conditions for the realization of an economic optimum (in the sense of either 1 or 2), economists represent the firms in terms of their production functions. They then write the equations that account for the flow of goods and the

---

*In more elaborate formulations of the theory one is not constrained by this hypothesis.

production factors. Finally, economists deal with the related problem of maximization, which consists in either determining the maximum of q_n for given $q_1, \ldots, q_{n-1}$, or in determining the maximum of U_m for given $U_1, \ldots, U_{m-1}$.* This mathematical analysis arrives at the following conclusions:

a) Production optimum. An optimal state of production is realized when, implicitly or explicitly, the following conditions obtain:

1) within an undifferentiated sector, the average cost is at a minimum for the chosen production, the selling price is equal to the marginal cost, and the entire production is sold;

2) within a differentiated sector the average cost of each unit of production is at a minimum, the selling price of each unit is equal to its marginal cost, and the entire production is sold. Furthermore, in the case of those branches of industry in which the units have the same cost structure, the marginal cost of each unit is equal to the average cost. This does not arise from company policy but from the adjustment of a number of firms to market conditions. In addition, in the case of those branches of industry in which the units do not have the same cost structure, the marginal cost is equal to the average cost only in the case of the last unit; as for the others, the average cost is lower than the marginal cost.

With regard to the differentiated sector, it can be demonstrated that such conditions are attained in a system of perfect competition. There must prevail, implicitly or explicitly, a price system which is equivalent to that which would be the result of perfect competition.

b) General optimum. A state of economic optimum is realized when, in addition to the preceding conditions, individuals have freedom of choice on the consumer goods market.

The states of economic optimum are infinite. To each of these corresponds one, and only one, allocation of income. Therefore, the theory of economic optimum is not predicated on an allocation of income, at least to the extent that income allocation does not affect the PQ curve.

2. Significance of the theory of economic optimum.

The theory of economic optimum is so frequently misinterpreted that we must discuss it now in order to appreciate the validity of the rule of marginal cost and price equality.

Since the preceding discussion did not contain any illustrations, let us first attempt, with the help of a few examples, to demonstrate the manner in which economic losses are introduced when optimum conditions are not realized.

---

*A detailed and precise outline of this question will be found in writings by M. Allais [1] [5].

The first example is by G. Dessus, who tells the following story: The inhabitants of a village, in order to provide heat for themselves, can either extract coal from a neighboring mine or cut some timber in a forest spreading on the side of a hill overlooking the village. Coal and wood both render the same service, which amounts to saying that, for all consumers, there is a certain amount of wood equal to a ton of coal. In this mythical village, manpower is the sole factor of production. The number of hours currently required to extract a ton of coal is hardly affected by the extent of previous extraction. On the other hand, the number of hours required to cut and saw a cubic meter of wood increases with production, because as the latter increases the inhabitants, who began by exploiting the forest nearest the valley, must climb higher and higher up the hill.

An economic optimum requires: 1) equality in the selling price of equivalent quantities of coal and of wood; 2) equality in these prices to the average and marginal costs of coal extraction on the one hand and, on the other, to the marginal cost of cutting down the trees (in this case, these two costs can be translated directly into work hours).

In a situation of economic optimum, a firm, either private or public, which cuts the trees will make some profit because the cost of such an operation will be lower than the selling price, except in the case of cords felled at the highest altitude on the hill. Assuming that one finds oneself in this "scandalous" situation and that instead of confiscating such profits and redistributing them—which would change the income distribution without affecting the situation of economic optimum—it is decided that the tree-cutting enterprise must sell at the average price, the market will then tend to realize the following equalities: cost of coal = price of coal = price of wood = average cost of wood.

Because the cost of coal does not change, the average cost of the wood will increase in relation to the previous situation, and the

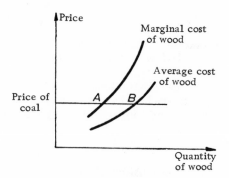

Fig. 2.

marginal cost of cutting trees will become higher than the marginal cost of extracting coal. In Fig. 2, which represents this phenomenon, we move from point A to point B. The quantity of wood produced will increase. In other words, there will be more woodcutters and the latter will have to go up higher along the hill in order to fell the trees. Because the selling price does not change, the total coal-wood demand remains the same. This means that the inhabitants will stop mining coal at the point at which they produce Q calories per hour and will be sent to a part of the hill where, taking into account the time spent going and coming, they will produce less than Q calories per hour. Under these conditions, the price system results in a waste of manpower. However, in a system of economic optimum the number of hours of work required to obtain one additional calorie is the same in the mine as on the hill. A small reallocation of manpower will not improve the total quantity of available calories.

As a second example, let us take the case of a metallurgist who plans to build a steel plant and who must decide between installing electric ovens or Martin ovens using fuel oil. He will have his department engage in a profit-ability study comparing the effective incomes deriving from the alternative methods on the basis of prices which the firm will actually pay. What consequences will the metallurgist's decision have upon the economy as a whole? If he decides upon electric ovens, this will require the production of an additional amount of electricity in order to meet his demand. If he chooses the Martin ovens, this will require an increase in availability of fuel oils. In both cases his decision can cause a modification in the marginal production of the energy he plans to use. The metallurgist's decision, therefore, will not conform to the general interest unless he takes the cost of these marginal modifications into consideration in his calculations. This is so only when the selling price of electricity and of fuel oil are equal to their marginal costs.

The S.N.C.F.—and this will be the third and last example—sells passenger tickets at the same price throughout the entire year. However, the influx of travelers from July 30 to August 2 is such that the S.N.C.F. must have surplus rolling stock constantly available in order to meet the peak demand during this short period. In other words, the marginal cost of transportation is then a peak marginal cost and is very high. The cost of the factors of production required to transport a passenger is therefore much higher than the price of the ticket. Suppose this price were increased and the passengers during that period were required to pay the actual cost of their transportation. Then all passengers who could find an alternative use for this expenditure having a greater "utility" would give up their trip. For its part, the S.N.C.F. could reduce its rolling stock; the value of the factors of production thus liberated would have greater benefit to the economy than the transit services they would otherwise render [4].

Having considered, by example, the essence of the theory, we will now examine its implications critically.

1. At the very outset, let us note that the theory does not specify that true competition will make it possible to attain an economic optimum. It contains a reference merely to perfect competition which sociologically has little meaning. To settle the debate between free market advocates and planners requires the examination of an entirely different problem, in terms of the following question: Between deliberate planning and free market competition, which state is closer to engendering perfect competition? This problem is not related to the theory of economic optimum.

The theory states simply that there must prevail, implicitly or explicitly: 1) a system of prices equal to marginal costs in the undifferentiated sector, and 2) a system of prices equivalent to that of perfect competition in the differentiated sector.

In this form, the significance of prices is more apparent. For the man in the street, in France at least, the main function of price is only to regulate the distribution of income and purchasing power. A high price means essentially, to quote a favorite expression of M. Allais: "Use this product with care, for it is scarce." In a competitive situation, the role of prices is to insure a distribution of factors of production such that it will be impossible to produce more than one type of goods without producing less of another. This result is obtained when the value of a factor of production has the same margin in all uses, because it is then impossible to increase the production of all goods by a reallocation of factors.

2. The theory teaches us that, when an economic optimum is attained, profits, calculated at constant prices, are at a maximum. It is often deduced therefrom as a practical rule that an economic optimum is attained when each enterprise maximizes its profit at constant prices. In point of fact, this is only an approximation. As has already been mentioned in Chapter 2, the behavior of a firm can affect other firms and the community in ways other than those expressed by the system of prices.

3. The theory may be limited somewhat by its essentially static framework, but it is possible to improve it greatly in more general presentations. More debatable, however, is the implicit hypothesis that demand and output are independent of income distribution. It is probable that excessively equal or excessively unequal distributions of income will have an unfavorable effect on the level of production. The purely theoretical postulate of independence between optimal income distribution and optimal production is solely an initial, working hypothesis.

4. Society is interested in an economic optimum to the extent that it promotes the optimization of social benefits. However, it is

generally preferable to pursue that policy which also optimizes the economic relationships. For example, it is more desirable to improve the distribution of income by a transfer than by a subsidy which would artificially lower consumer prices. Rather than subsidize an unprofitable plant, it is economically preferable to close the plant, give unemployment compensation to the workers, and help them find other employment.

The reasons which make it possible to justify a compromise between economic and social objectives are well known to the 20th-century Frenchman. These are mainly: a) the practical difficulties in modifying the distribution of income without affecting the system of prices; b) the adjustment difficulties which could result from an abrupt application of an economically optimum policy; c) a purely objective determination to establish economic and political independence on a national level (this is the motivating force which leads underdeveloped countries to spark their economic birth by installing a heavy industry).

5. If we now turn toward the actual content of the rules outlined, it becomes evident that the undifferentiated sector is the one of greater interest to us. In effect, within a differentiated sector the true problem relates less to the policy of the firm than to the choice of rules of the competitive game.

Let us therefore review, point by point, what the theory of economic optimum teaches us in the case of the undifferentiated sector.

a) It requires, first of all, an optimal organization of the firm. Production must be at a maximum for the quantities of factors or production utilized, and the average cost must be at a minimum for the production chosen. Because competition does not insure the realization of these two objectives in this sector, it may be necessary to institute mechanisms which will induce the directors constantly to improve the quality of management and which will make it possible to detect and eliminate incapable managers.

b) The proposed policy has a dual aspect: a production aspect and a price aspect. Production is adjusted in such a way that the product can be sold on the market at a price equal to the marginal cost.

As we have seen in Chapter 10, the rule of equality between selling price and marginal cost can be expressed in such a form as to avoid using the concept of marginal cost. In an undifferentiated sector, a firm must maximize its income for given sales prices.*

---

*Designating Q as the production, $D(Q)$ as the total costs, and $p(Q)$ as the curve of demand, income is: $R = p(Q) Q - D(Q)$. When $D(Q)$ is differentiable, the maximization of R for given $p(Q)$ leads

This second formula is more useful when considering several periods or when important modifications in production equipment are considered.

In order to maximize income, different solutions must be compared. The rule is not capable of providing these comparisons, but technical competence and imagination can provide a basis for decision making.

c) When competition within a differentiated sector is not perfect, the price system is not responsive to costs of production. One may then wonder, in the case of a firm in an undifferentiated sector, whether it would be in conformity with the general interest to sell at marginal cost, since this cost is calculated on the basis of incorrect prices for the factors of production.

In pure theory, a firm in the differentiated sector should exercise policies tending to compensate for the uneconomic aspects of an imperfect market. To do so would require abandoning the policy of pricing at marginal cost. We are now faced with the question of whether it is desirable to practice a policy of pricing at marginal cost only in certain sectors of the economy. Theoretically the question remains open and the models proposed provide fragmentary and diverse results [16]. From the practical standpoint, however, it is apparent that a failure to apply a marginal cost pricing policy in all sectors precludes the attainment of an economic optimum. There is also, perhaps, a tendency to overestimate the distortions of price in a differentiated sector.

d) When marginal cost is constantly lower than average cost, the application of the rule results in receipts which are smaller than costs—a deficit which must be made up by the State.

Anticipating a public reaction against a permanent deficit, the French school of economists [3], [20] has, during recent years, tackled the following problem. Given the necessity for a firm to be in a state of budgetary equilibrium, what price policy best lends itself to the promotion of an economic optimum?

This is a problem of linked optimum. The point here (taking into consideration the production of goods (B), (C), etc. and the fact that the firm producing (A) is in a state of budgetary equilibrium) is to ascertain under what conditions the production of (A) is maximized. To grasp the nature of this problem, it must be noted

---

to the condition: $p(Q) = D'(Q)$. If $D(Q)$ is not differentiable, a direct determination of the maximum of R is preferable.

A policy that would be noncompatible with an economic optimum would be to raise R to a maximum by taking into account the relationship of p and Q. It would lead, when $D'(Q)$ is differentiable, to the condition: $p + Q \dfrac{dp}{dQ} = D'(Q)$.

that the condition of budgetary equilibrium does not define company policy unless this company produces but one product, sells it on a single market, and does not vary the mix of factors of production. The equation, in which the notations are obvious, is:

$$R = p(Q)Q - D(Q) = 0$$

which, in fact, determines Q. But this is no longer the case when two goods are produced:

$$R = p_1(Q_1)Q_1 + p_2(Q_2)Q_2 - D(Q_1, Q_2) = 0$$

or if the same product is sold in quantities Q_1 and Q_2 on two markets:

$$p_1(Q_1)Q_1 + p_2(Q_2)q_2 - D(Q_1 + Q_2) = 0$$

or, finally, if one varies the mix of the factors of production which makes the function D (Q) become indeterminate.

M. Boiteux has recently developed a solution to this problem [20]. Although the theoretical implications of this solution are important, it is unfortunately too complex to be examined here.

Until now we have discussed marginal costs at great length but have carefully refrained from identifying specific marginal costs. In Chapter 10 we reviewed the complexity of this concept, and the reader will not be surprised to learn that the rule of sales at marginal cost presents difficulties of practical application and creates apparent paradoxes because of faulty interpretation.

An examination of these difficulties is the subject of the second section.

II

THE PRACTICAL ASPECTS OF SALES
AT MARGINAL COST

Two groups of questions will be considered.

The first group relates to difficulties of principle, i.e., those which give rise to apparent paradoxes. These difficulties emanate essentially from uncertainty as to the future and the indivisibility of investments [7]. The second group relates to the pricing of related products with emphasis on periodic or random demand.

Answers to these questions will make it possible to apply the foregoing concepts to a few industries and, further, to develop the example provided by the survey made by Vickrey in connection with the New York subway.

1. Sales at marginal cost and difficulties of principle.

a) First, let us consider the case of the construction of a bridge. The firm which has built the bridge and subsequently manages it for the community collects a toll charge. How should this toll charge be determined?

Let us take for granted that the demand curve (i.e., the traffic for various toll charges) is accurately known, and let us suppose that this curve is invariant during the bridge's lifetime.

The bridge's construction cost is a function of its capacity, i.e., of traffic T which is likely to cross the bridge per unit of time. By assuming a constant annual amortization, the annual accountable expenditures appear as a function D (T) and the long-run marginal cost is D'(T) if maintenance costs are omitted. The short-term marginal cost is zero when traffic is less than the bridge's capacity, and becomes infinite for traffic which is greater than or equal to such capacity.

If the toll charge is p, the maximization of income on the basis of a constant toll charge would require that the toll charge p be equal to the long-run marginal cost D' (T). But it is important to note (Fig. 3) that under such conditions the traffic which crosses the bridge is exactly equal to its capacity, and that the short-term marginal cost is then equal to the long-run marginal cost.

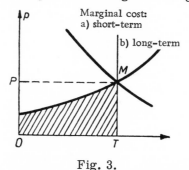

Fig. 3.

Thus, in this very simple case, in which a new unit of production is created and in which demand remains unchanged during the unit's lifetime, optimal decisions result in equality of demand and of production capacity, and in equality of selling price, short-term marginal cost, and long-run marginal cost.

The income derived from the use of the bridge is represented in Fig. 3 by the difference between the area of rectangle OTMP and the shaded area equal to

$$\int_0^T D' (T) \, \mathrm{d}T = D (T).$$

Net income is positive if the long-run marginal cost is an increasing function of traffic and negative in the contrary case. This does not mean, however, that the construction of the bridge should be pursued if positive income can be forecast, or dropped if negative income is forecast; the sole criterion of positive income is not always sufficient to decide on investments that are not extremely small (see Chapter 13).

b) Let us now turn to an example regarding the production and sale of coal. All mines are assumed to be small and to have different costs. The situation is represented in Fig. 4. The initial point is M, at which the production of all mines operating at capacity is T_0 and the price p_0.

Assuming that demand increases in a predictable and definitive manner, new mines will be opened to increase the productive capacity. If the entire group of mines is in a state of technical equilibrium, the new mines will show a higher average cost and will be opened in the order of increasing average costs. The curve representing the average cost of the least productive mine in relation to total capacity is none other than the curve of long-run marginal cost.

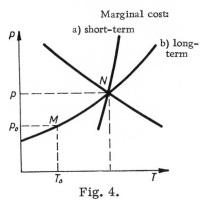

Fig. 4.

The total capacity will be controlled so that production capacity will equal demand and the selling price will be equal to the long-run marginal cost, i.e., to the average cost of the least productive mine.

Because capacity is fully utilized, the short-term marginal cost is also equal to the selling price. As the curve of long-run marginal cost is a growing one, the last mine is in a state of financial equilibrium and all the other mines have a positive revenue.

c) Let us return now to the example of the bridge, but let us assume that an error was made in the original prediction of demand so that the bridge, once constructed, does not have optimal capacity. There are three possibilities, represented in Fig. 5 by curves D_1, D_2, and D_3.

If the demand is D_1, the bridge is too large. Optimal traffic, in fact, would have been given by the abscissa of N_1. The toll charge must be p_1, at which level demand is equal to capacity and the toll charge is equal to the short-term marginal cost but less than the long-run marginal cost.

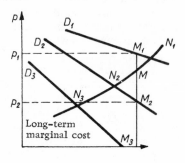

If the demand is D_2, capacity is excessive. Optimal traffic would have been given by the abscissa of N_2. The toll charge here must be equal to the short-term marginal cost and consequently zero. Under such conditions, the traffic remains less than the bridge's capacity.

The foregoing example illustrates a few important facts:

Fig. 5.

1. Once the bridge has been constructed, the toll charge cannot be equal to the long-run marginal cost if an incorrect demand level has been forecast and capacity is, therefore, not optimal.

2. On the other hand, equality of short-term marginal cost and the toll charge must be maintained.

The first equality listed above is the consequence of an investment policy, whereas the second, always realized, corresponds to operational policy. When there are no investments to be made, equality of selling price and short-term marginal cost must be realized (the latter is the cost of producing one additional unit according to the most economic procedure under prevailing conditions). When there are investments to be made, an attempt must be made to give them optimal volume which, in addition to the foregoing equality, necessitates equality of sales price and long-run marginal cost.

d) Until now we have not touched on problems of expansion and replacement.

First, let us consider the case of a plant which must be replaced. In Fig. 6, the plant is assumed to be too large.

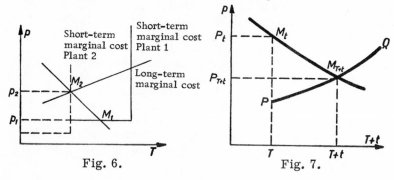

Fig. 6.   Fig. 7.

At replacement time the optimal point will go from M_1 to M_2, at which point the selling price is equal both to the short-term marginal cost and to the long-run marginal cost for the new plant. The new plant, obviously, will only be constructed if it is deemed profitable. The expansion of a plant at replacement time is handled in the same manner.

The problem of expansion (or of a decrease in capacity) of an existing plant is different. This can be considered in the same terms as the example concerning the bridge. The traffic being found to be much heavier than foreseen, there is a need to know whether a new bridge should be constructed. Designate as T the (fixed) capacity of the first bridge and as t the capacity (to be determined) of the second. Before the construction of the second bridge, the optimal point is M_T. The curve of long-run marginal cost for the second bridge is the curve PQ which begins only at leaving abscissa T. It intersects the demand curve at the new optimal point M_{T+t}. Curve PQ is naturally contingent upon the capacity of the first bridge. If this bridge did not exist, the outcome would be different and there would be another curve of long-run marginal cost. This curve would naturally lead, for any kind of traffic, to total costs less than or at most equal to those indicated by PQ. The final optimal capacity would probably not be the same, and we would perhaps have one bridge instead of two.

These conclusions are very important, especially with regard to the rule of sales at marginal cost. To summarize, whatever equipment may be available, it must always be operated in such a way that the selling price will be equal to the short-term marginal cost. This policy does not always lead to low selling prices because marginal cost grows very fast as maximum capacity is approached. Equipment productivity must be adapted to demand. If demand is correctly anticipated there is, for optimal equipment, equality of selling price and of long-run marginal cost.

The foregoing caveats are not always strictly applicable. Let us imagine that demand is increasing at a regular pace and that the productive apparatus consists of identical units of considerable size which are constructed as demand develops. Because it is not economically feasible to alter production schedules continually as demand changes, price flexibility might be considered a satisfactory alternative. However, continual fluctuations in prices are so harmful that it is preferable to maintain a constant price schedule to give the same receipts on the average.

2. Sales at marginal cost and adaptation of rate schedules
   to services rendered.

One of the characteristics of sales at marginal cost is the close correspondence between prices and services rendered. It shows up clearly in rate schedule problems for periodic or random demands and, more generally, for demands for related products and multiple services.

a) Periodic demand [15]. We will briefly consider the most interesting case, that of nonstorable goods. Let us imagine, for example, that this is a case involving the production of electricity and that there are two flows of demand, one occurring during the daytime and the other at night. Let us designate as p_1 and p_2 the consumer rates applicable respectively to daytime and to night-time, C_p the peak marginal cost independent of the level of such a peak, and C_r the marginal cost during slack hours.

In order to simplify, we will assume that the two functions of demand for energy are expressed (1 = day, 2 = night): $d_1 = a_1 - b_1 p_1 + c_1 p_2$; $d_2 = a_2 - b_2 p_2 + c_2 p_1$ (the coefficients a_1, a_2, b_1, b_2, c_1, c_2 are positive).

Finally, it is assumed that the power required is constant during each of these two periods.

If it is proposed to replace a certain rate schedule for which d_1 is greater than d_2 by selling at marginal cost, then the peak demand d_1 would require a rate equal to the peak marginal cost C_p, and the demand d_2 during slack hours would require a rate equal to the marginal cost of slack hours C_r. However, this rate correction can be valid only if d_1 remains the peak demand and d_2 the demand during slack hours. To insure this, the inequality:

$$a_1 - b_1 C_p + c_1 C_r > a_2 - b_2 C_r + c_2 C_p$$
$$a_2 - a_1 < (b_2 + c_1) C_r - (c_2 + b_1) C_p$$

must be satisfied. If it is not, an application of these rates tends to reverse the peak. The high rate during the day and the low one at night can lead consumers to switch their consumption patterns so that peaking now develops during the night.

Since the peak is now occurring at night, an attempt can be made to rate the night demand at the C_p cost, and the day demand at the C_r cost. Theoretically, this method of rate correction is possible if d_2 remains greater than d_1, i.e., if the inequality:

$$a_1 - b_1 C_r + c_1 C_p < a_2 - b_2 C_p + c_2 C_r$$
$$(b_2 + c_1) C_p - (b_1 + c_2) C_r < a_2 - a_1.$$

is satisfied.

But it is likely that this correction will again reverse the peak. In mathematical terms, none of the foregoing inequalities is satisfied and:

$$(b_2 + c_1) C_r - (c_2 + b_1) C_p < a_2 - a_1 < (b_2 + c_1) C_p - (b_1 + c_2) C,$$

In other words, none of the demands can support the peak price. The only balanced rate setting, consequently, is that rating which will level the peak and transform the demand into a perfectly steady demand.

Prices p_1 and p_2 must therefore first fulfill the equation:

$$a_1 - b_1 p_1 + c_1 p_2 = a_2 - b_2 + c_2 p_1.$$

Furthermore, they must insure the coverage of marginal costs resulting from an increase in one or the other of the demands. However, if one of the demands increases slightly, it does result in additional costs equal to C_p per unit, but the other demand then becomes a slack hour demand, of which the marginal cost is only C_r. Therefore, a relation between p_1 and p_2 must exist:

$$p_1 + p_2 = C_p + C_r$$

which, combined with the foregoing, gives:

$$p_1 = \frac{(c_1 + b_2)(C_p + C_r) - (a_2 - a_1)}{b_1 + b_2 + c_1 + c_2}$$

$$p_2 = \frac{(b_1 + c_2)(C_p + C_r) + (a_2 - a_1)}{b_1 + b_2 + c_1 + c_2}.$$

Note: As we have emphasized in Chapter 10, the peak marginal cost is a long-run marginal cost. The foregoing calculation determines, therefore, the best rate-setting method for the case of optimal equipment. The level of the peak or of the steady demand which develops determines the size of such equipment.

If the equipment existed and there was no intention of adapting it, the two rates would be determined by the intersection of the demand curves and the curve of short-term marginal cost. The latter is a horizontal of ordinate C_r for a demand less than the capacity of production D, and a vertical for a demand equal to such production capacity. Mathematically, the four cases which follow should be distinguished:

First case:
$$a_1 - b_1 C_r + c_1 C_r < D \tag{1}$$
$$a_2 - b_2 C_r + c_2 C_r < D \tag{2}$$

These two demands are rated at the cost of slack hours, and production capacity is never fully utilized.

Second case:
$$a_1 - b_1 p_1 + c_1 C_r = D \tag{3}$$
$$a_2 - b_2 C_r + c_2 p_1 < D \tag{4}$$

Production capacity is not completely utilized at night. Therefore $p_2 = C_r$. On the other hand, inequality (1) not having been verified, the p_1 price is such that production capacity will be fully utilized during the day.

Third case: This case is similar to the second. The production capacity is utilized at night, not by day.

Fourth case: The production capacity is fully utilized during the day and at night. p_1 and p_2 are determined by the relations:

$$a_1 - b_1 p_1 + c_1 p_2 = D$$
$$a_2 - b_2 p_2 + c_2 p_1 = D$$

b) Random demand. Chapter 10 has already stressed the importance of random demand. One of Mr. Boiteux's great accomplishments is that he was the first to approach the rate-setting problems in this field [21]. The new element which enters into consideration is that of guarantee. In effect, when demand is random it is impossible for a firm to have an inventory (storable goods) or a capacity of production (nonstorable goods) sufficient to avoid stockout completely.

As a first step, it can be taken for granted that the firm selects its probability of stockout. In Chapter 10 we considered the case of nonstorable goods and a random demand of average value Q with standard deviation s. We saw that the marginal cost of a customer's demand can be considered as the sum of two terms: 1) the marginal cost of his average demand, which will be noted here as c_m and 2) the marginal cost of the random demand (using the notations of Chapter 10) for a customer i with standard deviation s_i:

$$\frac{s_i}{s} C'(Q_0) k(p).$$

Finally, if his average demand is Q_i, the customer i must pay:

$$c_m Q_i + \frac{s_i^2}{s} C'(Q_0) k(p).$$

The second term is easily determined if a meter records the consumption irregularity of customer i. This second term is actually the payment by the consumer for the guarantee related to his demand.

Naturally, however, certain consumers would be most happy to consume goods Q without guarantee or, on the contrary, with a guarantee much greater than p. Instead of offering a single type of goods with a guarantee p, the firm should offer alternative goods with varying guarantees.

The advantage of this type of rate setting is that it becomes possible to avoid the construction of productive facilities whose capacity far exceeds normal utilization.

c) Related products and multiple services. With regard to related products, two principal cases should be considered. We will consider two related products. If the production relationship can be varied regularly, the total cost is a function of the two variables represented by the quantities produced of both goods. Each of these has a marginal cost, and the general theory may be applied.

The problem is different if the relationship of quantitites produced is technologically fixed. Consider two products A and B such that the ratio B/A is equal to a constant m, the total cost is a function D(A), the selling prices are a and b, and the functions of demand are A(a) and B(b). The a and b prices must be determined in such a way that:

$$a + mb = D'(A)$$

$$\frac{B(b)}{A(a)} = m$$

The marginal cost is equal to total marginal receipts at constant prices as is the relationship of demands to the production relationships, so that the equality of supply and demand can be realized for the two products.*

With regard to the services which generally accompany the sale of a product, the rule of rate setting at marginal cost results in an important corollary: the price must be the same for consumers situated in comparable economic conditions, and the differences in price among various consumers must be equal to the differences in marginal costs. Consequently, related services should be rated separately.

Thus, for example, when a family decides to consume gas but the facilities for delivery are not yet installed, Gaz de France must install conduits in the neighborhood, attach pipes to the conduit, install a meter, etc. Then the installation has to be maintained. All these operations have a cost which is not contingent upon the quantity of gas consumed but which is, nevertheless, a consequence of the decision of a household to consume gas. It is reasonable that a charge, independent of gas consumption, be assessed against the household as payment of the marginal cost of extending the network. This payment can be made at one time, or it can be staggered over a series of regular payments of equivalent present value. These costs should not be incorporated into the price per cubic meter of gas, because this would amount to penalizing regular consumers who have long been using the installed power.

Likewise, in the case of rail transportation of freight, the rate must include a cost for receipt and delivery independent of distance,

---

*In a large number of concrete cases the above solution is somewhat theoretical, because the form of demand functions is such that a small uncertainty in demand leads to a considerable price ambiguity.

and a transportation cost which is a function of the distance covered and of the rail network used.

We must also consider that the final sales price must equal the cost of both the product and its transportation. This would be one of the conditions required in order that an allocation of production factors should tend toward an optimum in a geographical area.

Up to now, the pricing policy of selling at marginal cost has been considered from an academic point of view rather than from within the actual framework of specific firms. In the following, we will consider examples in specific context. These will contain illustrations of the preceding rules, but no propositions will be stated. It is quite obvious that actual propositions would have to take into account numerous practical aspects which are beyond the scope of this book.

3. Sales at marginal cost in certain branches of industry.

Among the branches of industry in the undifferentiated sector which pose the most interesting problems are railroads, bridges and highways, waterways, the telephone, electricity, and gas.

a) Railroads [4]. This is an industry which is usually referred to in discussions on sales policy at marginal cost. In fact, it is one of the first industries to have been nationalized in Europe; it is an industry in which the characteristic of public service has been universally recognized; finally, and particularly, it is an industry in which the average cost continues to decrease as utilization increases in both the short and the long run. Consequently, the long-run marginal cost is smaller than the average cost; sales at marginal cost would therefore result in a substantial deficit which would have to be made up by the State and, therefore, by taxes. A reduction in rates, however, is not the inevitable aspect of sales at marginal cost in railroads. In accordance with the principle of price standardization, transportation rates would not be affected by the value of merchandise transported. They would be contingent only upon actual conditions of transportation (departure and arrival stations, transportation in single freight cars or complete trains, etc.). Reductions accorded to certain categories of users would also be eliminated, at least when there is no clause limiting them to slack-hour periods. Thus there would no longer be reductions for employees of the S.N.C.F., for military personnel, for large families, etc. In the latter examples, economic considerations are in conflict with sociological considerations. Although modifications in income distribution may be arrived at by other procedures, manipulation of rates may be one convenient way of accomplishing this. The procedure is questionable, however, because it can have undesirable side effects. For example, granting subsidies or reductions to people in accordance with the distance traveled by rail is neither rational nor generally beneficial [17]. By granting reductions to commuters, the situation of those who live in suburbs and must work in Paris is improved; at the same time, however, this encourages an industrial concentration in the metropolitan area of Paris which everyone agrees is now excessive.

Another application of the theory of economic optimum would require that transportation rates reflect receiving and delivery charges as well as actual transportation charges. Services specially requested by the customer (storage, insurance, etc.) should be billed separately.

Finally, because freight and passenger traffic varies considerably during the year, additional charges should be instituted for transportation during peak periods.

Public opinion is obviously not yet prepared to accept such measures and in the name of common sense and justice would not fail to attack this new method of setting rates. However, public opinion changes; the public must be prepared by educating it to understand the advantage of a rational price policy.

b) Bridges, highways, and waterways. This is a controversial field; however, following the discussions at the beginning of this chapter, the questions become rather apparent (theoretically, at least). As an example, let us consider the case of a bridge.

If the bridge exists and has excess capacity* the marginal cost is zero, because maintenance costs are practically independent of traffic. Exacting a high toll charge (as in the United States) would tend to discourage traffic and increase the deficit.

If the bridge exists but is of insufficient capacity, a toll charge is justified. The amount of toll should equate demand during peak hours to capacity. During slack hours, there would be no occasion to charge a toll.

Finally, if the bridge does not exist, and if a survey indicates that its construction is justified, its capacity must be such that it will be fully utilized at a toll charge equal to the long-run marginal cost.

These observations apply, without modification, to roads, tunnels, and canals. In order not to extend the discussion overly, we will merely point up a few more important problems:

1) the effect of the cost of collecting toll charges on a new bridge;

2) the problem of the stability of the charge when, with traffic increasing and investments being made by stages, the marginal cost fluctuates over a period of time.

---

*In actual practice, the capacity of a bridge cannot be defined very simply; however, this is of little importance because the presentation of this section is entirely schematic.

3) the problem of collecting toll charges on a new bridge when no toll is charged on existing bridges, although their capacity is insufficient. This latter problem relates to optimal price policy in an imperfect environment and, as such, is one of the most difficult to analyze and resolve.

c) The telephone. The rule of sales at marginal cost may have important consequences with regard to the utilization of a telephone network. In addition to a determination of the general level of rates, this rule would lead to a standardization of rates for various types of consumers; to the collection of separate charges for the installation, the subscription, and the calls; to an adjustment of rates according to the hour and the day; and to the fixing of rates from town to town in relation to line and switchboard capacities.

d) Electricity and gas. These two branches of industry pose very similar problems. The only notable differences are the existence of a complete network of interconnections in the case of electricity, and the possibility of storage capacity as a control of production in the case of gas. Here we find again most of the aspects, already noted, of sales at marginal cost:

1) The standardization of rates for consumers having similar requirements. Excluded are contracts with industrialists, in which the rates granted are lower because the industrialist can just as easily make use of another source of energy, and which necessitates a geographical differentiation of rates actually reflecting the cost structure. In order to be guided in their price policy, the offices of Electricité de France constructed a model of the French production and distribution apparatus. The purpose of the model was to assist in determining in each region the marginal costs incurred by an increase in demand.

2) The subdivision of the rate into several fractions relating to connection charges, the total consumption of energy, and the irregularity of consumption.

3) The adjustment of rates according to the hour of the day and the period of the year. Electricité de France already charges different rates for night and for day. In the near future it is to modify its rates still further.

4) The existence of different rates in relation to the guarantee granted to customers. In the case of gas, this can assume the form of interruptible contracts according to which the consumer accepts a low (delivery) guarantee in exchange for particularly advantageous rates.

These are the various principles which Electricité de France plans to apply by introducing a new rate, to be called the green rate [19].

Although hardly exhausting all aspects of sales at marginal cost, the above brief enumeration will be sufficient, we hope, to provide an idea of the essential points. The analysis of Vickrey's survey on New York subway fares will complete this discussion.

4. The change in New York subway fares [63].

At the beginning of 1951, the New York subway reported a moderate deficit (total receipts 213.6 million, total costs 215.1 million) which would have been higher had capital charges been taken into account. The municipality therefore decided to have a survey made of the fare problem to ascertain whether it would be desirable to modify its rate structure. W. S. Vickrey, who was called upon to make this survey, immediately placed the problem within an economic framework.

"Of the various aspects of the problem of fares, perhaps the least understood relates to an optimal utilization of the transit network, account being taken of costs involved. In order to present this aspect clearly we will examine it first, momentarily excluding all other aspects. In order to do this, we have to ask ourselves what the appropriate fare structure would be if certain assumptions were postulated:

1) if there were no fare collection costs;

2) if that revenue which the city is in need of could be obtained by other means (for instance, if the city were to have at its disposal an ideal income tax which would involve no administrations costs, no harmful economic repercussions, and would make it possible to derive the desired revenue from desired economic groups);

3) if no other economic and sociological considerations (such as the effect of a fare structure on population concentration, criminality, delinquency, and other sociological phenomena) were to be of importance.

Under such conditions, if we wished to determine fares on the basis of cost and optimal utilization, transportation would be treated as a service which would not differ materially from a hotel room, a razor, a theater ticket, or the rental for an apartment. For convenience, the following approach will be considered as economic, remembering, however, that there are economic factors other than utilization and cost..." [62].

The standpoint to be adopted having been defined, the first stages of the survey consisted in looking at the traffic structure and at marginal costs. It then became possible to study various fare proposals and to discuss the financial and economic consequences of these various proposals.

a) Traffic structure. A complete analysis of the origins and destinations of traffic at various hours of the day should have been utilized. On the basis of the fragmentary data available, Vickrey established a simplified table of traffic flow in which the origins and destinations were divided into three zones: the central area of

Manhattan, a four-mile-wide zone surrounding the central area, and an outer zone. Each day was divided into seven periods: the peak hours (7-9), the other morning hours (6-7, 9-10), midday (10-4), the peak afternoon hours (5-6), the other afternoon hours (4-5, 6-7), the evening hours (7-12), and the night hours (12-6).

This traffic analysis demonstrated that about a third of the traffic occurred during peak hours (550 million passengers transported of a total of 1,683 million). Moreover, actual peak flows did not exceed 22%; the balance was for trips which were either in the opposite direction of the peak flow or outside the zone of congestion. Any reduction in slack-hour fares, therefore, could only result in a substantial reduction in receipts or require a substantial increase in peak fares.

b) Structure of marginal costs. Vickrey began by studying the cost consequences of various parameters characterizing the traffic, such as: the number of miles traveled by the trains, the number of miles traveled by the subway cars, the maximum number of cars in service, the number of passengers transported, the number of passengers transported during peak hours, the network structure.

From the foregoing he was able to estimate the marginal costs for the different distances covered at the various hours. Table I shows marginal costs, in cents, for traffic originating in the central zone.

Table I

Marginal costs in cents

Traffic originating in the central zone	Toward the outer zone	Toward the median zone	Toward the central zone
Morning peak	5	5	10
Other morning hours . . .	2	2	5
Afternoon peak	25	20	10
Other afternoon hours. . .	15	10	5
Slack hours	5	5	2

c) Examination of various alternative fares. If this problem had been a strictly economic one, the analysis could have been limited to a study of the fare system based on marginal costs. Because it was necessary, however, to take other factors into consideration (financial condition of the company, fare collection costs, socio-logical repercussions), it was important to examine a considerable number of fare alternatives. Vickrey considered the following possibilities:

1. Free transportation.

2. Uniform fares. At the time of the survey, a fixed rate of $.10 was in effect. There was a possibility of returning to $.05 or of raising the fare to $.11, $.12, or $.15.

3. A flexible system of fares varying with the station of boarding (central zone at $.20, median zone at $.15, outer zone at $.10). This system had one drawback in that it did not take the hour of travel into account.

4. Adjustment of fares according to the hour of boarding. This adjustment, however, did not take into account the direction of traffic at peak hours.

5. Adjustment of fares according to the station and hour of boarding. For example: a) during the morning peak period $.20 in the outer zone, $.15 in the median zone, and $.10 in the central zone; b) during the afternoon peak hour, the reverse of the preceding schedule; c) during slack hours, $.05 everywhere; and d) during the remaining hours, an intermediate rate.

6. To minimize collection costs, one could adopt a system of collecting fares in the central zone only, and according to the hour, as passengers enter or leave.

d) Financial and economic repercussion of the various fares. In order to evaluate these, it was necessary to understand traffic reaction to the various projected fares; in other words, to ascertain the elasticity of demand. We do not need to dwell on the complexity of such a problem. The only figures which were available related to traffic reaction when the uniform fare was increased from $.05 to $.10. It was impossible, however, to deduce from these ob-servations the substitutions that would not fail to occur with a differential rate. Vickrey set up a table indicating, for each course, the annual change in traffic pattern in millions of passengers for each $.01 change in fare.

On the basis of these estimates, he calculated: a) the volume of revenue to anticipate from each type of fare, and b) the economic loss associated with each fare structure.

This loss was obtained by multiplying the difference between marginal cost and fare (in cents) by the change in traffic in millions of passengers per year for each $.01 change in fare.

Some of the results have been summarized in Table II. They indicate notably that uniform fares lead to significant economic losses.

With the help of the foregoing data it became possible to consider the problem of fare structure revision as a whole, because all quantitative elements had been evaluated.

Table II[1]

Fare structure	Millions of passengers per year	Receipts (millions of dollars)	Collection costs	Economic losses	Operating costs[2]
1. Free transportation	2,207	0	0	37.9	171
2. Marginal cost . . .	1,914	152 (118)	15.0	0	119.2 (95)
3. Uniform fares:					
5 cents	1,945	97.3	12.5	27.7	156.5
10 cents	1,683	168.3	12.5	30.4	142.0
15 cents	1,421	213.5	12.5	46.8	127.5
4. Collection in central zone: from 5 to 20 cents during the 7 full hours	2,004	90 (83)	3.5	7.3	138.4
5. Fares equal to marginal costs within the limit of a minimum of 5 cents and a maximum of 25 cents .	1,817	163 (151)	15.0	3.1	118.0 (101.0)

[1]The figures in parentheses take into account substitutions in traffic during various hours of the day.

[2]Long-run operating costs for an adjusted network.

We have analyzed this survey because it is an excellent example of the problems encountered in this book: from a study of the market and from a discussion of costs, it deduces various proposals as to price policy and evaluates their economic and financial consequences.

We turn now from the general interest viewpoint to that of the firm.

III

PRICE POLICY AND THE INTEREST OF THE FIRM

Considered solely from the standpoint of the firm, a price policy is intended to maximize long-run profit. This objective is not pursued in an isolated environment but in an environment in which both random events and reactions emanating from other economic organisms have to be taken into account. It is therefore impossible to consider company policy in the somewhat mechanical form used at the beginning of this chapter when the perspective was that of the general interest.

At the outset we will assume that a firm sells only one product at a single price. The firm has a certain independence of choice in determining this price. The next section will approach the problem of related products and the third that of price differentiation, i.e., the sale of one product at different prices.

1. Price policy and market conditions.

Price policy will be examined in the following contexts: a) perfect competition; b) monopoly by law or de facto; c) temporary monopoly (by this we mean the case of a firm that places a new product on the market and thereby benefits from a temporary monopoly. This monopoly will decline as the market for the product tends to develop a competitive market); and d) imperfect competition, characterized by duopoly, oligopoly, and monopolistic competition.

a) Perfect competition. A firm can only sell its production at the market price; it determines its production volume in such a way as to realize equality of sales price and marginal cost. The number of firms in competition is fixed at such a level that, in the case of the least efficient firm, the sales price will be at least equal to the average cost.

b) Monopoly by law or de facto. Monopolies are practically always nationalized enterprises for which the criterion of maximization of profit is hardly justifiable. De facto monopolies are rather scarce, because technical progress will frequently disturb monopolistic situations which were thought to be absolutely firm.

A discussion of this case, however, is interesting, for it is the converse of perfect competiton and facilitates comprehension of intermediate situations.

In Chapter 10 we demonstrated that a monopolistic enterprise fixes its production in such a way as to realize an equality between marginal cost and marginal income. The latter is less than the selling price because, to increase the quantity sold, a reduction in price must be granted for all quantities previously sold. As a consequence the following results: a) the selling price is higher than the marginal cost, and b) the quantity produced is less than that which would be produced if the monopolistic enterprise considered the price as fixed.

Such are the underlying reasons (restriction of production, increase in price) why the policy of a monopoly is in contradiction with the pursuit of the general interest. The foregoing underlies antitrust legislation in the United States and elsewhere.

Reality, however, tends to temper the strictness of this judgment. A firm enjoys a de facto monopoly only because it has succeeded in eliminating or absorbing its competitors. It is therefore probable that, initially, it was better organized and more efficient. The technical advantages which benefit large firms in certain branches of industry can also offset the harmful effects of a monopoly. Finally, any de facto monopoly must be prepared to defend itself, on the one hand, against the emergence of possible competitors and, on the other, against the competition of substitute products, which imposes a limitation on its profit realization.

In order to prevent the emergence of competitors, a monopoly must hold prices at a level which will tend to discourage new firms from entering that particular branch of industry. This presupposes an estimation, implicitly at least, of production costs of possible competitors and of the profits which will be required to attract them.

In order to fight the competition of substitute products, a monopoly must establish its price policy on the basis of a demand curve which will actually take these products into account. When the uses of goods produced by a monopoly are many, the degree of monopoly can vary enormously from one use to another. For instance, in the case of coal, sales range from the industrial market, in which the fuel oil competition is extremely active, to the blast furnace coke market, in which coal enjoys, for the present, a technical monopoly.

Rational management (i.e., management which actually attempts to maximize profit) requires much more detailed econometric data in the environment of monopoly than in that of perfect competition.

c) Temporary monopoly. This situation occurs frequently. A firm invents a new product and places it on the market. For a certain length of time the demand will remain low, for consumers are not yet aware of the product. The firm will enjoy a de facto monopoly under the protection of its patents. Then, as the product enters into common usage, demand develops rapidly. Additional firms try to enter the market. They develop new production techniques. In time, prices and techniques tend to stabilize; the market evolves toward an ordinary competitive market.

J. Dean, who has thoroughly analyzed this cycle of the evolution of the market for a particular product, distinguishes three characteristics toward which the market moves simultaneously.*

"A technical maturity, which is characterized by a decreasing rate in the development of the product, by an increasing

---

*Cf. [20], Chapter 10.

standardization of the different trademarks, by an increasing stability of production techniques, and by a knowledge of these techniques.

"The maturity of a market which is characterized by the consumer's familiarization with the idea that this is a necessary product, by a generalized belief in the quality of the products of the various manufacturers, by a familiarity and a knowledge of the product which make it possible for the consumer to compare the brands competently.

"A maturity in competition which is characterized by increasing stability in the distribution of the market and in price structure."

A firm which invents a new product must determine a strategy relating to prices and production which leads to a maximum effective income, with all of the nuances such a phrase implies in a field in which uncertainty and the reactions of competitors play a major part. This strategy, moreover, can be revised at all times. In order to present a range of possible strategies, it will be more convenient, following J. Dean's example, to consider two extreme cases: that of the skimming of demand and that of creating a broad market.

1) Skimming of demand. This policy is characterized by very high initial prices and by a major promotional effort. The prices are reduced as the market develops and competitors tend to appear. Remembering the significance of effective income, one can pinpoint fairly easily the conditions which contribute to making such a policy satisfactory.

First, demand is only slightly elastic. The chances are great that this will be the case when the product is brand-new. Consumers are not yet accustomed to the service it can render and many are drawn by the novelty of the product, all of which contributes to reduce the influence of price.

Second, advertising is very effective in promoting sales. This is also likely because advertising brings the product to the attention of the public and excites curiosity.

Third, in time the elasticity of demand will increase and the firm will progressively reduce its prices. If the product is a durable good, the policy takes the form of maximizing the price to the initial market, consisting of a relatively small number of eager buyers. As the market potential is broadened, the price is lowered to convert potential sales to actual revenues. This phenomenon of differentiation in price over a period of time makes it possible for the producer to appropriate the consumer's income. It is quite comparable to other price differentiations to be discussed later. The skimming policy is, therefore, particularly appropriate when consumer behavior is heterogeneous.

Fourth, if a firm is aware of the fact that it cannot prevent the emergence of new competitors, this policy avoids sacrificing current receipts for less probable future receipts.

A final economic advantage of this policy derives from the fact that it obviates the necessity of making large investments because large-scale development in the demand for the product is not anticipated.

2) The creation of a broad market. This policy, on the contrary, is characterized by relatively low initial prices, and consists essentially in exchanging present heavy costs against the expectation of future returns. Which are the most favorable conditions for this approach?

First, a strong initial elasticity of demand is needed. This, in effect, permits lowering prices without severely reducing receipts.*

Next is the requirement for a large market potential. This has many complex implications but, stated simply, the product should be potentially attractive to consumers of various environments.

Third, the productive process should yield increasing returns. In fact, by creating a broad market, a firm can avoid working below optimal production capacity and can effect substantial savings in expenditures.

Finally, there should be some way of minimizing the emergence of new competitors on the market.

The success of such a policy is contingent upon numerous conditions: the size of the market, reductions in cost made possible by mass production, the possibility of producing substitutes, and the vitality of firms in neighboring branches of production. The policy of creating a broad market is profitable for the firm if it can outdistance its competitors and benefit from the advantages of the large market before their arrival. If it reaches a fair size, it can be in a better condition to defend itself.

The parallel which has just been drawn may appear to be too rigid, but it must be remembered that these are extreme cases and that the price policy must be reexamined periodically.

d. Imperfect competition. Halfway between monopoly and perfect competition, this covers, as its name indicates, the majority of actual situations, within which can be distinguished duopoly, oligopoly, and monopolistic competition.

1) Duopoly. This is the case where only two firms are in a certain market. Let us designate p_1 and p_2 as the prices of the two enterprises, q_1 and q_2 as the quantities produced, and $D(q_1)$ and $D(q_2)$ as the corresponding costs. If demand functions are expressed as:

$$p_1 = p_1 (q_1, q_2)$$
$$p_2 = p_2 (q_1, q_2)$$

---

*It is seldom that, at the beginning, elasticity will be such that a reduction in price will increase the returns.

the income or receipts of the duopolists are expressed as:

$$R_1 = p_1 (q_1, q_2) q_1 - D (q_1) = R_1 (q_1, q_2)$$
$$R_2 = p_2 (q_1, q_2) q_2 - D (q_2) = R_2 (q_1, q_2)$$

The first duopolist choses q_1, the second q_2, and as a result the first collects $R_1(q_1, q_2)$, the second $R_2(q_1, q_2)$. Duopoly, therefore, appears as a two-person game in which pure strategies are represented by the values of q_1 and q_2, and in which the payments made to the players are the returns. This is not a zero-sum game; that is, what is won by one duopolist is not necessarily lost by the other.

A great number of patterns of behavior are possible.

Each duopolist can choose his production in such a way as to maximize his income for a given value of the production of the other enterprise. q_1 and q_2 are then determined by the system of equations:

$$\frac{\partial R_1}{\partial q_1} (q_1, q_2) = 0 \qquad \frac{\partial R_2}{\partial q_2} (q_1, q_2) = 0.$$

The point attained is an equilibrium point in the sense which Nash attributes to it in the theory of games. Each duopolist has no interest in modifying his behavior as long as the other does not modify his.

One of the duopolists (for example, the first) can continue to behave as heretofore, whereas the other attempts to maximize his profit while taking into account the reaction of his adversary. For the first, the relation:

$$\frac{\partial R_1}{\partial q_1} (q_1, q_2) = 0 \text{ defines } q_1 = q_1 (q_2).$$

R_2 becomes a function of q_2 only, and the second duopolist behaves in such a manner as to maximize:

$$\frac{\partial R_2}{\partial q_1} \frac{dq_1}{dq_2} + \frac{\partial R_2}{\partial q_2} = 0.$$

Naturally, the second duopolist is in a more advantageous situation than previously.

If both duopolists attempt to take one another's reactions into account, the problem is no longer predetermined. An economic model explains very well, therefore, the instability which historically has often characterized situations bordering on duopoly. Through price wars, duopolists have attempted to eliminate their competitors. Another procedure has been that of agreements. In effect, it can be demonstrated that duopolists can assure themselves, by cooperating, a total income greater than the sum of the revenues that each can insure for himself by noncooperative behavior. This is the objective of negotiating. This distribution can concretely assume varied forms: production quotas, price agreements, geographical shares of markets, etc. The nature of such agreements is contingent upon the respective power of the two enterprises.

2) Oligopoly. This situation is realized when a small number of sellers face each other in a small market, each holding a fair share of the market. In fact, oligopoly is common. It exists strongly in most of the industrial markets in the United States; in France, it is found in the metallurgical industry, in the automobile industry, in the aluminum industry, etc. The frequency of oligopolies is not surprising because perfect competition and monopolistic situations tend to disintegrate and to terminate in oligopolistic situations. Technical progress, by increasing the optimal capacity of factories, also contributes to the potential growth of oligopoly.

By constructing a model similar to that of duopoly, it could be easily observed that the problem of oligopoly can be brought back to a non-zero-sum game in which the number of players is equal to the number of entrepreneurs.

The number of possible situations increases very rapidly, depending on the number of participants. Following Nash, they can be separated into two groups: those in which oligopolists "play" independently of one another and do not cooperate, and those in which they form coalitions. In the latter case, the strength of the various coalitions, their probability of formation, the manner in which each distributes income among its members, should all be studied. Much work remains to be done in this area.

In oligopolistic situations, entrepreneurs attempt to avoid price wars which are ruinous for the industry. Aware of the fact that their competitors can do the same, they refrain from seeking to increase their share of the market through price reductions. As a result, oligopoly can attain a certain stability characterized by: a) the "price leadership" of a firm, b) the reduction of hidden prices, and c) competition in fields other than that of price.

Price leadership is a widespread institution in the United States. A firm in a particular branch of industry plays the role of "leader": it takes the initiative by announcing its price changes. The other firms follow suit either precisely or approximately but invariably in the same direction. In order for such a situation to hold, the leader must have a price policy which will be acceptable to the greater part of the industry. The leader cannot, therefore, select his prices to fit only his own situation. Moreover, if his policy is too conservative he runs the risk of losing his domination to a more dynamic enterprise. In a word, the leader must possess the necessary qualifications, ie., power, wisdom, and initiative. Very frequently, the leading firm is the largest one in the industry and offers the most varied goods and services. In order to preserve its prestige, it must avoid frequent changes in its official prices. The leading firm is the one which actually takes the initiative in raising prices. Reductions, on the contrary, are usually the result of hidden downgrading of official prices. When, in a great number of markets, the competitors and the leader agree to grant important discounts and the trend toward a decrease in prices seems to be a lasting one, the leader lowers his official prices to the level of prices actually practiced. The leader must also (and this is another aspect of his activity) evaluate the permissible price differences from one firm to another.

The lowering of hidden prices has just been touched upon. It can assume various forms. It is contingent at one time upon the customer, upon the size of the order, and upon the geographical area. The existence of inferior brands further increases the latitude in this respect. On the general interest level, this lowering of hidden prices is condemnable because it constitutes an infringement of the principle of price standardization. Its only advantage is that it precedes adjustments of official prices and in this way contributes to the stability of oligopolies.

Competition in fields other than that of price (promotion, packaging, etc.) is, in a way, a substitute for price competition. It is much less dangerous because its effects are long-term and the possibilities of reactions from competitors are more limited.

3) Monopolistic competition. This is a form of competition in which there is a large number of sellers but in which each sells a product which is slightly different from that of his competitors. Each firm is therefore faced with a demand curve as well as a market price. On the basis of such a demand curve a firm maximizes its income, but, contrary to what occurs in a monopolistic situation, new firms can easily enter the industry. They contribute to a lowering of the level of demand for each enterprise and to a reduction in profits.

In reality, price policies are extremely varied. The analysis may be developed further when game theory can be successfully applied to large numbers of players.

2. Establishing prices of related products.

Economists have often studied a price policy only for firms which place a single product on the market, but this hypothesis rarely corresponds to reality. Most firms manufacture numerous products which are basically different (i.e., gas, coke, and tar, by-products of a coke-making plant) or constitute, on the contrary, a homogeneous range in which differences relate only to size and to quality (the various models and styles of refrigerators manufactured by one company). To understand the logical solution to the problem, it is helpful to start by quickly examining some of the standard rules.

a) Critique of certain standard rules.

One rule states that the prices of different products must be proportionate to average costs. Unfortunately, in the case of related products the concept of average cost has no operational significance and can result only from arbitrary agreement. By applying this rule, a firm can find itself hemmed in by a rigid price policy in the face of changing market conditions.

A second rule suggests, on the other hand, that prices be proportionate to short-term marginal costs [3]. This rule does not suffer from the arbitrary nature of the preceding rule, because marginal costs can be determined without ambiguity. The advocates of this rule justify it by citing the example of rate setting for public utilities. The elasticity of demand in relation to prices for utilities as a whole is generally low. Any increase in price would, therefore, have small effect on the existing situation; consequently, a price increase would lead to little economic loss. On the other hand, the sensitivity of demand to prices for the various types of energy is extremely great, so that any modification in related prices would entail great economic loss. Because the optimum corresponds to the price setting for each of the different types of energy at a price equal to marginal cost, it follows that the economic loss corresponding to setting prices proportionate to marginal costs will be small. Nevertheless, the justification of this rule is not decisive: it certainly does not lead to a maximization of income because it does not take market conditions into account; neither is it in strict conformity with the general interest, which requires equality and not proportionality of prices and marginal costs. It is conceivable that this is the best rule if an enterprise wishes to be in a state of budgetary equilibrium (i.e., financially sound) while pursuing the best possible policy in the general interest. M. Boiteux recently demonstrated that this was not the case [20].

A final rule suggests prices such that profit margins on each product would be proportionate to the value added; a moment's thought will show that this rule is subject to the criticisms directed against the first two rules.

The foregoing rules all have the serious defect of suggesting a mode of systematic price fixing which takes only costs into account and omits market conditions.

b) The solution from the standpoint of maximization of profit. Let us take the case of a monopoly which manufactures two products q_1 and q_2 and sells them on markets in which the functions of demand are $p_1(q_1)$ and $p_2(q_2)$. If the monopoly's costs are $D(q_1, q_2)$, the income $p_1q_1 + p_2q_2 - D$ is at a maximum when, for each product, the marginal revenue is equal to marginal cost:

$$\frac{d}{dq_i}(p_iq_i) = \frac{\partial D}{\partial q_i} \qquad i = 1, 2.$$

These relations are written, designating by $e_i = -\dfrac{dq_i}{dp_i}\dfrac{p_i}{q_i}$ the elasticity of demand i:

$$p_i\left(1 - \frac{1}{e_i}\right) = \frac{\partial D}{\partial q_i}.$$

For a given marginal cost, the lower e_i the more $1 - \dfrac{1}{e_i}$ will also be low, and the greater p_i. Thus, if the marginal cost is substantially the same for the two products, the prices can vary widely if the elasticities of demand are very different. It is to a firm's advantage to establish a higher price for inelastic demands and a lower price for elastic demands. In other words, the price is high when the consumer does not restrict his consumption as price increases.

Very frequently, the products of a company are complementary or substitute products. In the first case, we find machines and their spare parts. It is possible to lower the price of the machines and to increase the prices of the spare parts, for which the demand is entirely inelastic for those in possession of the end-item. A second case of automobiles of varying horsepower can be cited. The manufacturer will then attempt to design models to sell to consumers of different social classes. Because the elasticity of demand is lower for consumers in the higher income classes than for consumers in the lower income classes, the difference in price between the products sold in the two markets will tend to be greater than the difference in marginal costs.

From the moment we recognize that there is an advantage for a firm to take into account the elasticity of demand (when demand curves exist), it will be more apparent that the individual firm must pattern its price policy upon competitive conditions. The number of competitors, the respective shares of the market they retain, and the exact characteristics of their product are the main elements in the evaluation. Neither should one lose sight of the possibility of new competitors appearing on the scene.

The establishment of prices for special orders constitutes an especially important criterion in price policy.

c) The establishment of prices for special orders. Some firms, such as printers, do not produce a specific product but fill successive orders placed by various customers. Each time they receive a request for printing, they must prepare an estimate for the client. This is a particularly delicate decision, because it is difficult to adjust progressively to market conditions.

A convenient method of approaching the problem is to determine the upper and lower limits of the zone within which the price could vary. The lower limit is reached when it is to the advantage of the firm to do nothing or to do something else. If, for the period considered, the firm has no other order in sight, the limit is the short-term marginal cost. If, on the other hand, the available capacity can be used otherwise, the limit depends on the income that would be realized by the other orders available to the firm. The upper limit, which is the price at which a firm loses the market, is less rigid, but here also a consideration of alternatives offered to the buyer can be valuable. An attempt can be made at evaluating bids which would be offered by competitors.

In order to complete this examination of price policy, we will discuss the case of the sales of a single product on several markets.

3. Price differentiation.

The distinction between the problems touched upon in this section and those which have been studied above is somewhat artificial. It presupposes that the manufacturer has no choice as to the nature of the products he sells on the market. The preceding section, therefore, dealt with the establishment of prices for distinct products, whereas this section describes a price policy which consists in selling identical products at different prices on different markets. In actual fact, however, a manufacturer can to a large extent determine the range of his products; this is one of the means at his disposal to divide his market into partial demands of differing elasticity.

Price differentiation is open to criticism from the standpoint of the general interest because the theory of economic optimum strongly insists upon the principle of equating price to marginal costs for all consumers. In the imperfect world in which we live, however, discrimination is not necessarily harmful. M. Boiteux has recently demonstrated that a certain amount of discrimination could be justified when it was requested of a public utility to comply with the general interest while attempting to maintain a budgetary equilibrium.

Price differentiation can assume many guises, but the most important are partitioning the market, differentiating prices within a geographical area, and granting discounts to distributors.

a) Partitioning of the market. Dividing a market consists of separating it into distinct sections of differing elasticity. The same pair of shoes will be sold at a higher price in a high-income district than in a poorer district, keeping in mind that: a) on the average, rich buyers will not buy their shoes in a poorer district, and b) the elasticity of their demand is lower.

Therefore, if tastes, habits, and incomes of social classes can be increasingly differentiated, then an enterprise can make use of this to increase its profit. In this respect, the possibilities are certainly much greater in Europe than in the United States. This is so because in the United States social homogeneity is greater.

By thus permitting an increase in revenue, the partition of a market enables a firm to remain in business whereas under a single price system it might be forced out. This phenomenon has played an important part in the policy of certain companies (such as railroads) and, for this reason, deserves attention. Let us consider (Fig. 8) an enterprise with a decreasing average cost where the average cost is constantly below the demand curve. In the absence of price differentiation the firm operates at a loss for any production Q because the rectangle of costs OQCA is a

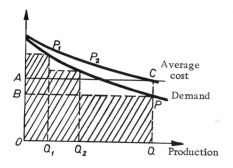

Fig. 8

larger area than that of receipts OQPB. The demand decreases as the price rises because there is an increasing number of consumers who forego the services offered by the firm. If one can succeed in isolating the consumers who are anxious to retain that service, one can, for example, sell them a quantity OQ_1 at price Q_1P_1. One can also sell Q_1Q_2 to intermediate consumers at price Q_2P_2. Finally, Q_2Q will be sold to marginal consumers at a price QP. The receipts will now be represented by the shaded area. They exceed the previous receipts by the portion above BP and can be greater than costs.

The price policies of the S.N.C.F. and of the Régie des Tabacs have frequently been influenced in the past by the foregoing analysis. But (although this demonstrates the influence which is beginning to be exerted by the theory of economic optimum) it would seem that they will not apply the same policy to the sale of natural gas. Yet this is a field in which prices can be differentiated with respect to classes of consumers; by confiscating their income, receipts can be brought closer to the area located below the curve of demand.

The existence of brands and subbrands constitutes, for certain industries, a means of realizing price differentiation. Another famous example is the practice of pricing the same goods differently for export as compared to domestic markets.

b) Price differentiation within a geographical area. The theory of the economic optimum requires that at each point the price of a product will be equal to the sum of the factory price plus a transportation cost. However, it is quite obvious that, in order to maximize profit, it is to a firm's advantage to break away from this rule.

To demonstrate this point, we will examine a very simple model. A monopoly located at point 0 sells to complexes that are equidistant from each other and symmetrically located in relation to 0. A community is at 0. Because the solution will be symmetrical, we can designate the symmetrical communities by the same index (Fig. 9). The transportation of the merchandise is assumed to take place at the

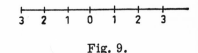

Fig. 9.

expense of the monopolist, subject to a constant cost t from one community to the neighboring community. In order to facilitate the geometrical presentation, it is also assumed that the marginal cost of production is not related to the quantity produced.

Assuming q_i to be the quantity sold in community i and p_i the price, the demand curves of the different communities will be hypothesized to be identical. Still in order to simplify, we will represent them by the straight line $a - bq_i$. The curve of marginal income, under these conditions, is the straight line $a - 2bq_i$. In Fig. 10, the straight lines of demand and of marginal income are MN_0 and MP_0 respectively. The straight lines of marginal costs at delivery are parallel to the straight line P_0N_0 marginal cost at the factory and are located at distances from this line equal to multiples of t.

Sales at marginal cost would consist in assigning prices and selling quantities represented by the coordinates of points N_0, N_1, N_2, N_3, ..., (in which the indices designate the communities). The policy of maximization of profit leads to an equalization of marginal income and marginal cost delivered for each community. Marginal incomes and quantities sold are consequently the coordinates of P_0, P_1, P_2, P_3, ..., and the corresponding prices are the ordinates of N_0', N_1', N_2', N_3', ... It will be noted in Fig. 10 that the difference between marginal cost and price decreases

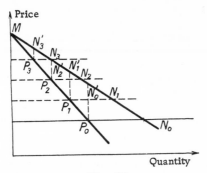

Fig. 10.

continuously. In addition, N_3' is much nearer to N_3 than N_0 is to N_0', and the difference in price between two communities N_0, N_1', N_2', N_3', ..., is smaller than the cost of transportation t. In other words, the monopoly has a range of prices which is much more restricted than the range of marginal costs. Everything occurs as though the monopoly charged relatively much higher transportation costs to neighboring consumers than to more distant ones. For a very long time firms have felt the advantage of such policies. These policies are found in a somewhat disguised form in the systems used in actual practice which we discuss below.

F.o.b. prices. This method of rate setting consists in having the consumer pay the sum of the factory delivered price plus actual transportation costs. It excludes, therefore, any unjustified geographical discrimination and, for this reason, is not incompatible with an economic optimum. In such a price system, each factory theoretically controls a sales zone within which its delivered prices are smaller than those of the other factories (the zone boundaries corresponding to equality). Nevertheless, in the case of certain industries, such a price system may lead to a certain instability. These are industries which have: 1) an oligopolic structure; 2) strongly decreasing average costs and, consequently, high fixed charges and low short-term marginal costs; 3) high transportation costs in relation to the factory delivered price; and 4) an unstable geographical demand as the business cycle varies, with strong possibilities of substitution between the products of the various factories.

In fact, the foregoing factors encourage firms to vary their factory delivered price in order to modify the effect of varying transportation costs, and price wars may result.

Uniform prices. Under this policy, price is independent of the geographical proximity of seller to buyer. When transportation costs are insignificant, this practice has the advantage of convenience. But when this is not so, the neighboring consumers are, in effect, helping to pay the cost of shipping to more distant consumers. By failing to take advantage of greater sales opportunities in nearby markets, firms using a uniform pricing policy are failing to optimize the allocation of the factors of production.

In the case of oligopolies, on the other hand, this policy does not present the drawbacks of the preceding one.

Zone prices. When company policy scales prices by zone, the customer is actually billed the sum of the factory delivered price plus a transportation cost but the factory price varies according to the zone, i.e., according to the customer's geographical location. It is generally lower for distant zones. Zone prices therefore constitute price discrimination. They permit firms to extend their areas of sale while maintaining high prices for neighboring consumers who can derive no advantage from more distant competition.

Parity prices. This system selects a point of parity, the same for all firms. The price scale of a company gives delivery prices at the parity point. Customers are not charged actual transportation costs but fictitious ones from the point of parity to the point of consumption. One of the results of this system is the appearance either of a phantom freight or of freight absorption. The first exists when the fictitious transportation charges are higher than the real ones, and the latter in the contrary case. If the firms are widely scattered geographically, this system results in considerable discrimination against consumers who are distant from the base point.

Multiple-parity prices. In order to reduce this last inconvenience the system of multiple-parity prices has been created, in which several centers are used as base points. Under this system, delivery charges are agreed upon to the different base points. The consumer is billed the sum of the factory delivered price at the nearest point of parity plus a transportation charge from there.

One application of this system is the practice of equalization of freight charges. All factories become points of parity. There is, therefore, in most cases absorption of freight charges by the sender, an absorption compensated for by an increase in the average factory delivery price. From a standpoint of economic optimum, this system is subject to the same criticisms as the previous systems.

On the other hand, by limiting geographical competition all systems of parity prices assist the oligopolies in achieving an equilibrium in which price competition is minimized.

c) Discounts to distributors. These are reductions in price that vary with the extent to which the distributor controls the market for the producer's products. The producer attempts to influence important distributors by trade discounts so that the distributor will favor his products on the retail market.

Trade discounts influence profits obtained by distributors and, if large enough, attract their interest. An expanding industry may grant large trade discounts in order to attract large numbers of distributors very quickly.

The structure of distribution networks can be modified by a play on margins. For example, with a view to shortening distribution networks, a large margin can be given to distributors who obtain goods directly from the factory and resell them immediately to consumers. Discounts granted to distributors often have much more important repercussions upon product sales than do reductions in consumer prices. Finally, these trade discounts are valuable in the partitioning of markets. They make it possible to reinforce the effect of differences in chains of distribution. As such, they are cumulative, that is, additive to the other means which have been mentioned in this chapter.

In view of this summary it would appear that company price policy must utilize the results of all economic studies, whether they relate to market analyses, surveys of costs, or policies of operation, stockage, and investment. The theory of economic optimum helps to provide a better understanding of the underlying significance of these relationships. Price is thus the connecting link between the firm and the outer world: it summarizes the demand situation for the firm, and it summarizes for the outside world a firm's conditions of operation. This intermediary role makes it possible to decentralize the decision function. In order that an economic optimum may be attained, this role should be perfectly played. Essentially, the rules of sale at marginal cost express nothing else. In actual practice, however, the price system is imperfect. The third part of this chapter has enumerated a certain number of means available to a company whereby it can alter the price system for its own benefit. The role of the State is to insure that the rules of the game are followed in order that the price system may effectively provide the various economic organisms with choices conforming to the general interest. Its price policy, therefore, blends the economic methods of industrial management with national economic action.

BIBLIOGRAPHY

1. M. ALLAIS:
   Traité d'Economie pure (Treatise on pure economics). Paris, Imprimerie nationale, 1953. (A first edition of this book was published in 1943 under the title, "A la recherche d'une discipline économique" [In search of an economic discipline].)

2. M. ALLAIS:
   Rendement social et productivité sociale (Corporate returns and corporate productivity). Econometrica, vol. XVII, supplement, July 1949.

3. M. ALLAIS:
La gestion des Houillères nationalisées et la théorie économique (Management of nationalized coal mines and economic theory). Imprimerie nationale, 1953.

4. M. ALLAIS:
Le problème de la coordination des transports et la théorie économique (The problem of transportation coordination and economic theory). Revue d'Economie politique, vol. LVII, March-April 1948.

5. M. ALLAIS:
Economie pure et rendement social. Contribution de la science économique moderne à la construction d'une économie de bien-être (Pure economics and corporate returns. Contribution of the modern science of economics to the establishment of a welfare economy). Paris, Sirey, 1945.

6. M. ALLAIS:
Quelques réflexions sur l'intérêt général et les intérêts particuliers (A few observations on the matter of the general interest and special interests). Nouvelle revue de l'Economie Contemporaine, 1951.

7. M. ALLAIS:
Problèmes posés par l'application de la théorie du coût marginal (Problems raised by the application of marginal cost theory). Multilithed document, 1951.

8. K. J. ARROW:
Social choices and individual values. Cowles Commission Monograph No. 12, New York, Wiley, 1951.

9. J. S. BAIN:
Price and production policies, in: A Survey of Contemporary Economics. Edited by H. S. Ellis. Published for the American Economic Association by the Blakiston Company, Philadelphia, Toronto, 1949.

10. BARONE:
Le Ministère de la production dans un Etat collectiviste (The Ministry of Production in a collectivist state). Article published in 1908, and republished in 1939 as an appendix to "L'économie dirigée en régime collectiviste" (Controlled economy in a collectivist regime), Librairie de Médicis, Paris.

11. W. J. BAUMOL:
Welfare economics and the theory of the state. The London School of Economics and Political Science. Longmans, Green and Co., London, New York, Toronto, 1952.

12. P. BECKWITH:
The economic theory of a socialist economy. Stanford University Press, California, and Oxford University Press, Geoffrey Camberley, London, 1948.

13. B. P. BECKWITH:
Marginal-cost price-output control, New York, Columbia University Press, 1955.

14. A. BERGSON:
"Socialist economics," in: A Survey of Contemporary Economics. Howard S. Ellis, ed., American Economic Association, 1949.

15. M. BOITEUX:
La tarification des demandes en pointe: application de la théorie de la vente au coût marginal (Pricing of peak demands: application of the theory of sales at marginal cost). Revue générale de l'électricité, August, 1949, vol. LVIII, No. 8.

16. M. BOITEUX:
La vente au coût marginal dans un environnement imparfait (Sales at marginal cost in an imperfect environment). Document of Electricité de France, 1951.

17. M. BOITEUX:
Réflexions sur la concurrence du rail et de la route (Observations on rail and road competition). Document of the Fédération nationale des transporteurs routiers, 1951.

18. M. BOITEUX:
La vente au coût marginal (Sales at marginal cost). Revue française de l'énergie, December 1956.

19. M. BOITEUX:
Le tarif vert d'Electricité de France (Electricité de France's green rate). Revue française de l'energie, January 1957.

20. M. BOITEUX:
Sur la gestion des monopoles publics astreints a l'équilibre budgetaire (On the management of public monopolies subject to budgetary equilibrium). Econometrica, vol. XXIV, No. 1, January 1956.

21. M. BOITEUX:
La tarification du coût marginal et les demandes aléatoires (Pricing of marginal cost and random demand). Cahiers du Séminaire d'Econometrie, No. 1, 1951.

22. James BONBRIGHT:
Major controversies as to the criteria of reasonable public utility rates. American Economic Review, XXX, supplement, 1940.

23. W. CLEMENS:
Price discrimination in a decreasing cost industry. American Economic Review, XXXI, December 1941.

24. E. H. CHAMBERLIN:
Une formulation nouvelle de la théorie de la concurrence monopolistique (A new formulation of the theory of monopolistic competition). Archives de l'I.S.E.A., vol. V, 1952, Nos. 2-3, April–September.

25. E. H. CHAMBERLIN:
The theory of monopolistic competition. Harvard Economic Studies, Cambridge, Harvard University Press, 1933.

26. R. H. COASE:
The marginal cost controversy. Economica, August 1946.

27. J. DEAN:
Managerial economics. Prentice-Hall, New York, 1951.

28. Henri DENIS:
Le Monopole bilateral (Bilateral monopoly). Paris, P.U.F., 1943.

29. G. DESSUS and FLEURQUIN:
Les tarifs du gaz et de l'électricité et l'orientation du consommateur (Gas and electricity rates and consumer orientation). Report to the World Conference on Energy held at the Hague, 1947, Rev, Econ. Pol., 1948, 4.

30. G. DESSUS:
La tarification des services publics (The price setting of public utilities). Lecture to the I.S.E.A., Monday, February 19, 1951.

32. G. DESSUS:
Le sens d'une tarification (Meaning of rate-setting). Lecture to a meeting of various chiefs of the Service Commercial National of the E.D.F., April 18-20, 1950.

33. DESSUS and FLEURQUIN:
    Sur les tarifications d'intérêt général dans les services
    publics industriels (Rate-setting in industrial public utilities
    and the general interest). Report to a special session of the
    Commission de tarification de l'UNIPEDE, 1949.

34. M. FLEMING:
    Price and output policy of state enterprise. Economica,
    XVII, February 1950. Production and price policy in public
    enterprise. Economica, vol. XVII, No. 65, February 1950.

35. G. Th. GUILBAUD:
    Les théories de l'intérêt général et le problème logique de
    l'agrégation (Theories on general interest and the logical
    problem of aggregation). Economie appliquée, October-
    December 1952.

36. A. M. HENDERSON:
    The pricing of public utility undertakings. Manchester School
    of Economic and Social Studies, vol. XV, No. 3, September
    1949.

37. H. HOTELLING:
    The relation of prices to marginal costs in an optimum
    system. Econometrica, VII, April 1939.

38. H. HOTELLING:
    The general welfare in relation to problems of taxation and
    of railway and utility rates. Econometrica, July 1945.

39. M. R. HUTTER:
    La théorie économique et la gestion commerciale des
    chemins de fer (Economic theory and the commerical
    management of railroads).
    I. Qu'est-ce que le coût marginal? (What is marginal cost?)
    II. Le problème tarifaire (The pricing problem).
    III. La coordination des transports (The coordination of
        transportation).
    Revue générale des chemins de fer, February 1950. Dunod,
    1951.

40. KALDOR:
    Welfare propositions of economics and interpersonal com-
    parisons of utility. Economic journal, September 1939.

41. B. V. KRISHNAMURTI:
    Pricing in planned economy, Bombay Oxford University
    Press, 1949.

42. A. P. LERNER:
Theory and practice in socialist economics. Review of economic studies, VI, October 1938.

43. A. P. LERNER:
The economics of control, principles of welfare economics. New York, 1949.

44. I. M. D. LITTLE:
A critique of welfare economics. Clarendon Press, 1950.

45. I. M. D. LITTLE:
L'avantage collectif (The collective advantage). Economie appliquée, October-December 1952.

46. J. MARCHAL:
Le mécanisme des prix (The mechanism of prices). Librairie de Médicis, Paris, 2nd edition, 1948.

47. J. E. MEADE:
Planning and the price mechanism. The liberal-socialist solution, London, 1948.

48. J. E. MEADE:
Price and output policy of state enterprise. The Economic Journal, December 1944.

49. J. E. MEADE:
The theory of international economic policy. Oxford University Press, 1955.

50. Hla MYINT:
Theories of welfare economics. Longmans, Green and Co., London, 1948.

51. Harry NORRIS:
State enterprise price and output policy and the problem of cost imputation, Economica, February 1949.

52. G. NYBLEN:
Quelques réflexions sur le vieux problème de l'avantage collectif à la lumière des développements récents (A few observations on the old problem of the collective advantage in the light of recent developments). Economie appliquée, October-December 1952.

53. A. C. PIGOU:
The economics of welfare. MacMillan and Co., Ltd., 4th ed., London, 1950.

54. A. C. PIGOU:
Some aspects of welfare economics. American Economic
Review, June 1951.

55. M. W. REDER:
Studies in the theory of welfare economics. New York,
Columbia University Press, 1947.

56. (Mrs.) J. ROBINSON:
The economics of imperfect competition. London, MacMillan,
1933.

57. P. A. SAMUELSON:
Foundations of economic analysis. Cambridge, Harvard
University Press.

58. A. SAUVY:
A propos de la coordination des transports: répartition d'un
objectif production entre deux activités (In regard to the
coordination of transportation: apportionment of a production
objective between two activities). Revue d'économie politique,
January 1949.

59. T. SCITOVSKY:
The state of welfare economics. American Economic Review,
vol. XVI, No. 3, June 1951.

60. T. SCITOVSKY:
Welfare and competition.

61. P. STREETEN:
La théorie moderne de l'économie de bien-être. (The modern
theory of welfare economics). Economie appliquée, Archieves
de l'I.S.E.A., vol. V, No. 4, October-December 1952.

62. W. VICKREY:
Some objections to marginal cost pricing. Journal of Political
Economy, June 1948.

63. W. VICKREY:
A proposal for revising New York's fare structure. Journal
of the Operations Research Society of America, vol. III, No. 1,
1955. The same study appeared as a brochure in 1952 (The
revision of the subway fare structure of the City of New York.
Mayor's Committee on management survey of the city of New
York).

CONCLUSION

Chapter 15

Economic analysis and
the organization of the firm

If we consider the variety of economic applications in the life of a firm, it is not surprising that the use of the economic method should raise problems of organization. If these problems are not studied and resolved, any action taken by the economic analysts runs the risk of being ineffective while arousing psychological hostility. For this reason, this book closes with a brief chapter devoted to the administrative aspects of the use of the economic method.

Our objective will not be that of suggesting ready-made solutions, because the basic organization of the firm and the degree of development of the economic studies have a controlling influence upon the outcome. The objective is rather to review problems while referring to an example of an important firm that has introduced or developed the use of economic analysis without calling upon outside assistance. (Incidentally, reference will also be made to the case of a firm that hires the services of a specialized group). So that the discussion may be introduced logically, the first part will recall briefly those tasks which can be entrusted to analysts. Then we will analyze, in the following order:

a) the anatomy of possible organizations;
b) the internal structure of economic departments;
c) communication between the economic and other departments of a firm.

A last portion of this chapter will cover questions relative to the training of personnel, fundamental questions because it is the lack of a sufficient number of specialists that currently limits the development of the economic method.

I

THE TASKS OF ECONOMIC ANALYSTS

The role of economic analysts in a firm should now be more apparent than it was when we attempted to provide a definition of economic method at the book's beginning. Their role is essentially that of carrying studies through successfully, to provide quantitative bases for decisions as a function of the price system. From it spring the three great tasks which have formed the three parts of this book:

a) the gathering of data on the external environment: business cycle analyses, detailed surveys of competitive conditions in industry, market studies;

b) the analysis of the internal operating conditions of the firm in terms of a survey of cost structure;

c) the synthesis of policies relating to production, stockage, investment, and price.

Secondarily, economic analysts are called upon to perform an educational function. This function, however, is merely a transitory one which should decrease in importance as the development of economic method progresses. Its main objectives are:

a) the training of specialists;

b) explaining to various members of the firm, especially to the executives and to the top-level personnel at the central office and in the research departments, the assistance which economic analysts can provide in the fulfillment of their responsibilities.

As a matter of fact, we know of no official training program covering the subjects which we have attempted to outline in this book, and there are so few specialists at present that no firm can readily establish an economics department specializing in modern methods. It is therefore quite normal to assign experienced analysts to training duties both in and out of the firm. Despite the variety of their functions, economic analysts should not have the authority to make decisions. This caveat, of course, does not pertain to decisions which are necessary to their studies; in this area it is desirable that they should have the widest latitude. We refer here only to decisions relative to company policy which are reached on the basis of their analyses. A separation of powers is desirable for two sets of reasons:

1) Economic surveys are essentially studies of synthesis prepared for the higher levels in the hierarchy; it is difficult simultaneously to be a good economic analyst and a good executive. An economist must devote his time to thinking without giving any concern to immediate action, and in the course of his research he is constantly led to discuss and to criticize. Furthermore, he must concentrate on the economic aspect of problems. An executive, on the contrary, must act, frequently taking into account nonquantitative factors known only to him. He has neither the time nor the peace of mind required to bring detailed studies to a successful conclusion. His role is merely to take cognizance of the hypotheses and conclusions contained in analyses presented by the economics department.

2) To mix research and executive functions would also contribute to irritating the echelons in the hierarchy that supervise those departments in the firm where economic research is being performed. Suppose, for example, that a study on inventory management is made in one of the plants of a firm at the request of the general manager. The analysts who are to spend a few months in the plant in question are likely to be received coolly. The plant managers are likely to assume that the visitors have come to inspect the plant. As veterans and specialists, they will view with mistrust and jealousy the newcomers, probably younger then they, who are attempting to apply mathematical methods to the delicate and special area of their craft. Cooperation between these two groups is more likely to be assured if the first group is aware of the fact that the second group has no power of decision, and if they know that consequently they can present their viewpoint to an executive, whose turn of mind they understand better. If the analysts respect the authority and experience of plant management while explaining their objectives and methodologies in direct, lay terms, cooperation will be possible. Plant managers and engineers will then look more spontaneously to the economics department for assistance.

Despite this separation of the research and decision functions, the economics department, to do its job effectively, must be afforded the possibility of closely following the policy of the firm.

II

ANATOMY OF ORGANIZATIONS

The problems directed toward economic analysis are management problems. To start with, the anatomy of possible organizations should be visualized at the top level.

Traditionally, the following is the organizational setup encountered:

1) a sales department;

2) a financial department, whose many activities include accounting and the administration of short and long term loans;

3) a production department engaged in operations, in new projects, in provisioning, and in technical research;

4) a personnel department which deals with all personnel problems, and wage matters;

5) a legal department.

All of these departments, with the possible exception of the last one, may become involved in questions of economic analysis. One type of organization might distribute its economic analysts to each of the standard departments instead of setting up a separate economics department, but such an organization is not, by far, the most efficient.

With the exception of very large organizations, it is likely that the various departments could not occupy their economists full time. They would therefore be inclined to assign them supplementary duties of a different nature. This would be a manifest waste because individuals possessing such training are few in number.

Although there is a considerable amount of routine work in economic analysis, there is also room for intensive research. Moreover, experience has demonstrated (an observation which may not be in accord with our old individualism) that group endeavor facilitates creativity). It tends to eliminate errors in reasoning, simplifies formulations, smooths technical difficulties (mathematical, for example), and permits a better exploration of consequences. To scatter analysts among management services would therefore deprive the firm of the benefits of group effort in a field in which the development of method can be very rapid during the next few years.

Finally, such an organization runs the risk of instability because there would always be occasions when the various economic analysts scattered among the various departments would have to work together "temporarily" and thus, progressively, a central economics department would emerge.

It would seem, therefore, that the best solution is the formation of a separate economics department or an operations research group. However, if sufficient specialists are available it may be desirable to assign a liaison economist to each of the top departments.

Eventually, an economics department can be divided into two groups: a) a group operating for the benefit of the sales department whose efforts would be directed essentially toward market research; and b) a group operating for the benefit of the other departments, dealing with problems of cost, production, and investment.

Research relating to price policy should come within the jurisdiction of the first group. However, because this policy must take cost structure into account and because, correspondingly, many studies on production must also incorporate elements relative to demand, a close relationship should exist between the two groups. The solution to be adopted is contingent upon the company's organizational form and the personalities of the directors in charge of the various departments.

In the case of those firms which, in addition to a central echelon, include important directorates in charge of different factories or various sales areas, some advantage might be gained by assigning one or two economic analysts to each directorate. They would deal with specific problems which may arise in their factory complex or their area, and would be valuable as assistants to a director. Furthermore, they would be collaborators with and liaison for the central economics group:

a) as collaborators, they would participate in studies by the central group when the problems under study related to their factory;

b) as liaison, they would be able to elaborate and forward data needed by the central group to enable it to bring its studies to a successful conclusion.

A sensitive aspect of organization that should be considered here is that relationships existing between the central group and the individual analysts located in the area offices or local factories must be functional, not hierarchical. The central group must not become involved in a factory's internal problems, and the local analyst must never cease to be subject to the authority of his director. An analogous problem arose during the last war with regard to the organization of operations research in the United States. The central group was located in Washington, whereas several subgroups functioned for the benefit of theaters of operations. From this experience and several other similar instances, it would appear that the following broad lines of a solution can be drawn [1]:

a) to insure community of thought it is desirable, fairly frequently, to detail members of a central group to factories, and vice versa;

b) exchange of information and of ideas should circulate freely between a central group and local economists;

c) both the central group and the local analysts should respect the proprietary aspects of the sources of exchanged information and should not release the results of studies using such data without prior approval from the management concerned.

When, to pursue operations research or economic analysis successfully, a firm engages the services of a specialized group, two distinct possibilities must be considered.

1) The consultant group places a specialist at the disposal of the client. This is the solution generally adopted by management engineering groups. It is satisfactory for problems of limited scope. An engineer specialist works directly with the engineers in charge of the problems within the firm.

2) A second possibility, which seems to be more widespread in the United States and which is better adapted to economic analysis—at least when the application of simple and proven methods is not contemplated—consists in setting up a permanent group comprised of representatives of the consulting firm and representatives from the client firm. This group functions as an economics department, but its functions are limited to the specific problem only. If a permanent central economics department exists, a few of its members are, of course, included in the work

group. It is preferable, however, that there also be representatives from the other departments in order to facilitate communication between the group and the firm as a whole.

III

INTERNAL ORGANIZATION OF AN ECONOMICS DEPARTMENT

The internal organization of an economics department must attempt to preserve the possibilities of group work; the best method for attaining such an objective, however, depends very much upon the size of the department. If the department is limited to two or three persons, specialization should be limited and routine tasks should not be assigned.

The entire effort must be directed toward the realization of long-term research and to the elaboration of methods. When the size of a firm permits an expansion of this department, it becomes possible to increase the differentiation within the group and to set up an individual section for market research and one for production surveys. Within these two sections, a few specialized tasks can be assigned to specific analysts: general information (analysis of business cycles and short-term forecasts), long-term forecasts, cost analyses, investment studies. The other analysts, on the other hand, should be released from specific assignments and should constitute an "operations research group" working as a team and bending every effort to bringing new studies to successful completion. This group must enjoy complete freedom; normally, two or three years are required before it starts paying off.

For an economics department so conceived it would seem advisable to turn toward rather flexible types of organization. This amounts to saying that the value of the economics service will be contingent to a high degree upon the efficacy of its chief. Among the qualifications the latter must possess, diplomacy ranks first, for it alone can make it possible to establish relationships of confidence with other headquarters offices and executives. Furthermore, it makes it possible to maintain a fertile spirit of cooperation within the economics department. In addition to diplomacy, the head of an economics department must possess a thorough knowledge of the problems of the firm. Such knowledge will make it possible for him to suggest new analyses to the executives and to orient the work of his department toward the most fruitful research. In addition, the head of the department should have the rather rare intuitive ability which permits him to distinguish between problems that have potential payoff and those whose potential has been exhausted and should be discontinued. This intuition, of course, is developed by experience derived from long association with economic method.

Aside from that of the chief, what training should be required of the other members of the staff of an economics department? Group activity provides a certain latitude in this respect. The general information assignments and market studies which do not require either a strong mathematical basis or a thorough technical knowledge of the firm but which do require adequate general training in economics can be entrusted to economists who have not taken the usual science courses in school. The group must include at least one professional statistician, since many problems of economic analysis pose difficult statistical questions (as we have seen in Chapters 6, 10, and 11). As to the other members of the department, they should possess a good knowledge of mathematics, of the mechanics of the firm, and of economics. These three elements are essential requirements, but their respective importance will naturally vary from one member to another. It would seem, however, that of these three elements the economics background would be the easiest to acquire, while the mathematical knowledge might be the most difficult. An engineer who still has an eager mind can quickly acquire a knowledge of economic analysis, provided he is willing to concede that this is a new technique whose mastery requires hard work. On the other hand, experience shows that if one has not acquired a solid background in mathematics during formal schooling, there is little hope of acquiring it subsequently. Finally, a convenient way of acquiring familiarity with the mechanics of an enterprise is to spend, at the beginning of one's career, a few years in a purely technical position. It is not, however, particularly desirable that such a contact be extended over too long a period.

All of the foregoing relates only to the background knowledge of economic analysts; such knowledge is of little value if they do not possess, in addition, the qualities which make them particularly suitable for their positions. These qualities are fairly numerous and somewhat inconsistent. Let us attempt to enumerate them:

1) Creativity is first among them, because economic analyses must define concepts, isolate variables, establish the relationships between them, and more often than not develop new methods. Unfortunately, only experience can prove whether an individual possesses this precious quality. Titles, intellectual brilliance, and learning are rarely valid indications.

2) To the above should be added a certain humility in the face of problems. Those who exclaim, after having listened briefly to the explanation of a problem, "This is a linear program," or "such-and-such a mathematical model should be used," rarely become good analysts inasmuch as they conceive of economic analysis as a catalog of methods, and attempt to force problems submitted to them into the framework of a predetermined mathematic

tool. On the contrary, it is necessary to start from an analysis of the problem and then to deduce its theoretical formulation.

3) The attraction of the new is another quality. A conservative turn of mind which is satisfied with things as they are and which conceals, beneath a belief in experience, a lack of interest in change cannot look upon economic analysis without sterile doubts. As a matter of fact, everyday industrial experience indicates that many engineers who showed great promise in their youth have allowed themselves to become hardened by factory life and regard anything new without enthusiasm. For this reason, engineers who have held positions of responsibility in factories for many years are usually not likely to be successfully integrated into an economics department. When it is desired to switch an engineer from a factory to the economics department, it is therefore preferable to select him from a group of younger engineers.

4) A desire to learn would appear to be a corollary of the above qualities. The economic method develops with such rapidity that it is necessary to maintain constant contact with recent discoveries. An analyst who did not read the main journals and periodicals and did not attend seminars would very soon lose all such contact. In other words, he would not be aware of a certain number of problems which he could analyze in his firm. Properly directed and apportioned, reading constitutes the best stimulant for a creative imagination.

5) We have already stressed diplomacy several times; this, so as not be be tinged with hypocrisy, must reflect modesty, a thorough comprehension of the psychology of others, and a spontaneous recognition of the limitations of the economic method.

6) Diplomacy, however, should not mean weakness. The points of view of others can be discussed with understanding without in any way abandoning an opinion believed to be legitimate. Analysts likely to be constantly working with other members of the enterprise must give proof of firmness. This blend of diplomacy and firmness results in opinions slightly ahead of the average. A state of mind must be adopted which will not offend deep convictions but which will cause reflection and which will lead in due course to a change in the average state of mind.

7) One last quality required of economic analysts is discretion. Because economists are constantly engaged in analyzing a firm's operations in seeking to determine the most effective policies to be followed, they are inclined to be critical of the status quo. Such criticism is fruitful because it gives birth to the planning of reforms and future improvements. It must, therefore, be allowed to develop freely within the group. But it should not be inconsiderately disseminated outside the organization. This could only create discontent and resentment and shake personnel faith in the good management of the company. Furthermore, at the beginning of a

survey economists run the risk, by systematically discussing the existing state of things, of criticizing rules which may later prove to be very judicious. If the change in position of the department were to leak to the outside, its authority would be needlessly weakened. Finally, the group needs a great amount of data. The members of the firm who provide this information are generally the very same ones who may feel themselves under criticism, which constitutes an added reason for discretion. Members of an economics department should therefore not express any opinions on the outside as long as a report has not been submitted containing the department's official conclusions.

Most of the qualities listed above are scarcely more than those which can be easily developed in individuals. Two among them, however, can be reinforced by the organization of the economics department: a) the creation of a documentation service can awaken a desire to learn; and b) the strict enforcement of rules as to the circulation of documents can help develop and maintain discretion.

A documentation service makes three types of documents available to an economics department:

1) The internal statistics of the firm. These statistics are of great value in routine work but, as all operations researchers have emphasized, generally they do not provide the data required for more detailed analyses.

2) Statistics relating to the overall economy and, especially, the publications of the I.N.S.E.E., of the O.E.E.C., and of the U.N.

3) Books and periodicals dealing with economic analysis. The most interesting publications have been listed in the bibliographies. As for the periodicals, which increase in number each day and which have been mentioned in the foreword, the following are some of the most outstanding:

In French: La revue française de Recherche opérationnelle,
               La revue de Statistique appliquée.

In English: Operations Research
               Management Science   } American
               Econometrica   journals
               Naval Research Logistics Quarterly
               Operational Research Quarterly } British
               Journal of the Royal Statistical Society } journals

In Italian: Bolletino del Centro per la Ricerca Operativa.

In Spanish: Trabajos de estadistica.

In German: Unternehmensforschung
               Statistischevierteljahresschrift.

It is also interesting to scan a few journals in the area of general economics (Economie appliquée, Revue d'Economie politique,

Banques, American Economic Review, Economica, Metroeconomica) or of demography (Population), but articles in these journals relating to economic problems of the firm are generally less numerous.

The circulation of documents must be organized in such a way as to make a careful distinction between departmental documents and memoranda and reports intended for dissemination. The former must be distributed to all members of the group in order to stimulate discussion, during which criticism can be expressed frankly and in the technical language commonly used. Unless so authorized by the chief, these papers are not distributed outside the department.

On the other hand, the object of memoranda and reports is to provide information to the executives or to the other departments as to the activity of the economics department. Memoranda contain brief informational material, whereas reports present an overall synthesis supported by statistical data. In preparing documents one should never lose sight of the fact that they are intended for individuals who are not economists and who, in addition, rarely have the time required for a complete study of all details. Under these conditions the report must include a main section, as brief as possible, which outlines in nontechnical terms the problem under study, the methods employed, the results obtained, and as many appendices as necessary to support statements made in the body of the report. An acceptable alternative would be to write two reports: a complete report for limited distribution and a short report in nontechnical terms for wider distribution.

Aside from reports and memoranda, an economics department may publish information bulletins for the use of all engineers. This must be regarded, however, as an aspect of its educational function.

IV

COMMUNICATION BETWEEN AN ECONOMICS DEPARTMENT
AND OTHER DEPARTMENTS

In any company, two networks of relations coexist: a network of authority and a communications network. The former is established when an individual, a subordinate, is willing to have his behavior directed by another, his superior; whereas, any process by means of which elements serving as a basis for decisions are transmitted from one member of an organization to another can be formally defined as communication. As indicated by H. A. Simon [2], information and orders which flow down through the network of authority constitute only a small part of the complete communications network.

What we have already mentioned regarding the economics department can therefore be summarized as follows: it must form part of a network of authority of small scope (which links it essentially to the executives of the firm), but within a very large network of communication. Before ascertaining the nature of this communication system, it is well to realize that this dissymmetry poses a problem since, in industrial organizations, there is always a tendency to pattern communications networks after the network of authority. Usually, knowledge, responsibility, and power go hand in hand. At a lower echelon, a supervisor knows just enough to perform his duties. His responsibilities and his authority are in agreement with his knowledge of the situation. A general manager, on the contrary, has access to all information regarding the condition of the firm and at the same time possesses the widest powers and the greatest responsibilities. By reason of this correlation between powers, responsibilities, and knowledge of a situation, the principle of "hierarchical channels" is particularly strong. Because knowledge of a situation grows with responsibilities and powers, it is taken for granted that information must be transmitted through the same channels as orders and requests. A very strict application of such a principle may affect the effectiveness of an economics department because:

a) hierarchical channels are a slow means of communication;

b) hierarchical channels are not conducive to an accurate transmission of technical information since the men who constitute the successive links in the chain are not specialists;

c) hierarchical channels have a low capacity since, in order to preserve independence and a certain initiative, each echelon tends to minimize any information transmitted to a higher level.

Does this amount to saying that the short-circuiting of hierarchical channels must assume an anarchical form? Definitely not. But it can be attained if, in each factory or regional office, the economics department is equipped with temporary or permanent antennas, i.e., analysts who are functionally linked to the central economics department and who are empowered to transmit information thereto. Naturally, before any analysis is undertaken, agreement at the various levels within the hierarchy is sought as to the procedure considered, and a copy of the information transmitted is also systematically distributed.

Assuming this difficulty to have been resolved, communications between the economics department and the other segments of the firm can be classed in two categories. These relate to the transmission of information to the economics department and a dissemination of the results of its studies. The input information is subdivided into reports and research effected by the other departments and documents prepared especially for the economics department. Particular care should be exercised in insuring that the reports of the other departments reach the economics department on a regular basis, because the latter is interested in multiple aspects of the life of the firm. Although theoretically obvious, this arrangement does not always work out smoothly.

A special system of communications links an economics department with a mechanical retrieval operation because many economic
studies require voluminous statistics which can be used only with
the help of automated processes. Finally, certain problems of
economic analysis require the use of computers. An economics
department will therefore maintain a close relationship with firms
specializing in the manufacture of computers and, at some future
time, may use a computer in its own enterprise. It is, therefore,
desirable that economists be aware of the potentialities of these
machines and the principles of programming, i.e., the series of
instructions fed to the computer in order that it may automatically
solve problems posed.

V

AN ECONOMICS DEPARTMENT AND THE TRAINING
OF PERSONNEL

The part which an economics department must play in the
training of personnel is quite varied, for objectives and methods are
closely connected with the groups this department services. Four
groups can be distinguished: the upper levels of the firm as a whole;
the executives; future leading groups; and future economic analysts.

a) The upper levels of the firm as a whole. The dissemination
of general information bulletins by an economics department, or the
publication of studies in the firm's periodicals, makes it possible to
enlarge the educational background of engineers and to create a
favorable climate for economic research. As a matter of fact, many
engineers are handicapped by knowing nothing whatever of the
economic aspects of their work. Confined, at the very outset of
their careers, to specialized techniques (at times conceived in a
routine manner), and ignorant of all or nearly all of the economic
context of their industry as well as of the elementary methods of
economic analysis, they ascend to the higher levels of a hierarchy
without adapting their knowledge to their new functions. Economic
bulletins can contribute toward maintaining in engineers the
intellectual curiosity they once possessed as students and young
engineers. A few possible subjects that could be presented are:
market studies by the firm, accounts of the place occupied by the
industry within the country's economy, the analysis of long-range
possibilities of development by the industry, and the simpler methods
of economic analysis such as cost analyses, the calculation of
amortization, and the utilization of the present value concept. These
outlines should never be in abstract form, but should be based on
specific examples drawn from problems being worked on by the
engineers. General information bulletins should contribute toward
facilitating the task of the economics department vis-à-vis the
other groups with which it must maintain contact.

b) Executives. By "executives" we do not mean here the directors of the enterprise itself, but rather the managers of the various plants when an enterprise is a sizeable one and relatively decentralized. The word "training," in this respect, is improper, because the objective is to present economic analysis and to give examples of problems which it can cover. One should therefore start with alternatives which actually face executives and attempt to demonstrate to them, without going into details regarding the methods, the assistance they can derive from economic analyses. In order to forestall any misunderstanding, it is wise to insist upon the limitations of the role of economic analysis and to underscore that it cannot be substituted for executives but is merely one more weapon for those who are the victims of the complexity of modern living.

This presentation of economic analysis can take place during seminars which the executives attend for a few days. It must assume the discussion form and avoid any formality.

c) Future executive cadres. The problem of presenting economic analysis to executives should, in the final analysis, remain an episodic event. The question arises now merely because we are at the very threshold of the development of economic analysis. In the future, executives will have had occasion during their careers to become aware of its utility and its limitations. The problem of training future executive cadres is one retaining topical interest, however; not even a change in curriculum in the large schools will cause it to disappear.

We must rid outselves of the ridiculous custom that one should not return to school during one's career; postgraduate work can be so beneficial. First of all, it is an intellectual stimulant as is any contact with something new. Next, it constitutes an excellent opportunity to bring oneself up to date and to evaluate what one has accomplished during the previous years. It enables one to relocate his practical experience within a more general framework and to make use of it, not merely in a repetitive routine, but in creative effort. Finally, it becomes a necessity if one wishes to adjust one's attitude to new responsibilities and, as one progresses, to avoid performing the same tasks at increasingly higher levels.

In this connection, a firm must have a long-range personnel policy, and must methodically insure the training of future executive cadres. There seems to be general agreement as to the proper time at which such training should begin. A "crisis" usually occurs in the lives of engineers in an industrial enterprise* four or five years after their graduation from college or university. They have

---

*Psychological problems are somewhat different for staff engineers.

mastered their profession and know the technique of their industry—at least as well as they ever will. They begin to feel that they have nothing more to learn. A few more years, and routine work will have killed in them the desire to create, to wander from traditional methods, or to keep up to date. This is the time which should be used by the executives to select the most promising engineers and to enlarge their training. Conferences and courses which can be organized for their benefit will require them to devote more thought to their work and will tend to demonstrate new aspects of such work.

In such preparation for management, economic analysis is naturally merely one of many components, including applied statistics, administrative technique, history and sociology of workers' movements, and financial technique. Nevertheless, it is an essential component for, as one rises within a hierarchy, economic aspects of choice become more important at the expense of technical aspects.

In order that a training program may be fruitful, it is necessary on the one hand to insure that the better men are chosen and, on the other, to create favorable conditions by prior discussion with factory directors.

d) Economic analysts. The problem here is to train specialists. The subject to be taught is of wide scope and must be studied in depth. Economic analysis must be approached in its full breadth, supplemented with applied statistics and general economics. Study should not be limited to courses and to textbooks; it should be extended to reading the most outstanding original works, and thus the habit of maintaining contact with current publications is acquired. Finally, practical training must go hand in hand with the acquisition of theoretical learning. The best procedure is to assign candidates for lengthy periods to the economics department, progressively leading them into participating in the activities of the group and entrusting them with more and more complex research.

However, this is an undertaking which a firm will find difficult to engage in successfuly through its own means. It is to be hoped than in the future there will be an adjustment in the courses of study provided by larger schools and universities; at the same time professional organizations, in conjunction with industry, will become interested in the training of higher-echelon cadres. Only in this manner will the country acquire the large number of specialists needed in this new and promising field, economic analysis.

BIBLIOGRAPHY

1. P. M. MORSE and G. E. KIMBALL:
    Methods of Operations Research. The Massachusetts Institute of Technology and John Wiley, New York, 1954.
2. H. A. SIMON:
    Administrative Behavior. MacMillan, New York, 1948.

Author index

Subject index